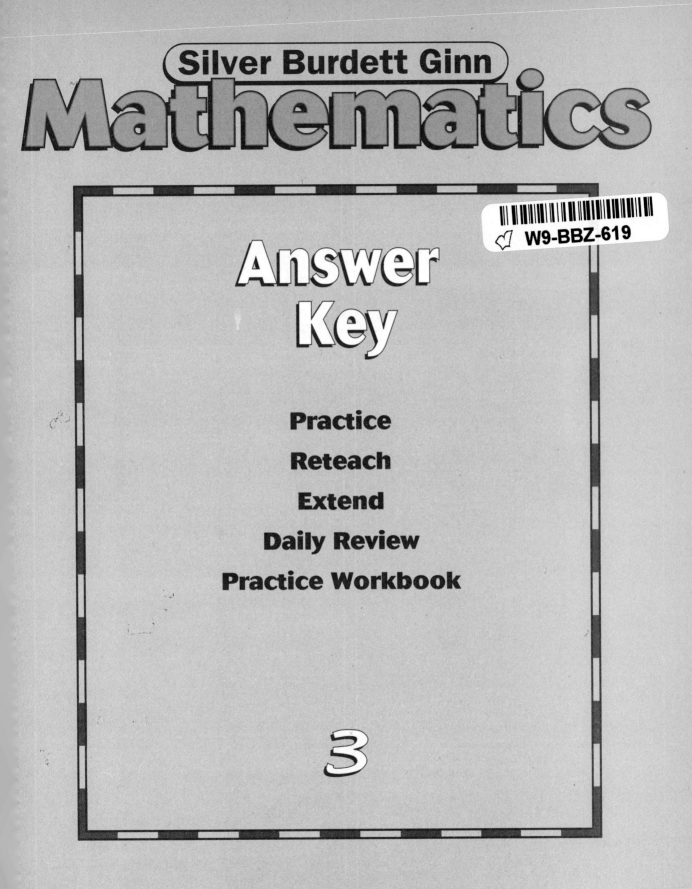

Silver Burdett Ginn

Mathematics

Answer Key

Practice

Reteach

Extend

Daily Review

Practice Workbook

3

Silver Burdett Ginn
Parsippany, NJ
Atlanta, GA • Deerfield, IL • Irving, TX • Needham, MA • Upland, CA

Silver Burdett Ginn

299 Jefferson Road, P.O. Box 480
Parsippany, NJ 07054-0480

1999 Printing

ISBN 0-382-37343-0

8 9-M-00 99

Contents

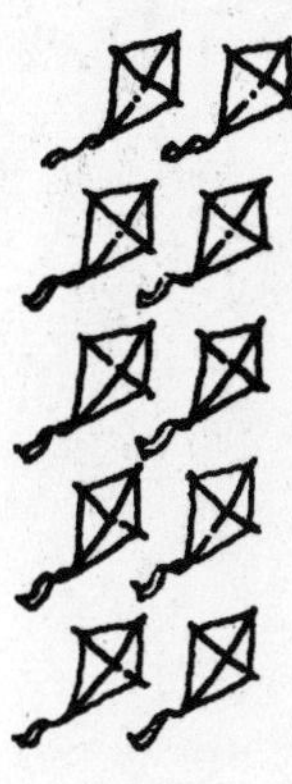

Chapter 1 • Lesson 1

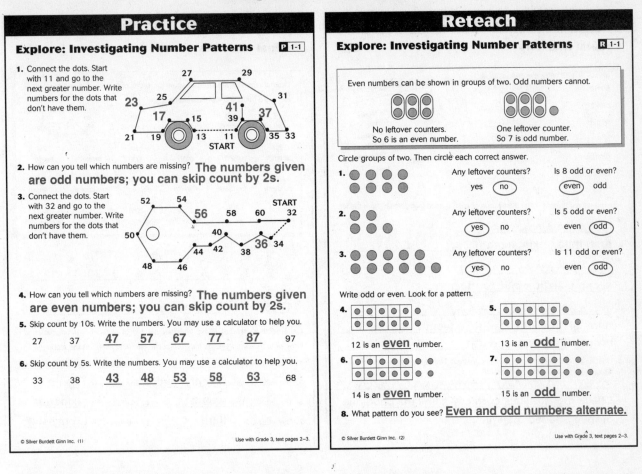

Practice

Explore: Investigating Number Patterns

P 1-1

1. Connect the dots. Start with 11 and go to the next greater number. Write numbers for the dots that don't have them.

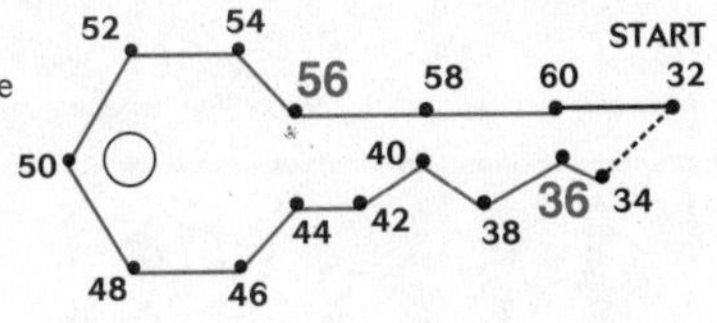

2. How can you tell which numbers are missing? The numbers given are odd numbers; you can skip count by 2s.

3. Connect the dots. Start with 32 and go to the next greater number. Write numbers for the dots that don't have them.

52 54 START 56 58 60 32 50 40 36 34 44 42 38 48 46

4. How can you tell which numbers are missing? The numbers given are even numbers; you can skip count by 2s.

5. Skip count by 10s. Write the numbers. You may use a calculator to help you.

27 37 47 57 67 77 87 97

6. Skip count by 5s. Write the numbers. You may use a calculator to help you.

33 38 43 48 53 58 63 68

 Use with Grade 3, text pages 2–3.

Reteach

Explore: Investigating Number Patterns

R 1-1

Even numbers can be shown in groups of two. Odd numbers cannot.

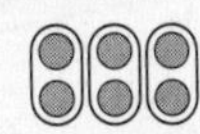

No leftover counters. So 6 is an even number.

One leftover counter. So 7 is odd number.

Circle groups of two. Then circle each correct answer.

1. Any leftover counters? yes (no) Is 8 odd or even? (even) odd
2. Any leftover counters? (yes) no Is 5 odd or even? even (odd)
3. Any leftover counters? (yes) no Is 11 odd or even? even (odd)

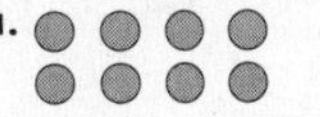

Write odd or even. Look for a pattern.

4. 12 is an even number.
5. 13 is an odd number.
6. 14 is an even number.
7. 15 is an odd number.
8. What pattern do you see? Even and odd numbers alternate.

 Use with Grade 3, text pages 2–3.

Extend

Hide and Seek

E 1-1 NUMBER SENSE

Work with a partner. Look at each group of numbers, then have your partner cover the group. Write down the numbers you remember. Look for a pattern in each group of numbers.

Answers for numbers will vary.

1. 67 68 69 70 71 72

Numbers ____

Pattern Numbers increase by 1.

2. 100 102 104 106 108 110

Numbers ____

Pattern Numbers increase by 2.

3. 56 66 76 86 96 106

Numbers ____

Pattern Numbers increase by 10.

4. B-1200 C-1300 D-1400 E-1500 F-1600

Numbers ____

Pattern Letters advance by 1; numbers by 100.

5. 55 60 65 70 75 80

Numbers ____

Pattern Numbers increase by 5.

6. 1980 1982 1984 1986 1988 1990

Numbers ____

Pattern Numbers increase by 2.

 Use with Grade 3, text pages 2–3.

Daily Review

Name ____ Daily Review 1-1

EXPLORE: Investigating Number Patterns

Circle the numbers that are odd.

Place an X on the numbers that are even.

1. (21) 2. (33) 3. ~~98~~
4. ~~90~~ 5. ~~76~~ 6. (45)
7. (67) 8. ~~84~~ 9. (99)

Write the missing numbers in each pattern. Use a hundreds chart to help you.

10. 5, 10, 15, 20, 25
11. 32, 34, 36, 38, 40
12. 4, 8, 12, 16, 20

Problem Solving

Solve.

13. Juan's design has 12 squares and 3 triangles. Which shape is made of an odd number? triangle
14. Which shape in Juan's design is made of an even number? square
15. A hundreds chart has these numbers circled: 5, 9, 13, 17, 21. Are odd numbers or even numbers circled? odd

Review and Remember

Add or subtract.

16. 12 + 4 = 16 17. 5 − 2 = 3 18. 8 + 2 = 10
19. 7 − 5 = 2 20. 4 + 5 = 9 21. 9 − 3 = 6
22. 8 − 7 = 1 23. 10 + 8 = 18 24. 6 − 5 = 1

Chapter 1 • Lesson 2

Practice

Ordinal Numbers

P 1-2

1. Sara has written a list of her favorite animals. In what position is each animal listed? Write the ordinal name.

horses	second
cats	third
rabbits	sixth
monkeys	eighth
giraffes	ninth
elephants	tenth

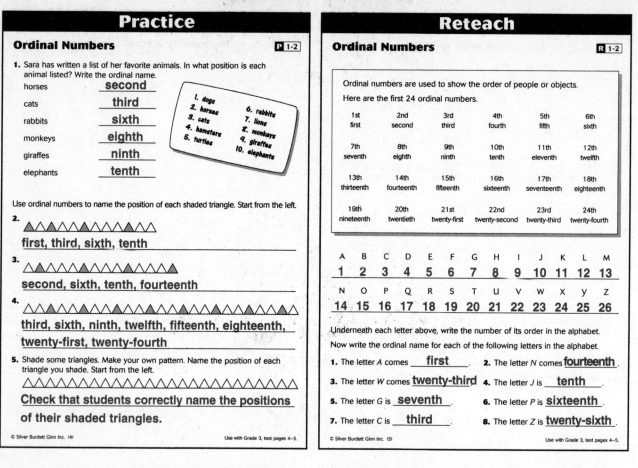

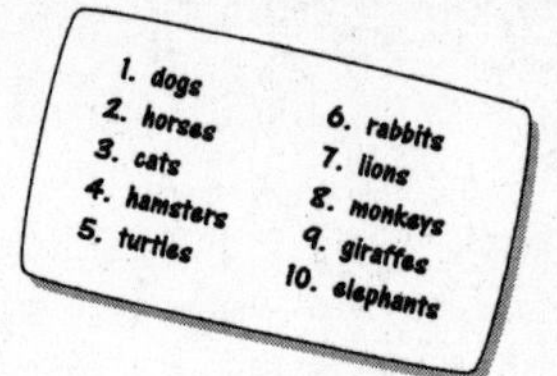

1. dogs
2. horses
3. cats
4. hamsters
5. turtles
6. rabbits
7. lions
8. monkeys
9. giraffes
10. elephants

Use ordinal numbers to name the position of each shaded triangle. Start from the left.

2. first, third, sixth, tenth

3. second, sixth, tenth, fourteenth

4. third, sixth, ninth, twelfth, fifteenth, eighteenth, twenty-first, twenty-fourth

5. Shade some triangles. Make your own pattern. Name the position of each triangle you shade. Start from the left.

Check that students correctly name the positions of their shaded triangles.

Use with Grade 3, text pages 4–5.

Reteach

Ordinal Numbers

R 1-2

Ordinal numbers are used to show the order of people or objects.

Here are the first 24 ordinal numbers.

1st first	2nd second	3rd third	4th fourth	5th fifth	6th sixth
7th seventh	8th eighth	9th ninth	10th tenth	11th eleventh	12th twelfth
13th thirteenth	14th fourteenth	15th fifteenth	16th sixteenth	17th seventeenth	18th eighteenth
19th nineteenth	20th twentieth	21st twenty-first	22nd twenty-second	23rd twenty-third	24th twenty-fourth

A	B	C	D	E	F	G	H	I	J	K	L	M
1	2	3	4	5	6	7	8	9	10	11	12	13

N	O	P	Q	R	S	T	U	V	W	X	Y	Z
14	15	16	17	18	19	20	21	22	23	24	25	26

Underneath each letter above, write the number of its order in the alphabet.

Now write the ordinal name for each of the following letters in the alphabet.

1. The letter *A* comes first.
2. The letter *N* comes fourteenth.
3. The letter *W* comes twenty-third
4. The letter *J* is tenth.
5. The letter *G* is seventh.
6. The letter *P* is sixteenth.
7. The letter *C* is third.
8. The letter *Z* is twenty-sixth.

Use with Grade 3, text pages 4–5.

Extend

Racing Results

E 1-2
REASONING

Solve each puzzle.

HINT: Draw a picture to help you solve each problem.

1. Shaun, Angel, and Chris ran in a race. One finished 3rd, one finished 5th, and one finished 8th. If Chris ran faster than Shaun, and Angel ran faster than Chris, who finished 5th? Chris
2. The 4 winners of a race posed for a picture. Margaret stood between Pete and Isaac. Isaac stood between Margaret and Isabel. What 2 winners stood at the ends of the line? Pete and Isabel
3. Three of the Cougars finished 1st, 4th, and 6th in the 100-meter dash. If Sara ran faster than Carol, and Carol ran faster than Nicole, who finished 4th? Carol
4. Tara has not won as many medals as Nadia. Grace has won two more medals than Nadia. Which of the three runners has won the most medals? Grace

Try these tough teasers.

5. The Gazelles, the Cheetahs, and the Falcons competed in a track meet. The coaches of these teams are Stan, Pam, and Ted. Stan's team won. Pam's team beat the Gazelles. If Stan coaches the Falcons, what team does Ted coach? The Gazelles
6. Three boys watched their sisters run the 50-yard dash. Sue beat Meg. Jim's sister beat Max's sister, and Max's sister beat Josh's sister. If Jill came in 1st, who is Josh's sister? Meg

Use with Grade 3, text pages 4–5.

Daily Review

Name ______________________

Daily Review 1-2

Ordinal Numbers

Write the name for each ordinal number.

1. sixth 6th
2. 10th tenth
3. 29th twenty-ninth
4. twenty-first 21st
5. seventy-sixth 76th
6. 15th fifteenth
7. thirty-third 33rd
8. 17th seventeenth
9. 42nd forty-second

Problem Solving

Use what you know about ordinal numbers to help you solve these problems.

10. If there are thirteen students ahead of you in line for a movie, what place in line are you? fourteenth
11. Write your birthday as an ordinal number. Answers will vary.
12. What are the four ordinal numbers after forty-fifth? forty-sixth, forty-seventh, forty-eighth, forty-ninth

Review and Remember

Add or subtract.

13. $14 + 0 = 14$
14. $4 + 7 = 11$
15. $12 - 9 = 3$
16. $7 - 6 = 1$
17. $9 - 4 = 5$
18. $4 + 9 = 13$
19. $16 - 0 = 16$
20. $11 - 3 = 8$
21. $6 + 3 = 9$

Chapter 1 • Lesson 3

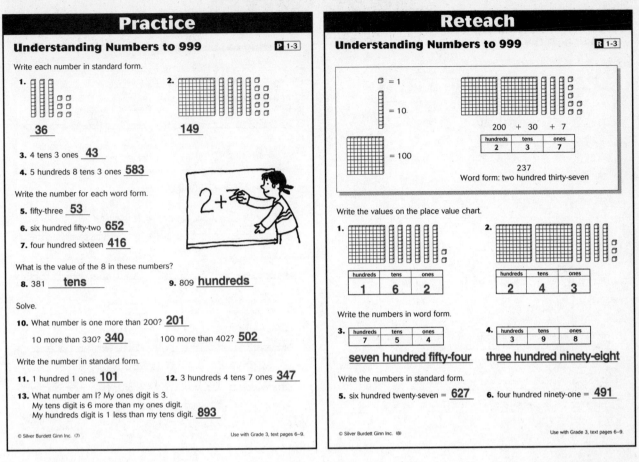

Practice

Understanding Numbers to 999

P 1-3

Write each number in standard form.

1. 36

2. 149

3. 4 tens 3 ones 43

4. 5 hundreds 8 tens 3 ones 583

Write the number for each word form.

5. fifty-three 53

6. six hundred fifty-two 652

7. four hundred sixteen 416

What is the value of the 8 in these numbers?

8. 381 tens

9. 809 hundreds

Solve.

10. What number is one more than 200? 201

10 more than 330? 340

100 more than 402? 502

Write the number in standard form.

11. 1 hundred 1 ones 101

12. 3 hundreds 4 tens 7 ones 347

13. What number am I? My ones digit is 3.
My tens digit is 6 more than my ones digit.
My hundreds digit is 1 less than my tens digit. 893

Use with Grade 3, text pages 6–9.

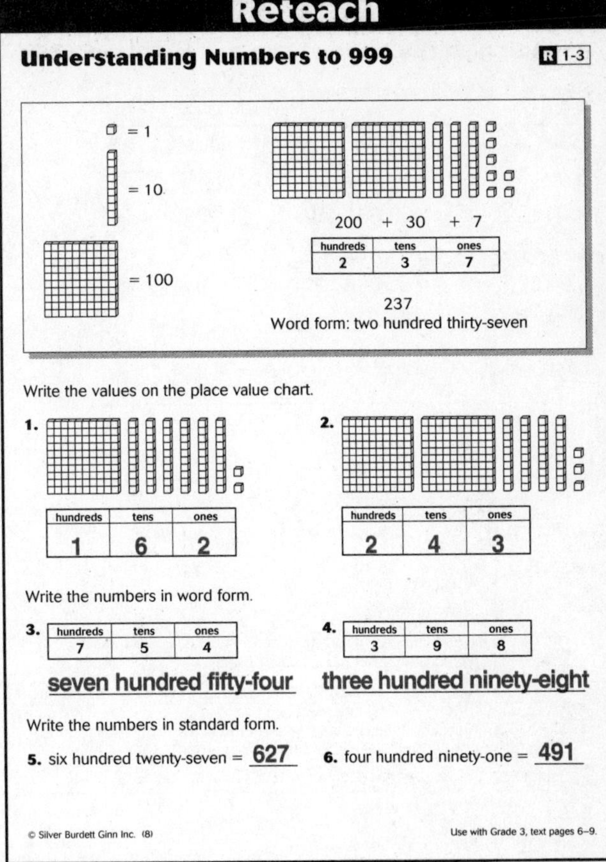

Reteach

Understanding Numbers to 999

R 1-3

= 1

= 10

= 100

200 + 30 + 7

hundreds	tens	ones
2	3	7

237

Word form: two hundred thirty-seven

Write the values on the place value chart.

1.

hundreds	tens	ones
1	6	2

2.

hundreds	tens	ones
2	4	3

Write the numbers in word form.

3.

hundreds	tens	ones
7	5	4

seven hundred fifty-four

4.

hundreds	tens	ones
3	9	8

three hundred ninety-eight

Write the numbers in standard form.

5. six hundred twenty-seven = 627

6. four hundred ninety-one = 491

Use with Grade 3, text pages 6–9.

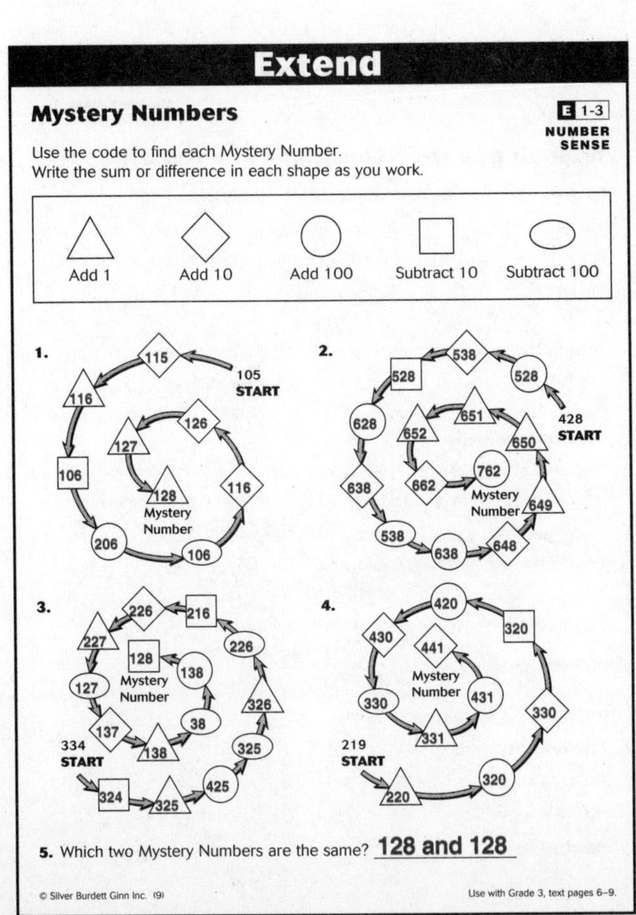

Extend

Mystery Numbers

E 1-3

NUMBER SENSE

Use the code to find each Mystery Number.
Write the sum or difference in each shape as you work.

Triangle	Diamond	Circle	Square	Oval
Add 1	Add 10	Add 100	Subtract 10	Subtract 100

5. Which two Mystery Numbers are the same? 128 and 128

Use with Grade 3, text pages 6–9.

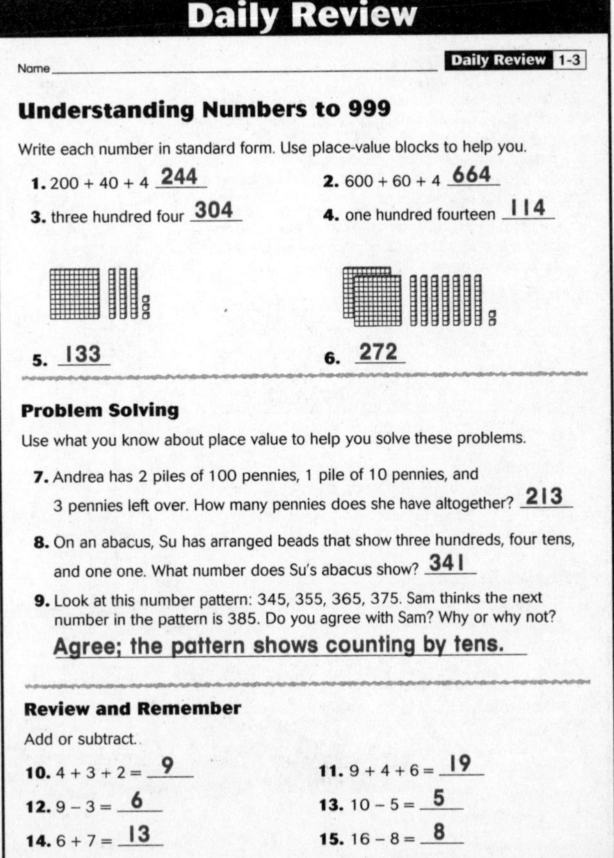

Daily Review

Name ______________________

Daily Review 1-3

Understanding Numbers to 999

Write each number in standard form. Use place-value blocks to help you.

1. 200 + 40 + 4 244

2. 600 + 60 + 4 664

3. three hundred four 304

4. one hundred fourteen 114

5. 133

6. 272

Problem Solving

Use what you know about place value to help you solve these problems.

7. Andrea has 2 piles of 100 pennies, 1 pile of 10 pennies, and 3 pennies left over. How many pennies does she have altogether? 213

8. On an abacus, Su has arranged beads that show three hundreds, four tens, and one one. What number does Su's abacus show? 341

9. Look at this number pattern: 345, 355, 365, 375. Sam thinks the next number in the pattern is 385. Do you agree with Sam? Why or why not?
Agree; the pattern shows counting by tens.

Review and Remember

Add or subtract.

10. 4 + 3 + 2 = 9

11. 9 + 4 + 6 = 19

12. 9 − 3 = 6

13. 10 − 5 = 5

14. 6 + 7 = 13

15. 16 − 8 = 8

Chapter 1 • Lesson 4

Practice

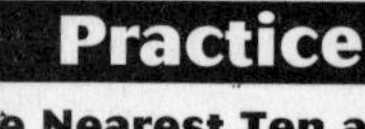

Rounding to the Nearest Ten and Hundred P 1-4

Use the number line. Round to the nearest ten or ten cents.

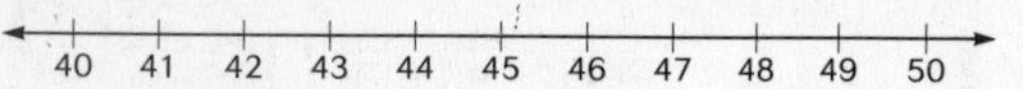

1. 42 40
2. 47 50
3. 48 50
4. 41¢ 40¢
5. 32 30
6. 46¢ 50¢

Round to the nearest ten or ten cents.

7. 24 20
8. 18¢ 20¢
9. 52 50
10. 68¢ 70¢
11. 29¢ 30¢
12. 98 100

Use the number line. Round to the nearest hundred or dollar.

500 510 520 530 540 550 560 570 580 590 600

13. 516 500
14. 551 600
15. $5.49 $5.00

Round to the nearest hundred or dollar.

16. 393 400
17. $8.79 $9.00
18. $4.23 $4.00
19. $7.25 $7.00
20. 681 700
21. $9.64 $10.00

Solve.

22. Hal said, "I have about $20." If he had either $14.37 or $18.98 exactly, which figure would you expect him to have? Explain.
$18.98; it rounds to $20, while $14.37 rounds to $10.

23. Gigi had 379 stickers. Then she bought a few more. How can she estimate the amount when telling friends about her collection?
She can say she has about 400 stickers.

 Use with Grade 3, text pages 10–13.

Reteach

Rounding to the Nearest Ten and Hundred R 1-4

A rounded number tells about how many instead of exactly how many.

14 is between 10 and 20.
Think of cubes.

10 11 12 13 14 15 16 17 18 19 20

14 is closer to 10 than to 20.
14 rounded is 10.

190 is between 100 and 200.
Think of cubes again.

100 110 120 130 140 150 160 170 180 190 200

190 is closer to 200 than 100.
190 rounded is 200.

Round each number to the nearest ten.
Shade the blocks for help.

1. 12 rounded is 10.
2. 27 rounded is 30.
3. 64 rounded is 60.
4. 46 rounded is 50.

Round each number to the nearest hundred.
Shade blocks and label for help.

5. 120 rounded is 100.
6. 670 rounded is 700.
7. 440 rounded is 400.

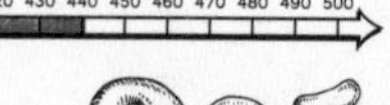

8. 580 rounded is 600.

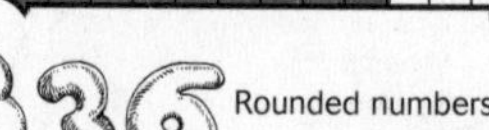

Rounded numbers!

 Use with Grade 3, text pages 10–13.

Extend

Break the Buzzer

E 1-4 NUMBER SENSE

How tough is your math muscle? Find out on the Math Muscle Buzzer. List your answers to each of the questions. You can use each digit only once in the same number. Then shade one box on the Math Muscle Buzzer for every number you made. A score of 30 is terrific. Go beyond that, and you break the Buzzer!

1. Use the digits 1, 3, 6, and 9. Write all the numbers you can that round to 300 when rounded to the nearest hundred.
316, 319

2. Use the digits 1, 2, 6, and 7. Write all the numbers you can that round to 200 when rounded to the nearest hundred.
216, 217, 167, 176, 162, 172

3. Use the digits 1, 2, 3, 5, and 8. Write all the numbers you can that round to 200 when rounded to the nearest hundred.
152, 153, 158, 182, 183, 185,
213, 231, 215, 235, 218, 238

4. Use the digits 2, 4, 5, 6, and 8. Write all the numbers you can that round to 500 when rounded to the nearest hundred.
452, 456, 458, 462, 465, 468, 482,
485, 486, 524, 526, 528,
542, 546,
548

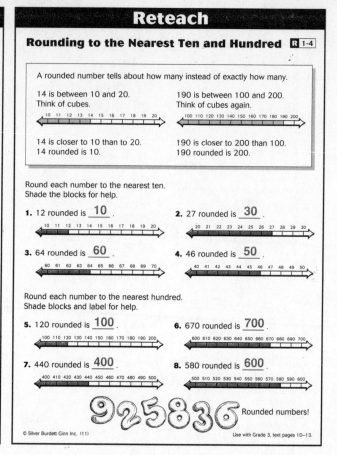

You broke the buzzer
30 Wow
25 You're humming
20 Getting there
15 Gaining steam
10 Warming up
5 Beginner

 Use with Grade 3, text pages 10–13.

Daily Review

Name ______ Daily Review 1-4

Rounding to the Nearest Ten and Hundred

Round to the nearest ten or ten cents. Draw a number line to help.

1. 74 70
2. 27 30
3. 82¢ 80¢

Round to the nearest hundred or dollar. Draw a number line to help.

4. $9.67 $10.00
5. 532 500
6. 847 800

What are the least and greatest whole numbers that round to each number?

7. 250, 300, 349
8. 550, 600, 649

Problem Solving

Use what you know about rounding to help you solve these problems.

9. Tom has $7.61 to spend on a gift. About how much money does he have to spend? about $8.00
10. A crayon box holds 64 crayons. About how many crayons are in the box? about 60
11. Explain why you round 323 to 300 instead of 400. 323 is closer to 300 than to 400.

Review and Remember

Add or subtract.

12. 9 − 6 = 3
13. 8 + 9 = 17
14. 14 − 7 = 7
15. 6 + 3 = 9
16. 11 − 5 = 6
17. 8 − 3 = 5
18. 7 + 8 = 15
19. 12 − 5 = 7
20. 8 + 6 = 14

Practice

Name ____________________

P 1-5

Problem Solving

Exact Numbers or Estimates

Circle the best choice for each question.

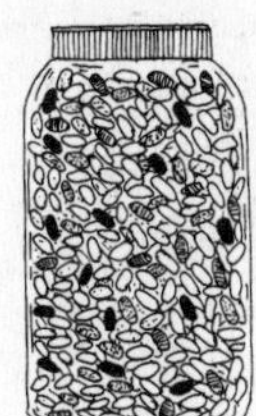

Jaime's school had a jelly bean contest. About 60 students tried to guess the number of jelly beans in a jar without going over the total. Most students guessed about 400. There were exactly 281 jelly beans in the jar. Jaime's guess of 270 was the closest. He won the jar of jelly beans and $10.

1. Which word helps you know that *400 jelly beans* is an estimate?
   - a. thought
   - (b.) about
   - c. guesses

2. Which sentence tells you how many jelly beans were in the jar?
   - a. Most students guessed about 400.
   - b. Jaime's guess of 270 was the closest.
   - (c.) There were exactly 281 jelly beans in the jar.

3. Which word helps you know that 60 is an estimate?
   - a. about
   - (b.) students
   - c. guesses

4. Is $10 a guess, an exact amount, or an estimate?
   - a. a guess
   - (b.) an exact amount
   - c. an estimate

5. There are 5 numbers in the story. How many of the numbers are estimates?
   - a. all of the numbers
   - b. one of the numbers
   - (c.) three of the numbers

6. Which number below could tell how many students took part in the contest?
   - a. 42
   - (b.) 58
   - c. 67

Reteach

R 1-5

Problem Solving

Exact Numbers or Estimates

An estimate is a number that is not exact. These words can help you recognize a number that is an estimate rather than an exact number.

more than *almost* *about*

Linda works 4 hours a day at a trading-card counter. On Fridays, she helps about 30 customers; on Saturdays, about 50. Last Saturday Linda sold almost 150 cards to one customer. One card cost $75.

Exact Number	Estimated Number
• Linda works 4 hours a day. • 4 is an *exact amount.*	• Linda helps *about* 30 customers a day. • 30 is an *estimated amount.*

1. Did Linda sell exactly 150 cards? If not, did she sell more than 150 or less? How can you tell?
   No; she sold less than 150 cards. The text states that she sold *almost* 150.

2. Does Linda help exactly 50 customers on a Saturday? If not, does she help more than or less than 50 customers? Explain.
   No; she helps about 50 customers, which may be more than or less than 50 customers.

3. Linda sold a card for $75. Is that an estimate or an exact number? How do you know?
   Exact; no words indicate an estimate. Also, a greater estimated number usually ends in zero.

 Use with Grade 3, text pages 14–15.

Extend

E 1-5 ESTIMATION

May Fair Shopping

Molly and Craig are planning the school May Fair. Write *estimate* or *exact* to show what kind of number they need for each amount.

1. How much peanut butter and jelly they will need. **Estimate**
2. How much a peanut butter and jelly sandwich will cost. **Exact**
3. How much to spend on decorations. **Estimate**
4. How much a ticket will cost. **Exact**
5. How many people will come to the fair. **Estimate**
6. How many game booths to set up. **Exact**

Solve.

7. Using the information above, what do Molly and Craig need to do to be ready for the fair? Make a list of tasks for the two classmates. **Possible answers:**
   Buy peanut butter, jelly, and bread.
   Decide price for sandwich and make sign.
   Decide on and buy decorations.
   Decide on ticket price and have tickets printed.
   Decide on game booths to build and get people to help.
   Decide on when the fair will be and advertise.

8. On the back of this page, write an ad for the school May Fair. Put four numbers in the ad. Make two of the numbers estimates and two of the numbers exact. Give your ad to a classmate to tell which numbers are estimates and which are exact numbers. **Ads will vary.**

 Use with Grade 3, text pages 14–15.

Daily Review

Name ____________________ Daily Review 1-5

Problem Solving

Exact Numbers or Estimates

Read each pair of sentences. Write which numbers are estimates and which are exact.

1. There are more than 20,000 runners in the marathon, but only the first 6 to cross the finish line can win any of the $300,000 prize money.
   exact **6; $300,000** estimate **20,000**
2. The weather report said that the afternoon temperature could reach 89°. In the evening temperatures will be around 72°.
   exact **89°** estimate **72°**
3. She said we should read about 25 pages each night. Then we could finish all 19 chapters by the end of the month.
   exact **19** estimate **25**
4. Jake wants to make sure he has 10 healthy plants. He is putting more than 15 plants in each of his 2 gardens.
   exact **10; 2** estimate **15**

Review and Remember

Round each number to the nearest ten.

5. 68 **70**
6. 213 **210**
7. 119 **120**
8. 834 **830**
9. 6 **10**
10. 75 **80**
11. 709 **710**
12. 1,999 **2,000**
13. 82 **80**
14. 418 **420**

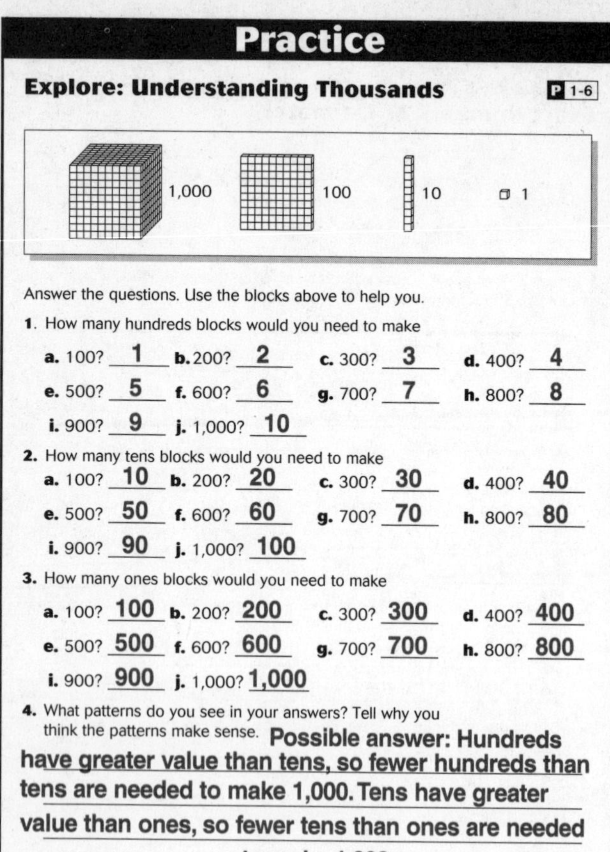

Practice

Explore: Understanding Thousands

P 1-6

Answer the questions. Use the blocks above to help you.

1. How many hundreds blocks would you need to make
   a. 100? 1 b. 200? 2 c. 300? 3 d. 400? 4
   e. 500? 5 f. 600? 6 g. 700? 7 h. 800? 8
   i. 900? 9 j. 1,000? 10
2. How many tens blocks would you need to make
   a. 100? 10 b. 200? 20 c. 300? 30 d. 400? 40
   e. 500? 50 f. 600? 60 g. 700? 70 h. 800? 80
   i. 900? 90 j. 1,000? 100
3. How many ones blocks would you need to make
   a. 100? 100 b. 200? 200 c. 300? 300 d. 400? 400
   e. 500? 500 f. 600? 600 g. 700? 700 h. 800? 800
   i. 900? 900 j. 1,000? 1,000
4. What patterns do you see in your answers? Tell why you think the patterns make sense. Possible answer: Hundreds have greater value than tens, so fewer hundreds than tens are needed to make 1,000. Tens have greater value than ones, so fewer tens than ones are needed to make 1,000.

 Use with Grade 3, text pages 18–19.

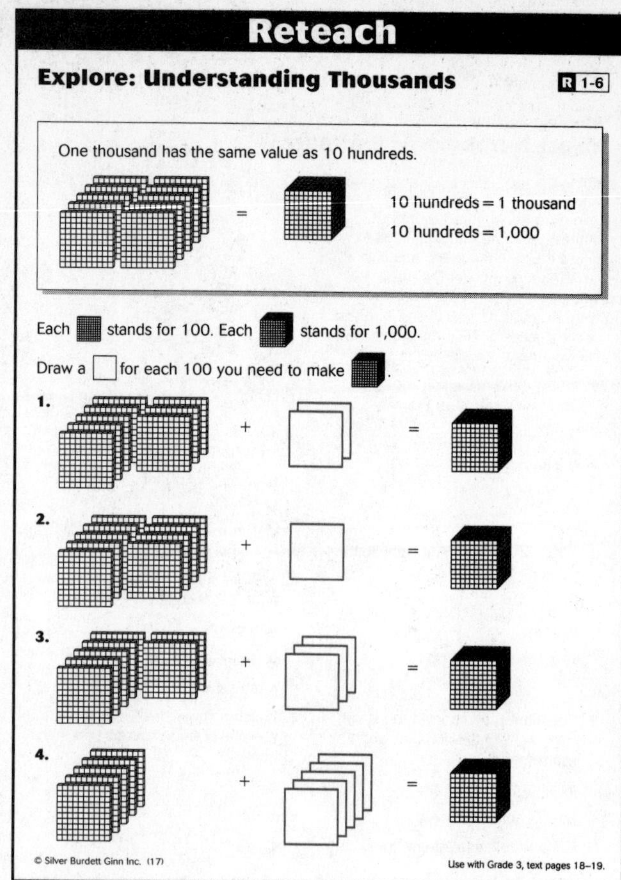

Reteach

Explore: Understanding Thousands

R 1-6

One thousand has the same value as 10 hundreds.

Each [hundred] stands for 100. Each [thousand] stands for 1,000.

Draw a □ for each 100 you need to make [thousand].

1. + =
2. + =
3. + =
4. + =

 Use with Grade 3, text pages 18–19.

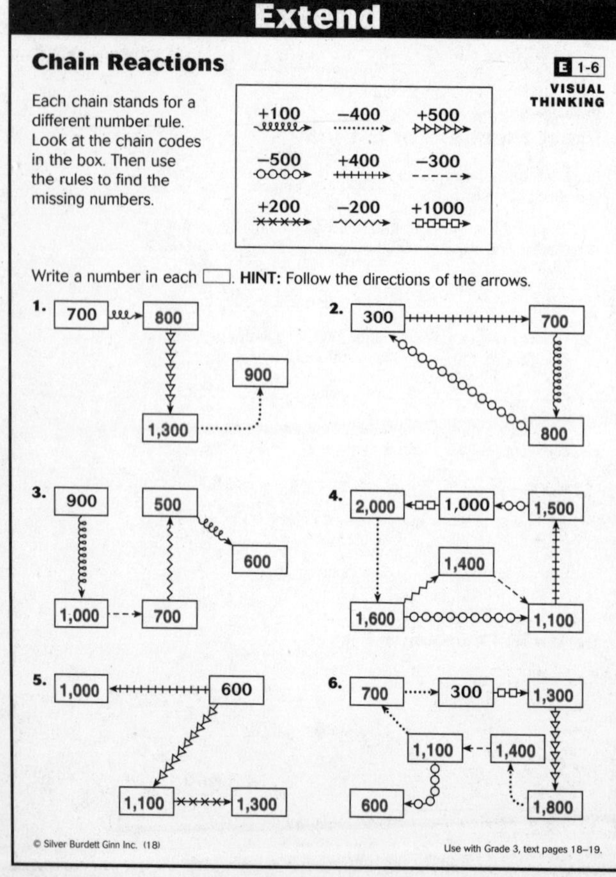

Extend

Chain Reactions

E 1-6 VISUAL THINKING

Each chain stands for a different number rule. Look at the chain codes in the box. Then use the rules to find the missing numbers.

Write a number in each □. HINT: Follow the directions of the arrows.

 Use with Grade 3, text pages 18–19.

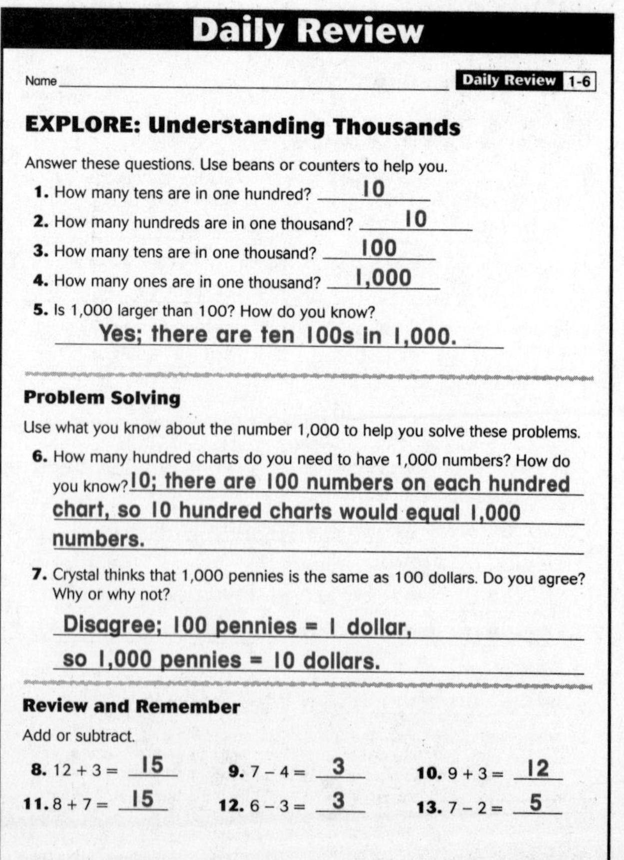

Daily Review

Name ____________________ Daily Review 1-6

EXPLORE: Understanding Thousands

Answer these questions. Use beans or counters to help you.

1. How many tens are in one hundred? 10
2. How many hundreds are in one thousand? 10
3. How many tens are in one thousand? 100
4. How many ones are in one thousand? 1,000
5. Is 1,000 larger than 100? How do you know? Yes; there are ten 100s in 1,000.

Problem Solving

Use what you know about the number 1,000 to help you solve these problems.

6. How many hundred charts do you need to have 1,000 numbers? How do you know? 10; there are 100 numbers on each hundred chart, so 10 hundred charts would equal 1,000 numbers.
7. Crystal thinks that 1,000 pennies is the same as 100 dollars. Do you agree? Why or why not? Disagree; 100 pennies = 1 dollar, so 1,000 pennies = 10 dollars.

Review and Remember

Add or subtract.

8. 12 + 3 = 15 9. 7 − 4 = 3 10. 9 + 3 = 12
11. 8 + 7 = 15 12. 6 − 3 = 3 13. 7 − 2 = 5

Chapter 1 • Lesson 7

Practice

Reading and Writing Four-Digit Numbers P 1-7

Write each number in standard form.

1. 4 thousands 5 hundreds 3 tens 7 ones **4,537**
2. 7 thousands 1 hundred 5 tens 0 ones **7,150**
3. 2 thousands 0 hundreds 6 tens 2 ones **2,062**

Complete the table below.

	Expanded form	Standard form	What 1 means
4.	3,000 + 100 + 50 + 4	**3,154**	**one hundred**
5.	1,000 + 300 + 20 + 8	**1,328**	**one thousand**
6.	8,000 + 200 + 40 + 1	**8,241**	**one**
7.	5,000 + 400 + 10 + 9	**5,419**	**ten**
8.	4,000 + 100 + 30 + 0	**4,130**	**one hundred**

Write each number in words.

9. 459 **four hundred fifty-nine**
10. 6,205 **six thousand, two hundred five**
11. 8,981 **eight thousand, nine hundred eighty-one**

Solve.

12. During recess, you and a friend decide to walk a mile around the school track. A mile equals 5,280 feet. Write this distance in expanded form. **5,000 + 200 + 80**

13. Use the digits 4, 8, 3, and 6. Make the smallest number you can. Then make the largest number you can **3,468; 8,643**

 Use with Grade 3, text pages 20–21.

Reteach

Reading and Writing Four-Digit Numbers R 1-7

Numbers with four digits show thousands.

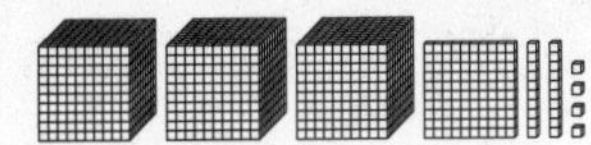

Write the number in expanded form.

3 thousands 1 hundreds 2 tens 4 ones

Write the number in standard form. 3,124

Write each number in expanded form. Then write the number in standard form.

1.

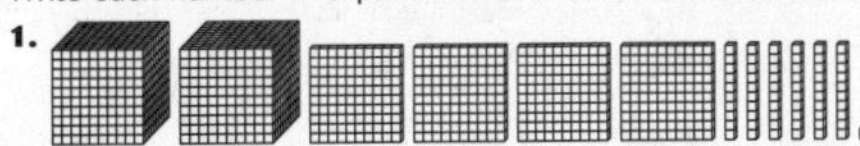

2 thousands **4** hundreds **6** tens **1** ones

standard form **2,461**

2.

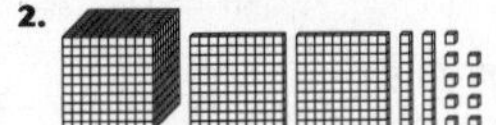

1 thousands **2** hundreds **2** tens **9** ones

standard form **1,229**

3.

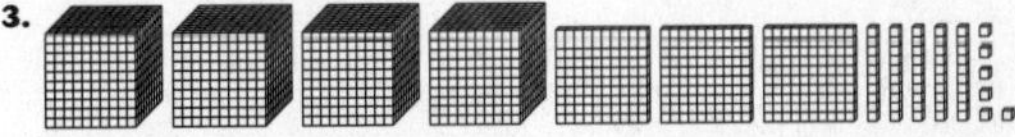

4 thousands **3** hundreds **5** tens **6** ones

standard form **4,356**

 Use with Grade 3, text pages 20–21.

Extend

A Place for Each Number E 1-7

NUMBER SENSE

Each number in the box has a place in the picture. Read the clues and write each number where it belongs.

HINT: Cross out the numbers as you use them.

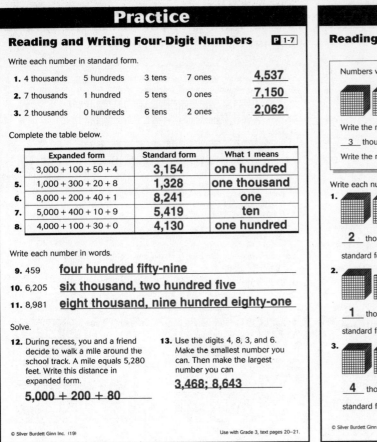

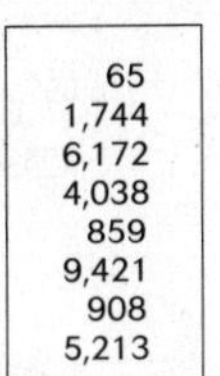

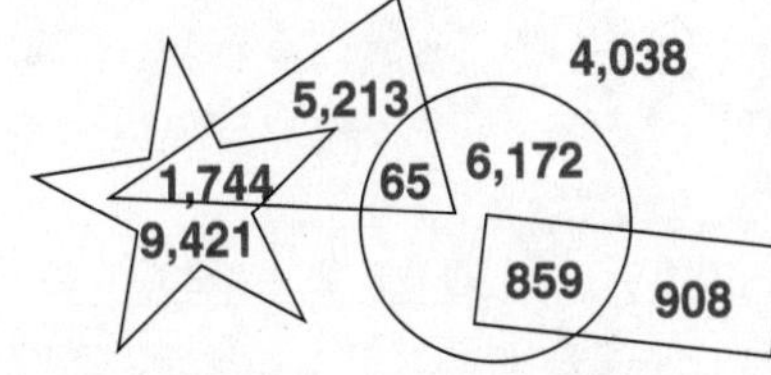

1. Write the number with 8 in the hundreds place inside the circle and the rectangle.
2. Write the number with 5 in the thousands place inside the triangle only.
3. Write the number with 6 in the thousands place inside the circle only.
4. Write the number with 5 in the ones place inside the circle and the triangle.
5. Write the number with 2 in the tens place inside the star only.
6. Write the number with 1 in the thousands place inside the star and the triangle.
7. Write the number with 3 in the tens place so that it is not inside any shape.
8. Write the number with 9 in the hundreds place inside the rectangle only.
9. Where is the two-digit number? **Inside the triangle and the circle.**
10. Where are two numbers whose digits add up to 16? **Inside the star.**
11. Where is the number whose digits add up to 17? **Inside the rectangle.**

 Use with Grade 3, text pages 20–21.

Daily Review

Name ______________________ Daily Review 1-7

Reading and Writing Four-Digit Numbers

Write each number in standard form. Use place-value blocks to help you.

1. 2,000 + 300 + 40 + 2 **2,342**
2. 6,000 + 200 + 60 + 5 **6,265**
3. 4 thousands 9 hundreds 7 tens 3 ones **4,973**
4. 7 thousands 6 hundreds 6 tens 2 ones **7,662**

Write each number in expanded form and in words.

5. 8,359 **8,000 + 300 + 50 + 9; eight thousand, three hundred fifty-nine**
6. 7,428 **7,000 + 400 + 20 + 8; seven thousand, four hundred twenty-eight**

Problem Solving

Solve.

7. A town has collected 1,236 tons of newspaper. If the town adds another collection of 4,000 tons, then how many tons of newspaper are there altogether? **5,236 tons**
8. Use the digits 4, 9, 2, and 1. Write the greatest possible four-digit number. Write the least possible four-digit number. **9,421** ; **1,249**

Review and Remember

Write the total amount.

9. 2 quarters, 6 dimes, 1 nickel **$1.15**
10. 1 quarter, 1 dime, 2 nickels **45¢**
11. 3 dimes, 3 nickels, 12 pennies **57¢**
12. 4 quarters, 4 pennies **$1.04**

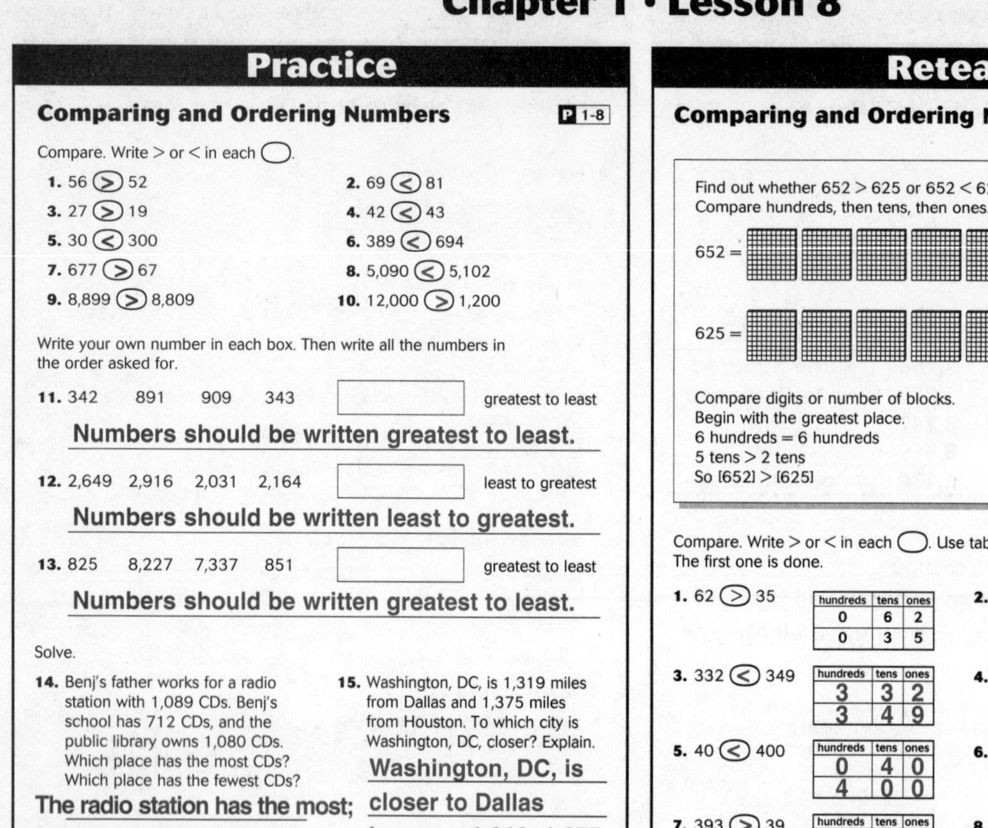

Practice

Comparing and Ordering Numbers

P 1-8

Compare. Write > or < in each ◯.

1. 56 (>) 52
2. 69 (<) 81
3. 27 (>) 19
4. 42 (<) 43
5. 30 (<) 300
6. 389 (<) 694
7. 677 (>) 67
8. 5,090 (<) 5,102
9. 8,899 (>) 8,809
10. 12,000 (>) 1,200

Write your own number in each box. Then write all the numbers in the order asked for.

11. 342 891 909 343 [ ] greatest to least

Numbers should be written greatest to least.

12. 2,649 2,916 2,031 2,164 [ ] least to greatest

Numbers should be written least to greatest.

13. 825 8,227 7,337 851 [ ] greatest to least

Numbers should be written greatest to least.

Solve.

14. Benj's father works for a radio station with 1,089 CDs. Benj's school has 712 CDs, and the public library owns 1,080 CDs. Which place has the most CDs? Which place has the fewest CDs?

The radio station has the most; Benj's school has the least.

15. Washington, DC, is 1,319 miles from Dallas and 1,375 miles from Houston. To which city is Washington, DC, closer? Explain.

Washington, DC, is closer to Dallas because 1,319<1,375.

 Use with Grade 3, text pages 22–25.

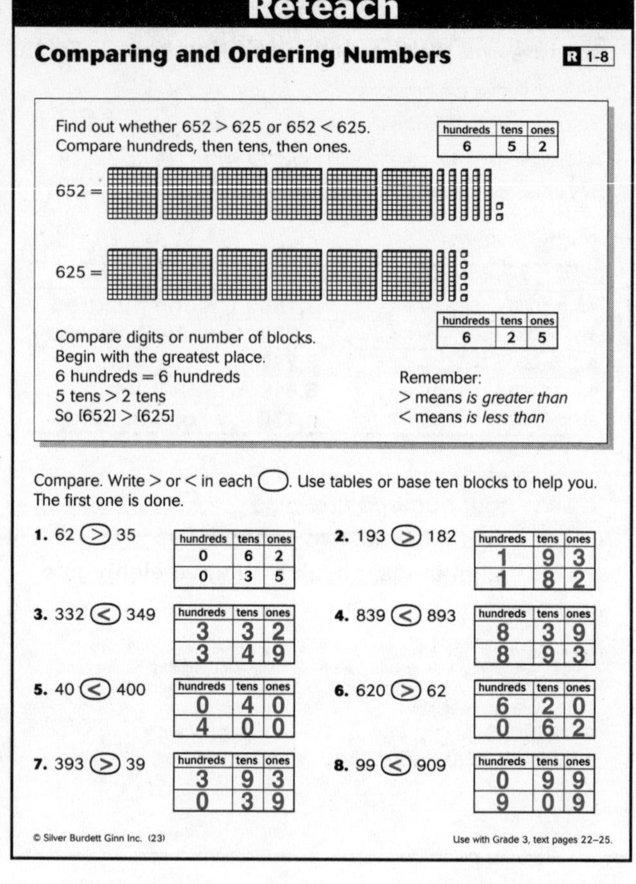

Reteach

Comparing and Ordering Numbers

R 1-8

Find out whether 652 > 625 or 652 < 625.
Compare hundreds, then tens, then ones.

hundreds	tens	ones
6	5	2

652 =

625 =

hundreds	tens	ones
6	2	5

Compare digits or number of blocks.
Begin with the greatest place.
6 hundreds = 6 hundreds
5 tens > 2 tens
So [652] > [625]

Remember:
> means *is greater than*
< means *is less than*

Compare. Write > or < in each ◯. Use tables or base ten blocks to help you. The first one is done.

1. 62 (>) 35

hundreds	tens	ones
0	6	2
0	3	5

2. 193 (>) 182

hundreds	tens	ones
1	9	3
1	8	2

3. 332 (<) 349

hundreds	tens	ones
3	3	2
3	4	9

4. 839 (<) 893

hundreds	tens	ones
8	3	9
8	9	3

5. 40 (<) 400

hundreds	tens	ones
0	4	0
4	0	0

6. 620 (>) 62

hundreds	tens	ones
6	2	0
0	6	2

7. 393 (>) 39

hundreds	tens	ones
3	9	3
0	3	9

8. 99 (<) 909

hundreds	tens	ones
0	9	9
9	0	9

 Use with Grade 3, text pages 22–25.

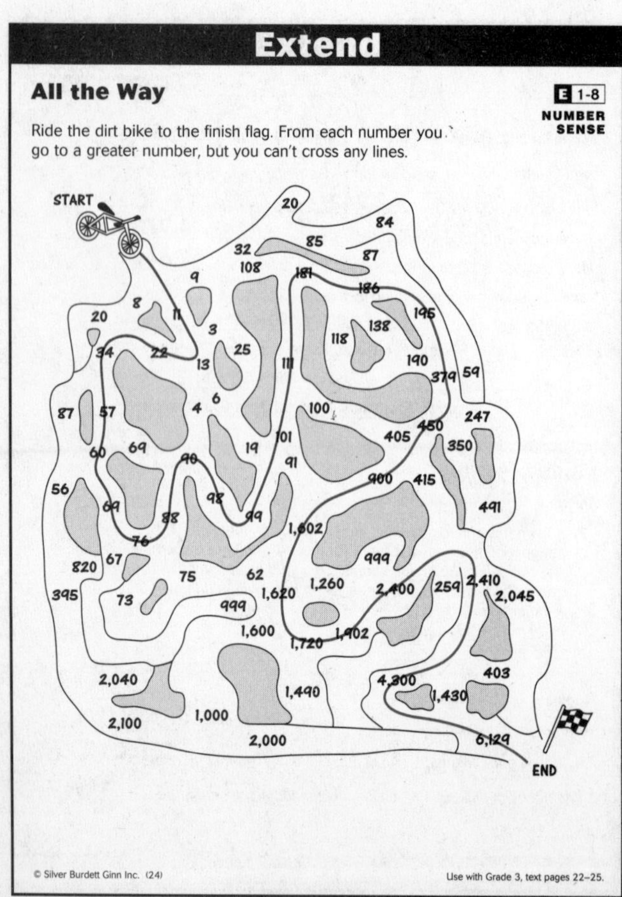

Extend

All the Way

E 1-8
NUMBER SENSE

Ride the dirt bike to the finish flag. From each number you go to a greater number, but you can't cross any lines.

 Use with Grade 3, text pages 22–25.

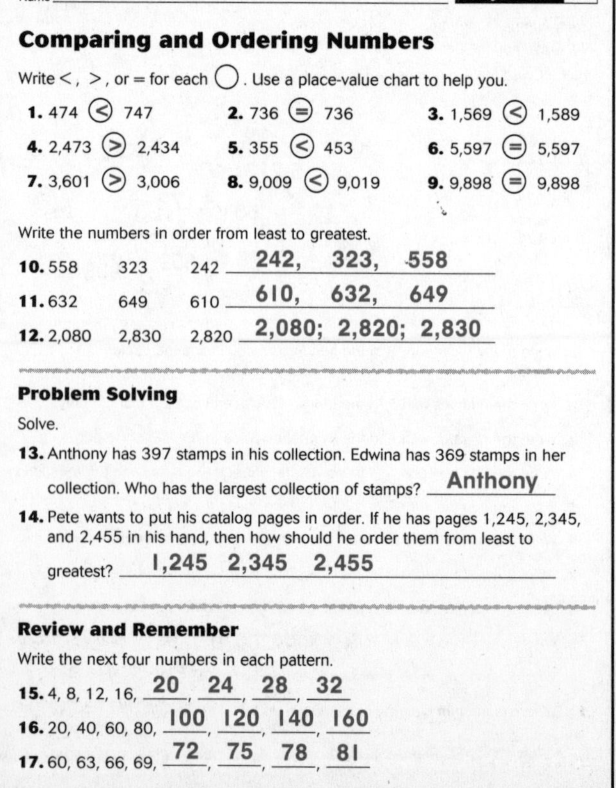

Daily Review

Name ______________________

Daily Review 1-8

Comparing and Ordering Numbers

Write <, >, or = for each ◯. Use a place-value chart to help you.

1. 474 (<) 747
2. 736 (=) 736
3. 1,569 (<) 1,589
4. 2,473 (>) 2,434
5. 355 (<) 453
6. 5,597 (=) 5,597
7. 3,601 (>) 3,006
8. 9,009 (<) 9,019
9. 9,898 (=) 9,898

Write the numbers in order from least to greatest.

10. 558 323 242 242, 323, 558
11. 632 649 610 610, 632, 649
12. 2,080 2,830 2,820 2,080; 2,820; 2,830

Problem Solving

Solve.

13. Anthony has 397 stamps in his collection. Edwina has 369 stamps in her collection. Who has the largest collection of stamps? Anthony

14. Pete wants to put his catalog pages in order. If he has pages 1,245, 2,345, and 2,455 in his hand, then how should he order them from least to greatest? 1,245 2,345 2,455

Review and Remember

Write the next four numbers in each pattern.

15. 4, 8, 12, 16, 20, 24, 28, 32
16. 20, 40, 60, 80, 100, 120, 140, 160
17. 60, 63, 66, 69, 72, 75, 78, 81

Practice

Problem Solving P 1-9

Use Logical Reasoning

Use logical reasoning to solve each problem.

1. Five students line up from shortest to tallest. Adam is taller than Jamie but shorter than Thuy. Kim is taller than Thuy but shorter than Staci. In what order do the students line up?
   Jamie, Adam, Thuy, Kim, and Staci

2. Hank asked Aaron how many runs Aaron's team scored in the softball game. Aaron said, "We scored an odd number of runs. It was more than 4, less than 9, and it was not 5." How many runs did Aaron's team score?
   7 runs

3. A cat, a dog, a bird, and an iguana line up. The dog is after the bird but before the iguana. The iguana is before the cat. Who is first in line?
   the bird

4. A dance class has between 10 and 18 students. There are fewer than 17 students but more than 13. The number of students is odd. How many students are in the class?
   15 students

5. Carl wrote a 3-digit number less than 300 with the digits 1, 3, and 5. The number in the tens place was greater than the number in the ones place. What number did Carl write?
   153

6. Don is younger than Marta but older than Suzie. Bill is older than Don but younger than Marta. Who is oldest? Who is youngest?
   Marta; Suzie

 Use with Grade 3, text pages 26–27.

Reteach

Problem Solving R 1-9

Use Logical Reasoning

The Links Company makes connecting cubes.
In one rod of connecting cubes, the red cube is on top of the yellow cube.
The blue cube is on top of the red cube.
The green cube is below the yellow cube.
What is the order of the cubes in the rod?

1. How can you solve the problem?

Understand You need to find the order of the cubes in the rod.

Plan You can write the names of the colors to show each clue in the problem.

Solve

The red cube is on top of the yellow cube.	The blue cube is on top of the red cube.	The green cube is below the yellow cube.
	blue	**blue**
red	**red**	**red**
yellow	**yellow**	**yellow**
		green

Look Back The answer matches each fact in the problem, so it makes sense.

Solve each problem. Use logical reasoning to help you.

2. In one rod, the blue cube is below the green cube. The red cube is above the green cube. The yellow cube is on the bottom. Tell the order of the cubes.
   red, green, blue, yellow

3. Four animals ran in the big race. The cheetah beat the horse. The dog came in after the cat. The horse beat the dog and the cat. In what order did the animals finish?
   cheetah, horse, cat, dog

 Use with Grade 3, text pages 26–27.

Extend

Track Meet

E 1-9 **REASONING**

Mr. Cohen's third-grade students had a track meet.

Use the high-scorers points from the table to solve each problem. Then, use each answer to list the order in which the students named finished the event.

Name	Points
Frank	8
Nancy	7
Trung	6
Judy	5
Dan	3
Virginia	2

For example: 286 would be Virginia, Frank, Trung.

1. **Long Jump Results**
   Nancy's, Judy's, and Dan's points make a number that is less than 600. The sum of the ones and hundreds digits is one more than the tens digit. The ones digit is greater than the hundreds digit.
   375; Dan, Nancy, Judy

2. **25-Yard Dash**
   Trung's, Virginia's, and Frank's points form a 3-digit number. The sum of the tens and ones digits equals the hundreds digit. The tens digit is greater than the ones digit.
   862; Frank, Trung, Virginia

3. **Jump Rope Medley**
   Dan's, Judy's, and Frank's points form a 3-digit number that is less than 400. The sum of the hundreds and tens digits equals the ones digit.
   358; Dan, Judy, Frank

4. **Obstacle Course**
   Judy, Dan, and Virginia won first, second, and third. On the back of this page, make up a number riddle for the their scores.
   Number should be 532.

Write down the point scores for Trung, Nancy, and Dan. Then try guessing the 3-digit number and check it against the clues. Can you find the answer that way?

5. Trung's, Nancy's and Dan's points form a 3-digit number. The hundreds digit is 3 more than the tens digit. The ones digit is the largest number.
   637; Trung, Dan, Nancy

 Use with Grade 3, text pages 26–27.

Daily Review

Name ____________________ Daily Review 1-9

Problem Solving

Use Logical Reasoning

Use logical reasoning to solve each problem.

1. Paul said that he couldn't meet the group until after 3:30. Renee had to work until 4:30, and Pat had to be home by 5:15. Carrie was available from 2:00 to 5:00. When could the group meet?
   from 4:30 to 5:00

2. Holly is trying to get her friend to guess the three digits of her address. The first digit is a 6, and the last two digits have a sum of 5. Her last clue is that the difference between the first and last digits is 4. What is Holly's address?
   632

3. Brian likes to put important messages on the bulletin board with red pins, and reminders with blue pins. There are 3 important messages and 5 reminders already posted. There are 10 red pins and 6 blue pins in all. How many red pins does Brian have left?
   7 red pins

4. Becca and Michael were hunting for caterpillars. They found 7 in the park and 4 more in the parking lot. Then Julene gave them 3 more. If Becca and Michael share the caterpillars equally, how many will each one have?
   7 caterpillars

Review and Remember

Write >, <, or = for each.

5. 213 **(>)** 132
6. 8,634 **(>)** 8,629
7. 908 **(<)** 918

Practice

Extending Place-Value Concepts

P 1-10

Write each number.

1. 33 thousands 9 hundreds 2 tens 2 ones **33,922**
2. 122 thousands 3 hundreds 5 tens 4 ones **122,354**
3. 989 thousands 3 hundreds 8 tens 8 ones **989,388**
4. 70,000 + 100 + 90 + 2 **70,192**
5. 902,000 + 500 + 40 + 1 **902,541**
6. ninety-nine thousand, thirty **99,030**
7. four hundred two thousand, six hundred one **402,601**

Write the value of the digit 5 in each number.

8. 50,143 **50,000**
9. 625,002 **5,000**
10. 99,945 **5**
11. 567,361 **500,000**
12. 29,567 **500**
13. 971,853 **50**

Give the next number in the pattern.

14. 810,000 820,000 830,000 **840,000**
15. 59,700 59,800 59,900 **60,000**

Solve.

16. A football stadium had 43,000 seats. A new section with 10,000 seats was added. How many seats are in the stadium now? **53,000**

17. A calculator display shows the number 850. You want it to show 9,850. What should you do to the displayed number? **Add 9,000 to the displayed number.**

 Use with Grade 3, text pages 28–29.

Reteach

Extending Place-Value Concepts

R 1-10

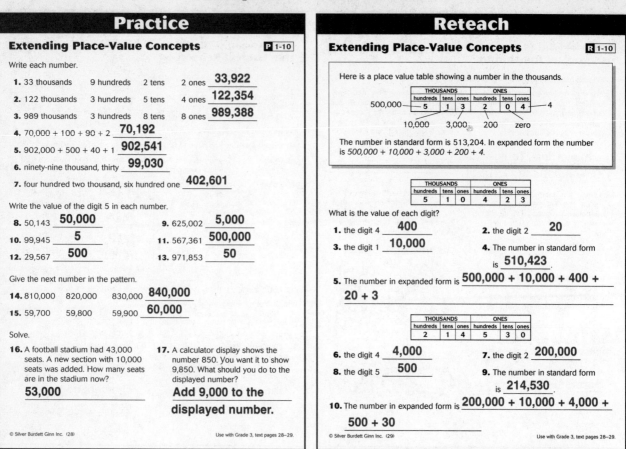

Here is a place value table showing a number in the thousands.

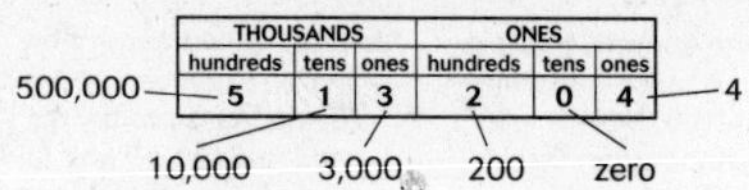

THOUSANDS			ONES		
hundreds	tens	ones	hundreds	tens	ones
5	1	3	2	0	4

The number in standard form is 513,204. In expanded form the number is *500,000 + 10,000 + 3,000 + 200 + 4.*

THOUSANDS			ONES		
hundreds	tens	ones	hundreds	tens	ones
5	1	0	4	2	3

What is the value of each digit?

1. the digit 4 **400**
2. the digit 2 **20**
3. the digit 1 **10,000**
4. The number in standard form is **510,423**.
5. The number in expanded form is **500,000 + 10,000 + 400 + 20 + 3**

THOUSANDS			ONES		
hundreds	tens	ones	hundreds	tens	ones
2	1	4	5	3	0

6. the digit 4 **4,000**
7. the digit 2 **200,000**
8. the digit 5 **500**
9. The number in standard form is **214,530**.
10. The number in expanded form is **200,000 + 10,000 + 4,000 + 500 + 30**

 Use with Grade 3, text pages 28–29.

Extend

True or False?

E 1-10

REASONING

Circle each answer. The first one is done for you.

1. My number is greater than 5. So my number could be 4. true (false)
2. My number is less than 50. So my number could not be 70. 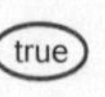 (true) false
3. Our numbers cannot be the same. So our numbers cannot both be 500. (true) false
4. James's number is greater than 2,000 but less than 5,000. So James's number could be 4,000.  (true) false
5. My number is 2 times your number. So my number is less than your number. true (false)
6. George's number is 14,000. Kelly's number is half of 14,000. So Kelly's number is 8,000. true (false)
7. Rich's number is 3,000. Loretta's number is 12,000. My number is 5,000 more than Rich's and 4,000 less than Loretta's. So my number could not be 4,000.  (true) false
8. Ursula's number is 600,000. My number is 200,000. So Ursula's number is twice my number. true  (false)

 Use with Grade 3, text pages 28–29.

Daily Review

Name ______________

Daily Review 1-10

Extending Place-Value Concepts

Write each number in standard form.

1. 500,000 + 80,000 + 6,000 + 300 + 20 + 5 **586,325**
2. six hundred fifty thousand, five hundred nine **650,509**
3. 7 hundred thousands, 5 thousands, 9 hundreds, 2 ones **705,902**

Write the value of the underlined number.

4. 46<u>6</u>,790 **6 thousands**
5. <u>6</u>93,805 **6 hundred thousands**
6. 395,<u>8</u>37 **8 hundreds**

Write each number in expanded form.

7. 68,002 **60,000 + 8,000 + 2**
8. 845,900 **800,000 + 40,000 + 5,000 + 900**

Problem Solving

Solve.

9. Pat's Printing Company has 400,000 boxes of white paper, 30,000 boxes of yellow paper, and 500 boxes of green paper. How many boxes of paper does the company have altogether? **430,500 boxes**
10. The printing company has an order for 109,000 notepads. If another order is received for 10,000 notepads, then how many notepads are ordered? **119,000 notepads**

Review and Remember

Write the next two numbers in each pattern.

11. 6, 11, 16, 21 **26**, **31**
12. 25, 45, 65, 85, **105**, **125**

Practice

Counting Coins and Bills

P 1-11

Write each value.

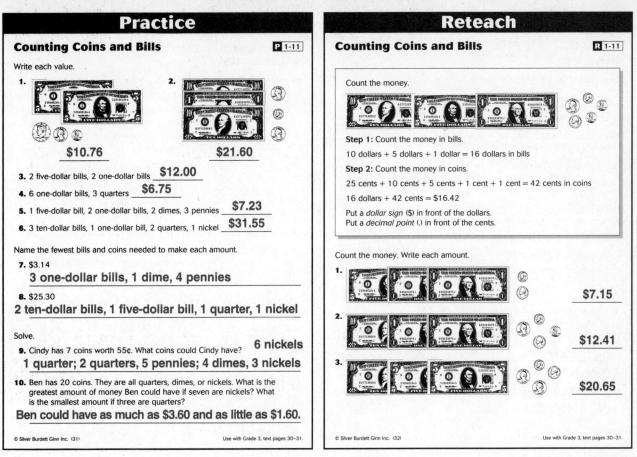

1. $10.76

2. $21.60

3. 2 five-dollar bills, 2 one-dollar bills $12.00

4. 6 one-dollar bills, 3 quarters $6.75

5. 1 five-dollar bill, 2 one-dollar bills, 2 dimes, 3 pennies $7.23

6. 3 ten-dollar bills, 1 one-dollar bill, 2 quarters, 1 nickel $31.55

Name the fewest bills and coins needed to make each amount.

7. $3.14

3 one-dollar bills, 1 dime, 4 pennies

8. $25.30

2 ten-dollar bills, 1 five-dollar bill, 1 quarter, 1 nickel

Solve.

9. Cindy has 7 coins worth 55¢. What coins could Cindy have? 6 nickels

1 quarter; 2 quarters, 5 pennies; 4 dimes, 3 nickels

10. Ben has 20 coins. They are all quarters, dimes, or nickels. What is the greatest amount of money Ben could have if seven are nickels? What is the smallest amount if three are quarters?

Ben could have as much as $3.60 and as little as $1.60.

 Use with Grade 3, text pages 30–31.

Reteach

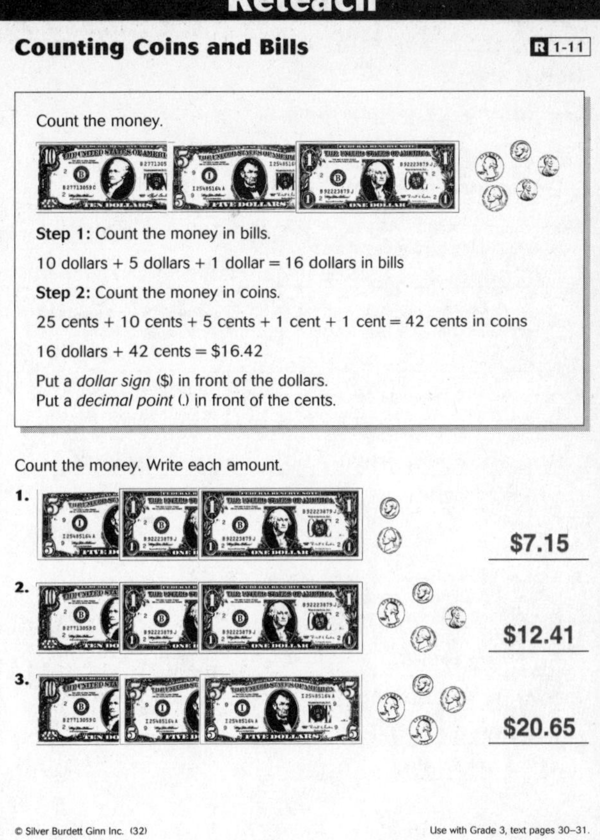

Counting Coins and Bills

R 1-11

Count the money.

Step 1: Count the money in bills.

10 dollars + 5 dollars + 1 dollar = 16 dollars in bills

Step 2: Count the money in coins.

25 cents + 10 cents + 5 cents + 1 cent + 1 cent = 42 cents in coins

16 dollars + 42 cents = $16.42

Put a *dollar sign* ($) in front of the dollars.
Put a *decimal point* (.) in front of the cents.

Count the money. Write each amount.

1. $7.15

2. $12.41

3. $20.65

 Use with Grade 3, text pages 30–31.

Extend

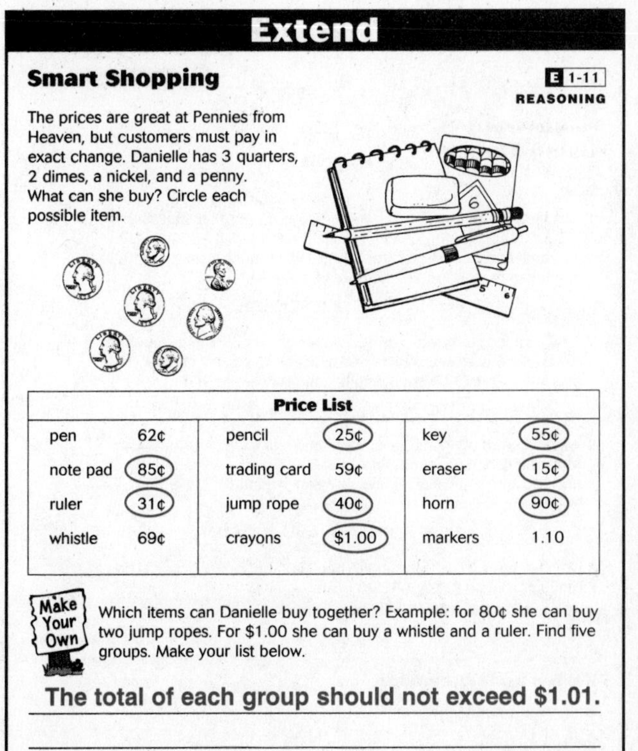

Smart Shopping

E 1-11
REASONING

The prices are great at Pennies from Heaven, but customers must pay in exact change. Danielle has 3 quarters, 2 dimes, a nickel, and a penny. What can she buy? Circle each possible item.

Price List					
pen	62¢	pencil	(25¢)	key	(55¢)
note pad	(85¢)	trading card	59¢	eraser	(15¢)
ruler	(31¢)	jump rope	(40¢)	horn	(90¢)
whistle	69¢	crayons	($1.00)	markers	1.10

Make Your Own

Which items can Danielle buy together? Example: for 80¢ she can buy two jump ropes. For $1.00 she can buy a whistle and a ruler. Find five groups. Make your list below.

The total of each group should not exceed $1.01.

 Use with Grade 3, text pages 30–31.

Daily Review

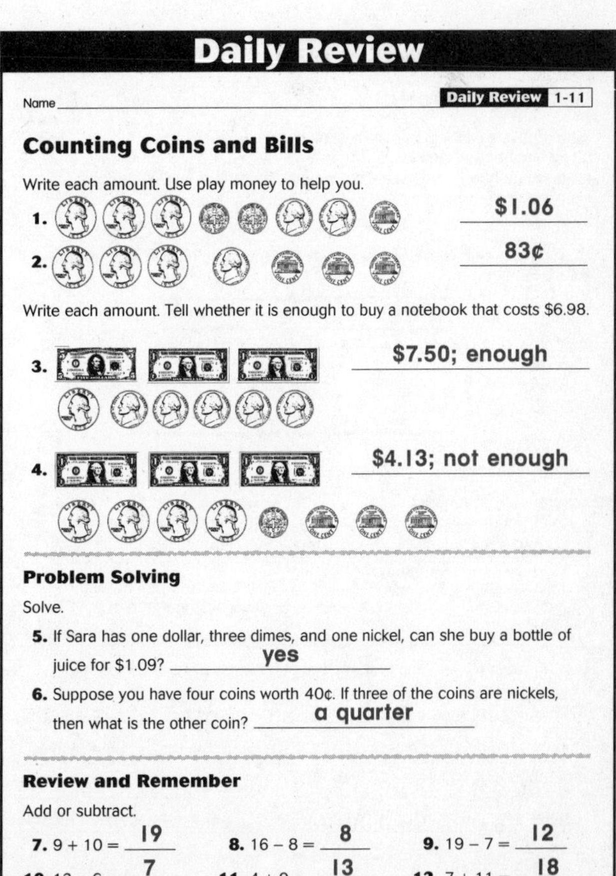

Name ____________________ Daily Review 1-11

Counting Coins and Bills

Write each amount. Use play money to help you.

1. $1.06

2. 83¢

Write each amount. Tell whether it is enough to buy a notebook that costs $6.98.

3. $7.50; enough

4. $4.13; not enough

Problem Solving

Solve.

5. If Sara has one dollar, three dimes, and one nickel, can she buy a bottle of juice for $1.09? yes

6. Suppose you have four coins worth 40¢. If three of the coins are nickels, then what is the other coin? a quarter

Review and Remember

Add or subtract.

7. 9 + 10 = 19 8. 16 − 8 = 8 9. 19 − 7 = 12

10. 13 − 6 = 7 11. 4 + 9 = 13 12. 7 + 11 = 18

Chapter 1 • Lesson 12

Practice

Problem Solving P 1-12

Using Money

Solve. **Possible answers given.**

1. Shelly gave the clerk $2.00 to pay for a birthday card that costs $1.59. What coins could Shelly have received for change?
   One penny, 1 nickel, 1 dime, and 1 quarter
2. Jules bought a game for $8.68. He gave the clerk a $10 bill. What coins and bills could Jules have received for change?
   Two pennies, 1 nickel, 1 quarter, and 1 dollar bill
3. Greta received 6 coins change from a $5 bill. She made a $4.37 purchase. Three of the coins were pennies. What were the other three coins?
   1 dime, 2 quarters
4. Ron spent $5.75 playing video games and $1.25 on a basketball-shooting game. Geraldo bought an all-day pass for $8.00. Who will receive more change back from a $10 bill? Explain.
   Ron; he spent only $7.00, so he will receive $3.00 change.

Create Your Own

5. Suppose you want to buy a painting set for $3.74. Decide how much you will give the clerk, and what change you will receive.
   Answers will vary; change should include 1 penny and 1 quarter or its equivalent.

 Use with Grade 3, text pages 32-33.

Reteach

Problem Solving R 1-12

Using Money

You give the clerk a $5.00 bill for a calculator that costs $3.69.

1. How much change should you get back?

Understand You need to get change to make up the difference between $3.69 and $5.00.

Plan Count up from $3.69 to $5.00.

You give the clerk $5.00 | You buy a calculator for $3.69 | You get back

$3.70 **$3.75** **$4.00** **$5.00**

The change is **$1.31**.

Look Back Add $1.31 + $3.69. It equals $5.00. The answer makes sense.

Suppose you give the clerk $5.00 for each item you buy. Count on to check the change. Write the amounts that you would say under each kind of coin. One is done for you. **Possible answers given.**

	Price of Item	Pennies	Nickels	Dimes	Quarters	Fifty-cents	Dollars	Your Change
2.	$2.49	$2.50	–	–	$2.75, $3.00	–	$4.00, $5.00	$2.51
3.	$4.58	**$4.59, $4.60**	**$4.65**	**$4.75**	**$5.00**	–	–	**$.42**
4.	$1.89	**$1.90**	–	**$2.00**	–	–	**$3.00, $4.00, $5.00**	**$3.11**

 Use with Grade 3, text pages 32-33.

Extend

Out of This World

E 1-12 NUMBER SENSE

John bought a package of snapshots on the planet Bruke. It cost $2.16 and he gave the clerk $5.00 of American money. The clerk gave John 2 foos, 4 too-foos, and a foo-bill. He counted out John's change as he gave it to him:

$2.18 $2.20 $2.40 $2.60 $2.80 $3.00 $5.00

How much is each Bruke coin or bill worth in American money? You can make a table to help you.

	Bruke Money	American Money
1.	foo	**2 cents**
2.	too-foo	**20 cents**
3.	foo-bill	**2 dollars**

Solve.

4. John used an American dollar to pay for a magnet that cost 70¢. What Bruke coins will John receive? Count the coins as the clerk would count them.
   72¢ 74¢ 76¢ 78¢ 80¢ $1.00
5. John bought a T-shirt with an American $10 bill. He received 1 foo, 2 too-foos, and 2 foo-bills in change. How much did the shirt cost?
   $5.58
6. John says, "No prices in Bruke can be odd numbers." He is correct. Can you explain why?
   Possible answer: All Bruke coin and bill values are even numbers. Sums and differences of even numbers are always even numbers; so there can be no odd numbers in costs or in change.

 Use with Grade 3, text pages 32-33.

Daily Review

Name ____________________ Daily Review 1-12

Problem Solving

Using Money

Solve.

1. Josh wanted to buy as many stickers as he could with $5. Package A has 18 stickers for $2.25. Package B has 11 stickers for $1.60. Package C has 35 stickers for $3.75. How should Josh spend his money to get the greatest number of stickers?
   Buy 2 A packages
2. Lauren needs to buy two notebooks which cost $1.89 each, two pens which cost $1.35 each, and a binder which costs $3.59. She has $10. Will that be enough to buy the supplies?
   No; the supplies cost $10.07
3. Sarah had $8.00 in her bank. When she emptied it, money spilled onto the floor. She found 3 dollar bills, 9 quarters, 19 dimes, 8 nickels, and 14 pennies. Three coins fell behind the table. What are they?
   1 quarter, 1 nickel, 1 penny
4. Ben bought a $2.19 book at the book fair with his $5 bill. Will he have enough change to buy a $2.60 poster?
   Yes

Review and Remember

Write each number in expanded form.

5. 20,712 **20,000 + 700 + 10 + 2**
6. 533 **500 + 30 + 3**
7. 1,076 **1,000 + 70 + 6**
8. 1,004,005 **1,000,000 + 4,000 + 5**

Chapter 2 • Lesson 1

Practice

Using Addition Strategies

P 2-1

Add. If you count on, color the section red.
If you make a ten, color the section yellow.
If you use doubles, color the section blue.

- $8 + 1 =$ **9** r
- $6 + 7 =$ **13** b
- $9 + 2 =$ **11** r
- $6 + 6 =$ **12** b
- $7 + 5 =$ **12** y
- $5 + 6 =$ **11** b
- $8 + 7 =$ **15** b
- $7 + 4 =$ **11** y
- $7 + 7 =$ **14** b
- $8 + 4 =$ **12** y
- $6 + 5 =$ **11** b
- $9 + 1 =$ **10** r
- $7 + 6 =$ **13** b
- $9 + 5 =$ **14** y
- $9 + 4 =$ **13** y
- $7 + 8 =$ **15** b
- $5 + 2 =$ **7** r
- $9 + 8 =$ **17** b
- $8 + 5 =$ **13** y
- $8 + 8 =$ **16** b
- $8 + 3 =$ **11** y
- $5 + 5 =$ **10** b
- $4 + 5 =$ **9** b
- $9 + 3 =$ **12** y
- $9 + 9 =$ **18** b
- $7 + 2 =$ **9** r
- $8 + 9 =$ **17** b
- $8 + 2 =$ **10** r

Which color did you use the most? **most likely blue**

Why do you think that is? **Most of the numbers were close to each other.**

 Use with Grade 3, text pages 44–47.

Reteach

Using Addition Strategies

R 2-1

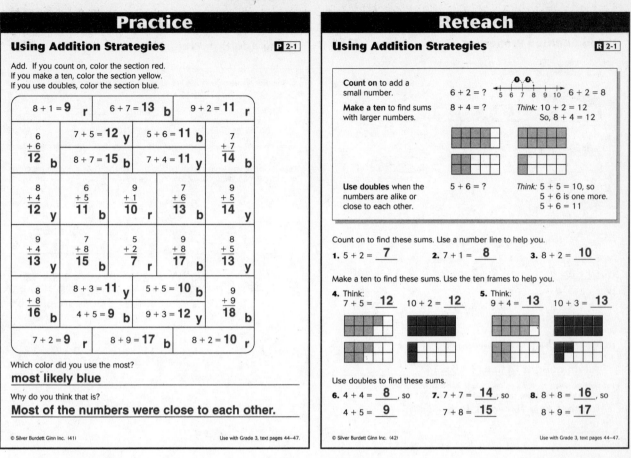

Count on to add a small number. $6 + 2 = ?$

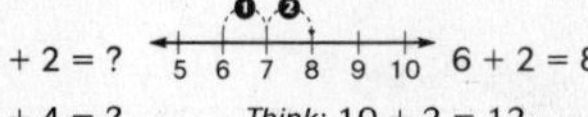

$6 + 2 = 8$

Make a ten to find sums with larger numbers. $8 + 4 = ?$ *Think:* $10 + 2 = 12$ So, $8 + 4 = 12$

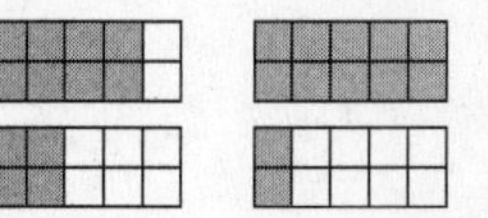

Use doubles when the numbers are alike or close to each other. $5 + 6 = ?$ *Think:* $5 + 5 = 10$, so $5 + 6$ is one more. $5 + 6 = 11$

Count on to find these sums. Use a number line to help you.

1. $5 + 2 =$ **7** **2.** $7 + 1 =$ **8** **3.** $8 + 2 =$ **10**

Make a ten to find these sums. Use the ten frames to help you.

4. Think: $7 + 5 =$ **12** $10 + 2 =$ **12**

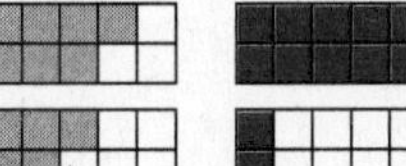

5. Think: $9 + 4 =$ **13** $10 + 3 =$ **13**

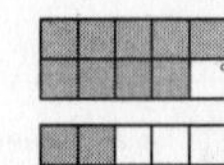

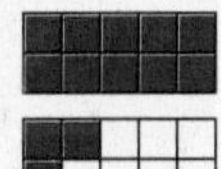

Use doubles to find these sums.

6. $4 + 4 =$ **8**, so $4 + 5 =$ **9**

7. $7 + 7 =$ **14**, so $7 + 8 =$ **15**

8. $8 + 8 =$ **16**, so $8 + 9 =$ **17**

 Use with Grade 3, text pages 44–47.

Extend

Double Puzzle

E 2-1 VISUAL THINKING

Work with a partner. Cut your puzzles into pieces. Mix the two sets together. Then work together to make two completed puzzles that are the same.

 Use with Grade 3, text pages 44–47.

Daily Review

Name________________ Daily Review 2-1

Using Addition Strategies

Count on to find these sums.

1. $4 + 3 =$ **7** **2.** $5 + 2 =$ **7** **3.** $4 + 2 =$ **6** **4.** $6 + 2 =$ **8**

Make a ten to find these sums.

5. $5 + 9 =$ **14** **6.** $8 + 5 =$ **13** **7.** $5 + 6 =$ **11** **8.** $7 + 6 =$ **13**

Use doubles to find these sums.

9. $8 + 9 =$ **17** **10.** $7 + 6 =$ **13** **11.** $4 + 3 =$ **7** **12.** $6 + 7 =$ **13**

Add.

13. $9 + 3 =$ **12** **14.** $2 + 7 =$ **9** **15.** $5 + 8 =$ **13** **16.** $7 + 8 =$ **15** **17.** $5 + 9 =$ **14**

Problem Solving

Write an addition sentence for each.

18. Salina found 5 cubes in her desk and 3 cubes on the floor. How many cubes did she find in all? **5 + 3 = 8**

19. Misha counted 6 stars in the Big Dipper and 5 stars in the Little Dipper. How many stars did he count? **6 + 5 = 11**

20. Henry had 4 eggs in one container an 9 eggs in another. How many eggs did he have in all? **4 + 9 = 13**

Review and Remember

Compare. Write <, >, or = for each.

21. 13 (>) 9 **22.** 63 (<) 630 **23.** 6,977 (=) 6,977

24. 7,533 (>) 7,333 **25.** 45 (<) 54 **26.** 744 (<) 755

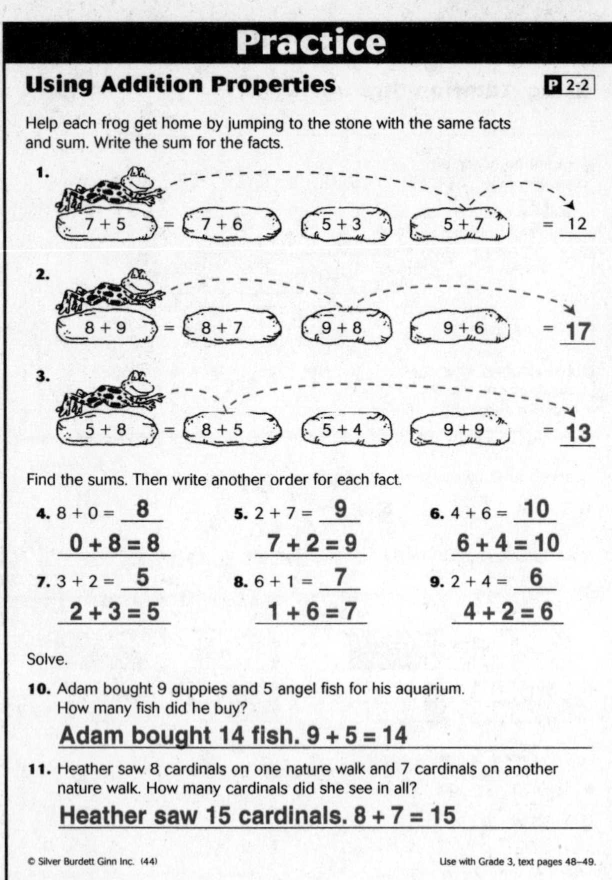

Practice

Using Addition Properties

P 2-2

Help each frog get home by jumping to the stone with the same facts and sum. Write the sum for the facts.

1. 7 + 5 = 7 + 6 | 5 + 3 | 5 + 7 = 12
2. 8 + 9 = 8 + 7 | 9 + 8 | 9 + 6 = 17
3. 5 + 8 = 8 + 5 | 5 + 4 | 9 + 9 = 13

Find the sums. Then write another order for each fact.

4. 8 + 0 = 8
   0 + 8 = 8
5. 2 + 7 = 9
   7 + 2 = 9
6. 4 + 6 = 10
   6 + 4 = 10
7. 3 + 2 = 5
   2 + 3 = 5
8. 6 + 1 = 7
   1 + 6 = 7
9. 2 + 4 = 6
   4 + 2 = 6

Solve.

10. Adam bought 9 guppies and 5 angel fish for his aquarium. How many fish did he buy?
    Adam bought 14 fish. 9 + 5 = 14
11. Heather saw 8 cardinals on one nature walk and 7 cardinals on another nature walk. How many cardinals did she see in all?
    Heather saw 15 cardinals. 8 + 7 = 15

 Use with Grade 3, text pages 48–49.

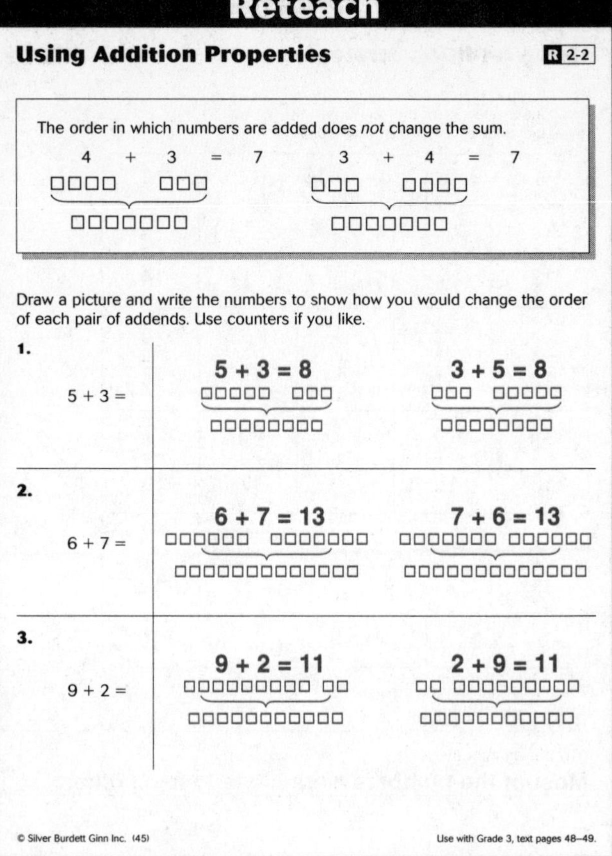

Reteach

Using Addition Properties

R 2-2

The order in which numbers are added does *not* change the sum.

4 + 3 = 7 □□□□ □□□ → □□□□□□□

3 + 4 = 7 □□□ □□□□ → □□□□□□□

Draw a picture and write the numbers to show how you would change the order of each pair of addends. Use counters if you like.

1. 5 + 3 = | 5 + 3 = 8 □□□□□ □□□ → □□□□□□□□ | 3 + 5 = 8 □□□ □□□□□ → □□□□□□□□
2. 6 + 7 = | 6 + 7 = 13 □□□□□□ □□□□□□□ → □□□□□□□□□□□□□ | 7 + 6 = 13 □□□□□□□ □□□□□□ → □□□□□□□□□□□□□
3. 9 + 2 = | 9 + 2 = 11 □□□□□□□□□ □□ → □□□□□□□□□□□ | 2 + 9 = 11 □□ □□□□□□□□□ → □□□□□□□□□□□

 Use with Grade 3, text pages 48–49.

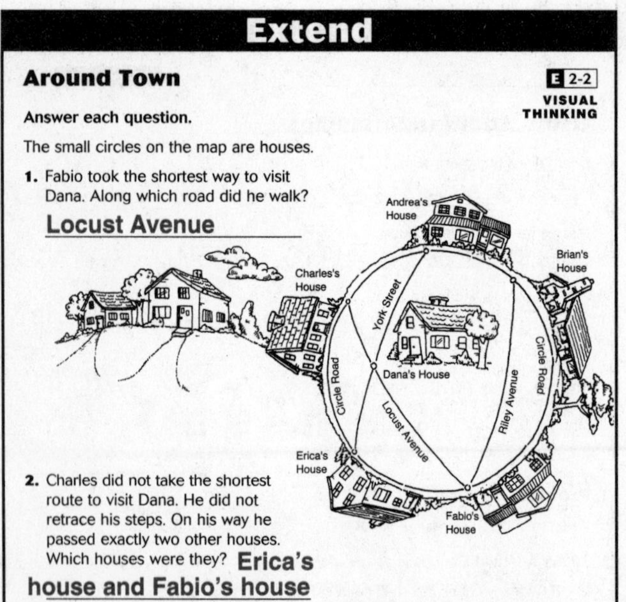

Extend

Around Town

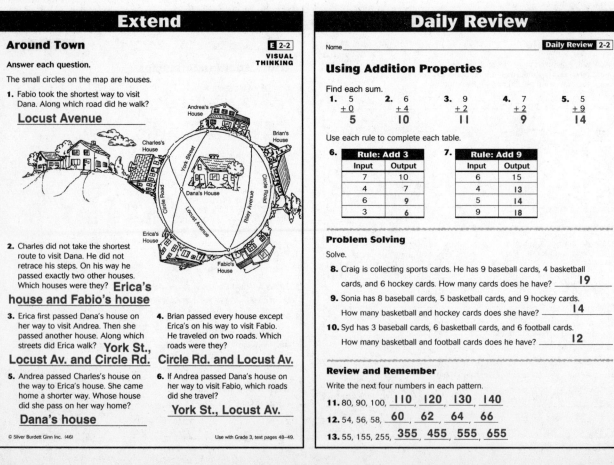

E 2-2 VISUAL THINKING

Answer each question.

The small circles on the map are houses.

1. Fabio took the shortest way to visit Dana. Along which road did he walk?
   Locust Avenue
2. Charles did not take the shortest route to visit Dana. He did not retrace his steps. On his way he passed exactly two other houses. Which houses were they? Erica's house and Fabio's house
3. Erica first passed Dana's house on her way to visit Andrea. Then she passed another house. Along which streets did Erica walk? York St., Locust Av. and Circle Rd.
4. Brian passed every house except Erica's on his way to visit Fabio. He traveled on two roads. Which roads were they?
   Circle Rd. and Locust Av.
5. Andrea passed Charles's house on the way to Erica's house. She came home a shorter way. Whose house did she pass on her way home?
   Dana's house
6. If Andrea passed Dana's house on her way to visit Fabio, which roads did she travel?
   York St., Locust Av.

 Use with Grade 3, text pages 48–49.

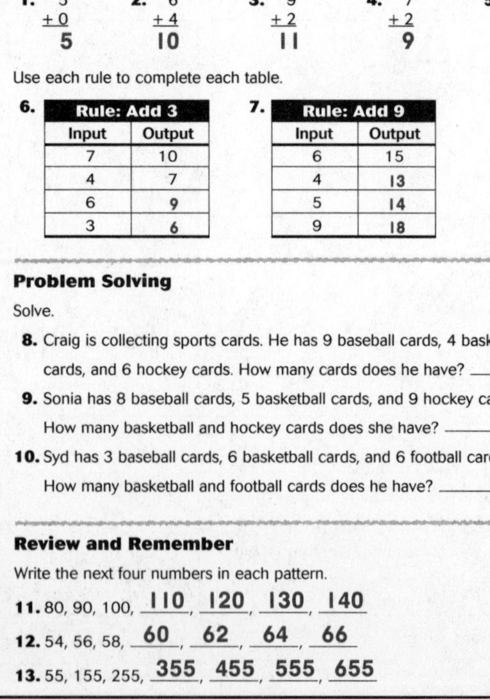

Daily Review

Name ____________ Daily Review 2-2

Using Addition Properties

Find each sum.

1. 5 + 0 = 5
2. 6 + 4 = 10
3. 9 + 2 = 11
4. 7 + 2 = 9
5. 5 + 9 = 14

Use each rule to complete each table.

6.

Rule: Add 3	
Input	Output
7	10
4	7
6	9
3	6

7.

Rule: Add 9	
Input	Output
6	15
4	13
5	14
9	18

Problem Solving

Solve.

8. Craig is collecting sports cards. He has 9 baseball cards, 4 basketball cards, and 6 hockey cards. How many cards does he have? 19
9. Sonia has 8 baseball cards, 5 basketball cards, and 9 hockey cards. How many basketball and hockey cards does she have? 14
10. Syd has 3 baseball cards, 6 basketball cards, and 6 football cards. How many basketball and football cards does he have? 12

Review and Remember

Write the next four numbers in each pattern.

11. 80, 90, 100, 110, 120, 130, 140
12. 54, 56, 58, 60, 62, 64, 66
13. 55, 155, 255, 355, 455, 555, 655

Chapter 2 • Lesson 3

Practice

Adding Three or More Numbers

P 2-3

Add.

1.	2.	3.	4.	5.	6.
6	6	4	5	1	3
1	3	4	4	3	0
+ 7	+ 2	+ 6	+ 0	+ 4	+ 7
14	**11**	**14**	**9**	**8**	**10**

7.	8.	9.	10.	11.	12.
4	6	8	2	3	5
6	0	1	3	2	4
+ 3	+ 5	+ 3	+ 8	+ 5	+ 4
13	**11**	**12**	**13**	**10**	**13**

Use these numbers: 4, 0, 2, 3, 6.

13. Write the sum of the numbers greater than 2. **13**

14. Write the sum of the numbers less than 4. **5**

Solve.

15. Esteban saw squirrels in his backyard. One day, he saw 5, then 4, then 2 squirrels. How many squirrels did Esteban see?

Esteban saw 11 squirrels.

16. Laura wanted to add fish to her tank. She bought 3 mollies on Monday, 5 guppies on Tuesday, and 6 angel fish on Wednesday. How many fish did Laura add to her tank?

Laura added 14 fish to her tank.

17. Tanya had 4 bear stickers, 6 deer stickers, and 3 fox stickers. How many stickers did Tanya have?

Tanya had 13 stickers.

 Use with Grade 3, text pages 50–51.

Reteach

Adding Three or More Numbers

R 2-3

You can group addends in different ways.

Add down				Add up		
3	ΔΔΔ	5	OR	3	ΔΔΔ	3
2	ΔΔ			2	ΔΔ	
+ 4	ΔΔΔΔ	+ 4		+ 4	ΔΔΔΔ	+ 6
		9				9

Either way, the sum is 9.

Group the addends to find the sums.

	Add down				Add up		
1.	2	ΔΔ		OR	2	ΔΔ	**2**
	5	ΔΔΔΔΔ	**7**		5	ΔΔΔΔΔ	
	+ 1	Δ	+ **1**		+ 1	Δ	+ **6**
			8				**8**
2.	7	ΔΔΔΔΔΔΔ		OR	7	ΔΔΔΔΔΔΔ	**7**
	4	ΔΔΔΔ	**11**		4	ΔΔΔΔ	
	+ 3	ΔΔΔ	+ **3**		+ 3	ΔΔΔ	+ **7**
			14				**14**
3.	5	ΔΔΔΔΔ		OR	5	ΔΔΔΔΔ	**5**
	3	ΔΔΔ	**8**		3	ΔΔΔ	
	+ 4	ΔΔΔΔ	+ **4**		+ 4	ΔΔΔΔ	+ **7**
			12				**12**
4.	8	ΔΔΔΔΔΔΔΔ		OR	8	ΔΔΔΔΔΔΔΔ	**8**
	1	Δ	**9**		1	Δ	
	+ 6	ΔΔΔΔΔΔ	+ **6**		+ 6	ΔΔΔΔΔΔ	+ **7**
			15				**15**

 Use with Grade 3, text pages 50–51.

Extend

Borrowing Books

E 2-3
REASONING

Here are the kinds of books borrowed from the library this week by students in Ms. Swann's third grade class.

Use the clues below to tally the missing information.
HINT: You may have to use clues out of order.

- 5 fewer fairy tales than novels were borrowed.
- The number of biographies borrowed was the same as the number of history books plus the number of fairy tales.
- One more history book than fairy tale was borrowed.
- The number of short-story books borrowed was two more than the number of fairy tales borrowed.
- The number of science books borrowed was the same as the number of history books borrowed.
- 7 people borrowed one novel each.

Now answer the questions.

1. How many nonfiction books were borrowed? Include biography, science, and history books. **11**
2. How many fiction books were borrowed? Include novels, fairy tales, and books of short stories. **13**
3. How many books were borrowed altogether? **24**
4. What kind of book is most popular? What kind is second most popular? What kind is third most popular?

first - novel; second - biography; third - short stories

 Use with Grade 3, text pages 50–51.

Daily Review

Name ____________________

Daily Review 2-3

Adding Three or More Numbers

Find each sum. Add in any order.

1.	2.	3.	4.	5.
5	6	9	7	8
0	3	5	2	5
+ 6	+ 4	+ 2	+ 6	+ 2
11	**13**	**16**	**15**	**15**

6.	7.	8.	9.	10.
4	9	5	7	9
5	3	1	6	7
+ 9	+ 5	6	0	9
		+ 4	+ 1	+ 0
18	**17**	**16**	**14**	**25**

11. 4 + 5 + 1 = **10** 12. 4 + 3 + 5 = **12** 13. 9 + 3 + 1 = **13**

Problem Solving

14. At the children's museum, Henry visited 4 animal exhibits, 3 art exhibits, and 5 science exhibits. How many exhibits did he visit altogether?

12

15. Philippa is sorting her photographs. She has 6 from vacation, 3 from school, and 7 from her birthday. How many photographs does she have to sort?

16

Review and Remember

Write the value of the underlined digit.

16. <u>3</u>,100	17. 54<u>5</u>	18. <u>1</u>0	19. <u>8</u>,450	20. <u>7</u>99
3,000	**5**	**10**	**8,000**	**700**

Chapter 2 • Lesson 4

Practice

Problem Solving

Choose the Operation

P 2-4

Circle the best choice for each question.

Zena and Boris sold wrapping paper for a fundraiser. Zena sold 7 cartons of wrapping paper. Boris sold 9 cartons.

1. Who sold more wrapping paper, Zena or Boris?

(a.) Boris

b. Zena

c. they sold the same amount

2. How would you find out how many more cartons of wrapping paper one student sold than another?

a. add 7 and 9

(b.) subtract 7 from 9

c. subtract 9 from 7

At the amusement park, Zena went on the bumper cars 9 times. Boris went on the bumper cars 8 times. How many more times did Zena ride the bumper cars than Boris?

3. What do you need to find?

a. the cost of a bumper car ride

b. the total number of rides Zena and Boris went on

(c.) the number of times Zena and Boris each rode the bumper cars

4. What number sentence could you use to find the answer?

(a.) 9 − 8 = 1

b. 9 + 8 = 17

c. 9 > 8

5. Suppose you want to know how many times Zena and Boris rode the bumper cars altogether. Would you add or subtract? Tell how you know.

You would add; you are combining the number of rides that both people took.

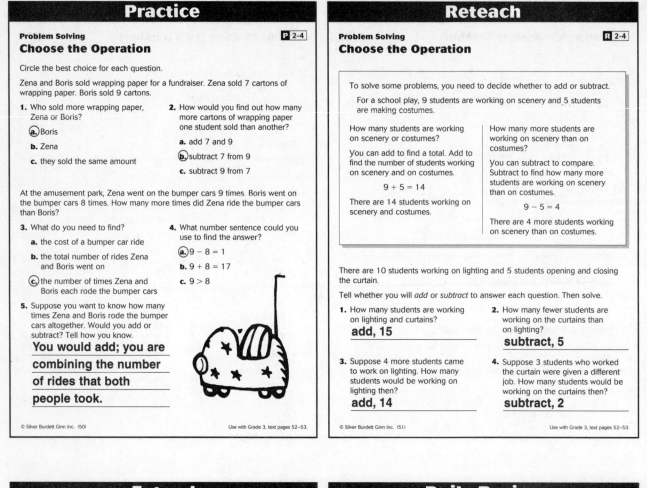

Use with Grade 3, text pages 52–53.

Reteach

Problem Solving

Choose the Operation

R 2-4

To solve some problems, you need to decide whether to add or subtract.

For a school play, 9 students are working on scenery and 5 students are making costumes.

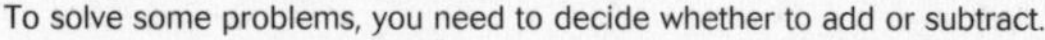

How many students are working on scenery or costumes?

You can add to find a total. Add to find the number of students working on scenery and on costumes.

9 + 5 = 14

There are 14 students working on scenery and costumes.

How many more students are working on scenery than on costumes?

You can subtract to compare. Subtract to find how many more students are working on scenery than on costumes.

9 − 5 = 4

There are 4 more students working on scenery than on costumes.

There are 10 students working on lighting and 5 students opening and closing the curtain.

Tell whether you will *add* or *subtract* to answer each question. Then solve.

1. How many students are working on lighting and curtains?

add, 15

2. How many fewer students are working on the curtains than on lighting?

subtract, 5

3. Suppose 4 more students came to work on lighting. How many students would be working on lighting then?

add, 14

4. Suppose 3 students who worked the curtain were given a different job. How many students would be working on the curtains then?

subtract, 2

Use with Grade 3, text pages 52–53.

Extend

Elevator Ride

E 2-4

DATA

Floor	People On and Off the Elevator
1	12 people get on
2	4 people get on; 6 get off
3	8 people get on; 4 get off
4	6 people get on, 5 get off
5	1 person gets off
6	2 people get on, no one gets off
7	
8	
9	
10	

Solve.

1. Look at the table. How many people are on the elevator for each floor 1 through 6? Choose when you need to add and subtract.

1st floor **12** 2nd floor **10**

3rd floor **14** 4th floor **15**

5th floor **14** 6th floor **16**

2. Trade papers with a classmate. Write your own numbers in the table for people on and off the elevator for floors 7 through 10. Trade back and tell how many people are on the elevator for each floor 7 through 10. Make a list to help. **Answers will vary. Check math.**

7th floor ____ 8th floor ____

9th floor ____ 10th floor ____

Use with Grade 3, text pages 52–53.

Daily Review

Name ____________________

Daily Review 2-4

Problem Solving

Choose the Operation

Solve.

1. Rob counted 32 children on the class field trip. When they got on the train the group paid for 46 tickets, which included the adults. How many adults went on the field trip?

a. What are you being asked to find out?

The number of adults

b. What information can you use to answer the question?

Number of tickets; number of children

c. What will you do to find the answer?

Subtract

d. How many adults went on the trip?

14 adults

2. Marissa learned that two states in the United States do not border any other states. She knows that the American flag has 50 stars, one for each state. Write the number sentence Marissa will use to find the number of states which border other states.

50 − 2 = 48

3. Cory went to the beach with his family and his neighbor's family. There were 3 people in his family and 5 in his neighbor's family. Each person had a beach chair. Write the sentence that shows how many beach chairs the group took.

3 + 5 = 8

Review and Remember

Add or subtract.

4. 23 + 8 = **31** **5.** 223 − 26 = **197** **6.** 304 + 6 = **310**

Practice

Using Subtraction Strategies
P 2-5

Write each difference.

1. 6 − 3 = **3**
2. 17 − 8 = **9**
3. 10 − 10 = **0**
4. 8 − 4 = **4**
5. 13 − 8 = **5**
6. 9 − 2 = **7**
7. 18 − 9 = **9**
8. 1 − 1 = **0**
9. 14 − 8 = **6**
10. 11 − 7 = **4**
11. 8 − 3 = **5**
12. 10 − 5 = **5**

Write the letter of the correct difference.

13. 15 − 6 = **b**
   a. 11 b. 9 c. 7 d. 3

14. **a** = 12 − 5
   a. 7 b. 9 c. 4 d. 17

15. 4 − 4 = **c**
   a. 8 b. 2 c. 0 d. 6

16. **d** = 6 − 0
   a. 5 b. 7 c. 0 d. 6

Solve.

17. Mrs. Tran needs 14 plates and 5 forks for the picnic at the wildlife preserve. She has 6 plates and 2 forks. How many more plates does Mrs. Tran need? How many forks?
   8 plates, 3 forks

18. Tomás needs 11 boxes and 4 long sticks to complete his birdhouse project. He has 6 boxes and 2 sticks. How many more boxes and sticks does Tomás need?
   5 boxes, 2 sticks

Use with Grade 3, text pages 56–57.

Reteach

Using Subtraction Strategies
R 2-5

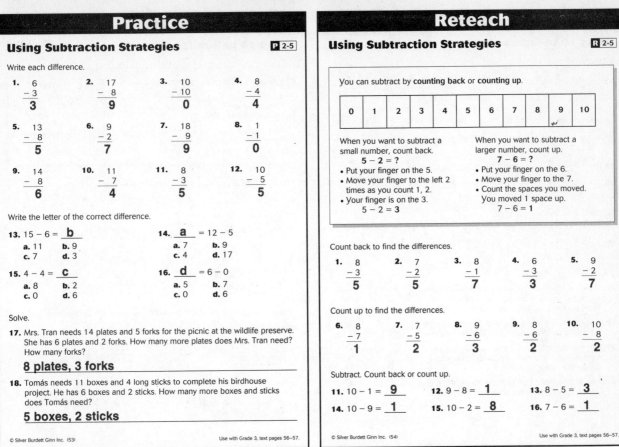

You can subtract by **counting back** or **counting up**.

0	1	2	3	4	5	6	7	8	9	10

When you want to subtract a small number, count back.
5 − 2 = ?
- Put your finger on the 5.
- Move your finger to the left 2 times as you count 1, 2.
- Your finger is on the 3.

5 − 2 = 3

When you want to subtract a larger number, count up.
7 − 6 = ?
- Put your finger on the 6.
- Move your finger to the 7.
- Count the spaces you moved. You moved 1 space up.

7 − 6 = 1

Count back to find the differences.

1. 8 − 3 = **5**
2. 7 − 2 = **5**
3. 8 − 1 = **7**
4. 6 − 3 = **3**
5. 9 − 2 = **7**

Count up to find the differences.

6. 8 − 7 = **1**
7. 7 − 5 = **2**
8. 9 − 6 = **3**
9. 8 − 6 = **2**
10. 10 − 8 = **2**

Subtract. Count back or count up.

11. 10 − 1 = **9**
12. 9 − 8 = **1**
13. 8 − 5 = **3**
14. 10 − 9 = **1**
15. 10 − 2 = **8**
16. 7 − 6 = **1**

Use with Grade 3, text pages 56–57.

Extend

A Snail's Homework
E 2-5 PROBLEM SOLVING

Complete each section of the snail's shell. Add and subtract.

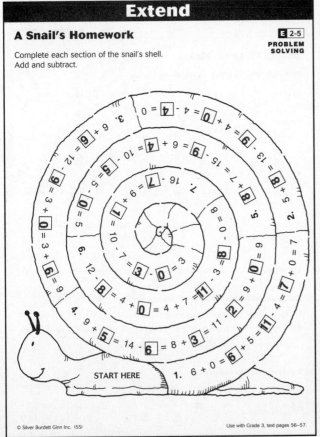

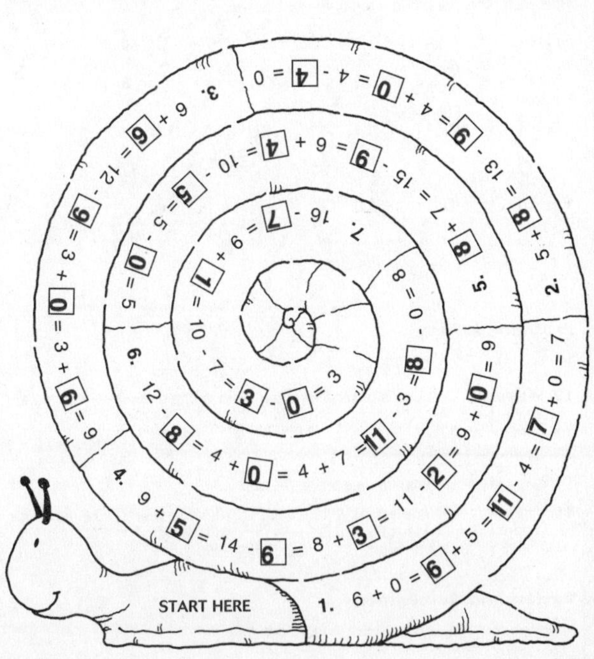

Use with Grade 3, text pages 56–57.

Daily Review

Name ______________________
Daily Review 2-5

Using Subtraction Strategies

Find each difference. Count back or up.

1. 5 − 0 = **5**
2. 7 − 3 = **4**
3. 9 − 5 = **4**
4. 14 − 9 = **5**
5. 8 − 2 = **6**
6. 9 − 2 = **7**
7. 8 − 3 = **5**
8. 10 − 6 = **4**
9. 12 − 5 = **7**
10. 6 − 4 = **2**
11. 4 − 4 = **0**
12. 4 − 3 = **1**
13. 9 − 3 = **6**
14. 7 − 1 = **6**

Problem Solving

Solve.

15. Philana checked out 3 books at the library. Eva checked out 4 books. Sam checked out 9 books. How many more books did Sam check out than Philana? **6**
16. Evon has 7 guppies in his aquarium. If he adds 3 guppies from Nini's aquarium, then how many guppies will Evon have? **10**
17. Clare needed 12 plates for her dinner party. She has 7 plates. How many plates does she need to borrow from Max? **5**

Review and Remember

Find each sum or difference.

18. 8 + 4 = **12**
19. 9 − 3 = **6**
20. 14 + 9 = **23**
21. 19 − 0 = **19**
22. 5 + 11 = **16**
23. 15 − 6 = **9**

Practice

Using 10 to Subtract

P 2-6

Subtract.

1. $16 - 9 = $ **7**
2. $9 - 2 = $ **7**
3. $13 - 8 = $ **5**
4. $12 - 8 = $ **4**
5. $15 - 9 = $ **6**
6. $8 - 1 = $ **7**
7. $11 - 4 = $ **7**
8. $17 - 9 = $ **8**
9. $16 - 8 = $ **8**
10. $14 - 7 = $ **7**
11. $17 - 13 = $ **4**
12. $15 - 8 = $ **7**

13. 10 − 6 = **4**
14. 11 − 5 = **6**
15. 13 − 6 = **7**
16. 17 − 8 = **9**
17. 18 − 9 = **9**
18. 9 − 7 = **2**

Compare. Write >, <, or = in ◯.

19. 16 − 12 (>) 16 − 14
20. 10 − 4 (=) 11 − 5
21. 16 − 8 (<) 13 − 4
22. 11 − 9 (<) 8 − 5
23. 14 − 6 (>) 4 − 4
24. 13 − 7 (>) 9 − 7

Solve.

25. Eleven ducklings are swimming behind their mother. Six follow her out of the water onto the shore. How many ducklings are still in the water? **5**

26. The gray squirrel makes a pile of 15 nuts. It carries 7 up to its nest. How many nuts are left in the pile? **8**

27. Kim's garden has 18 red flowers and 13 yellow flowers. How many more red flowers than yellow flowers are in Kim's garden? **5**

28. Mrs. Morgan has 14 plants in her garden. Nine are tomato plants. How many are not tomato plants? **5**

 Use with Grade 3, text pages 58–59.

Reteach

Using 10 to Subtract

R 2-6

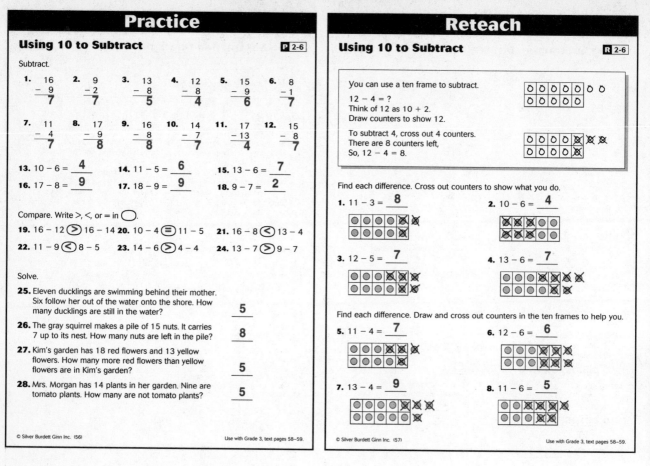

You can use a ten frame to subtract.

12 − 4 = ?
Think of 12 as 10 + 2.
Draw counters to show 12.

To subtract 4, cross out 4 counters.
There are 8 counters left.
So, 12 − 4 = 8.

Find each difference. Cross out counters to show what you do.

1. 11 − 3 = **8**
2. 10 − 6 = **4**
3. 12 − 5 = **7**
4. 13 − 6 = **7**

Find each difference. Draw and cross out counters in the ten frames to help you.

5. 11 − 4 = **7**
6. 12 − 6 = **6**
7. 13 − 4 = **9**
8. 11 − 6 = **5**

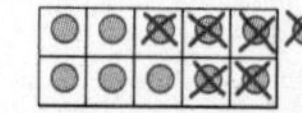

 Use with Grade 3, text pages 58–59.

Extend

Treasure Hunt

E 2-6 NUMBER SENSE

Toni and Jeff played Treasure Hunt.

Here are the rules they used:

Pick a number card and jump that many spaces.

If you land on a (storm cloud), move back one space.

If you land on a (ship), move forward one space.

If you land on the (island), go back four spaces.

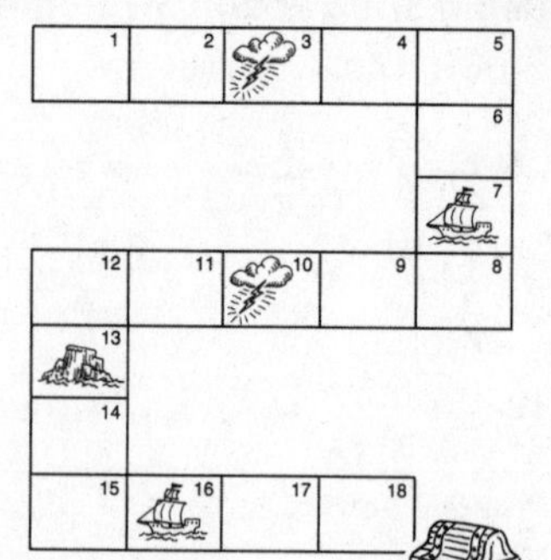

Complete each subtraction fact to answer the question.

1. Spaces 7 and 16 have (ship). How far apart are they? 16 − 7 = **9**

2. Toni landed on 5. How many spaces is she from (island)? 13 − 5 = **8**

3. Jeff got a 7 and landed on a (ship). How many more spaces does he have to go to reach 14? 7 + 1 = **8**; 14 − 8 = **6**

4. Toni is 8 spaces from 17. What space is she on? 17 − 8 = **9**

5. Jeff landed on space 13, the (island). How far is he from the end? 13 − 4 = **9**; 18 − 9 = **9**

 Use with Grade 3, text pages 58–59.

Daily Review

Name ______________________

Daily Review 2-6

Using 10 to Subtract

Find each difference. Use a ten-frame to help you.

1. 16 − 8 = **8**
2. 14 − 7 = **7**
3. 13 − 5 = **8**
4. 13 − 9 = **4**
5. 11 − 2 = **9**
6. 15 − 9 = **6**
7. 12 − 3 = **9**
8. 11 − 6 = **5**

Subtract.

9. $14 - 5 = $ **9**
10. $12 - 3 = $ **9**
11. $11 - 3 = $ **8**
12. $17 - 8 = $ **9**
13. $19 - 9 = $ **10**
14. $15 - 6 = $ **9**
15. $11 - 8 = $ **3**
16. $17 - 9 = $ **8**
17. $15 - 7 = $ **8**
18. $11 - 2 = $ **9**

Problem Solving

Solve.

19. Moneet has 16 ounces of sand for a terrarium. If she gives 9 ounces to her sister, then how many ounces will Moneet have? **7**

20. There are 15 dog bones in a container. If the veterinarian gives 6 bones away, then how many bones are left? **9**

21. Billy has used 7 ride tickets. If he started with 17 ride tickets, how may does he have left? **10**

Review and Remember

Write the numbers in order from least to greatest.

22. 8 14 36 — **8**, **14**, **36**

23. 24 19 11 — **11**, **19**, **24**

24. 449 409 419 — **409**, **419**, **449**

Chapter 2 • Lesson 7

Practice

Problem Solving P 2-7

Act It Out

Solve by acting it out. Or use objects or draw pictures to help you.

1. A group of trained dogs play a game with a plastic saucer. Fido passes the saucer to Spot. Spot passes the saucer to Max. Max passes the saucer to Rex. Rex passes the saucer back to Fido, who starts the relay again. Who has the saucer after 12 passes?
   Fido

2. The Green family opens a pet day care center in their home. The first month, 2 pets stay with them. Four pets stay with them the second month. Six pets stay with them the third month. If the pattern continues, in which month will the Green family have 10 pets stay with them?
   the fifth month

3. Joan feeds the animals in the zoo in a special order each day. She feeds the zebras before the penguins. She feeds the armadillos after the penguins. She feeds the giraffes before the zebras. In what order does Joan feed the animals?
   giraffes, zebras, penguins, armadillos

4. Ten puppies play in a barn. Two puppies leave the barn and hide in the hay. Later, three more puppies leave the barn and hide in the hay. Then one of the puppies returns to the barn. Finally, four puppies leave the barn and hide in the hay. How many puppies are in the barn? How many are hiding in the hay?
   two puppies in barn; 8 puppies hiding in hay

5. Hector has 5 dogs. He has 2 more cats than dogs, and 4 fewer horses than dogs. How many of each animal does Hector have?
   Hector has 5 dogs, 7 cats, and 1 horse.

 Use with Grade 3, text pages 60–61.

Reteach

Problem Solving R 2-7

Act It Out

Kate has 3 goldfish. Noah has 2 more goldfish than Kate. Yvette has 1 fewer goldfish than Noah. Who has the fewest fish?

1. How can you compare the number of goldfish each person has?

Understand You know that Kate has 3 goldfish. You need to know how many goldfish Noah and Yvette have. Then you can compare them.

Plan Your classmates can pretend they are Kate's, Noah's, and Yvette's goldfish.

Solve

☺ ☺ ☺	☺ ☺ ☺ ☺ ☺	☺ ☺ ☺ ☺
Start with 3 children for Kate's 3 fish.	Noah has 2 more fish than Kate, so add 2 children. Noah has 5 fish.	Yvette has 1 less fish than Noah, so take away 1 child. Yvette has 4 fish.

So, **Kate** has the fewest goldfish.

Look Back Read the problem again. Does your answer make sense?

2. Farmer Dan has 5 cows. Farmer Vic has 3 fewer cows than Farmer Dan. Farmer Ned has 6 cows more than Farmer Vic. Which farmer has the most cows?
   Farmer Ned

3. Ava watched 4 groups of students perform with hula hoops. The first group used 1 hula hoop. The next group used 3 hula hoops. The third group used 5 hula hoops. How many hula hoops would you predict that the fourth group used?
   7 hula hoops

4. Jeremy had some pennies. He spent 4¢, then earned 8¢. When he counted all of his pennies, he had 18¢. How many pennies did he begin with?
   14 pennies

 Use with Grade 3, text pages 60–61.

Extend

Try, Try Again

E 2-7 REASONING

Act out these exercises or draw a picture.

1. The neighborhood children are marching their stuffed animals in a parade. The bear is ahead of the lion. The monkey is ahead of the bear. The elephant is behind the lion. The horse is first in line. What is the order of the stuffed animals in the parade?

horse	monkey	bear	lion	elephant

2. Burt is making a banner for his classroom. He wants the banner to be red, blue, and yellow. How can he color the banner so that he has a red, a blue, and a yellow section in every row and column without the same color next to each other or on top of each other?

b	r	y
r	y	b
y	b	r

3. Carmen keeps her games on a shelf in her room. The checkers game is under the marbles game. The chess game is on the left side of the checkers game. Chase is to the left of marbles, between marbles and dominoes. Dominoes are above the Babble game. Where is each game on Carmen's shelf?

dominoes	Chase	marbles
Babble	chess	checkers

Use logical reasoning for the following.

4. John is in front of Paul. Raymond is between Stu and Jorge. Jorge is behind Paul. Stu is last. In what order are the boys?
   John, Paul, Jorge, Raymond, Stu

5. Ryan made a tile design using these colors:

   red yellow blue red yellow blue

   What color will the tenth tile be in the design? **red**

 Use with Grade 3, text pages 60–61.

Daily Review

Name ______________________ Daily Review 2-7

Problem Solving

Act It Out

Solve each problem by acting it out.

1. On Monday Sam found 4 shiny stones. He gave 2 stones to his friend and 1 stone to his mother. On Tuesday, Sam found 5 shiny stones and gave 1 away. On Wednesday, Charlene gave him 1 shiny stone. How many shiny stones did Sam have on Wednesday?
   6 stones

2. The class needs 4 vans for a trip to the museum. Each van holds 9 people. There is one empty seat in each of three vans. How many people go on the class trip?
   33 people

3. Rachel stands in line to buy a ticket at the movies. There are 9 people in line. Four people are in front of Rachel. Susan gets in line behind the ninth person. How many people are between Rachel and Susan?
   4 people

4. Five chickens walked out of the chicken coop. Two walked back in, then 6 walked out. Finally, 3 walked back into the coop. How many chickens are out of the chicken coop right now?
   6 chickens

Review and Remember

Find each difference.

5. 13 − 7 = **6** 6. 15 − 9 = **6** 7. 11 − 5 = **6**
8. 12 − 3 = **9** 9. 23 − 7 = **16** 10. 17 − 8 = **9**
11. 17 − 9 = **8** 12. 45 − 6 = **39** 13. 32 − 4 = **28**

Practice

Thinking Addition to Subtract

P 2-8

Write each missing addend. Then write each difference.

1. 7 + 6 = 13; 13 − 7 = 6
2. 6 + 9 = 15; 15 − 6 = 9
3. 5 + 0 = 5; 5 − 5 = 0

Subtract.

4. 11 − 8 = 3
5. 12 − 5 = 7
6. 10 − 2 = 8
7. 9 − 7 = 2
8. 14 − 9 = 5

9. 8 − 5 = 3
10. 10 − 7 = 3
11. 13 − 5 = 8
12. 15 − 7 = 8
13. 13 − 4 = 9
14. 12 − 8 = 4

Complete each table.

15. Rule: Add 7
Then: Subtract 7

Input	Output
3	3
8	8
7	7

16. Rule: Add 6
Then: Subtract 6

Input	Output
8	8
3	3
5	5

17. Rule: Add 3
Then: Subtract 3

Input	Output
9	9
4	4
6	6

Solve.

18. Danny had 9 tickets to the circus. He gave some away. Now he has 3. How many tickets did he give away? 6 tickets

19. Sam had 8 books. Luis borrowed some. Now Sam has 5 books. How many books did Luis borrow? 3 books

 Use with Grade 3, with text pages 62–63.

Reteach

Thinking Addition to Subtract

R 2-8

You can use addition to find the answer to a subtraction fact.

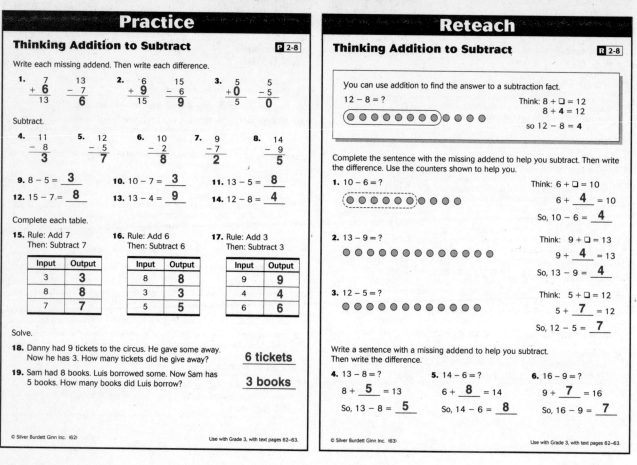

12 − 8 = ?

Think: 8 + ☐ = 12
8 + **4** = 12
so 12 − 8 = **4**

Complete the sentence with the missing addend to help you subtract. Then write the difference. Use the counters shown to help you.

1. 10 − 6 = ?
Think: 6 + ☐ = 10
6 + 4 = 10
So, 10 − 6 = 4

2. 13 − 9 = ?
Think: 9 + ☐ = 13
9 + 4 = 13
So, 13 − 9 = 4

3. 12 − 5 = ?
Think: 5 + ☐ = 12
5 + 7 = 12
So, 12 − 5 = 7

Write a sentence with a missing addend to help you subtract. Then write the difference.

4. 13 − 8 = ?
8 + 5 = 13
So, 13 − 8 = 5

5. 14 − 6 = ?
6 + 8 = 14
So, 14 − 6 = 8

6. 16 − 9 = ?
9 + 7 = 16
So, 16 − 9 = 7

 Use with Grade 3, with text pages 62–63.

Extend

Meet the Winners

E 2-8
REASONING

Here are the winners of the Junior Track Meet. Note the total miles run by each child.

Miles	8	7	5	12	15	10
Name	Pete	Jan	Bob	Nan	Rita	Lee

Read each clue. Write the names of the runners under the miles.

- Bob ran 5 miles.
- Rita ran 3 times as many miles as Bob.
- Jan ran 2 more miles than Bob.
- Nan ran as far as Bob and Jan together.
- Pete ran 4 miles less than Nan.
- Lee ran twice as many miles as Bob.

Now you can award the medals. The winners are the ones who ran the most miles. You may want to order the number of miles from greatest to least.

1. The gold medal is for the first-place winner. That winner is Rita.
2. The silver medal is for the second-place winner. Nan is that winner.
3. The bronze medal is for third place. It goes to Lee.

 Use with Grade 3, with text pages 62–63.

Daily Review

Name ____________

Daily Review 2-8

Thinking Addition to Subtract

Use the addition fact to find each difference.

1. 5 + 9 = 14
14 − 9 = 5
14 − 5 = 9

2. 6 + 5 = 11
11 − 5 = 6
11 − 6 = 5

3. 6 + 7 = 13
13 − 6 = 7
13 − 7 = 6

Think addition to help you find each difference.

4. 11 − 6 = 5
5. 13 − 8 = 5
6. 14 − 5 = 9
7. 16 − 9 = 7
8. 18 − 8 = 10
9. 15 − 9 = 6
10. 12 − 4 = 8
11. 11 − 6 = 5
12. 17 − 8 = 9
13. 16 − 7 = 9

Problem Solving

Solve.

14. Tamika has 11 cousins in her family. Six of them are boys. How many cousins are girls? 5

15. An animal shelter has 16 cats and dogs. If 8 animals are cats, then how many are dogs? 8

Review and Remember

Add or subtract.

16. 8 + 4 = 12
17. 13 − 4 = 9
18. 15 − 6 = 9
19. 2 + 10 = 12
20. 18 − 9 = 9
21. 8 + 3 = 11

Chapter 2 • Lesson 9

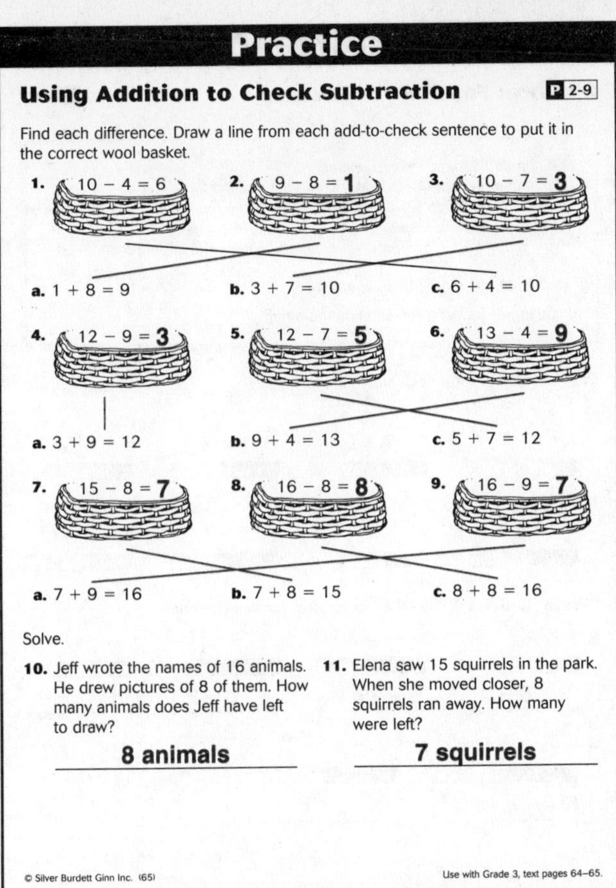

Practice

Using Addition to Check Subtraction

P 2-9

Find each difference. Draw a line from each add-to-check sentence to put it in the correct wool basket.

1. 10 − 4 = 6 2. 9 − 8 = **1** 3. 10 − 7 = **3**

a. 1 + 8 = 9 b. 3 + 7 = 10 c. 6 + 4 = 10

4. 12 − 9 = **3** 5. 12 − 7 = **5** 6. 13 − 4 = **9**

a. 3 + 9 = 12 b. 9 + 4 = 13 c. 5 + 7 = 12

7. 15 − 8 = **7** 8. 16 − 8 = **8** 9. 16 − 9 = **7**

a. 7 + 9 = 16 b. 7 + 8 = 15 c. 8 + 8 = 16

Solve.

10. Jeff wrote the names of 16 animals. He drew pictures of 8 of them. How many animals does Jeff have left to draw?

8 animals

11. Elena saw 15 squirrels in the park. When she moved closer, 8 squirrels ran away. How many were left?

7 squirrels

Use with Grade 3, text pages 64–65.

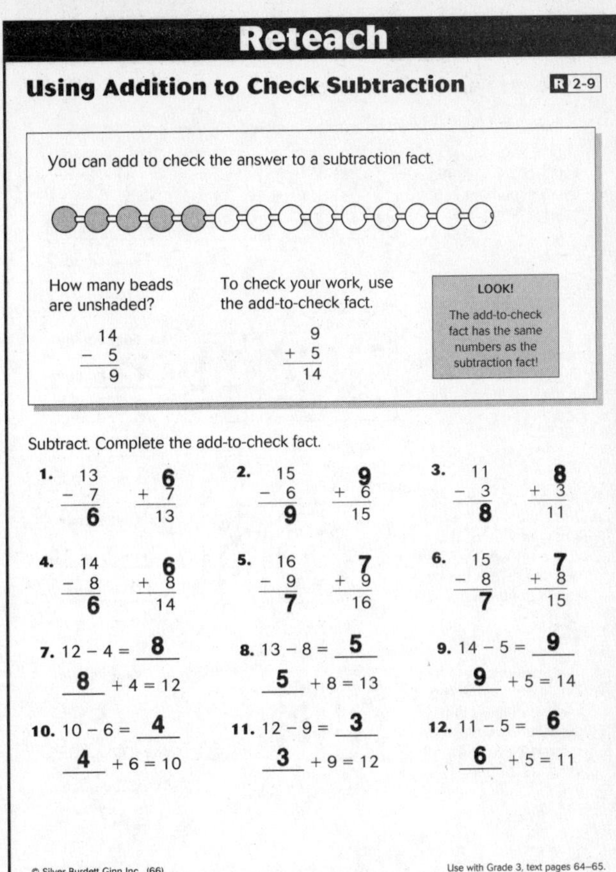

Reteach

Using Addition to Check Subtraction

R 2-9

You can add to check the answer to a subtraction fact.

How many beads are unshaded?

$$\begin{array}{r} 14 \\ -\ 5 \\ \hline 9 \end{array}$$

To check your work, use the add-to-check fact.

$$\begin{array}{r} 9 \\ +\ 5 \\ \hline 14 \end{array}$$

LOOK! The add-to-check fact has the same numbers as the subtraction fact!

Subtract. Complete the add-to-check fact.

1. 13 − 7 = **6**; **6** + 7 = 13
2. 15 − 6 = **9**; **9** + 6 = 15
3. 11 − 3 = **8**; **8** + 3 = 11
4. 14 − 8 = **6**; **6** + 8 = 14
5. 16 − 9 = **7**; **7** + 9 = 16
6. 15 − 8 = **7**; **7** + 8 = 15
7. 12 − 4 = **8**; **8** + 4 = 12
8. 13 − 8 = **5**; **5** + 8 = 13
9. 14 − 5 = **9**; **9** + 5 = 14
10. 10 − 6 = **4**; **4** + 6 = 10
11. 12 − 9 = **3**; **3** + 9 = 12
12. 11 − 5 = **6**; **6** + 5 = 11

Use with Grade 3, text pages 64–65.

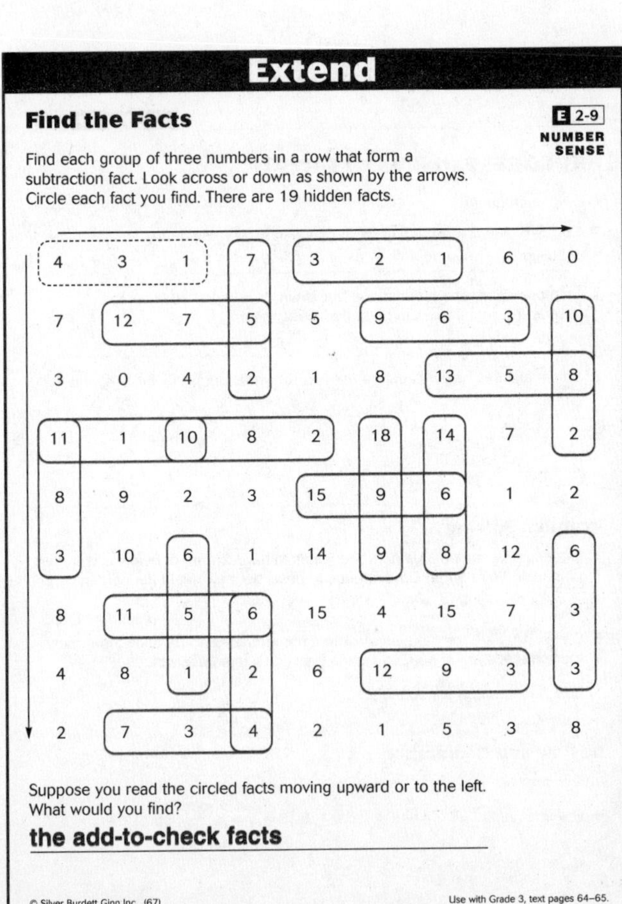

Extend

Find the Facts

E 2-9 NUMBER SENSE

Find each group of three numbers in a row that form a subtraction fact. Look across or down as shown by the arrows. Circle each fact you find. There are 19 hidden facts.

4	3	1	7	3	2	1	6	0
7	12	7	5	5	9	6	3	10
3	0	4	2	1	8	13	5	8
11	1	10	8	2	18	14	7	2
8	9	2	3	15	9	6	1	2
3	10	6	1	14	9	8	12	6
8	11	5	6	15	4	15	7	3
4	8	1	2	6	12	9	3	3
2	7	3	4	2	1	5	3	8

Suppose you read the circled facts moving upward or to the left. What would you find?

the add-to-check facts

Use with Grade 3, text pages 64–65.

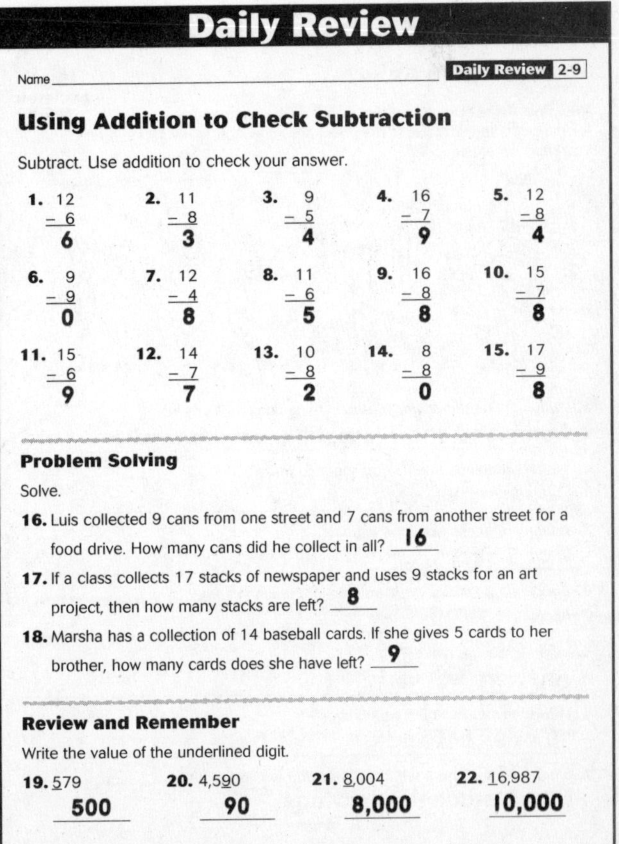

Daily Review

Daily Review 2-9

Name ____________________

Using Addition to Check Subtraction

Subtract. Use addition to check your answer.

1. 12 − 6 = **6**
2. 11 − 8 = **3**
3. 9 − 5 = **4**
4. 16 − 7 = **9**
5. 12 − 8 = **4**
6. 9 − 9 = **0**
7. 12 − 4 = **8**
8. 11 − 6 = **5**
9. 16 − 8 = **8**
10. 15 − 7 = **8**
11. 15 − 6 = **9**
12. 14 − 7 = **7**
13. 10 − 8 = **2**
14. 8 − 8 = **0**
15. 17 − 9 = **8**

Problem Solving

Solve.

16. Luis collected 9 cans from one street and 7 cans from another street for a food drive. How many cans did he collect in all? **16**
17. If a class collects 17 stacks of newspaper and uses 9 stacks for an art project, then how many stacks are left? **8**
18. Marsha has a collection of 14 baseball cards. If she gives 5 cards to her brother, how many cards does she have left? **9**

Review and Remember

Write the value of the underlined digit.

19. <u>5</u>79 **500**
20. 4,5<u>9</u>0 **90**
21. <u>8</u>,004 **8,000**
22. 1<u>6</u>,987 **10,000**

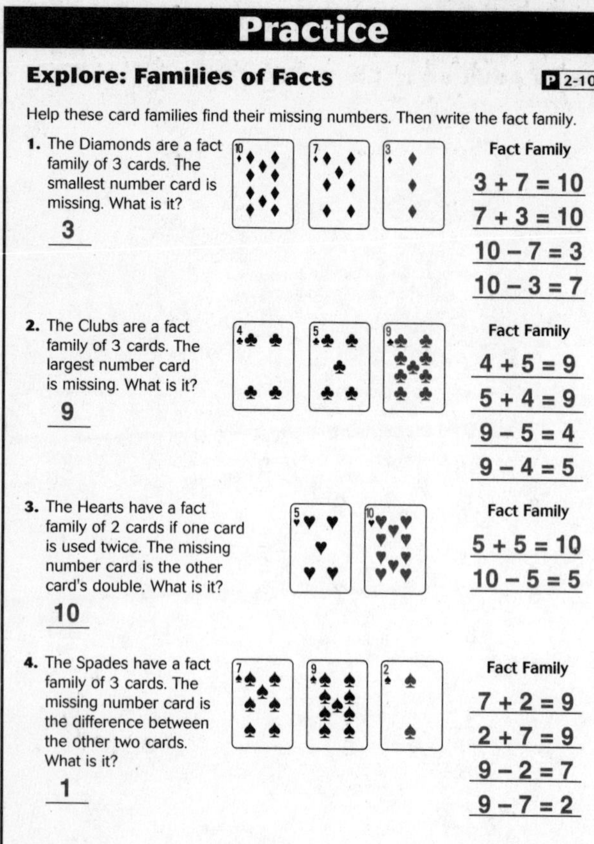

Practice

Explore: Families of Facts

P 2-10

Help these card families find their missing numbers. Then write the fact family.

1. The Diamonds are a fact family of 3 cards. The smallest number card is missing. What is it?
   3

   Fact Family
   3 + 7 = 10
   7 + 3 = 10
   10 − 7 = 3
   10 − 3 = 7

2. The Clubs are a fact family of 3 cards. The largest number card is missing. What is it?
   9

   Fact Family
   4 + 5 = 9
   5 + 4 = 9
   9 − 5 = 4
   9 − 4 = 5

3. The Hearts have a fact family of 2 cards if one card is used twice. The missing number card is the other card's double. What is it?
   10

   Fact Family
   5 + 5 = 10
   10 − 5 = 5

4. The Spades have a fact family of 3 cards. The missing number card is the difference between the other two cards. What is it?
   1

   Fact Family
   7 + 2 = 9
   2 + 7 = 9
   9 − 2 = 7
   9 − 7 = 2

Use with Grade 3, text pages 66–67.

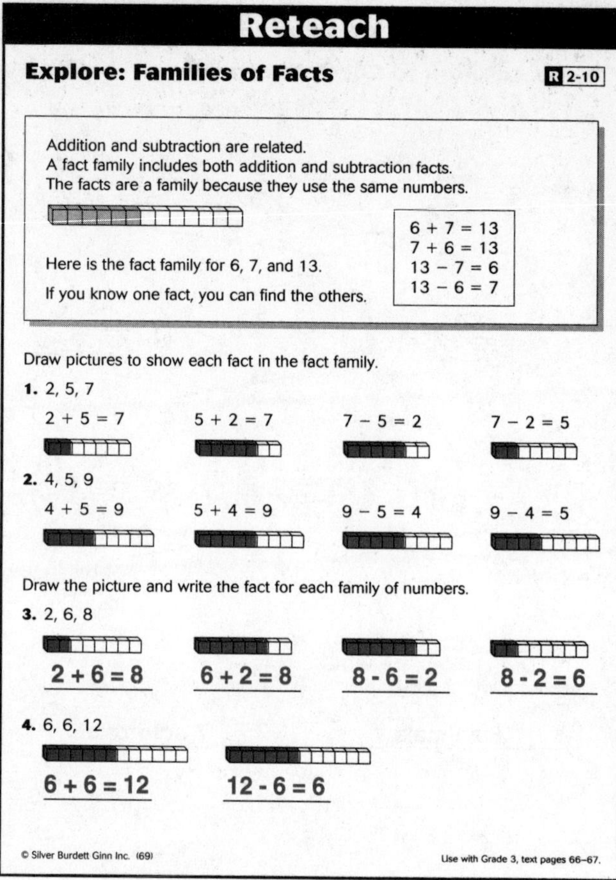

Reteach

Explore: Families of Facts

R 2-10

Addition and subtraction are related.
A fact family includes both addition and subtraction facts.
The facts are a family because they use the same numbers.

Here is the fact family for 6, 7, and 13.

If you know one fact, you can find the others.

6 + 7 = 13
7 + 6 = 13
13 − 7 = 6
13 − 6 = 7

Draw pictures to show each fact in the fact family.

1. 2, 5, 7
   2 + 5 = 7   5 + 2 = 7   7 − 5 = 2   7 − 2 = 5

2. 4, 5, 9
   4 + 5 = 9   5 + 4 = 9   9 − 5 = 4   9 − 4 = 5

Draw the picture and write the fact for each family of numbers.

3. 2, 6, 8
   2 + 6 = 8   6 + 2 = 8   8 - 6 = 2   8 - 2 = 6

4. 6, 6, 12
   6 + 6 = 12   12 - 6 = 6

Use with Grade 3, text pages 66–67.

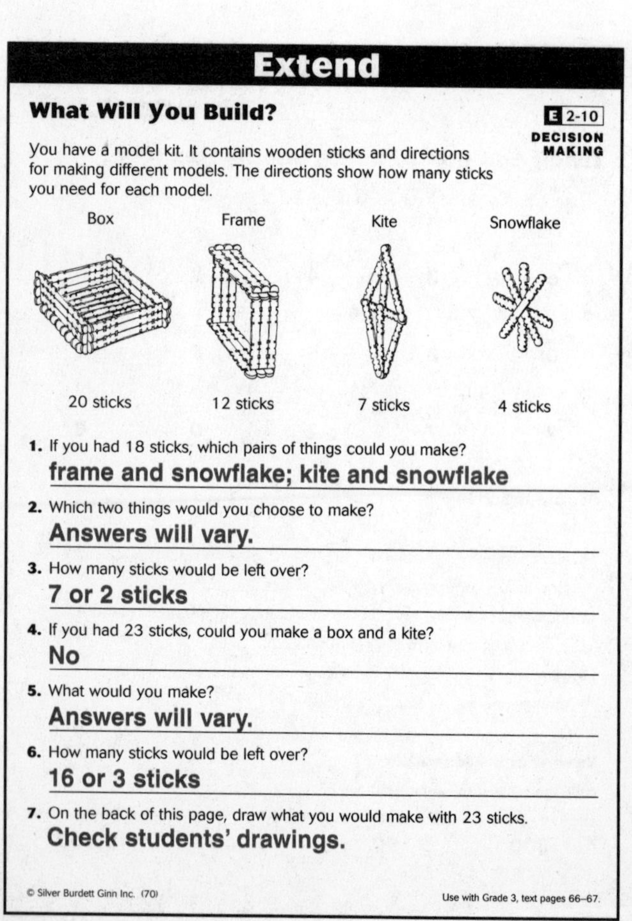

Extend

What Will You Build?

E 2-10
DECISION MAKING

You have a model kit. It contains wooden sticks and directions for making different models. The directions show how many sticks you need for each model.

Box	Frame	Kite	Snowflake
20 sticks	12 sticks	7 sticks	4 sticks

1. If you had 18 sticks, which pairs of things could you make?
   frame and snowflake; kite and snowflake
2. Which two things would you choose to make?
   Answers will vary.
3. How many sticks would be left over?
   7 or 2 sticks
4. If you had 23 sticks, could you make a box and a kite?
   No
5. What would you make?
   Answers will vary.
6. How many sticks would be left over?
   16 or 3 sticks
7. On the back of this page, draw what you would make with 23 sticks.
   Check students' drawings.

Use with Grade 3, text pages 66–67.

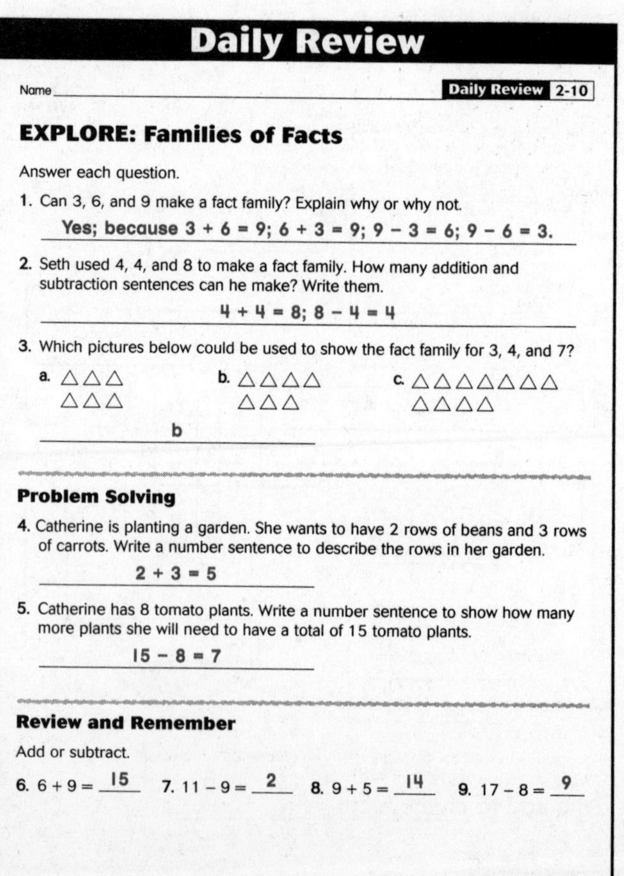

Daily Review

Name ____________ Daily Review 2-10

EXPLORE: Families of Facts

Answer each question.

1. Can 3, 6, and 9 make a fact family? Explain why or why not.
   Yes; because 3 + 6 = 9; 6 + 3 = 9; 9 − 3 = 6; 9 − 6 = 3.
2. Seth used 4, 4, and 8 to make a fact family. How many addition and subtraction sentences can he make? Write them.
   4 + 4 = 8; 8 − 4 = 4
3. Which pictures below could be used to show the fact family for 3, 4, and 7?
   a. △△△ △△△   b. △△△△ △△△   c. △△△△△△△ △△△△
   b

Problem Solving

4. Catherine is planting a garden. She wants to have 2 rows of beans and 3 rows of carrots. Write a number sentence to describe the rows in her garden.
   2 + 3 = 5
5. Catherine has 8 tomato plants. Write a number sentence to show how many more plants she will need to have a total of 15 tomato plants.
   15 − 8 = 7

Review and Remember

Add or subtract.

6. 6 + 9 = 15   7. 11 − 9 = 2   8. 9 + 5 = 14   9. 17 − 8 = 9

Practice

Problem Solving P 2-11

Using Data From a Graph

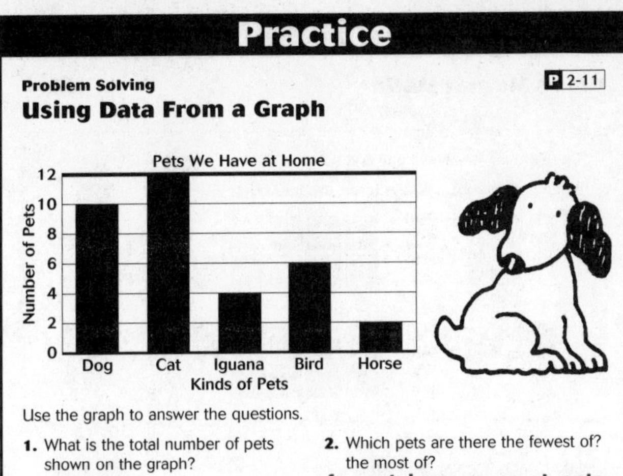

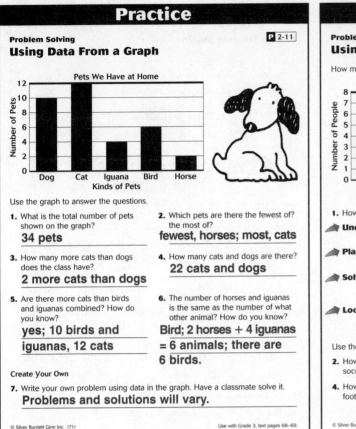

Use the graph to answer the questions.

1. What is the total number of pets shown on the graph? **34 pets**
2. Which pets are there the fewest of? the most of? **fewest, horses; most, cats**
3. How many more cats than dogs does the class have? **2 more cats than dogs**
4. How many cats and dogs are there? **22 cats and dogs**
5. Are there more cats than birds and iguanas combined? How do you know? **yes; 10 birds and iguanas, 12 cats**
6. The number of horses and iguanas is the same as the number of what other animal? How do you know? **Bird; 2 horses + 4 iguanas = 6 animals; there are 6 birds.**

Create Your Own

7. Write your own problem using data in the graph. Have a classmate solve it. **Problems and solutions will vary.**

 Use with Grade 3, text pages 68–69.

Reteach

Problem Solving R 2-11

Using Data From a Graph

How many people chose basketball or baseball?

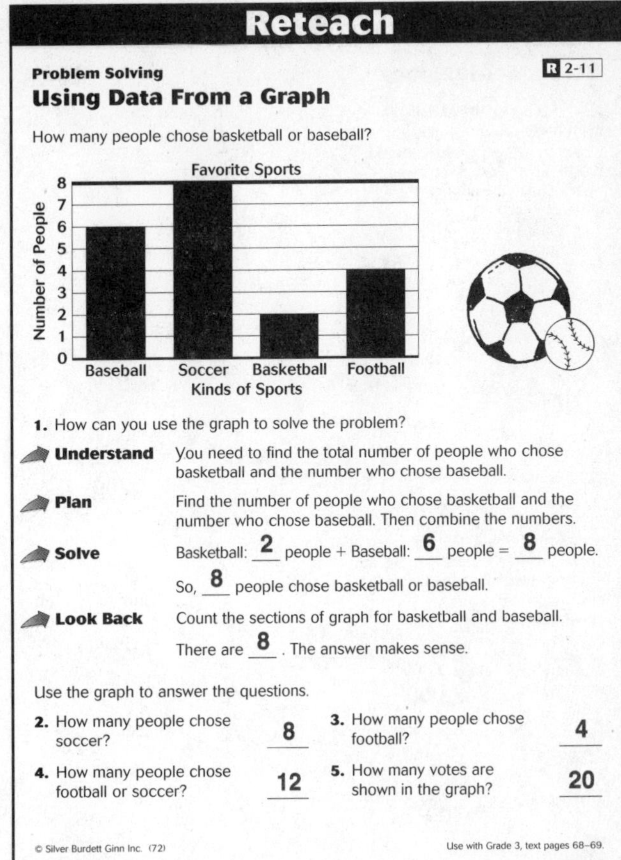

1. How can you use the graph to solve the problem?

Understand You need to find the total number of people who chose basketball and the number who chose baseball.

Plan Find the number of people who chose basketball and the number who chose baseball. Then combine the numbers.

Solve Basketball: **2** people + Baseball: **6** people = **8** people.

So, **8** people chose basketball or baseball.

Look Back Count the sections of graph for basketball and baseball.

There are **8**. The answer makes sense.

Use the graph to answer the questions.

2. How many people chose soccer? **8**
3. How many people chose football? **4**
4. How many people chose football or soccer? **12**
5. How many votes are shown in the graph? **20**

 Use with Grade 3, text pages 68–69.

Extend

Team Spirit

E 2-11 DATA

The Rockets are in a tournament. The outcome will decide if they can play in a state final. Read the final scores for each round. Shade the number of wins, losses, or ties for the Rockets in the Tournament Record graph.

Star Team Tournament

Game 1		Game 2		Game 3		Game 4	
Rockets	4	Rockets	9	Rockets	5	Rockets	8
Starbursts	2	Flyers	5	Beepers	6	Travelers	1
Game 5		**Game 6**		**Game 7**		**Game 8**	
Rockets	6	Rockets	7	Rockets	7	Rockets	6
Jets	4	Winners	7	Bops	9	Rainbows	6
Game 9		**Game 10**		**Game 11**		**Game 12**	
Rockets	8	Rockets	5	Rockets	9	Rockets	4
Inklings	6	Jazz	4	Victors	10	Arrows	3

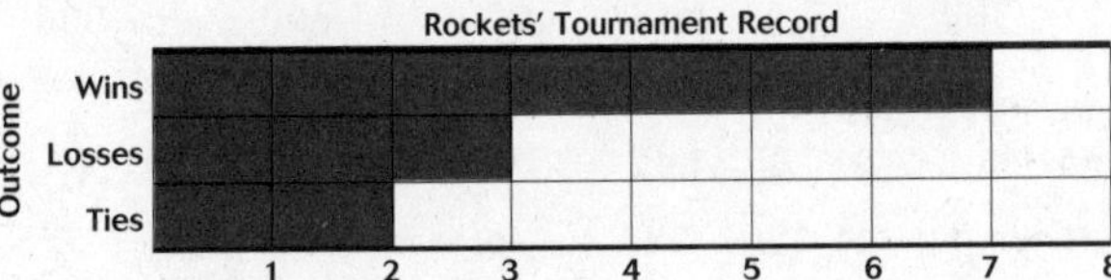

Use your graph to answer the questions.

1. How many games did the Rockets win? **7** lose? **3** tie? **2**
2. The Rockets need more wins than losses and ties combined in order to play in the state finals. Will they be able to play? **yes**
3. How would you find the total number of points that the Rockets scored in the last three games of the tournament? **Add the points from all three games.**
4. Is there a pattern to the scores of the Rockets? If the pattern continues and the Rockets play a 13th game, what will their score be? **10**

 Use with Grade 3, text pages 68–69.

Daily Review

Name ______________________ Daily Review 2-11

Problem Solving

Using Data from a Graph

Use the bar graph to answer the questions.

Students' Favorite Exhibit at the Zoo

Number of Students: 0, 2, 4, 6, 8, 10, 12, 14, 16, 18, 20

Sea Lion, Snake, Giraffe, Elephant, Tiger

Favorite Animal

1. How many students liked exhibits of animals that walk on four legs? **34 students**
2. Which exhibit was the least popular and which was the most popular? least popular **sea lion and giraffe** most popular **elephant**
3. How many students went to the zoo? **53 students**
4. How many more students liked the tiger exhibit than liked the snake exhibit? **1 more student**

Review and Remember

Give the value of the underlined digit.

5. 2,3<u>4</u>0 **40**
6. <u>9</u>88 **900**
7. <u>7</u>,042 **7,000**

Chapter 3 • Lesson 1

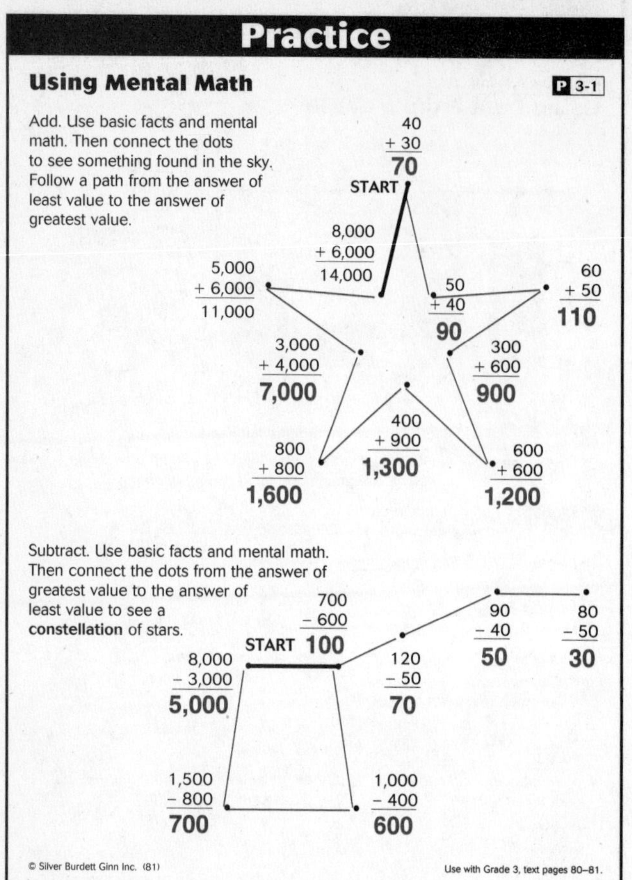

Practice

Using Mental Math

P 3-1

Add. Use basic facts and mental math. Then connect the dots to see something found in the sky. Follow a path from the answer of least value to the answer of greatest value.

START

- 40 + 30 = 70
- 50 + 40 = 90
- 60 + 50 = 110
- 300 + 600 = 900
- 600 + 600 = 1,200
- 400 + 900 = 1,300
- 800 + 800 = 1,600
- 3,000 + 4,000 = 7,000
- 5,000 + 6,000 = 11,000
- 8,000 + 6,000 = 14,000

Subtract. Use basic facts and mental math. Then connect the dots from the answer of greatest value to the answer of least value to see a **constellation** of stars.

START

- 700 − 600 = 100
- 90 − 40 = 50
- 80 − 50 = 30
- 8,000 − 3,000 = 5,000
- 120 − 50 = 70
- 1,500 − 800 = 700
- 1,000 − 400 = 600

© Silver Burdett Ginn Inc. (81) Use with Grade 3, text pages 80–81.

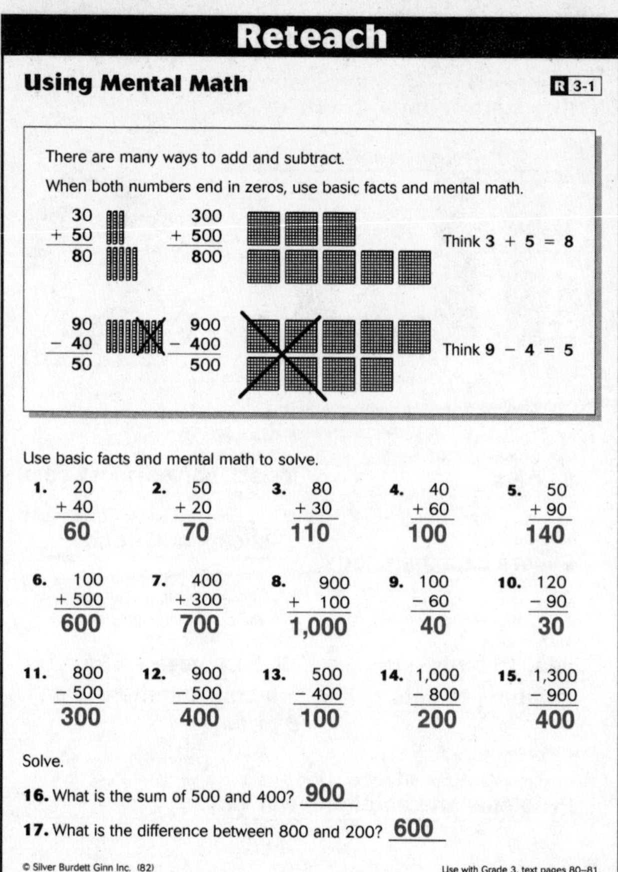

Reteach

Using Mental Math

R 3-1

There are many ways to add and subtract.

When both numbers end in zeros, use basic facts and mental math.

30 + 50 = 80 300 + 500 = 800 Think 3 + 5 = 8

90 − 40 = 50 900 − 400 = 500 Think 9 − 4 = 5

Use basic facts and mental math to solve.

1. 20 + 40 = 60
2. 50 + 20 = 70
3. 80 + 30 = 110
4. 40 + 60 = 100
5. 50 + 90 = 140
6. 100 + 500 = 600
7. 400 + 300 = 700
8. 900 + 100 = 1,000
9. 100 − 60 = 40
10. 120 − 90 = 30
11. 800 − 500 = 300
12. 900 − 500 = 400
13. 500 − 400 = 100
14. 1,000 − 800 = 200
15. 1,300 − 900 = 400

Solve.

16. What is the sum of 500 and 400? 900
17. What is the difference between 800 and 200? 600

© Silver Burdett Ginn Inc. (82) Use with Grade 3, text pages 80–81.

Extend

Take Off the Mask

E 3-1 NUMBER SENSE

The numbers in the equations below are hiding behind masks. Look at the clues and decide which number is behind each mask. The same mask always covers the same number.

HINT: As soon as you figure out one number, write it in the answer space and next to that shape in each equation.

1. Use the numbers 2, 3, 5, and 6.

6 − 5 = 1 5 − 3 = 2 3 + 3 = 6

3 + 5 = 2 + 6

= 3 = 6 = 2 = 5

2. Use the numbers 1, 4, 5, 8, and 9.

4 + 5 = 9 1 + 4 = 5 8 − 4 = 4 8 + 1 = 9

5 + 5 = 9 + 1

= 5 = 4 = 1 = 9 = 8

© Silver Burdett Ginn Inc. (83) Use with Grade 3, text pages 80–81.

Daily Review

Name ____________________

Daily Review 3-1

Using Mental Math

Use mental math to find each sum.

1. 6 + 3 = 9
2. 60 + 30 = 90
3. 600 + 300 = 900
4. 6,000 + 3,000 = 9,000

Find each sum or difference.

5. 40 − 30 = 10
6. 50 + 60 = 110
7. 600 − 200 = 400
8. 6,000 + 1,000 = 7,000
9. 700 − 0 = 700
10. 200 + 100 = 300
11. 3,000 − 1,000 = 2,000
12. 900 − 500 = 400
13. 700 + 900 = 1,600
14. 4,000 − 2,000 = 2,000

Complete each pattern.

15. 400, 500, 600, 700, 800
16. 4, 24, 44, 64, 84
17. 620, 520, 420, 320, 220
18. 85, 80, 75, 70, 65

Problem Solving

19. One library shelf holds 300 books. Another shelf holds 500 books. How many books do the shelves hold in all? 800
20. One library shelf has 500 books. 200 books are checked out. How many books are left on the shelf? 300

Review and Remember

Round each number to the nearest ten.

21. 89 90
22. 63 60
23. 47 50
24. 51 50

Practice

Estimating Sums One possible solution shown. P 3-2

Use the numbers in the boxes to solve each riddle.

Cross out each number once you have used it. You may use each number only once.

407	598	314	235	829	124	495
682	884	909	429	174	293	329

1. We are both between 300 and 500. Our estimated sum is 700. What numbers are we? **314 and 407**
2. One of our numbers is exactly 400 less than the other. Together, our estimated sum is 1,200. What numbers are we? **429 and 829**
3. We are both between 500 and 700. Our estimated sum is 1,300. What numbers are we? **598 and 682**
4. We are both between 200 and 300, and our estimated sum is 500. What numbers are we? **235 and 293**
5. We make the lowest estimated sum possible out of this list of numbers. What numbers are we? What is our estimated sum?
124 and 174; 300
6. We make the greatest estimated sum possible out of this list of numbers. What numbers are we? What is our estimated sum?
884 and 909; 1,800
7. Make up your own number riddle with the two remaining numbers.
495, 325 may remain; Numbers, riddles will vary.

 Use with Grade 3, text pages 82–83.

Reteach

Estimating Sums R 3-2

To estimate sums, round and add.

Round 2-digit numbers to the nearest ten.	Round 3-digit numbers to the nearest hundred.	Round money amounts to the nearest dollar.
47 → 50 + 23 → + 20 70	279 → 300 + 416 → + 400 700	\$1.89 → \$2.00 + 3.47 → + 3.00 \$5.00
The sum is about 70.	The sum is about 700.	The sum is about \$5.00.

Estimate the sum by rounding to the nearest ten.

1. 58 + 21 → 60 + 20 = **80**
2. 74 + 38 → 70 + 40 = **110**
3. 46 + 93 → 50 + 90 = **140**
4. 38 + 47 → 40 + 50 = **90**
5. 81 + 26 → 80 + 30 = **110**
6. 79 + 88 → 80 + 90 = **170**

Estimate the sum by rounding to the nearest hundred.

7. 684 + 131 → 700 + 100 = **800**
8. 579 + 285 → 600 + 300 = **900**
9. 782 + 807 → 800 + 800 = **1,600**

Estimate the sum by rounding to the nearest dollar.

10. \$3.95 + 2.39 → \$4.00 + 2.00 = **\$6.00**
11. \$7.19 + 3.22 → \$7.00 + 3.00 = **\$10.00**
12. \$8.89 + 4.12 → \$9.00 + 4.00 = **\$13.00**

 Use with Grade 3, text pages 82–83.

Extend

Puzzling Placements E 3-2 VISUAL THINKING

Solve each puzzle. Draw a picture to show the new arrangement. Then write sentences to tell how you solved each puzzle.

1. This triangle of coins is pointing up. Move just two coins to make the triangle point down.
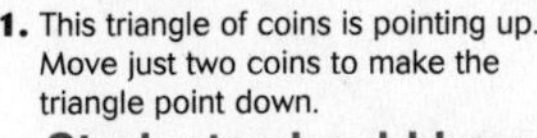
Students should have moved 4 and 6 up to top with 1 between them.

2. The house of toothpicks faces west. Move one toothpick to make the house face east.
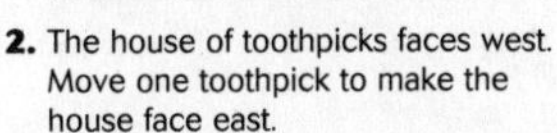
Students should have moved 3 to the point between 2 and 4.
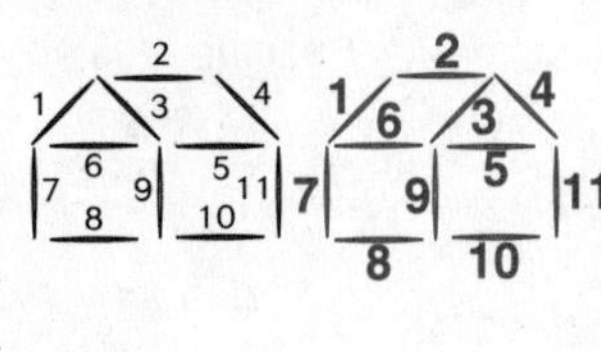

3. The toothpicks make three diamonds. Move four toothpicks to make four diamonds the same size as the original ones.
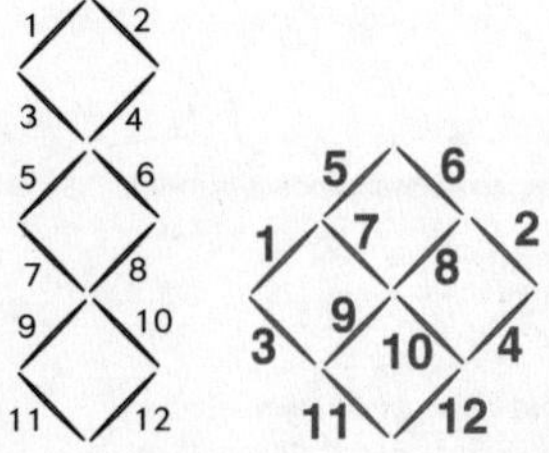
Students should have moved 1 and 3 opposite 7 and 9 and 2 and 4 opposite 8 and 10.

 Use with Grade 3, text pages 82–83.

Daily Review

Name ______________ Daily Review 3-2

Estimating Sums

Estimate by rounding to the nearest ten.

1. 36 + 81 **40 + 80 = 120**
2. 40 + 58 **40 + 60 = 100**
3. 66 + 44 **70 + 40 = 110**
4. 87 + 23 **90 + 20 = 110**
5. 79 + 21 **100**
6. 59 + 42 **100**
7. 91 + 54 **140**
8. 77 + 78 **160**

Estimate by rounding to the nearest hundred or dollar.

9. 402 + 314 **400 + 300 = 700**
10. 420 + 478 **400 + 500 = 900**
11. \$8.12 + \$9.90 **\$8.00 + \$10.00 = \$18.00**
12. \$7.67 + 1.21 **\$8.00 + 1.00 = \$9.00**
13. 589 + 321 **600 + 300 = 900**
14. 387 + 698 **400 + 700 = 1,100**

Problem Solving

15. If a book costs \$8.94 and a pad of paper costs \$3.13, about how much do both items cost? **\$12.00**
16. If two crates of books weigh 300 pounds, and one of the crates weighs 200 pounds, then how much does the other crate weigh? **100 pounds**

Review and Remember

Complete each pattern.

17. 89, 91, 93, **95**, **97**
18. 180, 182, 184, **186**, **188**
19. 111, 121, 131, **141**, **151**
20. 65, 75, 85, **95**, **105**
21. 13, 15, 17, **19**, **21**
22. 20, 23, 26, **29**, **32**

Practice

Problem Solving P 3-3

Deciding When to Estimate

Circle the best choice for each question.

Mikala makes puka-shell bracelets for his friends. Mikala needs about 72 shells for each bracelet. He wants to make 5 bracelets in all. About how many puka shells does Mikala need?

1. How many shell bracelets is Mikala making?

- **a.** about 5 bracelets
- ⓑ exactly 5 bracelets
- **c.** more than 5 bracelets

2. Which of the following is true for 100 shells?

- ⓐ enough for 1 bracelet
- **b.** enough for 2 bracelets
- **c.** enough for 3 bracelets

3. Mikala has made 4 bracelets so far. About how many shells has he used?

- **a.** about 100
- **b.** about 200
- ⓒ about 300

4. Which number sentence would you use to estimate the number of shells Mikala needs for 5 bracelets?

- **a.** 72 + 72 + 72 + 72 + 72 = □
- ⓑ 70 + 70 + 70 + 70 + 70 = □
- **c.** 72 + 5 = □

Mikala's father Randy sells puka-shell bracelets. He sold 198 on Saturday and 117 on Sunday. About how many bracelets did Randy sell during the two days?

5. What are you asked to find?

- **a.** on which day Randy sold more bracelets
- **b.** the exact number of bracelets sold Saturday and Sunday
- ⓒ an estimate of bracelets sold Saturday and Sunday

6. How could you find the answer to this problem?

Possible answer: Round to the nearest hundred the number sold on Saturday and on Sunday; then combine amounts to find the total—about 300.

 Use with Grade 3, text pages 84–85.

Reteach

Problem Solving R 3-3

Deciding When to Estimate

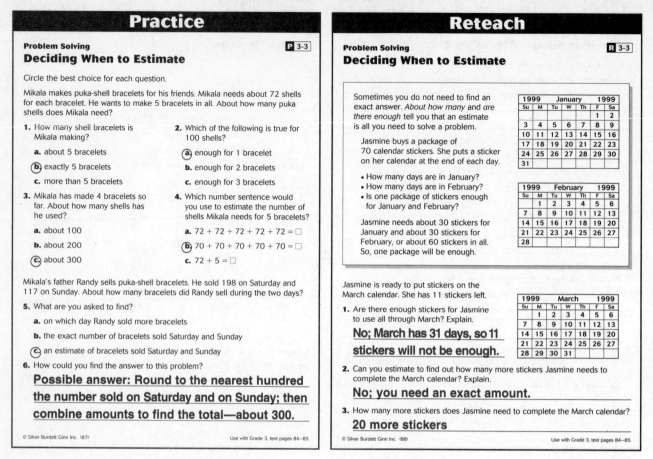

Sometimes you do not need to find an exact answer. *About how many* and *are there enough* tell you that an estimate is all you need to solve a problem.

Jasmine buys a package of 70 calendar stickers. She puts a sticker on her calendar at the end of each day.

- How many days are in January?
- How many days are in February?
- Is one package of stickers enough for January and February?

Jasmine needs about 30 stickers for January and about 30 stickers for February, or about 60 stickers in all. So, one package will be enough.

1999			January			1999
Su	M	Tu	W	Th	F	Sa
					1	2
3	4	5	6	7	8	9
10	11	12	13	14	15	16
17	18	19	20	21	22	23
24	25	26	27	28	29	30
31						

1999			February			1999
Su	M	Tu	W	Th	F	Sa
	1	2	3	4	5	6
7	8	9	10	11	12	13
14	15	16	17	18	19	20
21	22	23	24	25	26	27
28						

Jasmine is ready to put stickers on the March calendar. She has 11 stickers left.

1999			March			1999
Su	M	Tu	W	Th	F	Sa
	1	2	3	4	5	6
7	8	9	10	11	12	13
14	15	16	17	18	19	20
21	22	23	24	25	26	27
28	29	30	31			

1. Are there enough stickers for Jasmine to use all through March? Explain.

No; March has 31 days, so 11 stickers will not be enough.

2. Can you estimate to find out how many more stickers Jasmine needs to complete the March calendar? Explain.

No; you need an exact amount.

3. How many more stickers does Jasmine need to complete the March calendar?

20 more stickers

 Use with Grade 3, text pages 84–85.

Extend

Ticket Trade-In

E 3-3 REASONING

You can trade tickets in for gifts at the Amazing Amusement Park. Here are the gifts available today.

bookmark	key chain	big comb	stuffed bear
59 tickets	88 tickets	31 tickets	97 tickets

If you have 500 tickets, what are some of the different combinations of gifts you can get? Estimate and write your results in the table. **Possible answers are given. Check that students' totals do not exceed 500 tickets.**

Different Ways to Trade in 500 Tickets

	One Way		Another Way		A Third Way	
Item	Number of Each Item	Number of Tickets	Number of Each Item	Number of Tickets	Number of Each Item	Number of Tickets
Bookmark	1	60	2	120	3	180
Key chain	2	180	1	90	1	90
Big comb	4	120	1	30	4	120
Stuffed bear	1	100	2	200	1	100
Estimated Total of Tickets		460		440		490

Write a number sentence for the exact number of tickets needed for each different combination you chose.

1. **59 + 88 + 88 + 31 + 31 + 31 + 31 + 97 = 456**
2. **59 + 59 + 88 + 31 + 97 + 97 = 431**
3. **59 + 59 + 59 + 88 + 31 + 31 + 31 + 31 + 97 = 486**

Answers given for combinations in the table. Check students' choices and computations.

 Use with Grade 3, text pages 84–85.

Daily Review

Name ____________ Daily Review 3-3

Problem Solving

Deciding When to Estimate

Read each story and answer the questions.

1. David had a $20 bill. He spent $3.90 on school supplies. Write a sentence that will estimate his change.

$20 − $4 = $16

Write a sentence that will show his exact change.

$20.00 − $3.90 = $16.10

2. Madeline is buying a gift that costs $2.95 and a gift that costs $5.90. She has $10 to spend. Write a number sentence that estimates the total cost of the gifts. Does she have enough money to buy both gifts?

$3 + $6 = $9; yes

3. Lou packed 79 books and moved them to another room. He put 11 books into each box. Would 9 boxes be enough to pack all his books?

Yes

4. Laura walks about 1 mile in 15 minutes. If school is 2 miles away, can she walk to school in 20 minutes?

No

Review and Remember

Continue the pattern.

5. 110, 115, 120, **125**

6. 60, 80, 100, **120**

7. 800, 700, 600, **500**

8. 225, 325, 425, **525**

9. 75, 70, 65, **60**

10. 1, 3, 5, 7, **9**

Practice

Explore: Regrouping in Addition

P 3-4

Combine base-ten blocks.

Exchange to show the sum using the fewest blocks possible. The first one is done for you.

1. 3 tens 6 ones + 4 tens 5 ones = 7 tens 11 ones. Regroup

tens	ones
8	1

2. 5 tens 3 ones + 2 tens 7 ones = **7 tens 10 ones**. Regroup

tens	ones
8	0

3. 4 tens 7 ones + 2 tens 11 ones = **6 tens 18 ones**. Regroup

tens	ones
7	8

4. 5 tens 6 ones + 7 tens 5 ones = **12 tens 11 ones**. Regroup

hundreds	tens	ones
1	3	1

5. 3 hundreds 5 tens 6 ones + 2 hundreds 4 tens 10 ones = **5 hundreds 9 tens 16 ones**. Regroup

hundreds	tens	ones
6	0	6

Solve.

6. Neil and Judith are collecting rocks. Neil walks 118 paces in one direction. Judith walks 225 paces in the opposite direction. How many paces apart are Neil and Judith? **343 paces apart**

7. Neil finds 187 rocks. Judith brings back 243 rocks. How many rocks did Neil and Judith find?

430 rocks

 Use with Grade 3, text pages 86–87.

Reteach

Explore: Regrouping in Addition

R 3-4

Add.

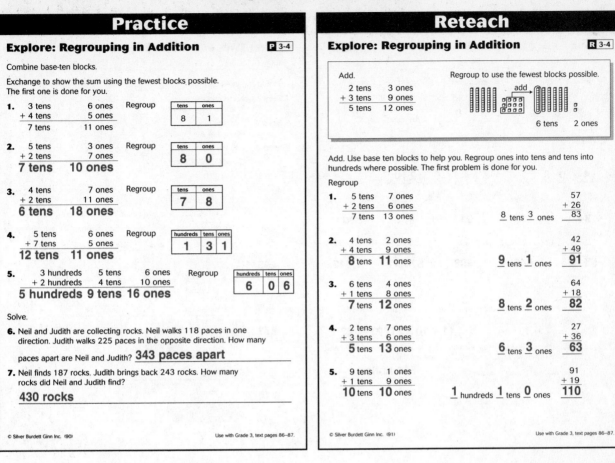

2 tens 3 ones + 3 tens 9 ones = 5 tens 12 ones

Regroup to use the fewest blocks possible.

add

6 tens 2 ones

Add. Use base ten blocks to help you. Regroup ones into tens and tens into hundreds where possible. The first problem is done for you.

Regroup

1. 5 tens 7 ones + 2 tens 6 ones = 7 tens 13 ones — 8 tens 3 ones — 57 + 26 = 83

2. 4 tens 2 ones + 4 tens 9 ones = **8** tens **11** ones — **9** tens **1** ones — 42 + 49 = **91**

3. 6 tens 4 ones + 1 tens 8 ones = **7** tens **12** ones — **8** tens **2** ones — 64 + 18 = **82**

4. 2 tens 7 ones + 3 tens 6 ones = **5** tens **13** ones — **6** tens **3** ones — 27 + 36 = **63**

5. 9 tens 1 ones + 1 tens 9 ones = **10** tens **10** ones — **1** hundreds **1** tens **0** ones — 91 + 19 = **110**

 Use with Grade 3, text pages 86–87.

Extend

What Could It Be?

E 3-4 NUMBER SENSE

Use numbers from the box to answer each problem. You may use a number more than once.

4 18 1962
23065 25
0 7371092
62 1956
2803613 19
70607 1000
726 6161385
9 3334
1987 1999 3

1. Which numbers could be a phone number?

7371092, 2803613, 6161385

2. Which numbers could be the year someone in your family was born?

1962, 1956, 1987

3. Which numbers could be a street address number?

4, 18, 1962, 25, 62, 1956, 19,
1,000 726, 9, 1987, 1999, 3,334

4. Which numbers could be a zip code?

23065, 70607

5. Which numbers could be the sum of two one-digit numbers?

4, 18, 9, 3

6. Which numbers could be the sum of a three-digit number and a two-digit number? **1000, 726**

7. Which numbers have a 3 in the thousands place?

23065, 2803613, 3334

8. Which numbers could be the difference between two two-digit numbers?

4, 18, 25, 0, 62, 19, 9, 3

9. Which number has the same digit in in the ones place as it has in the ten thousands place? **70607**

 Use with Grade 3, text pages 86–87.

Daily Review

Name ____________________

Daily Review 3-4

Explore: Regrouping in Addition

Use base-ten blocks to help you decide if you will need to regroup. Then complete the chart.

	Addition Sentence	Did I regroup 10 ones for 1 ten?	Did I regroup 10 tens for 1 hundred?	Did I regroup 10 hundreds for 1 thousand?
1.	543 + 72 = 615	no	yes	no
2.	644 + 89 = 733	yes	yes	no
3.	491 + 99 = 590	yes	yes	no
4.	133 + 647 = 780	yes	no	no
5.	229 + 140 = 369	no	no	no
6.	73 + 32 = 105	no	yes	no
7.	866 + 82 = 948	no	yes	no
8.	909 + 101 = 1,010	yes	no	yes
9.	56 + 45 = 101	yes	yes	no

Problem Solving

10. Jamal showed the numbers 490 and 212 with blocks. Will he need to regroup when he adds his numbers together? What is his total?

yes; 702

11. Hillary looked at the problem 809 + 111. She said she needs to regroup 10 tens for one hundred. Do you agree or disagree? Why?

Disagree; ten ones must be regrouped for one ten.

Review and Remember

Give the value of the underlined digit.

12. <u>6</u>9 **60** **13.** <u>8</u>62 **800** **14.** <u>1</u>,829 **1,000**

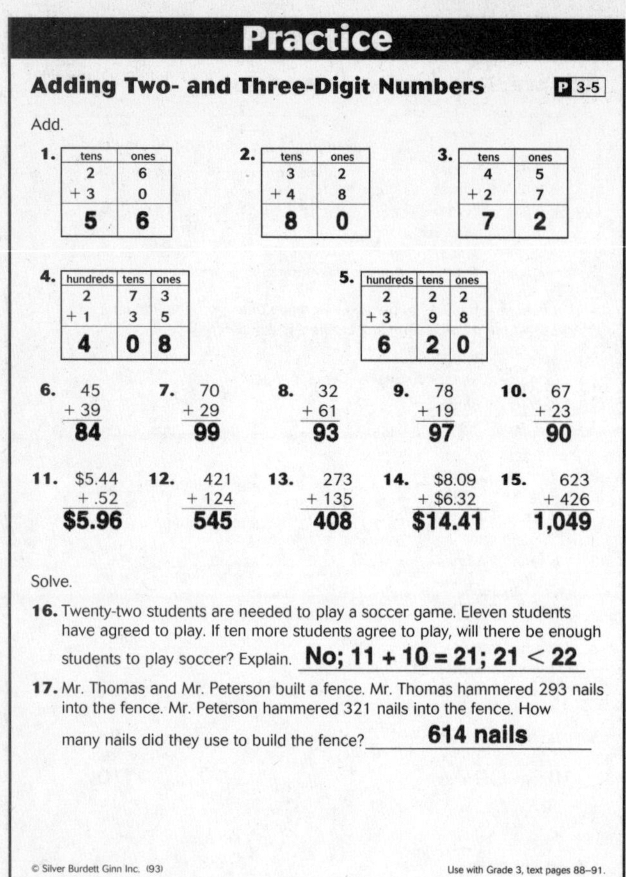

Practice

Adding Two- and Three-Digit Numbers

P 3-5

Add.

1.

tens	ones
2	6
+ 3	0
5	**6**

2.

tens	ones
3	2
+ 4	8
8	**0**

3.

tens	ones
4	5
+ 2	7
7	**2**

4.

hundreds	tens	ones
2	7	3
+ 1	3	5
4	**0**	**8**

5.

hundreds	tens	ones
2	2	2
+ 3	9	8
6	**2**	**0**

6. 45 + 39 = **84**
7. 70 + 29 = **99**
8. 32 + 61 = **93**
9. 78 + 19 = **97**
10. 67 + 23 = **90**

11. $5.44 + .52 = **$5.96**
12. 421 + 124 = **545**
13. 273 + 135 = **408**
14. $8.09 + $6.32 = **$14.41**
15. 623 + 426 = **1,049**

Solve.

16. Twenty-two students are needed to play a soccer game. Eleven students have agreed to play. If ten more students agree to play, will there be enough students to play soccer? Explain. **No; 11 + 10 = 21; 21 < 22**

17. Mr. Thomas and Mr. Peterson built a fence. Mr. Thomas hammered 293 nails into the fence. Mr. Peterson hammered 321 nails into the fence. How many nails did they use to build the fence? **614 nails**

 Use with Grade 3, text pages 88–91.

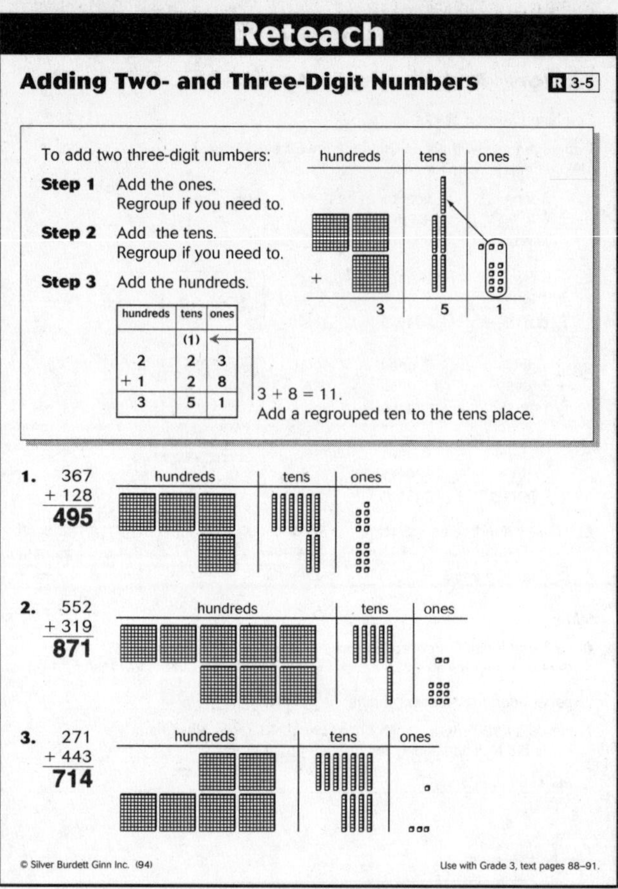

Reteach

Adding Two- and Three-Digit Numbers

R 3-5

To add two three-digit numbers:

Step 1 Add the ones. Regroup if you need to.

Step 2 Add the tens. Regroup if you need to.

Step 3 Add the hundreds.

hundreds	tens	ones
	(1)	
2	2	3
+ 1	2	8
3	5	1

3 + 8 = 11.
Add a regrouped ten to the tens place.

1. 367 + 128 = **495**
2. 552 + 319 = **871**
3. 271 + 443 = **714**

 Use with Grade 3, text pages 88–91.

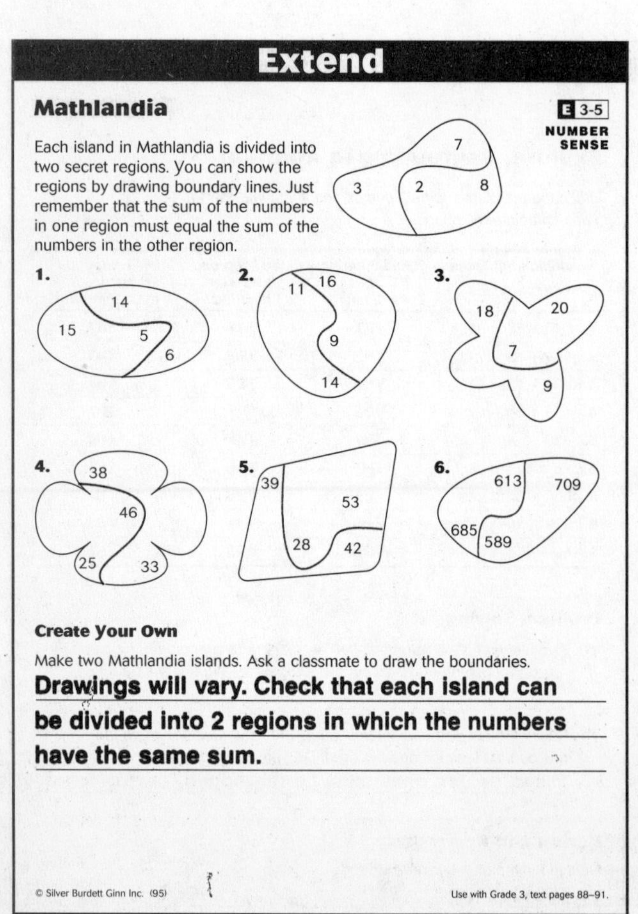

Extend

Mathlandia

E 3-5 NUMBER SENSE

Each island in Mathlandia is divided into two secret regions. You can show the regions by drawing boundary lines. Just remember that the sum of the numbers in one region must equal the sum of the numbers in the other region.

Create Your Own

Make two Mathlandia islands. Ask a classmate to draw the boundaries.

Drawings will vary. Check that each island can be divided into 2 regions in which the numbers have the same sum.

 Use with Grade 3, text pages 88–91.

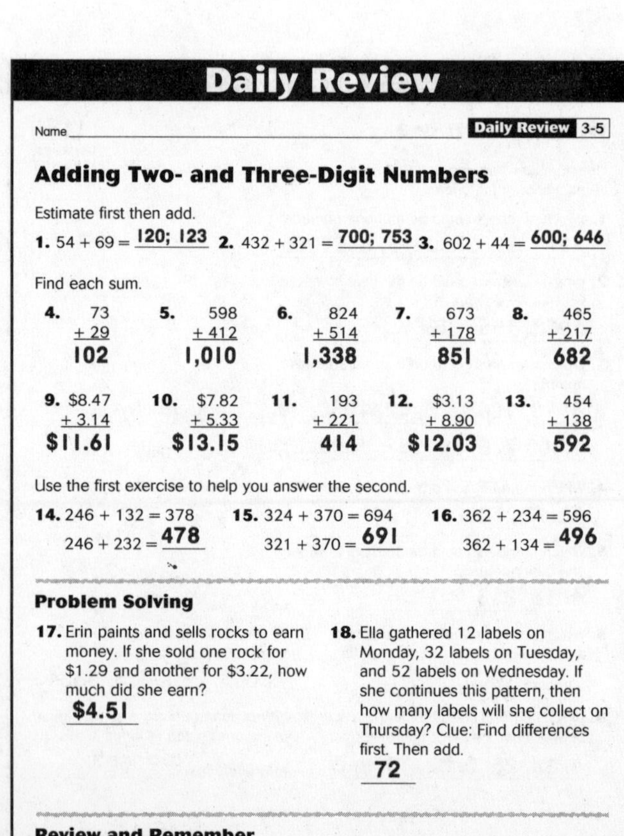

Daily Review

Name ____________________ Daily Review 3-5

Adding Two- and Three-Digit Numbers

Estimate first then add.

1. 54 + 69 = **120; 123**
2. 432 + 321 = **700; 753**
3. 602 + 44 = **600; 646**

Find each sum.

4. 73 + 29 = **102**
5. 598 + 412 = **1,010**
6. 824 + 514 = **1,338**
7. 673 + 178 = **851**
8. 465 + 217 = **682**
9. $8.47 + 3.14 = **$11.61**
10. $7.82 + 5.33 = **$13.15**
11. 193 + 221 = **414**
12. $3.13 + 8.90 = **$12.03**
13. 454 + 138 = **592**

Use the first exercise to help you answer the second.

14. 246 + 132 = 378; 246 + 232 = **478**
15. 324 + 370 = 694; 321 + 370 = **691**
16. 362 + 234 = 596; 362 + 134 = **496**

Problem Solving

17. Erin paints and sells rocks to earn money. If she sold one rock for $1.29 and another for $3.22, how much did she earn? **$4.51**

18. Ella gathered 12 labels on Monday, 32 labels on Tuesday, and 52 labels on Wednesday. If she continues this pattern, then how many labels will she collect on Thursday? Clue: Find differences first. Then add. **72**

Review and Remember

Draw a clock that shows each time.

19. 9:30 20. 12:00 21. 8:30

Practice

Adding Greater Numbers

P 3-6

1. 473 + 6,138 = **6,611**
2. 5,752 + 3,523 = **9,275**
3. 8,648 + 6,372 = **15,020**
4. 1,374 + 6,211 = **7,585**
5. $49.50 + 28.90 = **$78.40**
6. $39.28 + 50.63 = **$89.91**
7. $38.76 + 25.40 = **$64.16**
8. $22.48 + 98.75 = **$121.23**

9. 5,720 + 3,376 = **9,096**
10. 7,483 + 4,631 = **12,114**
11. 3,287 + 4,165 = **7,452**
12. 2,760 + 1,404 = **4,164**

Use the numbers on the number cards. Find the sum of every possible number pair. Then use your answers to complete the sentences below.

7,475	7,924	7,478	7,923

13. Write the pair of numbers with the greatest sum: **7,924 + 7,923 = 15,847**
14. The number pair with smallest sum is: **7,475 + 7,478 = 14,953**
15. The number pair with a sum that has all odd number digits is: **7,475 + 7,924 = 15,399**

Solve.

16. Shelly has $14.50 in her bank. She adds $5.50 baby-sitting money to her bank account. How much does Shelly have now? **$20.00**
17. A trip down the Moon Rapids costs $12.95. You also want to rent an underwater camera for $2.79. What will the rapids trip cost? **$15.74**

 Use with Grade 3, text pages 92–93.

Reteach

Adding Greater Numbers

R 3-6

Adding four-digit numbers is like adding two-digit and three-digit numbers: sometimes you have to regroup.

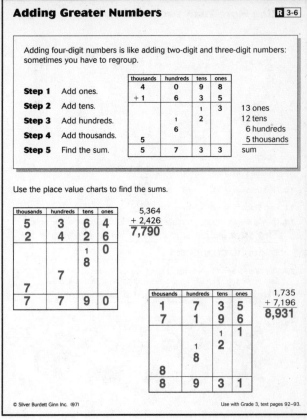

		thousands	hundreds	tens	ones	
		4	0	9	8	
		+ 1	6	3	5	
Step 1	Add ones.			1	3	13 ones
Step 2	Add tens.		1	2		12 tens
Step 3	Add hundreds.		6			6 hundreds
Step 4	Add thousands.	5				5 thousands
Step 5	Find the sum.	5	7	3	3	sum

Use the place value charts to find the sums.

thousands	hundreds	tens	ones
5	3	6	4
2	4	2	6
		1	0
		8	
	7		
7			
7	7	9	0

5,364 + 2,426 = **7,790**

thousands	hundreds	tens	ones
1	7	3	5
7	1	9	6
		1	1
	1	2	
	8		
8			
8	9	3	1

1,735 + 7,196 = **8,931**

 Use with Grade 3, text pages 92–93.

Extend

Pinball Wizard

E 3-6 REASONING

Your scores for each round of pinball are shown below. Which two targets did you hit? Write the numbers.

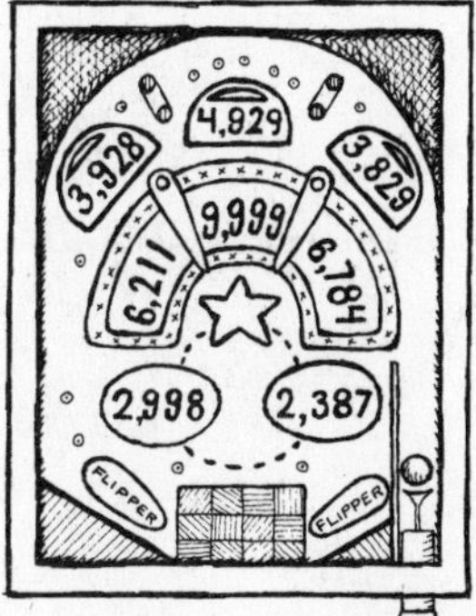

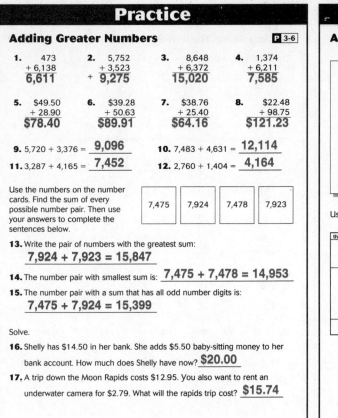

1. **3,928 + 6,211** = 10,139
2. **4,929 + 9,999** = 14,928
3. **2,387 + 6,784** = 9,171
4. **2,998 + 9,999** = 12,997
5. **6,784 + 6,211** = 12,995
6. **4,929 + 6,784** = 11,713
7. **2,998 + 3,928** = 6,926
8. **3,829 + 4,929** = 8,758
9. **3,829 + 2,998** = 6,827
10. **2,387 + 6,211** = 8,598
11. **4,929 + 3,928** = 8,857
12. **9,999 + 2,387** = 12,386

Suppose you hit two targets and each target is different.

13. What is the highest possible score you could get? **16,783**
14. What is the lowest possible score you could get? **5,385**

 Use with Grade 3, text pages 92–93.

Daily Review

Name ____________________ Daily Review 3-6

Adding Greater Numbers

Find each sum. Regroup if you need to.

1. 2,154 + 2,269 = **4,423**
2. 4,532 + 3,201 = **7,733**
3. $8.02 + 4.04 = **$12.06**
4. 6,187 + 1,522 = **7,709**

Use paper and pencil or a calculator to find each sum. Tell which method you used. **Methods will vary.**

5. 3,592 + 2,107 = **5,699**
6. 4,392 + 5,211 = **9,603**
7. $18.22 + 21.04 = **$39.26**
8. 4,127 + 2,542 = **6,669**
9. $24.27 + 33.64 = **$57.91**
10. $67.72 + 2.31 = **$70.03**
11. 1,373 + 3,221 = **4,594**
12. 3,256 + 2,081 = **5,337**

Problem Solving

13. On one day, 2,198 people visited the theater in the afternoon. That night, 3,123 people visited the theater. How many people visited the theater that day? **5,321**
14. One round of mini-golf costs $5.50? One game of bowling costs $2.95. One game of lawn darts costs $1.50. How much would it cost to play mini-golf and lawn darts? **$7.00**

Review and Remember

Add or subtract.

15. 9 + 8 = **17**
16. 16 − 9 = **7**
17. 3 + 7 = **10**
18. 17 − 9 = **8**
19. 10 + 5 = **15**
20. 14 − 8 = **6**

Practice

Adding More Than Two Numbers

P 3-7

Find each sum.

1. 12 61 + 20 **93**	**2.** 24 19 + 53 **96**	**3.** 513 290 + 183 **986**	**4.** \$2.94 3.75 + 0.15 **\$6.84**
5. 1,234 357 + 2,701 **4,292**	**6.** 3,152 2,901 + 3,737 **9,790**	**7.** \$10.95 1.74 + 1.74 **\$14.43**	**8.** \$17.25 43.58 + 25.10 **\$85.93**

Add. Use paper and pencil or a calculator.

9. Find the sum of 213 + 514 + 179. **906**

10. Find the sum of 514 + 179 + 213. **906**

11. Find the sum of 179 + 514 + 213. **906**

12. Look at the answers to exercises 9–11 and write about what you notice.
The sum is the same, even if the order of addends changes.

13. The pirate wants to get to his treasure quickly. Predict which number path is shorter. Then add up the numbers on each path to find out.
Predictions will vary. Path A is shorter.

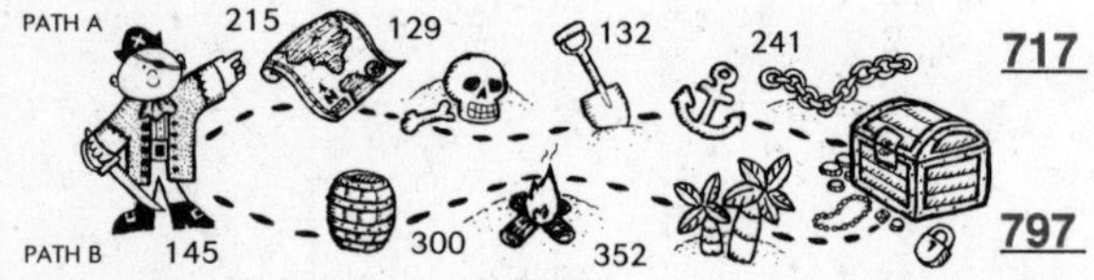

717

797

Reteach

Adding More Than Two Numbers

R 3-7

Add all the ones. Then add all the tens.

46 11 + 38	6 + 1 = 7 7 + 8 = 15 15 ones	4 + 1 = 5 5 + 1 = 6 6 + 3 = 9 tens	1 46 11 + 38 95

1. 45 21 + 32 **98**	**2.** 56 37 + 16 **109**	**3.** 81 49 + 27 **157**	**4.** 73 26 + 13 **112**	**5.** 21 12 + 66 **99**
6. 23 43 + 19 **85**	**7.** 57 78 + 32 **167**	**8.** 91 44 + 46 **181**	**9.** 53 50 + 39 **142**	**10.** 14 64 + 85 **163**
11. 64 26 + 75 **165**	**12.** 82 24 + 66 **172**	**13.** 59 42 + 33 **134**	**14.** 27 49 + 53 **129**	**15.** 36 52 + 75 **163**
16. 346 267 + 453 **1,066**	**17.** 568 419 + 766 **1,753**	**18.** 792 364 + 537 **1,693**	**19.** 237 504 + 862 **1,603**	**20.** 661 942 + 333 **1,936**

Extend

Summer Fun

E 3-7

VISUAL THINKING

Use the map to answer the questions about the Landrys' vacation.

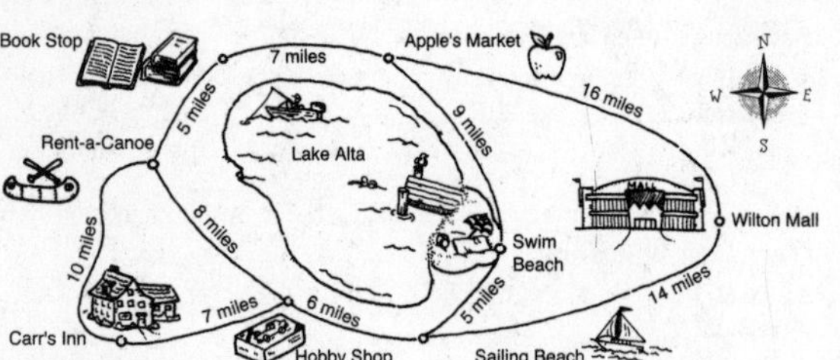

1. Fred biked north from Carr's Inn to The Book Stop. Suzanne biked north and then west from Swim Beach to meet Fred there. Who biked the greater distance?
Suzanne

2. Mr. Landry drove from Swim Beach to Wilton Mall. If he traveled the shortest route, did he turn north or south when he left Swim Beach?
South

3. Rachel biked the shortest route from the Rent-a-Canoe shop to Apple's Market. Suzanne biked the shortest route from Apple's Market to Sailing Beach. Who had the longer ride?
Suzanne

4. When Mr. Landry finished shopping at the mall, he drove the shorter route to The Book Stop. He bought a book and then returned to Carr's Inn. How far was his trip from the mall?
38 miles

5. Rachel started at Rent-a-Canoe and biked all around the lake. How far did she ride?
40 miles

6. Fred took the shorter route from The Book Stop to Sailing Beach. How far did he bike?
19 miles

Daily Review

Name ____________________

Daily Review 3-7

Adding More Than Two Numbers

Add. Check each answer by adding up.

1. 24 31 + 45 **100**	**2.** 182 242 + 422 **846**	**3.** 802 535 + 64 **1,401**	**4.** 3,211 5,747 + 4,312 **13,270**

Use paper and pencil or a calculator to find each sum. Tell which method you used.

5. 35 92 + 27 **154**	**6.** 42 54 + 21 **117**	**7.** 182 225 + 643 **1,050**	**8.** 715 654 + 322 **1,691**
9. 8,527 3,344 + 5,672 **17,543**	**10.** 2,531 1,377 + 3,221 **7,129**	**11.** 3,256 2,081 + 4,094 **9,431**	**12.** 5,469 2,001 + 3,533 **11,003**

Problem Solving

13. A bike rider travels 14 miles the first day, 21 miles the second day, and 28 miles the third day. If she continues this pattern, how far will she have ridden in the first four days?
98 miles

14. A bike rider buys an air pump for \$13.79; a helmet for \$79.22 and a mirror for \$11.09. How much does the rider spend?
\$104.10

Review and Remember

Add.

15. 1 + 4 + 3 = **8**
16. 6 + 3 + 5 = **14**
17. 3 + 7 + 5 = **15**
18. 7 + 9 + 1 = **17**
19. 3 + 6 + 2 = **11**
20. 5 + 2 + 5 = **12**

Practice

Problem Solving P 3-8

Make a Table

Make a table to solve each problem.

1. Rita lifts a weight 6 times in 1 minute. How many minutes will it take her to lift the same weight 30 times?

Number of weights	6	12	18	24	30
Minutes	1	2	3	4	5

5 minutes

2. Jeff is saving his money for a new exercise book. He saves 1¢ the first day and doubles what he saves each day for the next 7 days. How much will Jeff save on the seventh day?

Days	1	2	3	4	5	6	7
Pennies saved	1¢	2¢	4¢	8¢	16¢	32¢	64¢

64¢

3. Phil does 3 sit-ups on the first day of school. He doubles the number of sit-ups he does every day for 5 days. How many sit-ups will Phil do on the fifth day?

Days	1	2	3	4	5
Sit-ups	3	6	12	24	48

48 sit-ups

4. Yolanda runs 4 miles a day to stay in shape. How many days does it take for Yolanda to run 28 miles?

Days	1	2	3	4	5	6	7
Miles run	4	8	12	16	20	24	28

7 days

 Use with Grade 3, text pages 98-99.

Reteach

Problem Solving R 3-8

Make a Table

Max's teacher gives him 4 stickers each week he completes his homework. If Max turns in his homework every week, how many stickers does he have after 4 weeks?

You can make a table to solve this problem.

1. How many stickers does Max have at the end of each week?

Understand You need to know the number of stickers Max earns each week. You need to find the new total number of stickers Max has at the end of each week.

Plan Make a table to keep track of the stickers Max has. Remember to add the stickers for one week to the number of stickers for the week before to make a new total.

Solve Count each week of homework 1 through 4. Count the stickers by 4's, since Max gets 4 stickers each week.

Weeks	1	2	3	4
Stickers	4	8	12	16

Look Back Max will have 16 stickers after 4 weeks. That makes sense because 4 + 4 + 4 + 4 = 16.

Complete the table to solve the problem.

2. Max saves 5¢ a day. How much money does he save in 8 days?

Weeks	1	2	3	4	5	6	7	8
Money saved	5¢	10¢	15¢	20¢	25¢	30¢	35¢	40¢

Max saves 40¢ in 8 days.

 Use with Grade 3, text pages 98-99.

Extend

Step Right Up!

E 3-8 REASONING

Martha stacked some shoeboxes in the shape of a staircase.

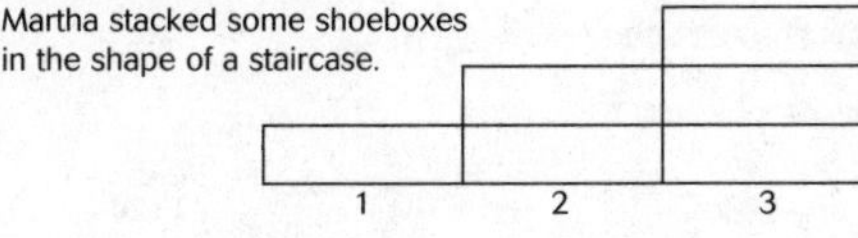

1. How many shoeboxes are used in the first step? 1 shoebox
2. How many shoeboxes are used in the first two steps? 3 shoeboxes
3. How many shoeboxes are used in the first three steps? 6 shoeboxes
4. Make a table. How many shoeboxes make a staircase 5 steps high?

Number of steps	1	2	3	4	5
Shoeboxes needed	1	3	6	10	15

5. Describe the pattern you see in the table.
Possible answer: shoeboxes needed increase one more than the shoeboxes needed the time before.
6. Martha has 40 shoeboxes. How many steps high can her staircase be? Explain.
Possible answer: Martha's staircase can be 8 steps high. She needs 21 shoeboxes for 6 steps, 28 shoeboxes for 7 steps, and 36 shoeboxes for 8 steps. She cannot make 9 steps, because she would need 45 shoeboxes.
7. How many boxes will Martha use if the staircase is 10 steps high?
55 shoeboxes

 Use with Grade 3, text pages 98-99.

Daily Review

Name__________ Daily Review 3-8

Problem Solving

Make a Table

Make a table to help you solve each problem. **Check students' tables.**

1. Ten minutes before the store opens, 30 people are in line. Each minute 10 more people arrive. How many people will be in line when the store finally opens?
130 people
2. Bob can frame 12 photographs in one day. He needs to frame 60 photographs for the gallery. After 3 days, how many more photographs will Bob have left to frame?
24 photographs
3. Joshua's cat eats 4 cans of cat food in one week. How many weeks will 24 cans of cat food last?
6 weeks
4. Matt is reading a 250 page book. So far, he has read 40 pages. If he reads 25 pages each night, how many nights will it take him to finish the book?
9 nights

Review and Remember

Add.

5. 344 + 456 = 800
6. 973 + 845 = 1,818
7. 55 + 66 = 121
8. 542 + 96 = 638
9. 48 + 29 = 77
10. 209 + 711 = 920

Practice

Estimating Differences

P 3-9

Estimate each difference.

1. 63 − 32 = **30**
2. 41 − 18 = **20**
3. 39 − 23 = **20**
4. 85 − 49 = **40**
5. 903 − 660 = **200**
6. 726 − 301 = **400**
7. 921 − 546 = **400**
8. $7.52 − .96 = **$7.00**
9. 707 − 233 = **500**
10. 57 − 28 = **30**
11. $3.42 − $1.85 = **$1.00**
12. 63 − 29 = **30**

Choose estimation, paper and pencil, or a calculator to compare the following numbers. Write >, <, or = for each ◯.

13. 47 − 10 **<** 97 − 26
14. 85 − 40 **>** 47 − 24
15. $7.68 − $3.25 **>** $5.00 − $2.01
16. 920 − 821 **<** 595 − 180
17. Larry is visiting the planet Dinopar. He began the day with $9.42 and spent $1.58 for lunch. Estimate and tell which pet and toys he might buy at the Dinosaur Pet Shop.

baby dinosaur	$2.83
teenage dinosaur	$3.63
dino ball	.86
dino food	$1.79
dino first aid kit	.67
bone for chewing	$1.46
dinosaur leash	$2.04

Larry might buy **Check to see that students' totals do not exceed $7.84.**

Use with text pages 100–101.

Reteach

Estimating Differences

R 3-9

To estimate differences, round each number before you subtract.

Round two-digit numbers to the nearest ten.	Round three-digit numbers to the nearest hundred.	Round dollars and cents to the nearest dollar.
82 → 80 − 25 → − 30 50	350 → 400 − 188 → − 200 200	$5.23 → $5 − 3.89 → − 4 $1
Remember: When there are 5 or more ones, you round up.	Remember: When there are 5 or more tens, you round up.	Remember, when there is more than 50¢, you round up.

Estimate each difference. The first one is done for you.

1. 52 → 50; − 21 → − 20; 30
2. 320 → **300**; − 240 → − **200**; **100**
3. 467 → **500**; − 172 → − **200**; **300**
4. 67 → **70**; − 23 → − **20**; **50**
5. 580 → **600**; − 410 → − **400**; **200**
6. 761 → **800**; − 493 → − **500**; **300**
7. $5.93 → **$6.00**; − $2.46 → − **$2.00**; **$4.00**
8. $7.34 → **$7.00**; − $5.82 → − **$6.00**; **$1.00**
9. $3.65 → **$4.00**; − $2.49 → − **$2.00**; **$2.00**

Use with Grade 3, text pages 100–101.

Extend

Sum Puzzles

E 3-9
NUMBER SENSE

Solve each puzzle. Use a number only once in each puzzle.

1. Put the numbers 1 through 6 along the sides of the triangle so that each side adds up to 9.

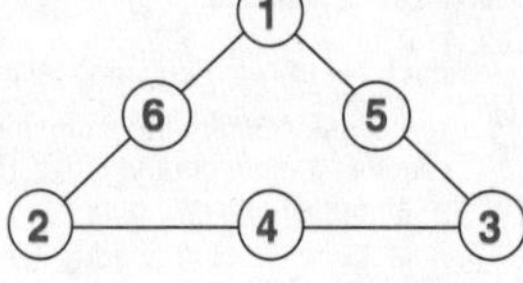

Note: answers may vary in orientation.

2. Put the numbers 1 through 9 in the square so that every horizontal and vertical row and the diagonals add up to 15.

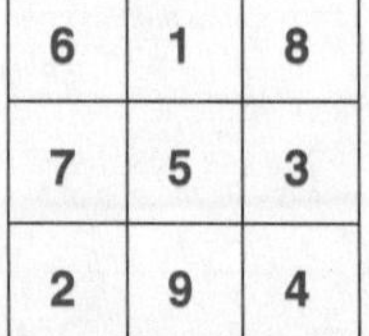

6	1	8
7	5	3
2	9	4

Note: answers may vary in orientation.

3. Put the numbers 1 through 13 in the circles so that any three circles on a straight line add up to 21.

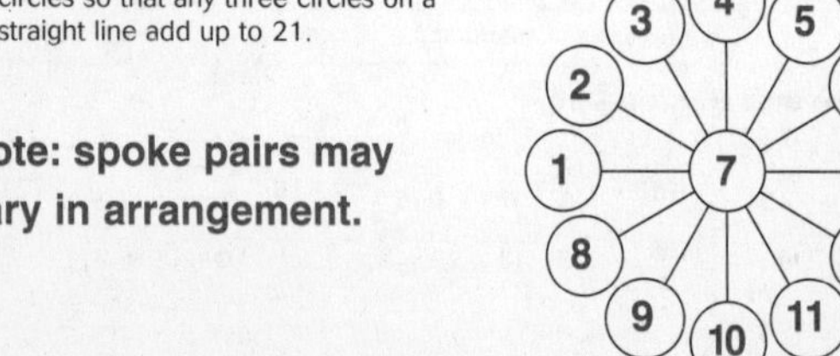

Note: spoke pairs may vary in arrangement.

Use with Grade 3, text pages 100–101.

Daily Review

Name ______________________

Daily Review 3-9

Estimating Differences

Estimate by rounding to the nearest ten.

1. 36 − 21 **20**
2. 49 − 28 **20**
3. 76 − 44 **40**
4. 87 − 13 **80**

Estimate by rounding to the nearest hundred or dollar.

5. 492 − 314 **200**
6. 430 − 318 **100**
7. $8.12 − 2.90 **$5.00**
8. $7.67 − 1.25 **$7.00**
9. 827 − 698 **100**
10. $6.21 − 5.02 **$1.00**
11. 782 − 291 **500**
12. 741 − 257 **400**

Problem Solving

13. A box of crackers weighs 795 grams. A box of cereal weighs 396 grams. Which box weighs more? About how much more? **crackers, 400 g**
14. A ream of paper contains 500 sheets. Which is closer to a ream: 2 stacks of 200 papers each, or 3 stacks of papers each? **3 stacks of 150 papers**

Review and Remember

Compare. Write >, <, or = for each.

15. 8 + 9 **<** 9 + 9
16. 4 − 1 **>** 4 − 4
17. 4 + 5 **<** 5 + 6
18. 6 + 3 **=** 4 + 5
19. 9 − 7 **<** 8 − 1
20. 6 + 0 **<** 4 + 3
21. 8 + 0 **=** 0 + 8
22. 7 − 1 **>** 6 − 2
23. 4 + 3 **<** 5 + 4

Practice

Explore: Regrouping in Subtraction

P 3-10

Stanley drove 762 miles to Grandma's farm. He made several stops along the way.

Write subtraction sentences to show how many miles Stanley had left to drive after each day. You may use base-ten blocks to help you solve the subtractions. Remember to regroup when necessary.

1. Day 1

Stanley drove 189 miles. He stopped to visit Uncle Jed. How many miles were left?

$$\begin{array}{r} 762 \\ -\,189 \\ \hline 573 \end{array}$$ miles

2. Day 2

Stanley drove 221 miles. He stopped to see a local fair. How many miles were left?

$$\begin{array}{r} 573 \\ -\,221 \\ \hline 352 \end{array}$$ miles

3. Day 3

Stanley drove 215 miles before he stopped to see Cousin Bill. How many miles were left?

$$\begin{array}{r} 352 \\ -\,215 \\ \hline 137 \end{array}$$ miles

4. Day 4

The fourth day he drove only 135 miles. He spent half of the day sightseeing. How many miles were left?

$$\begin{array}{r} 137 \\ -\,135 \\ \hline 2 \end{array}$$ miles

Use with Grade 3, text pages 102–103.

Reteach

Explore: Regrouping in Subtraction

R 3-10

The students of Edison School planted tulip bulbs. They had 452 tulip bulbs. Each student planted one bulb. The school is going to donate the bulbs left over to a local hospital. How many bulbs can the school donate?

Write a subtraction sentence for each exercise.
Use base-ten blocks to help you.

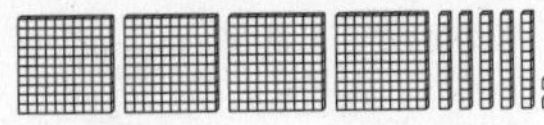

= 452 tulip bulbs

1. The first graders planted 43 bulbs. How many are left?
   452 – 43 = 409
2. The second graders planted 54 bulbs. How many are left?
   409 – 54 = 355
3. There are 66 third graders. How many bulbs are left when they finish planting?
   355 – 66 = 289
4. There are 63 fourth graders. How many bulbs are left when they finish planting?
   289 – 63 = 226
5. The fifth graders planted 59 tulip bulbs. How many are left?
   226 – 59 = 167
6. The sixth graders planted 64 bulbs. How many bulbs can be donated to the hospital?
   167 – 64 = 103

Use with Grade 3, text pages 102–103.

Extend

Subtracting Leaves

E 3-10

NUMBER SENSE

How many subtractions can you make with the numbers **146, 862, 313, 400, 794,** and **585?** Write a different subtraction in each tree. Then find the difference for each.

Arrangement may vary.
Check the accuracy of students' work.

Use with Grade 3, text pages 102–103.

Daily Review

Name ____________________

Daily Review 3-10

EXPLORE: Regrouping in Subtraction

Use base-ten blocks to help you decide whether you will need to regroup. Then complete the chart.

	Subtraction Sentence	Did I need to regroup a ten as 10 ones?	Did I need to regroup a hundred as 10 tens?
1.	624 – 36 = 588	yes	yes
2.	212 – 23 = 189	yes	yes
3.	958 – 31 = 927	no	no
4.	802 – 12 = 790	no	yes
5.	631 – 59 = 572	yes	yes
6.	236 – 89 = 147	yes	yes
7.	325 – 12 = 313	no	no
8.	963 – 521 = 442	no	no
9.	841 – 69 = 772	yes	yes
10.	921 – 36 = 885	yes	yes

Problem Solving

11. Anika showed the numbers 511 and 431 with base-ten blocks. Will she need to regroup when she subtracts the numbers to find the difference?

Yes; regroup a hundred as 10 tens.

12. Josh looked at the problem 989 – 191. He thinks he needs to regroup 1 ten for 10 ones. Do you agree or disagree? What would you tell Josh?

Disagree; he needs to regroup 1 hundred for tens, but not 1 ten for ones.

Review and Remember

Give the value of 6 in each number.

13. 36 **6** **14.** 569 **60** **15.** 6,214 **6,000** **16.** 963 **60**

Practice

Subtracting Two- and Three-Digit Numbers

P 3-11

Subtract. Color the balloon with the matching answer.

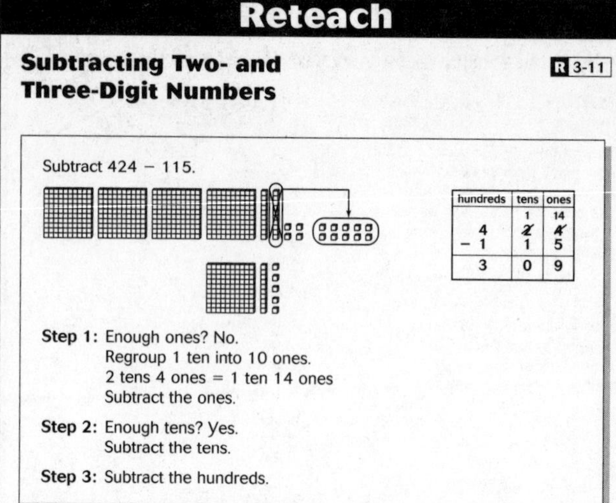

1. 53 − 12 = **41**
2. 47 − 19 = **28**
3. 41 − 25 = **16**
4. 81 − 15 = **66**
5. 90 − 34 = **56**
6. 72 − 68 = **4**
7. 563 − 128 = **435**
8. 671 − 134 = **537**
9. 926 − 432 = **494**
10. 736 − 317 = **419**
11. $7.94 − 5.85 = **$2.09**
12. $4.29 − 1.99 = **$2.30**
13. $6.92 − 0.38 = **$6.54**
14. $3.09 − 1.42 = **$1.67**

15. Write the number on the balloon that remains. **$1.00**

Solve.

A space camp has 25 astronauts, 51 technicians, and 16 scientists.

16. How many more technicians are there than scientists? **35 more technicians**

17. How many more astronauts are there than scientists? **9 more astronauts**

18. There are 612 seats on a space shuttle. 103 of the seats are window seats. How many seats are not next to a window? **509 seats are not next to a window**

 Use with Grade 3, text pages 104–107.

Reteach

Subtracting Two- and Three-Digit Numbers

R 3-11

Subtract 424 − 115.

hundreds	tens	ones
	1	14
4	~~2~~	~~4~~
− 1	1	5
3	0	9

Step 1: Enough ones? No.
Regroup 1 ten into 10 ones.
2 tens 4 ones = 1 ten 14 ones
Subtract the ones.

Step 2: Enough tens? Yes.
Subtract the tens.

Step 3: Subtract the hundreds.

Subtract. Regroup 1 ten into 10 ones or 1 hundred into 10 tens.
You may use base-ten blocks to help you.

1.

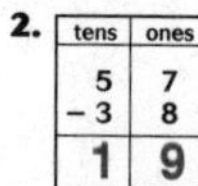

tens	ones
4	2
− 1	4
2	**8**

2.

tens	ones
5	7
− 3	8
1	**9**

3.

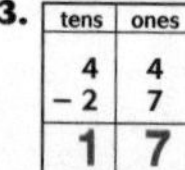

tens	ones
4	4
− 2	7
1	**7**

4.

hundreds	tens	ones
2	3	2
− 1	2	5
1	**0**	**7**

5.

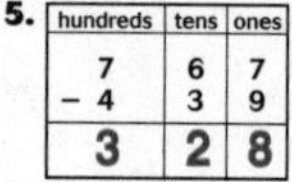

hundreds	tens	ones
7	6	7
− 4	3	9
3	**2**	**8**

 Use with Grade 3, text pages 104–107.

Extend

Weighty Sums and Differences

E 3-11 NUMBER SENSE

The weightlifter needs the same total weight on each side of the barbell. Find the weight that will make the barbell balance. You will need to add and then subtract. You will not use every weight in the pile.

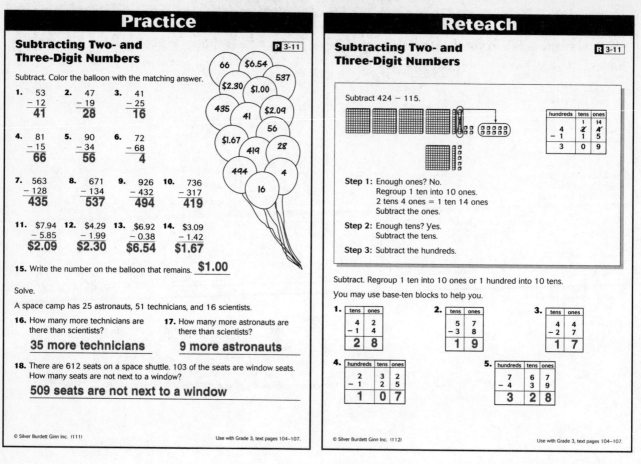

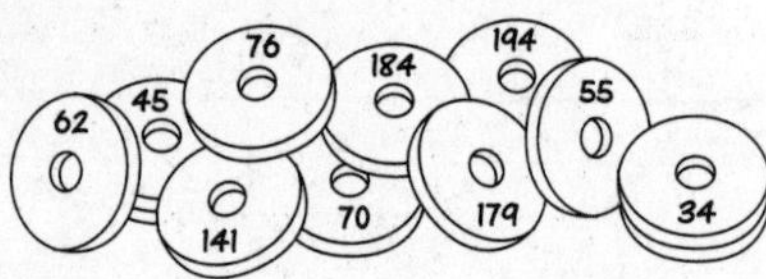

1.

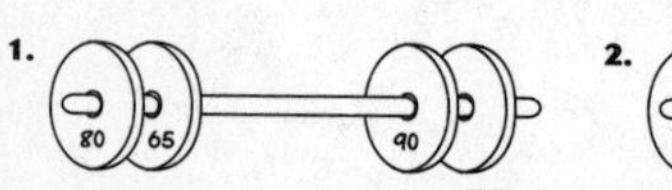

55

2.

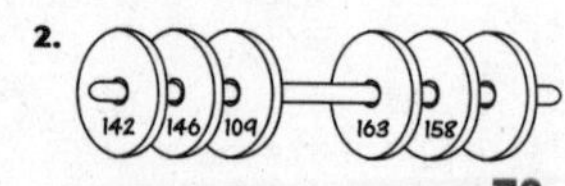

76

3.

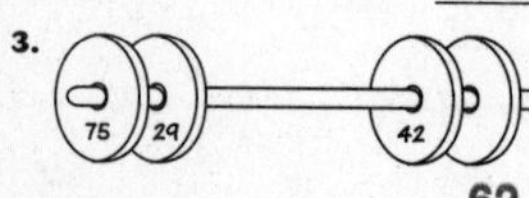

62

4.

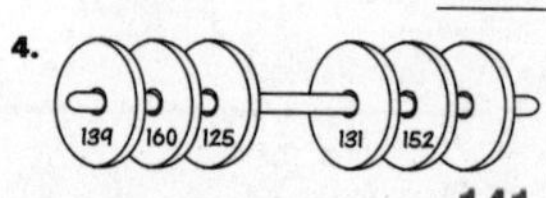

141

5.

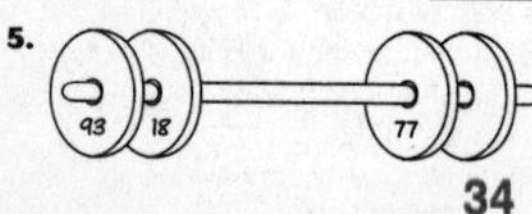

34

6.

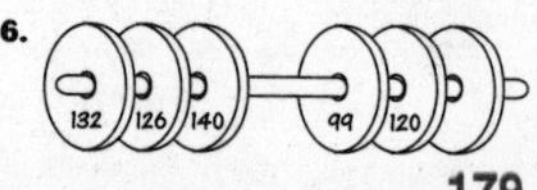

179

7.

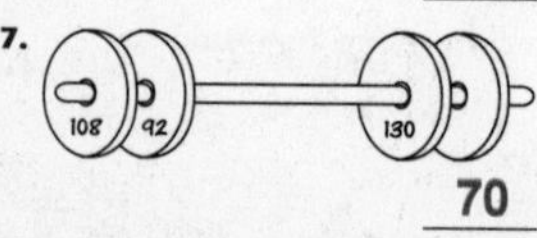

70

8.

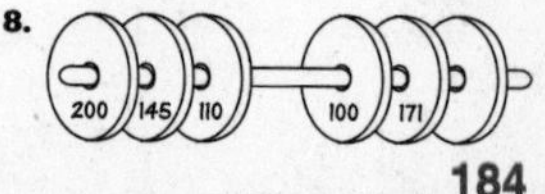

184

 Use with Grade 3, text pages 104–107.

Daily Review

Name ____________________

Daily Review 3-11

Subtracting Two- and Three-Digit Numbers

Subtract. Regroup if you need to.

1. 54 − 21 = **33**
2. 349 − 128 = **221**
3. 776 − 54 = **722**
4. 287 − 193 = **94**
5. 271 − 191 = **80**

Find each difference.

6. 998 − 314 = **684**
7. 43 − 31 = **12**
8. 862 − 201 = **661**
9. $7.65 − 4.25 = **$3.40**
10. 557 − 429 = **128**
11. 737 − 697 = **40**
12. $5.21 − 1.31 = **$3.90**
13. 982 − 273 = **709**
14. 771 − 247 = **524**
15. $9.69 − 3.71 = **$5.98**

Problem Solving

16. Sam weighs 110 pounds. His dog weighs 25 pounds. His cat weighs 11 pounds. How much more does Sam weigh than his cat? How much more does the dog weigh than the cat?
99 pounds; 14 pounds

17. Sam, his cat, and dog get on a scale at the vet's. The scale is broken and shows their weight to be 164 pounds. What's wrong with the scale?
Possible answer: The scale switches the last two digits.

Review and Remember

Find each missing number.

18. $5 + n = 9$ $n =$ **4**
19. $n - 9 = 7$ $n =$ **16**
20. $7 - n = 5$ $n =$ **2**
21. $8 + n = 15$ $n =$ **7**
22. $7 + 9 = n$ $n =$ **16**
23. $n - 6 = 9$ $n =$ **15**

Practice

Subtracting Greater Numbers

P 3-12

Subtract.

1. 9,829 − 5,431 = **4,398**
2. 3,245 − 2,026 = **1,219**
3. 4,170 − 500 = **3,670**
4. 5,916 − 2,007 = **3,909**
5. 9,704 − 243 = **9,461**
6. 6,400 − 3,700 = **2,700**
7. 4,852 − 941 = **3,911**
8. 7,444 − 2,353 = **5,091**
9. 6,930 − 37 = **6,893**
10. 5,888 − 688 = **5,200**

Choose estimation, paper and pencil, or a calculator to compare the following numbers. Write >, <, or = for each ◯.

11. 600 − 60 (>) 595 − 530
12. 2,000 − 666 (<) 8,750 − 2,000

Solve.

13. Ramon sold a fishing boat for $8,660. He bought a different boat for $5,490 and had it painted for $1,370. How much money did Ramon have left?
$1,800

14. The Rosemont school collected $1,346 to help plant trees in the park. They spent $228 advertising their fund raising. How much money can they give the city?
$1,118

15. Amelia has been saving pennies all her life. She has 2,357 of them. If she takes 400 pennies and turns them into bills, how many pennies will she have left?
1,957

Use with Grade 3, text pages 108–109.

Reteach

Subtracting Greater Numbers

R 3-12

Decide when to regroup.
Start with the ones and compare one place at a time.
If the top digit is less than the bottom digit, you need to regroup.

Step 1 You can subtract ones.
Step 2 4 < 6. So regroup 1 hundred into tens.
Step 3 You can subtract hundreds.
Step 4 You can subtract thousands.

6,7̸4̸5 (regrouped: 6 14) − 2,563 = **4,182**

Subtract. Show the regrouping.

1. 8,246 − 4,702 = **3,544** Regroup 1 thousand to make 10 hundreds.
2. 5,839 − 2,762 = **3,077** Regroup 1 hundred to make 10 tens.
3. 2,984 − 1,879 = **1,105**
4. 7,755 − 4,934 = **2,821**
5. 6,780 − 2,462 = **4,318**
6. 4,875 − 2,290 = **2,585**
7. 9,648 − 4,351 = **5,297**
8. 6,978 − 5,099 = **1,879**
9. 9,975 − 2,692 = **7,283**
10. 1,387 − 1,268 = **119**

Use with Grade 3, text pages 108–109.

Extend

Go With the Flow

E 3-12 NUMBER SENSE

A flowchart gives you directions. The arrows show you which way to go. Write the answer for each flowchart in its empty box. One is done for you.

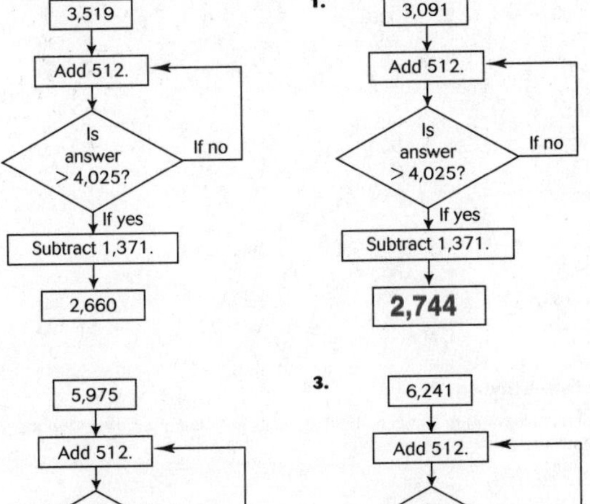

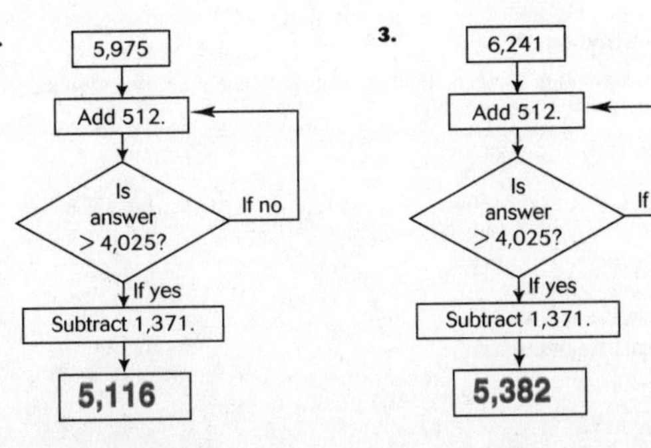

Use with Grade 3, text pages 108–109.

Daily Review

Name ______________________

Daily Review 3-12

Subtracting Greater Numbers

Subtract. Use addition to check your answer.

1. 5,764 − 2,951 = **2,813**
2. 3,849 − 1,728 = **2,121**
3. 7,476 − 4,554 = **2,922**
4. 9,187 − 7,193 = **1,994**

Use paper and pencil or a calculator to subtract. Tell which method you used.

5. 9,898 − 5,814 = **4,084**
6. 4,757 − 2,011 = **2,746**
7. 8,162 − 4,251 = **3,911**
8. 7,465 − 3,991 = **3,474**
9. 8,742 − 1,697 = **7,045**
10. $5,215 − 1,311 = **$3,904**
11. 4,771 − 2,471 = **2,300**
12. $9,009 − 3,990 = **$5,019**

Problem Solving

13. A mile is 5,280 feet. One-half mile is 2,640 feet. How many feet are in one and one-half miles?
7,920 ft.

14. The temperature on Sunday night was 32 degrees Celsius. On Monday morning the temperature was 24 degrees Celsius. Was it warmer on Sunday night or Monday morning? How much warmer or colder?
Sunday night; 8 degrees warmer

Review and Remember

What is the value of 6 in each number?

15. 64 **60**
16. 506 **6**
17. 639 **600**
18. 6,348 **6,000**
19. 69,047 **60,000**

Practice

Subtracting Across Zeros

P 3-13

Subtract. Estimate to be sure your answers make sense.

1. 506 − 137 = **369**
2. 903 − 146 = **757**
3. 600 − 235 = **365**
4. 809 − 509 = **300**
5. 700 − 463 = **237**
6. 803 − 297 = **506**
7. 400 − 88 = **312**
8. 307 − 118 = **189**
9. 707 − 103 = **604**
10. 403 − 227 = **176**
11. 602 − 73 = **529**
12. 500 − 6 = **494**

13. 402 − 257 = **145**
14. 100 − 24 = **76**
15. 602 − 504 = **98**
16. 303 − 249 = **54**

Choose mental math, paper and pencil, or a calculator to figure out the correct difference. Circle the appropriate letter.

17. 207 − 175 = ___?___
a. 23 **(b.) 32** c. 13 d. 31

18. 400 − 315 = ___?___
a. 58 b. 115 c. 105 **(d.) 85**

Solve.

19. Karen, Devin, and Kristin found the names of 508 caves in atlases and encyclopedias. Karen found 120 names of caves and Devin found 206 names. How many cave names did Kristin find?
182

 Use with Grade 3, text pages 110–111.

Reteach

Subtracting Across Zeros

R 3-13

Sometimes you must regroup 1 hundred before you can subtract.

hundreds	tens	ones
2	0	8
− 1	5	9

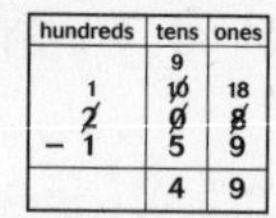

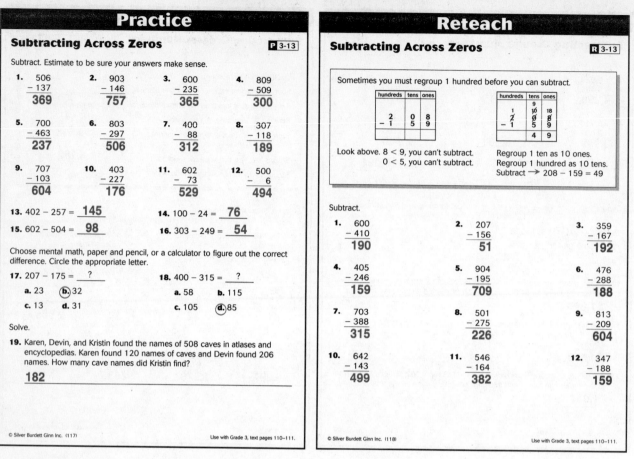

Look above. 8 < 9, you can't subtract.
0 < 5, you can't subtract.

Regroup 1 ten as 10 ones.
Regroup 1 hundred as 10 tens.
Subtract → 208 − 159 = 49

Subtract.

1. 600 − 410 = **190**
2. 207 − 156 = **51**
3. 359 − 167 = **192**
4. 405 − 246 = **159**
5. 904 − 195 = **709**
6. 476 − 288 = **188**
7. 703 − 388 = **315**
8. 501 − 275 = **226**
9. 813 − 209 = **604**
10. 642 − 143 = **499**
11. 546 − 164 = **382**
12. 347 − 188 = **159**

 Use with Grade 3, text pages 110–111.

Extend

Pick Up the Pieces

E 3-13 VISUAL THINKING

Draw lines to show how the shape on the left can be made from the smaller shapes on the right. Number the pieces. Study this example before you start.

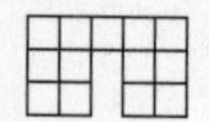
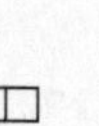

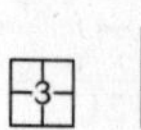
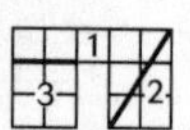

1.
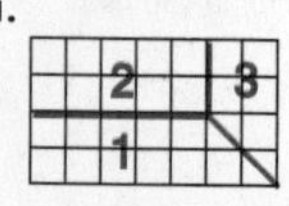
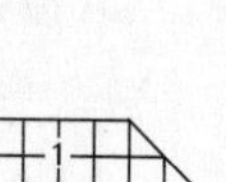
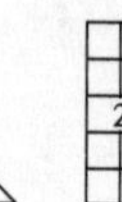
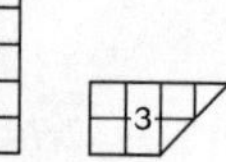

2.
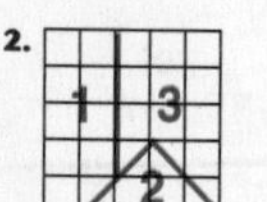
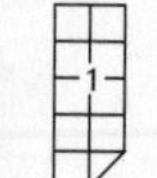
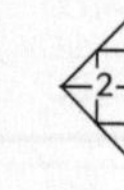
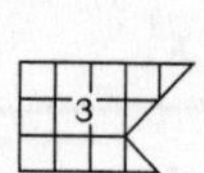

3.
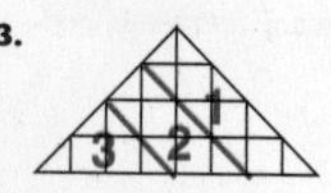
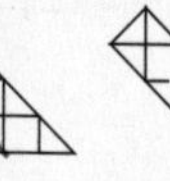
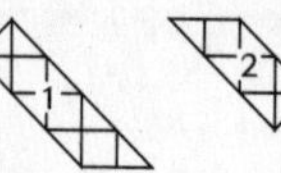

4.

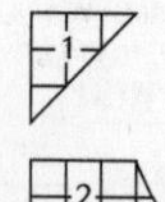
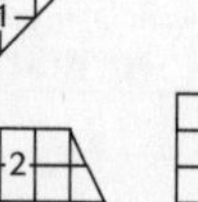
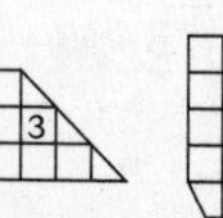

 Use with Grade 3, text pages 110–111.

Daily Review

Name ______________________ Daily Review 3-13

Subtracting Across Zeros

Find each difference. Regroup if you need to.

1. 500 − 251 = **249**
2. 3,000 − 1,785 = **1,215**
3. 7,000 − 3,594 = **3,406**
4. $8,000 − 2,678 = **$5,322**

Subtract.

5. 900 − 515 = **385**
6. 4,000 − 2,981 = **1,019**
7. 8,000 − 4,061 = **3,939**
8. $50.00 − 24.24 = **$25.76**

Use mental math to find each difference.

9. 400 − 90 = **310**
10. 9,000 − 900 = **8,100**
11. $70.00 − 5.00 = **$65.00**
12. $5.00 − 1.50 = **$3.50**

Problem Solving

13. A bus holds 100 passengers. If 28 students get on the bus, then how many seats are left for other passengers?
72

14. A farmer grows 1,000 acres of corn. He can harvest 150 acres in a day. How many days will it take to harvest all 1,000 acres?
7 days

Review and Remember

Add or subtract.

15. 6 + 4 = **10**
16. 5 + 6 = **11**
17. 13 − 6 = **7**
18. 16 − 9 = **7**
19. 6 + 9 = **15**

Practice

Choosing a Computation Method

P 3-14

Add or subtract. Use mental math, pencil and paper, or a calculator. Find each answer in the BINGO box below and circle it. When you have circled five answers in a row, you have BINGO and can stop!

1. 597 − 381 = **216**
2. 700 − 412 = **288**
3. 131 + 400 = **531**
4. 1,237 − 1,085 = **152**
5. 842 − 596 = **246**
6. 1,465 − 1,400 = **65**
7. 43 + 34 = **77**
8. 468 + 480 = **948**
9. 1,782 + 1,010 = **2792**
10. 489 + 136 = **625**
11. 4,326 − 3,548 = **778**
12. 1,300 + 1,076 = **2,376**
13. 631 + 369 = **1,000**
14. 807 − 787 = **20**
15. 1,000 − 257 = **743**
16. 688 − 99 = **589**

B	I	N	G	O
20	2,376	743	531	699
1,000	625	85	306	778
53	288	152	216	173
2,792	589	735	2,735	948
2,001	65	888	246	77

 Use with Grade 3, text pages 112–113.

Reteach

Choosing a Computation Method

R 3-14

There are many ways to find a sum.

Use mental math when the numbers are easy to combine. 400 + 310 = 710. Start with 310. Count on 4 hundreds. The sum is 710.

Use pencil and paper when you cannot use mental math. 2,578 + 6,156 = 8,734. Add ones and regroup. Add tens and regroup. Add hundreds. Add thousands.

Use a calculator: Press 2 5 7 8 + 6 1 5 6 = 8,734

Choose a computation method to solve each problem. Tell which method you will use. Then solve. **Methods will vary.**

1. 70 + 80 = **150** computation method: **mental math**
2. 39 + 36 = **75** computation method: **pencil and paper**
3. 40 + 65 = **105** computation method: **mental math**
4. 600 + 415 = **1,015** computation method: **mental math**
5. $3.15 + 2.79 = **$5.94** computation method: **pencil and paper**
6. 192 + 534 = **726** computation method: **pencil and paper**
7. 6,706 + 289 = **6,995** computation method: **calculator**
8. $35.50 + 20.00 = **$55.50** computation method: **mental math**

 Use with Grade 3, text pages 112–113.

Extend

Same All Around

E 3-14 VISUAL THINKING

Use a colored pencil or a crayon. Copy each design.

1.

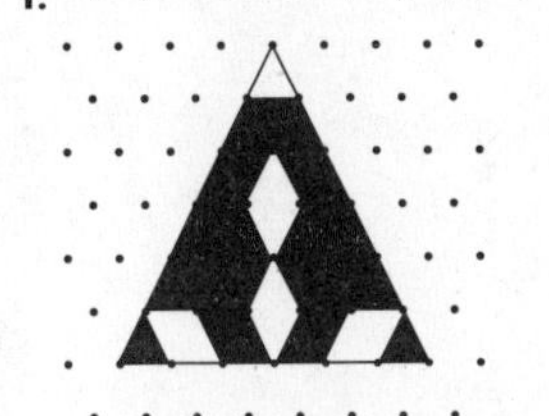
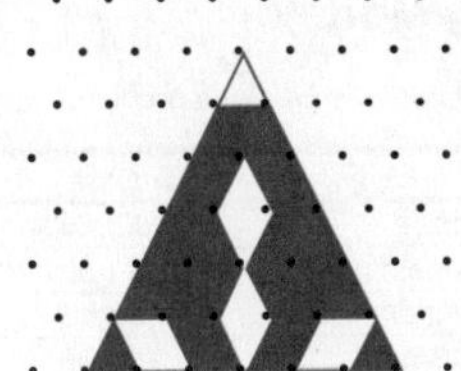

2.

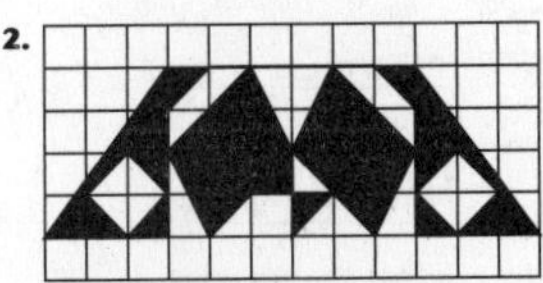

3.

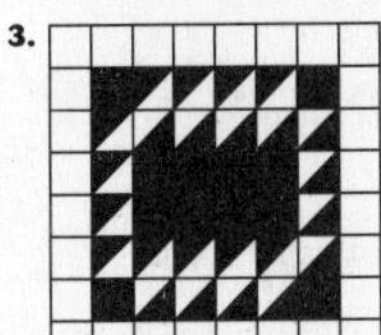
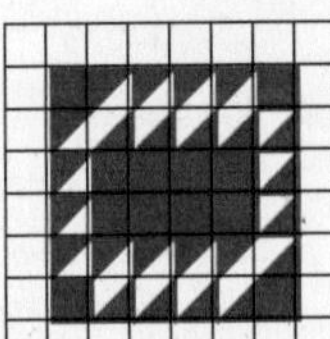

 Use with Grade 3, text pages 112–113.

Daily Review

Name ____________________

Daily Review 3-14

Choosing a Computation Method

Use mental math, paper and pencil, or a calculator to add or subtract. Tell which method you chose. **Methods may vary.**

1. 50 − 25 = **25**
2. 3,589 + 1,785 = **5,374**
3. 7,000 + 3,000 = **10,000**
4. $85.00 − 15.00 = **$70.00**
5. 9,890 − 5,515 = **4,375**
6. 846 − 406 = **440**
7. $67.69 − 15.91 = **51.78**
8. 5,000 − 900 = **4,100**
9. 4,600 + 9,648 = **14,248**
10. 6,986 − 986 = **6,000**
11. $77.00 + 15.37 = **$92.37**
12. 6,930 + 9,000 = **15,930**

Problem Solving

13. A museum displays 254 sculptures and 686 paintings in its Asian exhibit. How many items are in the exhibit altogether? **940**

14. The museum decides to loan 50 of the sculptures to a school's exhibit. How many more paintings than sculptures are left? **482**

Review and Remember

Write the numbers from least to greatest.

15. 61 44 54 — **44**, **54**, **61**
16. 158 155 515 — **155**, **158**, **515**
17. 3,580 3,499 3,229 — **3,229**, **3,499**, **3,580**

Chapter 3 • Lesson 15

Practice

Problem Solving P 3-15

Using Money

Niles received $35.00 for a birthday gift. He plans to spend his money at Out-Of-Doors, a sporting goods shop.

Price List
- walking stick.... $11.70
  sale price...... $ 8.50
- neon vest...... $ 9.49
  sale price...... $ 7.99
- gloves......... $ 6.75
- compass....... $ 2.99
- hiking boots.... $19.49

Solve. If items are on sale, assume Niles buys them on sale.

1. How much money will he save if he buys the walking stick while it is on sale? **$3.20**
2. Niles wants to buy a neon vest and hiking boots. About how much will he spend? **about $30**
3. Niles can't decide between the neon vest and the gloves. How much will he save by buying the gloves? **$1.24**
4. Niles is buying the boots and a compass. Does he have enough money left to buy a walking stick? Explain.
   The boots and compass cost $22.48. Niles has $12.52 left, so he can buy the walking stick.
5. Niles bought gloves and a compass. He gave the cashier $20. How much money should he receive in change? **$10.26**
6. About how much would it cost to buy a neon vest, a compass, and a walking stick? **about $20**
7. Hiking boots are on sale today for only $10.99. How much can Niles save if he buys them today? **$8.50**

 Use with Grade 3, text pages 114-115.

Reteach

Problem Solving R 3-15

Using Money

You go to Puzzles 4U and you want to buy the 500-piece puzzle.

Puzzles 4U

500-piece puzzle	1,000 piece puzzle
Tagged $5.95	Tagged $6.25
On sale for $4.80	On sale for $5.50

1. How much can you save if you buy the 500-piece puzzle on sale?

Understand You need to find the difference between the original and sale prices.

Plan *Subtract* to find a difference.

Solve
$5.95
− 4.80
$1.15

You save **$1.15** if you buy the 500-piece puzzle on sale.

Look Back Check your answer with addition.
$4.80
+ 1.15
$5.95

Your answer is the same as the original price, so it is correct.

Decide whether to add or subtract. Then solve.

2. How much will it cost to buy a 500-piece puzzle and a 1,000-piece puzzle on sale?
   $4.80 + 5.50 = $10.30
3. How much will you save if you buy the 1,000-piece puzzle on sale?
   $6.25 − 5.50 = $0.75

 Use with Grade 3, text pages 114-115.

Extend

Scuba, Dooba, Doo

E 3-15 **REASONING**

You and your friends are going snorkeling. You need some equipment for your trip.

Write the total amount of money each person spent. Then tell which items were purchased.

- goggles $ 9.75
- snorkel $12.50
- camera $19.30
- wet suit $21.55
- flippers $ 5.65

1. 1 $10 bill, 1 $5 bill, 4 dimes
   Total: **$15.40**
   Items bought: a. **goggles** b. **flippers**
2. 2 $10 bills, 2 $1 bills, 1 quarter
   Total: **$22.25**
   Items bought: a. **goggles** b. **snorkel**
3. 2 $20 bills, 3 quarters, 1 dime
   Total: **$40.85**
   Items bought: a. **camera** b. **vest**
4. 1 $20 bill, 1 $10 bill, 1 $1 bill, 3 quarters, 1 nickel
   Total: **$31.80**
   Items bought: a. **camera** b. **snorkel**
5. 2 $20 bills, 1 $10 bill, 2 quarters, 1 dime
   Total: **$50.60**
   Items bought: a. **goggles** b. **vest** c. **camera**
6. 2 $20 bills, 1 $1 bill, 2 quarters, 1 nickel
   Total: **$41.55**
   Items bought: a. **goggles** b. **snorkel** c. **camera**
7. Choose three items that you would purchase. Find their total. Then find the change from $50.00.
   Answers will vary.

 Use with Grade 3, text pages 114-115.

Daily Review

Name ______ Daily Review 3-15

Problem Solving

Using Money

Use the table to solve each problem.

Item	Cost
puzzle	$2.25
die-cast car	$1.89
paint set	$6.49
terrarium	$4.99
modeling clay	$3.19

1. Which two toys can you buy for about $4.00? **Puzzle and die-cast car**
2. About how much would you pay for the paint set and the terrarium? **$11.00**
3. Exactly how much would you spend for the paint set, the modeling clay, and the puzzle? **$11.93**
4. Can you buy the puzzle, the car, and the terrarium for $10.00? **Yes**
5. If you had $12.00 to spend, what would you buy from the list above? **Answers will vary.**

Review and Remember

Find each difference.

6. $4.50 − $1.25 = **$3.25**
7. $0.89 − $0.30 = **$0.59**
8. 4,820 − 1,200 = **3,620**
9. 8,000 − 6,500 = **1,500**

Practice

Telling Time to the Quarter Hour

P 4-1

Possible answers are given.

Write each time using words and numbers.

1. 11:15 — quarter past 11 — eleven fifteen
2. 8:30 — half past 8 — eight thirty
3. 5:45 — quarter to 6 — five forty-five

Fill in the letter that gives the same time.

4. d half past 4 in the afternoon — a. 6:30 P.M.
5. b seven o'clock in the morning — b. 7:00 A.M.
6. a six thirty in the evening — c. 4:45 A.M.
7. c quarter to five in the morning — d. 4:30 P.M.

Circle the time when each activity is more likely to happen.

8. going to school
   a. 7:30 P.M. b. 11 A.M. c. (8 A.M.) d. 1 P.M.
9. eating dinner
   a. (6 P.M.) b. 3 P.M. c. 9 A.M. d. 10 A.M.

Solve.

10. School ends at 3:15. Is this closer to 3:00 or 4:00?
    It is closer to 3:00.
11. Mary's soccer game ends at a quarter to 5. What will Mary's digital watch say at that time?
    The watch will say 4:45.

 Use with Grade 3, text pages 128–129.

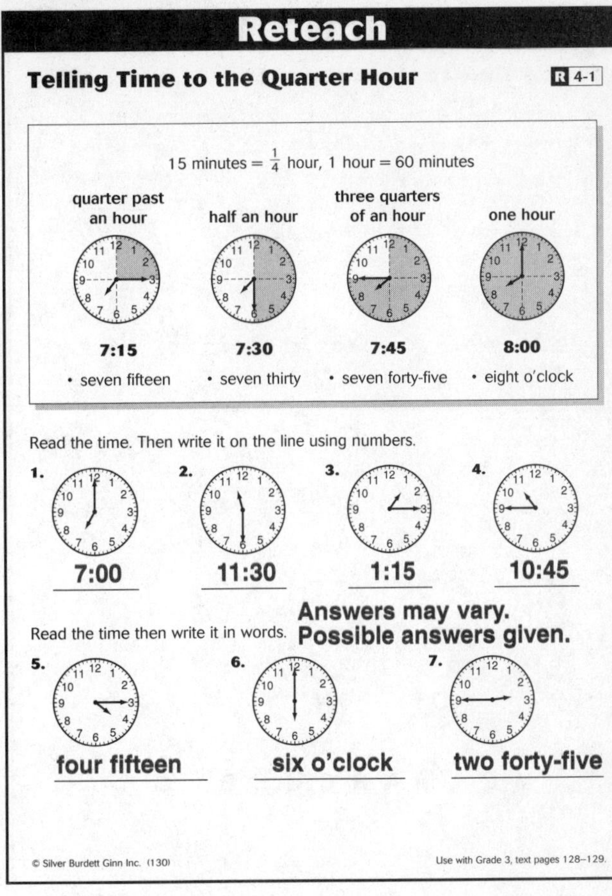

Reteach

Telling Time to the Quarter Hour

R 4-1

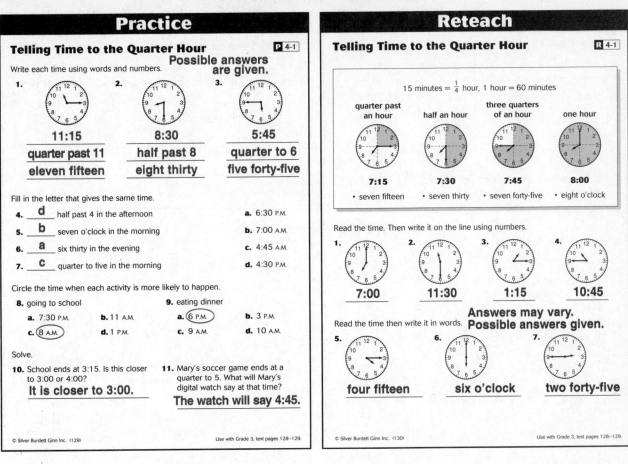

15 minutes = $\frac{1}{4}$ hour, 1 hour = 60 minutes

quarter past an hour	half an hour	three quarters of an hour	one hour
7:15	7:30	7:45	8:00
• seven fifteen	• seven thirty	• seven forty-five	• eight o'clock

Read the time. Then write it on the line using numbers.

1. 7:00
2. 11:30
3. 1:15
4. 10:45

Read the time then write it in words. Answers may vary. Possible answers given.

5. four fifteen
6. six o'clock
7. two forty-five

 Use with Grade 3, text pages 128–129.

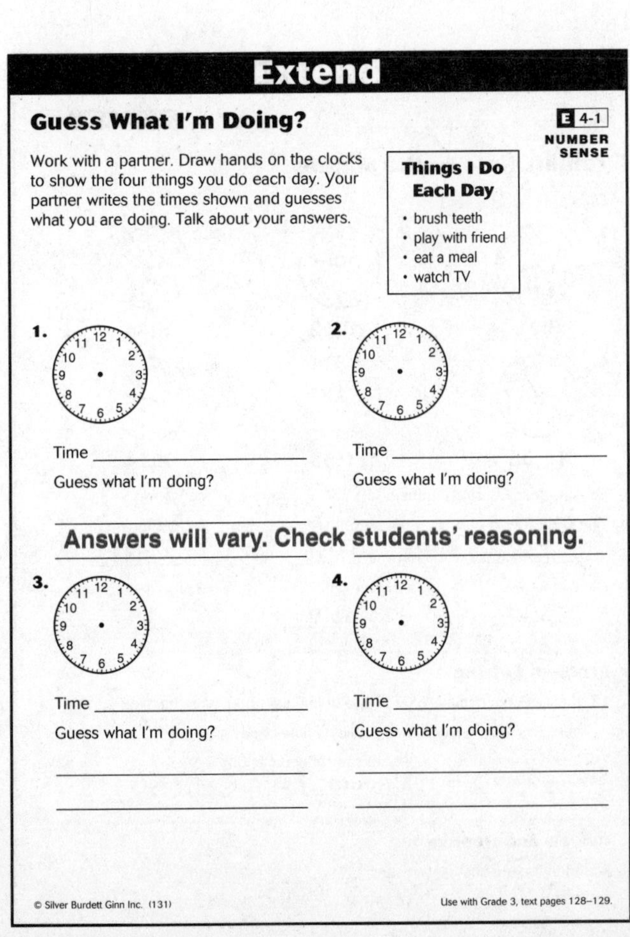

Extend

Guess What I'm Doing?

E 4-1 NUMBER SENSE

Work with a partner. Draw hands on the clocks to show the four things you do each day. Your partner writes the times shown and guesses what you are doing. Talk about your answers.

Things I Do Each Day
- brush teeth
- play with friend
- eat a meal
- watch TV

1. Time ______ Guess what I'm doing? ______
2. Time ______ Guess what I'm doing? ______

Answers will vary. Check students' reasoning.

3. Time ______ Guess what I'm doing? ______
4. Time ______ Guess what I'm doing? ______

 Use with Grade 3, text pages 128–129.

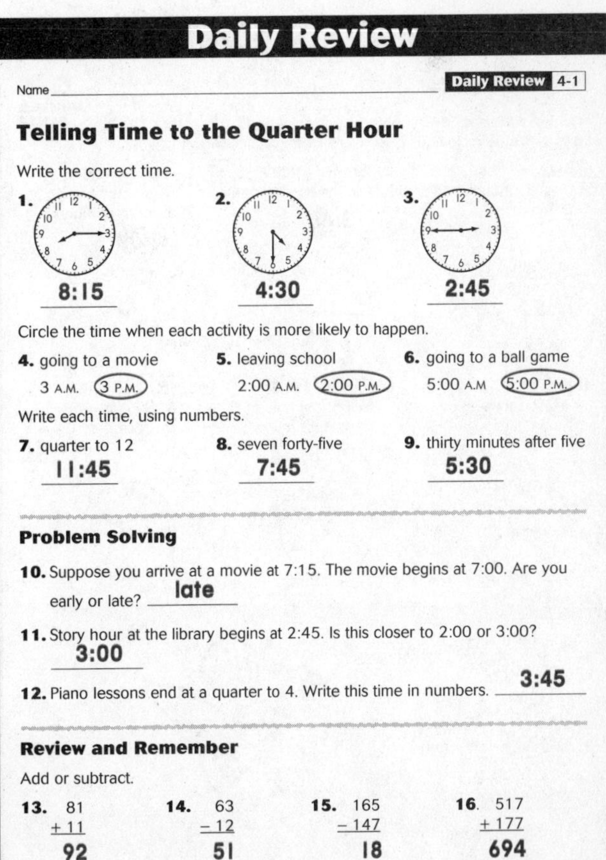

Daily Review

Name ______________________ Daily Review 4-1

Telling Time to the Quarter Hour

Write the correct time.

1. 8:15
2. 4:30
3. 2:45

Circle the time when each activity is more likely to happen.

4. going to a movie: 3 A.M. (3 P.M.)
5. leaving school: 2:00 A.M. (2:00 P.M.)
6. going to a ball game: 5:00 A.M. (5:00 P.M.)

Write each time, using numbers.

7. quarter to 12 — 11:45
8. seven forty-five — 7:45
9. thirty minutes after five — 5:30

Problem Solving

10. Suppose you arrive at a movie at 7:15. The movie begins at 7:00. Are you early or late? late
11. Story hour at the library begins at 2:45. Is this closer to 2:00 or 3:00? 3:00
12. Piano lessons end at a quarter to 4. Write this time in numbers. 3:45

Review and Remember

Add or subtract.

13. $81 + 11 = 92$
14. $63 - 12 = 51$
15. $165 - 147 = 18$
16. $517 + 177 = 694$

Chapter 4 • Lesson 2

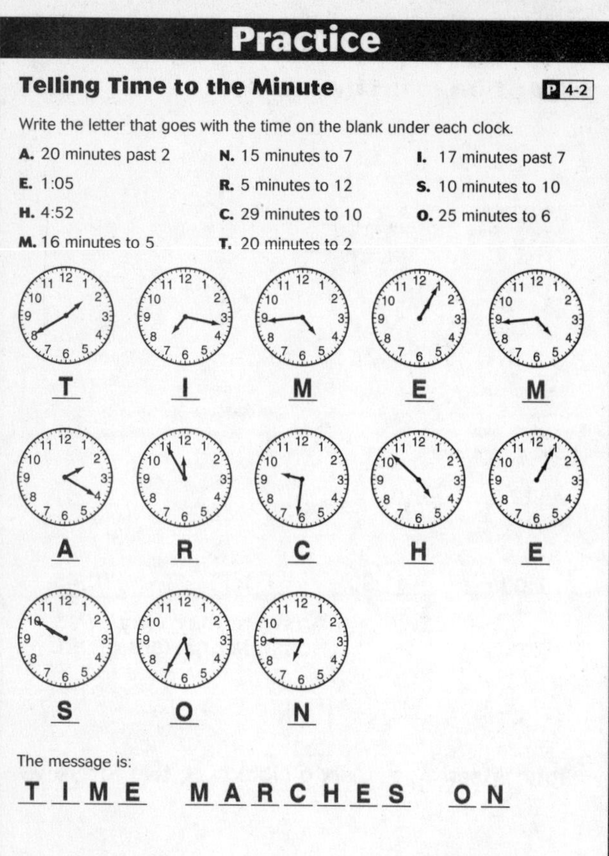

Practice

Telling Time to the Minute

P 4-2

Write the letter that goes with the time on the blank under each clock.

A. 20 minutes past 2
N. 15 minutes to 7
I. 17 minutes past 7
E. 1:05
R. 5 minutes to 12
S. 10 minutes to 10
H. 4:52
C. 29 minutes to 10
O. 25 minutes to 6
M. 16 minutes to 5
T. 20 minutes to 2

T I M E M

A R C H E

S O N

The message is:

T I M E   M A R C H E S   O N

 Use with Grade 3, text pages 130–131.

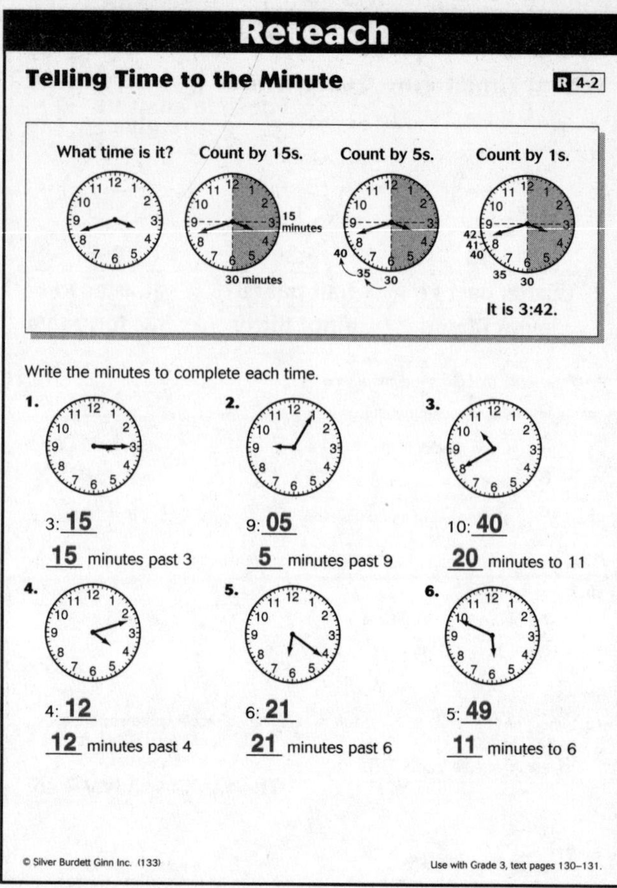

Reteach

Telling Time to the Minute

R 4-2

Write the minutes to complete each time.

1. 3: **15**
15 minutes past 3

2. 9: **05**
5 minutes past 9

3. 10: **40**
20 minutes to 11

4. 4: **12**
12 minutes past 4

5. 6: **21**
21 minutes past 6

6. 5: **49**
11 minutes to 6

 Use with Grade 3, text pages 130–131.

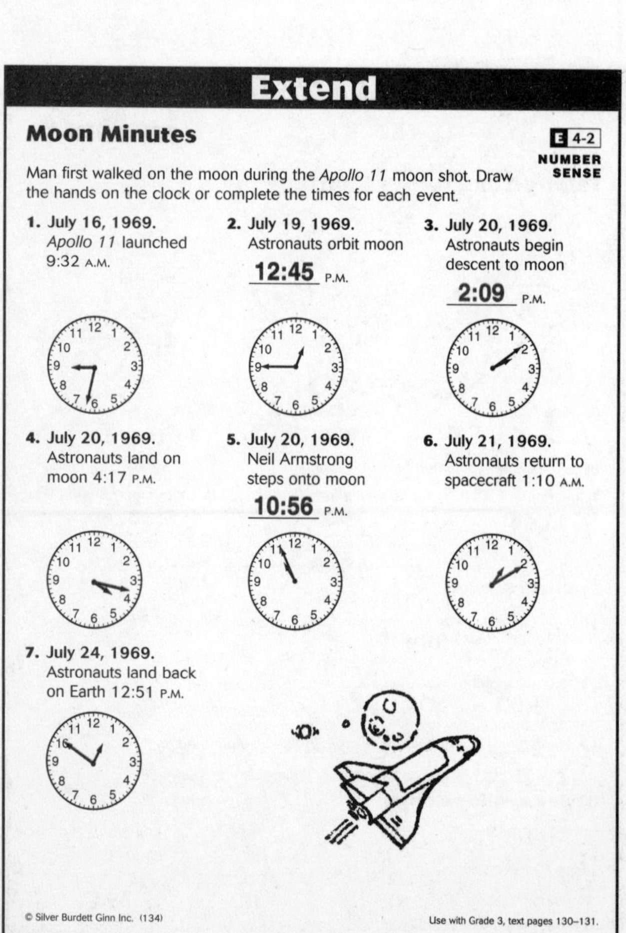

Extend

Moon Minutes

E 4-2 NUMBER SENSE

Man first walked on the moon during the *Apollo 11* moon shot. Draw the hands on the clock or complete the times for each event.

1. **July 16, 1969.** *Apollo 11* launched 9:32 A.M.
2. **July 19, 1969.** Astronauts orbit moon **12:45** P.M.
3. **July 20, 1969.** Astronauts begin descent to moon **2:09** P.M.
4. **July 20, 1969.** Astronauts land on moon 4:17 P.M.
5. **July 20, 1969.** Neil Armstrong steps onto moon **10:56** P.M.
6. **July 21, 1969.** Astronauts return to spacecraft 1:10 A.M.
7. **July 24, 1969.** Astronauts land back on Earth 12:51 P.M.

 Use with Grade 3, text pages 130–131.

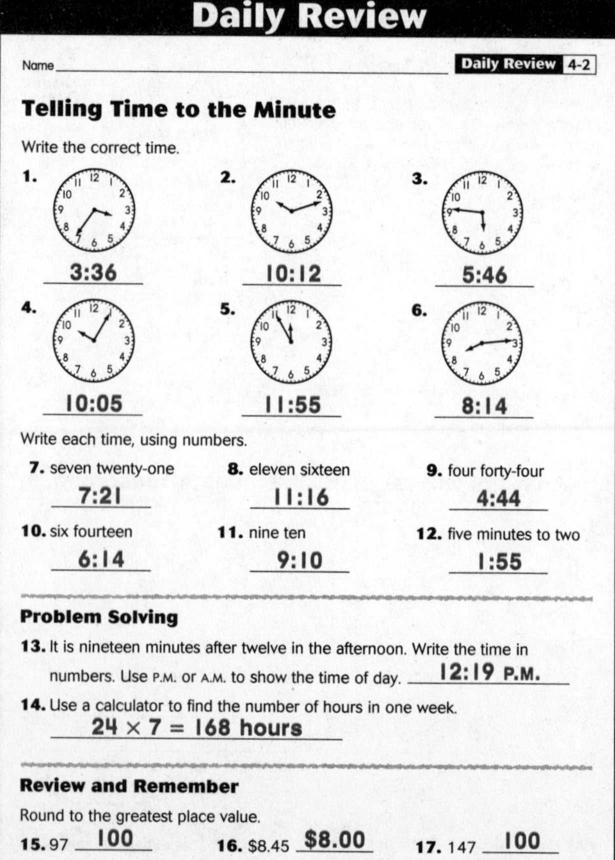

Daily Review

Name ____________ Daily Review 4-2

Telling Time to the Minute

Write the correct time.

1. **3:36**
2. **10:12**
3. **5:46**
4. **10:05**
5. **11:55**
6. **8:14**

Write each time, using numbers.

7. seven twenty-one **7:21**
8. eleven sixteen **11:16**
9. four forty-four **4:44**
10. six fourteen **6:14**
11. nine ten **9:10**
12. five minutes to two **1:55**

Problem Solving

13. It is nineteen minutes after twelve in the afternoon. Write the time in numbers. Use P.M. or A.M. to show the time of day. **12:19 P.M.**
14. Use a calculator to find the number of hours in one week. **24 × 7 = 168 hours**

Review and Remember

Round to the greatest place value.

15. 97 **100**
16. $8.45 **$8.00**
17. 147 **100**

Practice

Elapsed Time

P 4-3

Tell how much time has passed.

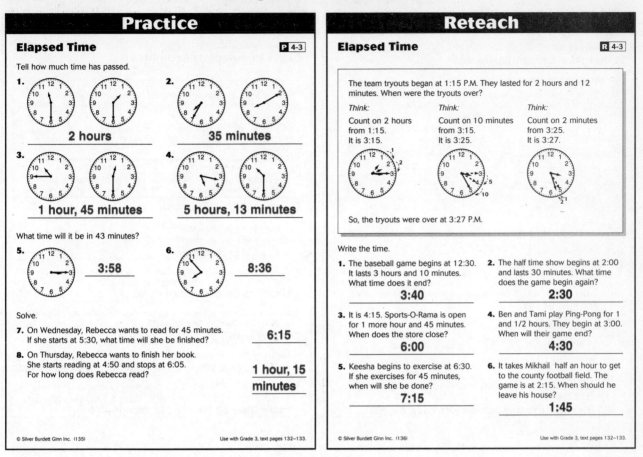

1. 2 hours
2. 35 minutes
3. 1 hour, 45 minutes
4. 5 hours, 13 minutes

What time will it be in 43 minutes?

5. 3:58
6. 8:36

Solve.

7. On Wednesday, Rebecca wants to read for 45 minutes. If she starts at 5:30, what time will she be finished? 6:15
8. On Thursday, Rebecca wants to finish her book. She starts reading at 4:50 and stops at 6:05. For how long does Rebecca read? 1 hour, 15 minutes

Use with Grade 3, text pages 132–133.

Reteach

Elapsed Time

R 4-3

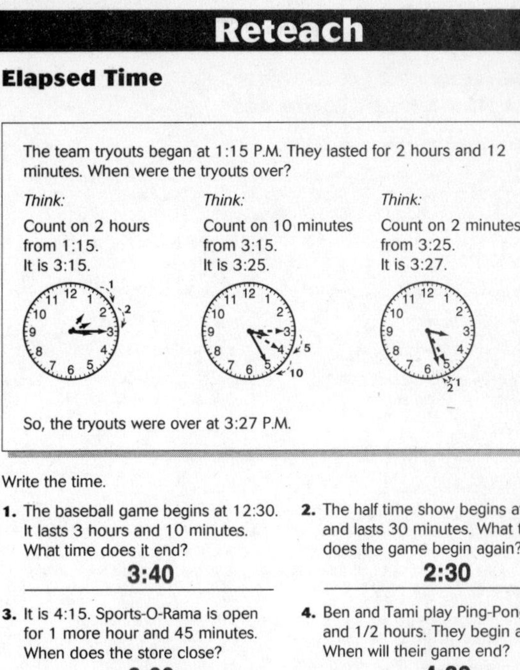
The team tryouts began at 1:15 P.M. They lasted for 2 hours and 12 minutes. When were the tryouts over?

Think:	*Think:*	*Think:*
Count on 2 hours from 1:15. It is 3:15.	Count on 10 minutes from 3:15. It is 3:25.	Count on 2 minutes from 3:25. It is 3:27.

So, the tryouts were over at 3:27 P.M.

Write the time.

1. The baseball game begins at 12:30. It lasts 3 hours and 10 minutes. What time does it end? 3:40
2. The half time show begins at 2:00 and lasts 30 minutes. What time does the game begin again? 2:30
3. It is 4:15. Sports-O-Rama is open for 1 more hour and 45 minutes. When does the store close? 6:00
4. Ben and Tami play Ping-Pong for 1 and 1/2 hours. They begin at 3:00. When will their game end? 4:30
5. Keesha begins to exercise at 6:30. If she exercises for 45 minutes, when will she be done? 7:15
6. It takes Mikhail half an hour to get to the county football field. The game is at 2:15. When should he leave his house? 1:45

Use with Grade 3, text pages 132–133.

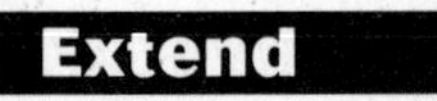

Extend

Maffle Math

E 4-3

REASONING

Mister Maffle likes to confuse people. He makes up strange tasks for them to do. Can you do Mr. Maffle's confusing tasks?

HINT: It helps to look at a clock face.

1. These times have been DIZBOED.

		Now DIZBOE these times.	
2:00 →	6:00	3:00 →	7:00
9:00 →	1:00	11:00 →	3:00
12:00 →	4:00	8:00 →	12:00

2. These times have been WHAMDUCKED.

		Now WHAMDUCK these times.	
6:40 →	20 minutes to 7	1:59 →	1 minute to 2
3:55 →	5 minutes to 4	5:35 →	25 minutes to 6
2:48 →	12 minutes to 3	9:56 →	4 minutes to 10

3. These times have been SUZZLED.

		Now SUZZLE these times.	
3:14 →	10:14	8:22 →	3:22
12:36 →	7:36	4:32 →	11:32
1:47 →	8:47	9:59 →	4:59

4. These times have been BODINGLED.

		Now BODINGLE these times.	
6:15 →	6:45	7:22 →	7:52
10:29 →	10:59	11:45 →	12:15
2:55 →	3:25	3:32 →	4:02

Use with Grade 3, text pages 132–133.

Daily Review

Name ____________________

Daily Review 4-3

Elapsed Time

Write the time that each clock will show in 5 minutes.

1. 5:05
2. 8:35
3. 2:50

Write the time that each clock will show in 20 minutes.

4. 10:30
5. 4:50
6. 5:10

Look at each pair of times. Write how much time has passed.

7. Start 11:30 P.M. End 12:30 A.M. 1 hour
8. Start 3:11 A.M. End 3:20 A.M. 9 minutes
9. Start 8:35 P.M. End 9:05 P.M. 30 minutes

Problem Solving

10. Social Studies starts at 9:50 A.M. It ends at 10:15 A.M. How long does it last? 25 minutes
11. The skating rink is open from 10:00 A.M. until 12:30 P.M. and from 1:30 P.M. until 4:30 P.M. How long is it open each day? $5\frac{1}{2}$ hours

Review and Remember

Use paper and pencil or mental math to solve. Name your method.
Methods will vary.

12. 26 + 36 = 62
13. $246 + $375 = $621
14. 66 − 60 = 6

Practice

Problem Solving P 4-4

Exact Numbers or Estimates

Circle the correct answer to each question.

Paula has been collecting postcards for more than 2 years. She has about 50 big postcards and at least 100 small postcards. Paula has 22 animal postcards. In all, Paula has postcards from 38 different places.

1. How long has Paula been collecting postcards?

a. less than 2 years

b. exactly 2 years

(c.) more than 2 years

2. How many small postcards does Paula have?

a. exactly 100

b. less than 100

(c.) more than 100

3. Look back at the problem. Which number is an estimate?

(a.) 2 years

b. 22 animal postcards

c. 38 different places

4. Which of these words tells you that 50 is an estimate?

a. has

(b.) about

c. big

In Rockville, almost 200 people jogged in a footrace to support a trip to Washington for the 32 students in Mr. Blue's class. The trip costs $58 a student. Joggers paid $6 to be in the 3-mile race and got breakfast when they crossed the finish line.

5. Exactly how many people might have jogged in the footrace?

a. 97 people

(b.) 197 people

c. 215 people

6. How long was the race?

a. less than 3 miles

(b.) exactly 3 miles

c. more than 3 miles

7. How much money did the race bring in? Does the class have enough money for the trip? Explain.

$1,200; no; the trip costs more than $1,800.

 Use with Grade 3, text pages 134–135.

Reteach

Problem Solving R 4-4

Exact Numbers or Estimates

An estimate is a number that tells *about* how many. If the number comes after a clue word such as *about, over, less than,* and *almost,* it is probably an estimated number.

Mrs. Wong sells Glad Hats for $4.95. She says she has sold about 40 in the last 8 days. Twelve hats come in one carton, and she orders almost 10 cartons a week.

Exact Number	Estimated Number
• Exactly 12 hats are in 1 carton. • 12 is an exact amount.	• Mrs. Wong sells about 40 hats. • 40 is an estimated amount.

1. How much does each hat cost? **$4.95**

Is your answer an exact number or an estimate?

It is an exact number.

2. Can you tell exactly how many cartons of hats Mrs. Wong orders each week? Why or why not? **No; she orders *about* 10, which is an estimated number.**

3. Suppose Mrs. Wong orders less than 10 cartons in one week. Exactly how many cartons might she have ordered?

8 or 9 cartons

4. Could Mrs. Wong have sold *exactly* 42 Glad Hats in one week? **42 is close to 40, so Mrs. Wong could have sold exactly 42 hats.**

5. Someone asks Mrs. Wong how much her hats cost. Would you say that *about $5.00* is a reasonable estimate? Explain. **Yes; $5.00 is only 5¢ more than $4.95, so it is reasonable.**

 Use with Grade 3, text pages 134–135.

Extend

At the Toy Store

E 4-4 **ESTIMATION**

Write four problems that can be solved using the information below. Decide whether an estimate or an exact answer is needed. Solve. Then write *estimate* or *exact* for each solution.

Mr. Haines He sells about 12 bicycles each week. He needs to lower the price of $69 for the December 20 sale.

Julie She bought one bicycle on December 12. She receives change from $100.

Andrew He has $60 to spend on a bicycle.

1. Problem: **Problems and solutions will vary. Check students' work.**

Solution: ________ Exact or Estimate? ________

2. Problem: ________

Solution: ________ Exact or Estimate? ________

3. Problem: ________

Solution: ________ Exact or Estimate? ________

4. Problem: ________

Solution: ________ Exact or Estimate? ________

 Use with Grade 3, text pages 134–135.

Daily Review

Name ________ **Daily Review 4-4**

Problem Solving

Exact Numbers or Estimates

Read each story. Then answer each question.

The car wash was a great success. Over 20 students came to wash cars, and nearly 85 cars were cleaned. The group charged $10 per car, so they raised a lot of money for the school newspaper.

1. Which numbers in the story are exact? **$10.00**

2. Can you tell exactly how much money was raised? Why or why not?

No; the exact number of cars is not given

3. Did the students make more or less than $850?

They made less than $850.

Emily's soccer game was exciting, but wet! It rained during the first half for over 15 minutes. During the second half, rain fell for at least 20 minutes. Emily's team scored 3 goals in the first half. The other team stopped them from scoring their usual 5 goals. In spite of everything, Emily's team won by 2 goals.

4. About how long did it rain during the game? **35 minutes**

5. How many goals did Emily's team score in the first half?

Emily's team scored 3 goals.

6. Can you tell the final score of the game? Why or why not?

No; it could be 4–2 or 3–1.

Review and Remember

Write how much time has passed.

7. 8:30 A.M. to 2:30 P.M. **6 hours** **8.** 9:30 A.M. to 11:00 A.M. **1 h 30 m**

9. 2:00 P.M. to 5:30 P.M. **3 h 30 m** **10.** 11:00 P.M. to 4:30 A.M. **5 h 30 m**

Practice

Using a Calendar

P 4-5

Use the calendar to answer the questions.

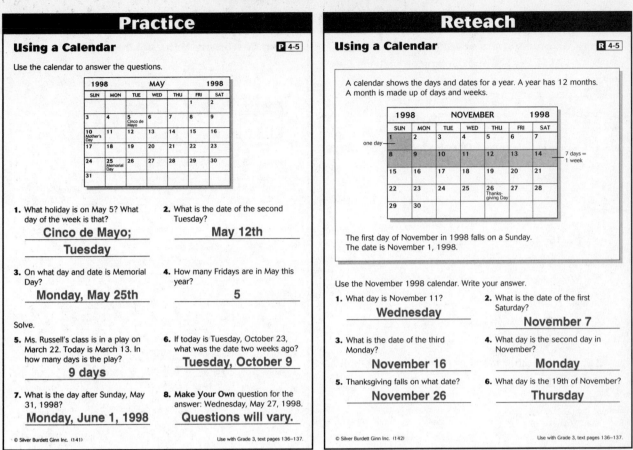

1998			MAY			1998
SUN	MON	TUE	WED	THU	FRI	SAT
					1	2
3	4	5 Cinco de Mayo	6	7	8	9
10 Mother's Day	11	12	13	14	15	16
17	18	19	20	21	22	23
24	25 Memorial Day	26	27	28	29	30
31						

1. What holiday is on May 5? What day of the week is that? **Cinco de Mayo; Tuesday**
2. What is the date of the second Tuesday? **May 12th**
3. On what day and date is Memorial Day? **Monday, May 25th**
4. How many Fridays are in May this year? **5**

Solve.

5. Ms. Russell's class is in a play on March 22. Today is March 13. In how many days is the play? **9 days**
6. If today is Tuesday, October 23, what was the date two weeks ago? **Tuesday, October 9**
7. What is the day after Sunday, May 31, 1998? **Monday, June 1, 1998**
8. **Make Your Own** question for the answer: Wednesday, May 27, 1998. **Questions will vary.**

 Use with Grade 3, text pages 136–137.

Reteach

Using a Calendar

R 4-5

A calendar shows the days and dates for a year. A year has 12 months. A month is made up of days and weeks.

1998			NOVEMBER			1998
SUN	MON	TUE	WED	THU	FRI	SAT
1	2	3	4	5	6	7
8	9	10	11	12	13	14
15	16	17	18	19	20	21
22	23	24	25	26 Thanks-giving Day	27	28
29	30					

one day

7 days = 1 week

The first day of November in 1998 falls on a Sunday. The date is November 1, 1998.

Use the November 1998 calendar. Write your answer.

1. What day is November 11? **Wednesday**
2. What is the date of the first Saturday? **November 7**
3. What is the date of the third Monday? **November 16**
4. What day is the second day in November? **Monday**
5. Thanksgiving falls on what date? **November 26**
6. What day is the 19th of November? **Thursday**

 Use with Grade 3, text pages 136–137.

Extend

Date Book Mix-up

E 4-5 REASONING

The pages of Wesley's date book have gotten mixed up. Help him arrange them correctly. He has figured out the first page. Give the remaining pages a number from 2 to 6 to tell the proper order. If you have trouble remembering the order, cut out the pages and then arrange them in order on a piece of paper. Paste them down.

dentist–3:30 (6)	• library books due tomorrow • movies with Mark–3:00 (2)	spelling test TODAY! (4)
ask Mark to go with me to tomorrow's movie (1)	• library books due today • buy baseball mitt • study for tomorrow's spelling test (3)	• baseball tryouts–4:00 • dentist tomorrow (5)

 Use with Grade 3, text pages 136–137.

Daily Review

Name ____________________

Daily Review 4-5

Using a Calendar

Use the calendar to help you solve Problems 1–6.

October						
Sun	Mon	Tue	Wed	Thu	Fri	Sat
	1	2	3	4	5	6
7	8	9	10	11	12	13
14	15	16	17	18	19	20
21	22	23	24	25	26	27
28	29	30	31			

1. Write the month. **October**

Write the day of the week.

2. October 22 **Monday**
3. October 2 **Tuesday**
4. October 10 **Wednesday**
5. What is the date of the third Monday? **October 15**
6. What is the date of the second Thursday? **October 11**

Name the month that follows each month.

7. July **August**
8. April **May**
9. December **January**

Problem Solving

10. If today is Wednesday, January 2, then how many days are there until January 19? **17 days**
11. A raffle will be held in 10 days. Today is February 12. When will the raffle be held? **February 22**

Review and Remember

Write the missing numbers in each pattern.

12. 275, **375**, 475, **575**, 675
13. 78, 76, **74**, 72, **70**

Chapter 4 • Lesson 6

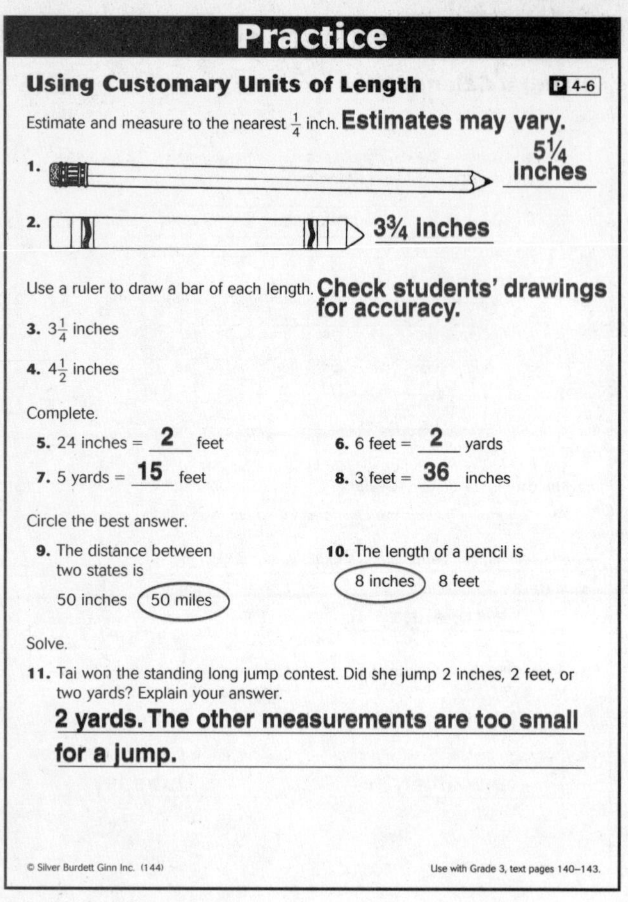

Practice

Using Customary Units of Length

P 4-6

Estimate and measure to the nearest $\frac{1}{4}$ inch. **Estimates may vary.**

1. **5¼ inches**

2. **3¾ inches**

Use a ruler to draw a bar of each length. **Check students' drawings for accuracy.**

3. $3\frac{1}{4}$ inches

4. $4\frac{1}{2}$ inches

Complete.

5. 24 inches = **2** feet
6. 6 feet = **2** yards
7. 5 yards = **15** feet
8. 3 feet = **36** inches

Circle the best answer.

9. The distance between two states is

   50 inches   (50 miles)

10. The length of a pencil is

    (8 inches)   8 feet

Solve.

11. Tai won the standing long jump contest. Did she jump 2 inches, 2 feet, or two yards? Explain your answer.

    2 yards. The other measurements are too small for a jump.

Use with Grade 3, text pages 140–143.

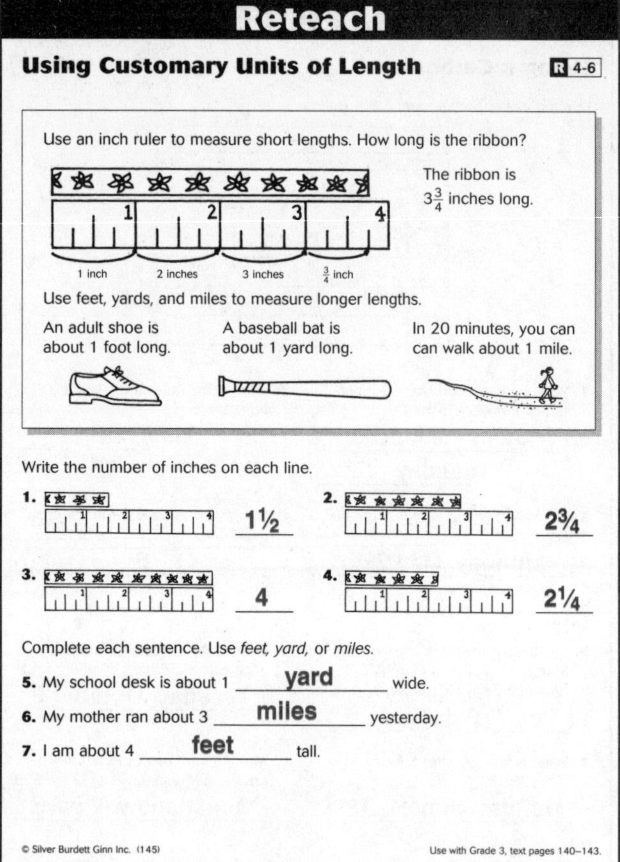

Reteach

Using Customary Units of Length

R 4-6

Use an inch ruler to measure short lengths. How long is the ribbon?

The ribbon is $3\frac{3}{4}$ inches long.

1 inch   2 inches   3 inches $\frac{3}{4}$ inch

Use feet, yards, and miles to measure longer lengths.

An adult shoe is about 1 foot long.

A baseball bat is about 1 yard long.

In 20 minutes, you can can walk about 1 mile.

Write the number of inches on each line.

1. **1½**
2. **2¾**
3. **4**
4. **2¼**

Complete each sentence. Use *feet, yard,* or *miles.*

5. My school desk is about 1 **yard** wide.
6. My mother ran about 3 **miles** yesterday.
7. I am about 4 **feet** tall.

Use with Grade 3, text pages 140–143.

Extend

Measure Mania

E 4-6

ESTIMATION

Work with a partner. Choose two different units below to measure the length of your classroom. Estimate first. Then measure.

Unit	Estimate	Actual Measure
inches		
your foot	**Estimates and**	**measurements**
	will vary.	
feet		
your pace		
yards		

Use the information in your table to answer the questions.

1. What was the least reasonable unit of measure to use? Why?

   Possible answer: Inches. The room was too large to measure using such a small unit.

2. Compare your actual measures with classmates. For which units do you have the same measurements? Why?

   Feet or yards might be the same; they are large standard units of measure.

Use with Grade 3, text pages 140–143.

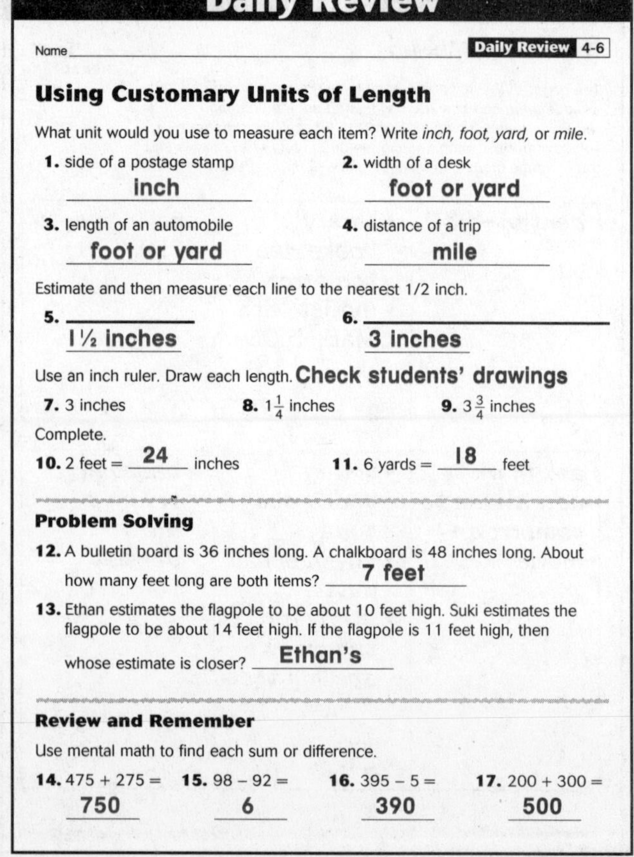

Daily Review

Name

Daily Review 4-6

Using Customary Units of Length

What unit would you use to measure each item? Write *inch, foot, yard,* or *mile.*

1. side of a postage stamp **inch**
2. width of a desk **foot or yard**
3. length of an automobile **foot or yard**
4. distance of a trip **mile**

Estimate and then measure each line to the nearest 1/2 inch.

5. **1½ inches**
6. **3 inches**

Use an inch ruler. Draw each length. **Check students' drawings**

7. 3 inches
8. $1\frac{1}{4}$ inches
9. $3\frac{3}{4}$ inches

Complete.

10. 2 feet = **24** inches
11. 6 yards = **18** feet

Problem Solving

12. A bulletin board is 36 inches long. A chalkboard is 48 inches long. About how many feet long are both items? **7 feet**

13. Ethan estimates the flagpole to be about 10 feet high. Suki estimates the flagpole to be about 14 feet high. If the flagpole is 11 feet high, then whose estimate is closer? **Ethan's**

Review and Remember

Use mental math to find each sum or difference.

14. 475 + 275 = **750**
15. 98 − 92 = **6**
16. 395 − 5 = **390**
17. 200 + 300 = **500**

Chapter 4 • Lesson 7

Practice

Explore: Using Customary Capacity

P 4-7

Circle the best estimate.

1. gas in a car's full tank
   10 cups or (10 gallons)
2. water to fill an ice cube tray
   (2 cups) or 2 quarts

What measure would you use to tell about each item below? Write *cup, pint, quart,* or *gallon.*

3. two glasses of juice **pint**
4. water in a bathtub **gallon**
5. the milk in a bowl of cereal **cup**
6. a large milk carton **quart**

Complete.

7. 1 pint = **2** cups
8. 1 gallon = **4** quarts
9. 2 pints = **1** quart
10. 3 pints = **6** cups

Solve.

11. Mahssa needs to fill her dog's bathtub. Should she pour water from a cup or a gallon jug? Why?
    Possible answers: Mahssa should use a gallon container. The bathtub may hold many gallons. She can make fewer trips from the sink to the bathtub.
12. Ms. Chiles told Lizzy to bring at least 2 quarts of juice for the party. Lizzy brought 5 pints of juice. Did she bring enough? Explain.
    Yes; 5 pints is more than 2 quarts.

 Use with Grade 3, text pages 144–145.

Reteach

Explore: Using Customary Capacity

R 4-7

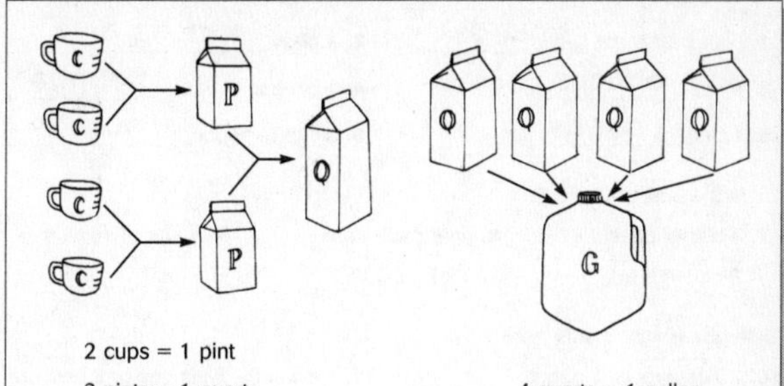

Circle the most likely measure for each.

1. juice in a glass
   (cup) quart
2. soup in a bowl
   gallon (pint)
3. water in an aquarium
   (gallon) cup
4. milk in a tall, thin container
   cup (quart)

Write *more* or *less* to complete each sentence.

5. A soup spoon holds **less** than a cup.
6. A glass holds **less** than a gallon.
7. A bucket holds **more** than a pint.
8. A watercooler holds **more** than a quart.

 Use with Grade 3, text pages 144–145.

Extend

Water Play

E 4-7
REASONING

1. Marc poured water from a 5-gallon jug into an empty 4-gallon jug. He stopped when the jug was full. How much was left in the 5-gallon jug?
   1 gallon
2. Marc wants to measure exactly 7 gallons this time. He has a 5-gallon jug and a 3-gallon jug. How can he do it?

   Write each step of your solution.
   You may draw pictures to help.
   He pours 5 gallons from 5 gallon jug. Then he refills 5 gallon jug, uses it to fill the 3 gallon jug, and adds the remaining 2 gallons to the original 5 gallons.
3. Choose a gallon amount from the choices below. Tell how Marc can measure the amount using the 5-gallon and 3-gallon jugs. Share your solution with a classmate.

11 gallons	12 gallons	14 gallons	17 gallons	19 gallons

Possible answers: 11: two 3 gallons and one 5 gallon; 12: four 3 gallons; 14: one 5 gallon and three 3 gallons; 17: four 3 gallons and one 5 gallon; 19: two 5 gallons and three 3 gallons.

 Use with Grade 3, text pages 144–145.

Daily Review

Name ____________________

Daily Review 4-7

EXPLORE: Using Customary Capacity

Complete the chart.

	Measure	Equivalent
1.	4 quarts	**1** gallon(s)
2.	**2** pint(s)	1 quart(s)
3.	2 cups	**1** pint(s)
4.	**16** cup(s)	1 gallon

Circle the best measure for each item.

5. water in a child's pool
   cup or (gallon)
6. milk for one bowl of cereal
   (cup) or quart
7. water in a clothes washer
   quart or (gallon)
8. milk in a baby bottle
   gallon or (cup)
9. hot chocolate in a mug
   quart or (pint)
10. paint for a house
    cup or (gallon)

Problem Solving

11. One quart of milk costs $1.49. One pint of milk costs 79 cents. What is the better buy if you need one quart of milk?
    There are 2 pints in 1 quart. Two pints would cost $1.58, which is more than the cost of one quart.
12. Sara eats one cup of yogurt each day. How many pints of yogurt does Sara eat in 4 days? **2 pints**

Review and Remember

Round to the nearest hundred.

13. 475 **500**
14. 632 **600**
15. 274 **300**
16. 889 **900**
17. 127 **100**

Practice

Using Ounces and Pounds

P 4-8

Choose a unit to measure each item. Write *ounces* or *pounds*.

1. your best friend **pounds**
2. a glass **ounces**
3. a key **ounces**
4. a big bag of flour **pounds**
5. a bed **pounds**
6. a cup of popcorn **ounces**

Circle the best estimate.

7. a dinner plate (9 oz) 9 lb
8. your math book 1 oz (1 lb)
9. a pair of mittens (7 oz) 7 lb

Circle the weight that is more.

10. (20 ounces) or 1 pound
11. 1 pound, 12 ounces or (2 pounds)
12. 30 ounces or (2 pounds)
13. (3 pounds, 24 ounces) or 4 pounds

Solve.

14. Ms. Suarez needs 24 oz of rice. How many 1-lb bags must Ms. Suarez buy? Explain. **2 bags; 1 bag is only 16 oz**
15. Liza's baseball glove weighs 14 oz. How much less than 1 lb does the glove weigh? **2 oz less than 1 lb**
16. Which weighs more, a big balloon or a little golf ball? **the golf ball**
17. How can something big be lighter than something small? **It depends on what objects are made of— light or heavy materials.**

 Use with Grade 3, text pages 146–147.

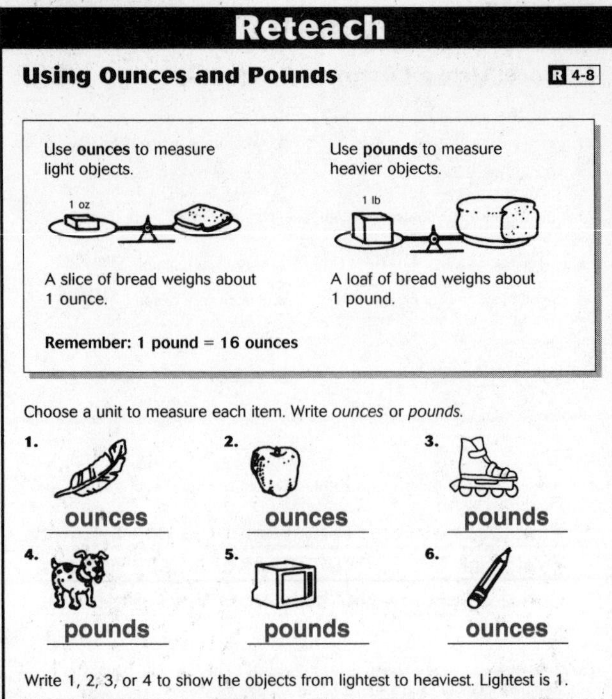

Reteach

Using Ounces and Pounds

R 4-8

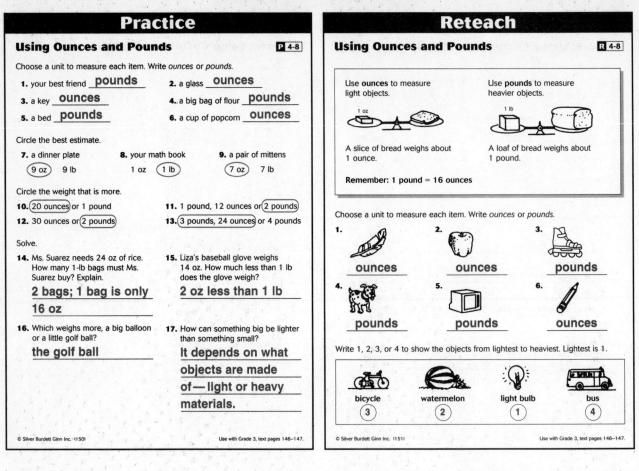

Use **ounces** to measure light objects.

1 oz

A slice of bread weighs about 1 ounce.

Use **pounds** to measure heavier objects.

1 lb

A loaf of bread weighs about 1 pound.

Remember: 1 pound = 16 ounces

Choose a unit to measure each item. Write *ounces* or *pounds*.

1. **ounces**
2. **ounces**
3. **pounds**
4. **pounds**
5. **pounds**
6. **ounces**

Write 1, 2, 3, or 4 to show the objects from lightest to heaviest. Lightest is 1.

bicycle	watermelon	light bulb	bus
(3)	(2)	(1)	(4)

 Use with Grade 3, text pages 146–147.

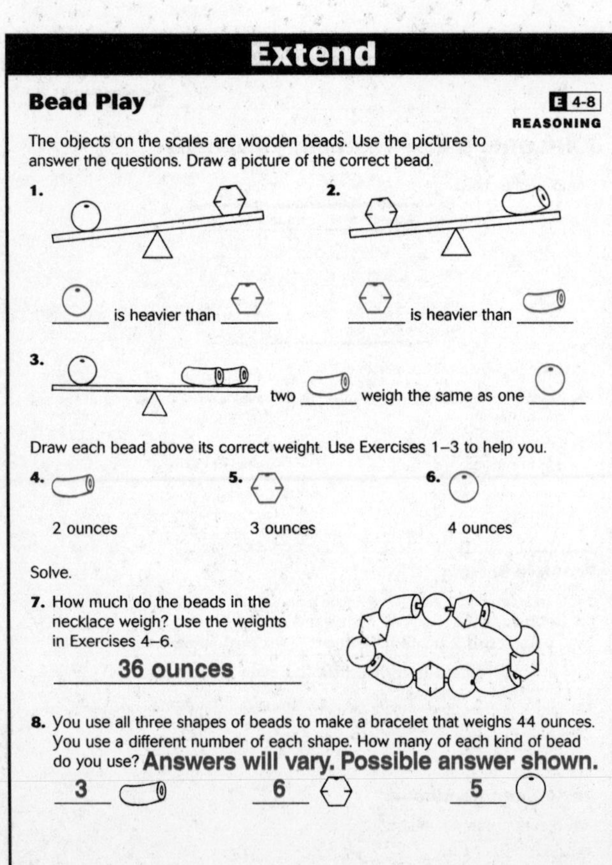

Extend

Bead Play

E 4-8
REASONING

The objects on the scales are wooden beads. Use the pictures to answer the questions. Draw a picture of the correct bead.

1. ○ is heavier than ⬡
2. ⬡ is heavier than ▭
3. two ▭ weigh the same as one ○

Draw each bead above its correct weight. Use Exercises 1–3 to help you.

4. 2 ounces
5. 3 ounces
6. 4 ounces

Solve.

7. How much do the beads in the necklace weigh? Use the weights in Exercises 4–6. **36 ounces**
8. You use all three shapes of beads to make a bracelet that weighs 44 ounces. You use a different number of each shape. How many of each kind of bead do you use? **Answers will vary. Possible answer shown.** **3** ▭ **6** ⬡ **5** ○

 Use with Grade 3, text pages 146–147.

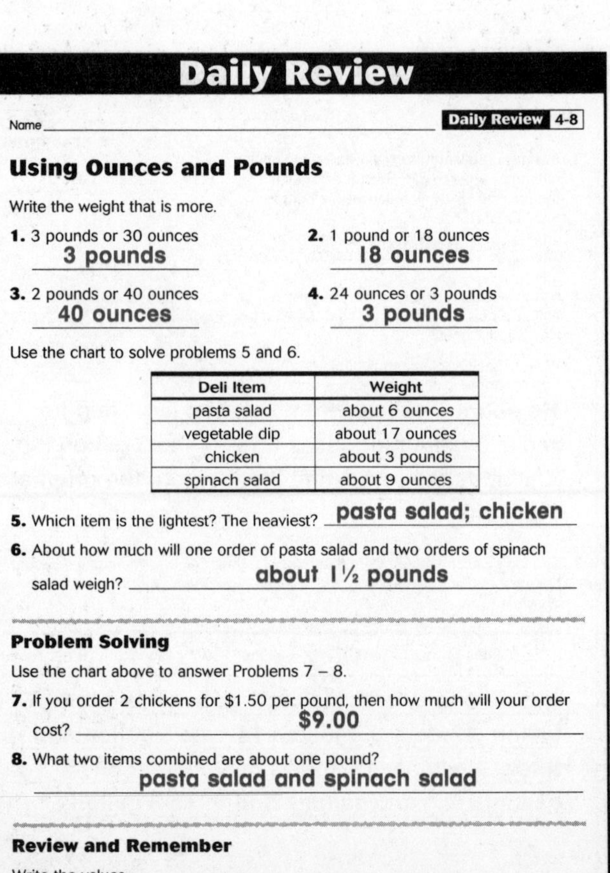

Daily Review

Name ______________________

Daily Review 4-8

Using Ounces and Pounds

Write the weight that is more.

1. 3 pounds or 30 ounces **3 pounds**
2. 1 pound or 18 ounces **18 ounces**
3. 2 pounds or 40 ounces **40 ounces**
4. 24 ounces or 3 pounds **3 pounds**

Use the chart to solve problems 5 and 6.

Deli Item	Weight
pasta salad	about 6 ounces
vegetable dip	about 17 ounces
chicken	about 3 pounds
spinach salad	about 9 ounces

5. Which item is the lightest? The heaviest? **pasta salad; chicken**
6. About how much will one order of pasta salad and two orders of spinach salad weigh? **about 1½ pounds**

Problem Solving

Use the chart above to answer Problems 7 – 8.

7. If you order 2 chickens for $1.50 per pound, then how much will your order cost? **$9.00**
8. What two items combined are about one pound? **pasta salad and spinach salad**

Review and Remember

Write the values.

9. 4 quarters and 2 dimes **$1.20**
10. 4 dimes and 6 pennies **46¢**

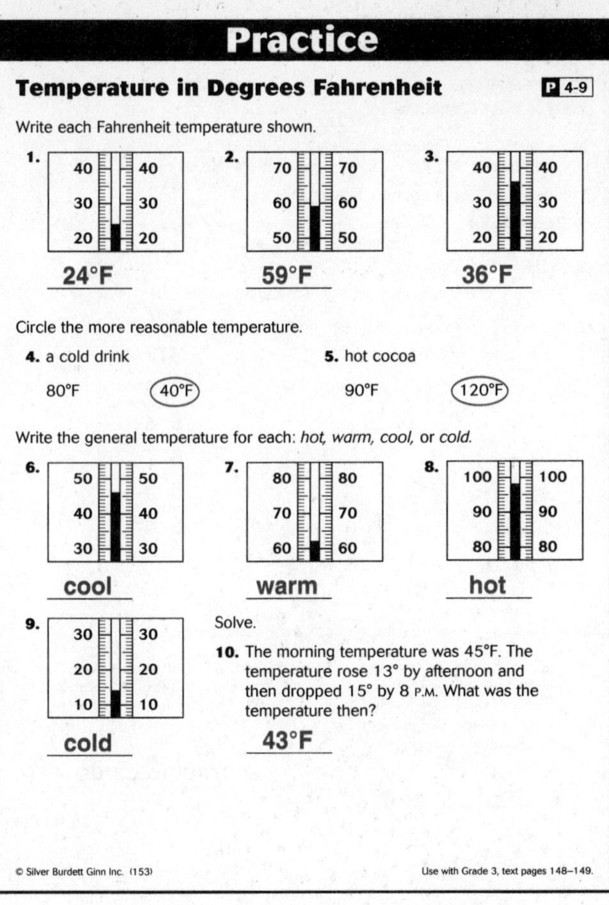

Practice

Temperature in Degrees Fahrenheit

P 4-9

Write each Fahrenheit temperature shown.

1. 24°F
2. 59°F
3. 36°F

Circle the more reasonable temperature.

4. a cold drink — 80°F — (40°F)
5. hot cocoa — 90°F — (120°F)

Write the general temperature for each: *hot, warm, cool,* or *cold.*

6. cool
7. warm
8. hot
9. cold

Solve.

10. The morning temperature was 45°F. The temperature rose 13° by afternoon and then dropped 15° by 8 P.M. What was the temperature then? 43°F

 Use with Grade 3, text pages 148–149.

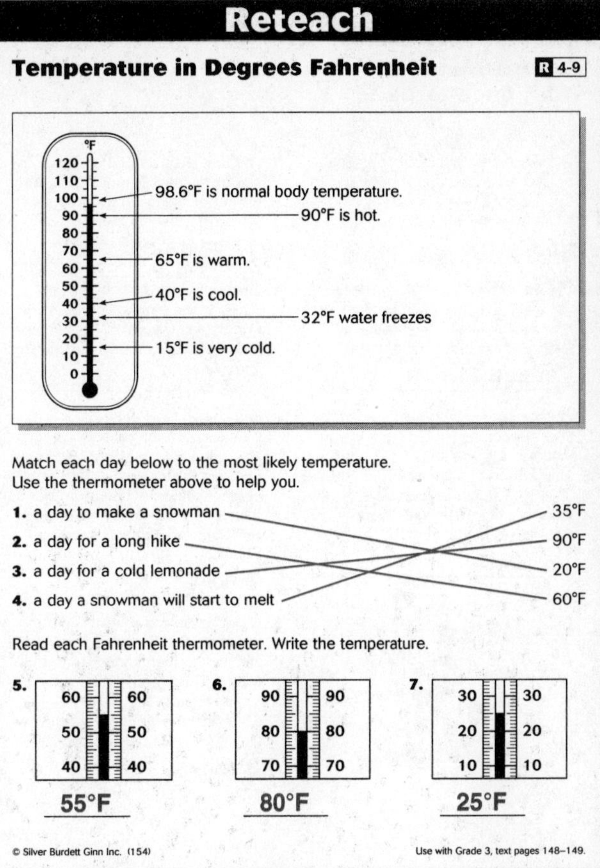

Reteach

Temperature in Degrees Fahrenheit

R 4-9

Match each day below to the most likely temperature. Use the thermometer above to help you.

1. a day to make a snowman — 20°F
2. a day for a long hike — 60°F
3. a day for a cold lemonade — 90°F
4. a day a snowman will start to melt — 35°F

Read each Fahrenheit thermometer. Write the temperature.

5. 55°F
6. 80°F
7. 25°F

 Use with Grade 3, text pages 148–149.

Extend

Wind Chill

E 4-9

DATA

On a cold day, the thermometer reading and the wind speed combine to make a wind chill. Wind chill is how cold the air feels to your skin.

Look at the table. What does a wind chill of 22° Fahrenheit mean?

Wind Chill (in °F)

Wind Speed (miles per hour)	Thermometer Reading			
	35°F	30°F	25°F	20°F
5	33°	27°	21°	19°
10	22°	16°	10°	3°
15	16°	9°	2°	−5°*

*−5° = 5° below 0

If it is 35°F and the wind is blowing 10 miles per hour, the wind chill is 22°F.

Use the table. Write the wind chill for each wind speed and temperature.

1. Wind Speed = 5 m.p.h.
Temperature = 35°F
Wind Chill = 33°F

2. Wind Speed = 10 m.p.h.
Temperature = 30°F
Wind Chill = 16°F

3. Wind Speed = 5 m.p.h.
Temperature = 25°F
Wind Chill = 21°F

4. Wind Speed = 10 m.p.h.
Temperature = 20°F
Wind Chill = 3°F

Which feels colder to your skin? Circle the answer.

5. (Wind Speed = 15 m.p.h. Temperature = 35°F) — Wind Speed = 5 m.p.h. Temperature = 20°F

6. Wind Speed = 5 m.p.h. Temperature = 30°F — (Wind Speed = 15 m.p.h. Temperature = 35°F)

 Use with Grade 3, text pages 148–149.

Daily Review

Name ______________________

Daily Review 4-9

Temperature in Degrees Fahrenheit

Write each temperature in °F. Describe the temperature as *hot, cold, warm,* or *cool.*

1. 90°, hot
2. 10°, cold
3. 70°, warm
4. 60°, cool

Which temperature is warmer?

5. 10°F or 40°F — 40°F
6. 14°F or 41°F — 41°F
7. 89°F or 86°F — 89°F
8. 12°F or 14°F — 14°F

Which temperature is colder?

9. 55°F or 15°F — 15°F
10. 65°F or 56°F — 56°F
11. 75°F or 55°F — 55°F
12. 63°F or 89°F — 63°F

Problem Solving

13. The temperature is 30°F in Denver, Colorado, and 98°F in Mexico City. In which city could you build a snowman? Denver

14. It is 15°F. Will you wear hat, mittens, and a coat, or shorts and a tee shirt? hat, mittens, coat

Review and Remember

Add or subtract.

15. 47 + 52 = 99
16. 96 − 19 = 77
17. 135 + 27 = 162
18. 980 − 235 = 745

Practice

Problem Solving P 4-10

Work Backwards

Try to work backwards to solve each problem.

1. Lisa spent $15 in December. She spent $4 in January. She has $18 in the bank now. How much did Lisa have to start with?

   $37

2. Lisa is 5 years older than Jeff. The piano teacher is 22 years older than Lisa. The piano teacher is 44 years old. How old is Jeff?

   17 years old

3. Maya visits her grandparents every 2 years. She was 15 when she went for the third time. At what age did Maya first visit her grandparents?

   at age 11

4. Sharon bought 3 books for $2 each and a magazine for $1.50. Her change was $2.50. How much money did Sharon give the clerk?

   $10.00

5. Wade likes to feed the ducks at the lake. When he started feeding the ducks, two flew away. Five more ducks came to the lake. Then there were 11 ducks to feed. How many ducks were there when Wade started to feed them?

   8 ducks

6. The time in New York City is 1 hour later than it is in Chicago. The time in Chicago is 2 hours later than it is in Los Angeles. The time in Los Angeles is 3 hours later than it is in Honolulu. It is 2:00 in Honolulu. What time is it in New York City?

   8:00

7. Lisa took several rolls of film from the photography club's storeroom. Jeff took 3, Clark took 5, and Meg took 4. There were 10 left after Lisa took hers. The storeroom had 25 rolls at the beginning of the day. How many rolls did Lisa take?

   3 rolls

 Use with Grade 3, text pages 150–151.

Reteach

Problem Solving R 4-10

Work Backwards

Juana had $24. She bought a gift for a friend for $12. Then she bought a ticket to the movies for $5, and she spent $3 on popcorn and soda.

1. How much does Juana have in her wallet now?

Understand You need to know how much money Juana had to start with. You also need to know how much she spent.

Plan You can work backward from the amount of money Juana had. Subtract $12, $5, and $3 from $24.

Solve

Juana's money to begin with	**$24**
Gift for friend	**– $12**
	$12
Ticket for movie	**– $ 5**
	$ 7
Popcorn and soda	**– $ 3**
Juana's money now	**$ 4**

Look Back You can add to check.
4 + 3 + 5 + 12 = $24 ✔

Work backwards to solve. Use the **Look Back** step to check your work.

2. Keith made party hats for his friends. He made some on Monday, 8 on Tuesday, and 7 on Wednesday. Keith made 20 party hats. How many did he make on Monday?

   5 hats

3. Lyle has some trading cards. He loses 1. He trades 10 cards for a ball. Now he has 9 trading cards. How many cards did Lyle have to start with?

   20 trading cards

 Use with Grade 3, text pages 150–151.

Extend

Plan Ahead

E 4-10 REASONING

Mrs. Chen meets her children at the school bus stop at 3:30 every day. Today, she leaves work at 12:30 so that she can run some errands. Here are the errands Mrs. Chen plans to run:

Travel time from work to bank:	5 minutes
Stay at bank:	10 minutes
Travel from bank to mall:	15 minutes
Shop at mall:	?
Travel from mall to grocery store:	10 minutes
Complete grocery shopping:	45 minutes
Travel from grocery store to bus stop:	15 minutes

You can use a table to track Mrs. Chen's times.

1. Work forward to know what time Mrs. Chen arrives at the mall.
2. Work backwards to find out what time Mrs. Chen must leave the mall.

Leaves work	**12:30**
Arrives at bank	**12:35**
Leaves bank	**12:45**
Arrives at mall	**1:00**
Leaves mall	**2:20**
Arrives at grocery store	**2:30**
Leaves grocery store	**3:15**
Meets school bus	**3:30**

3. How long can Mrs. Chen stay at the mall?

   1 hour and 20 minutes

 Use with Grade 3, text pages 150–151.

Daily Review

Name ____________________ Daily Review 4-10

Problem Solving

Work Backwards

Work backwards to solve each problem.

1. Jason's family stopped for gasoline every 5 hours on the first day of their vacation. They stopped for the third time at 9:00 P.M. What time was it when they began their drive?

   6 A.M.

2. Ramon went to the park every other day during the summer. On the tenth visit it was Sunday. On what day of the week was his first visit?

   Wednesday

3. Monica returned home with $2.10 in her pocket. She had bought an umbrella for $5.15, lunch for $4.25, and a pair of shoes for $23.50. How much money did she have when she went shopping?

   $35.00

4. Bob had 4 more apples than Jim. Jim had 1 less apple than Grace. Grace had 6 more than John, who had 3 less than Peter. Peter had 8 apples. How many apples did Bob have?

   14 apples

Review and Remember

Write <, >, or = for each ◯.

5. 68°F (<) 72°F
6. 16 oz (=) 1 lb
7. 35 oz (>) 2 lb
8. 80 min (>) 1 h
9. 15°C (>) 10°C
10. 8 ft (>) 2 yd
11. 5 ft (=) 60 in.
12. 2 c (=) 1 pt
13. 2 h (>) 110 min

Chapter 4 • Lesson 11

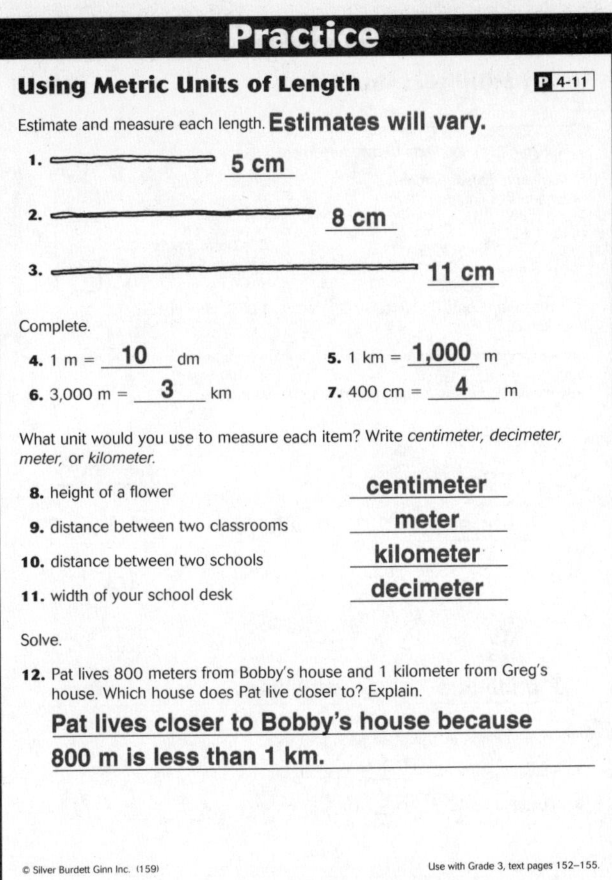

Practice

Using Metric Units of Length

P 4-11

Estimate and measure each length. **Estimates will vary.**

1. ________ **5 cm**
2. ________ **8 cm**
3. ________ **11 cm**

Complete.

4. 1 m = **10** dm
5. 1 km = **1,000** m
6. 3,000 m = **3** km
7. 400 cm = **4** m

What unit would you use to measure each item? Write *centimeter, decimeter, meter,* or *kilometer.*

8. height of a flower **centimeter**
9. distance between two classrooms **meter**
10. distance between two schools **kilometer**
11. width of your school desk **decimeter**

Solve.

12. Pat lives 800 meters from Bobby's house and 1 kilometer from Greg's house. Which house does Pat live closer to? Explain.
Pat lives closer to Bobby's house because 800 m is less than 1 km.

Use with Grade 3, text pages 152–155.

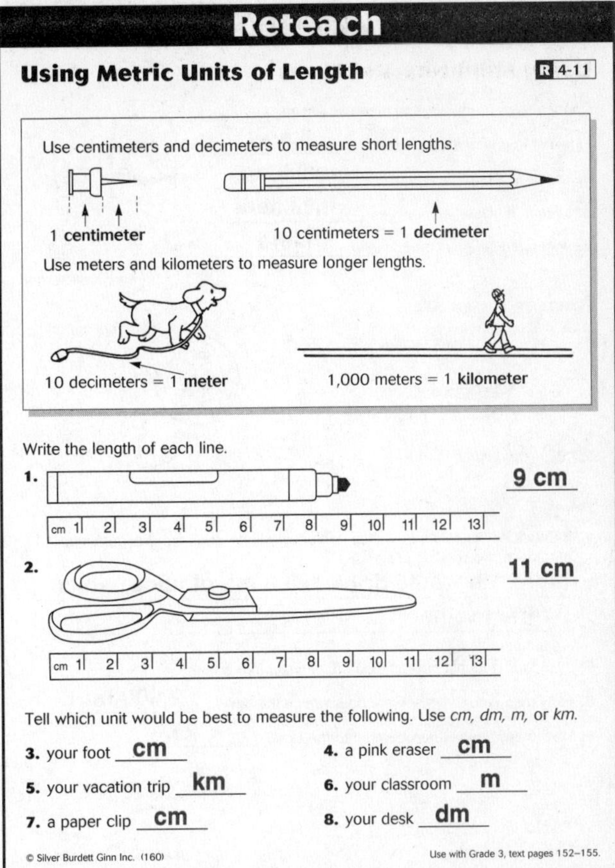

Reteach

Using Metric Units of Length

R 4-11

Use centimeters and decimeters to measure short lengths.

1 centimeter

10 centimeters = 1 decimeter

Use meters and kilometers to measure longer lengths.

10 decimeters = 1 meter

1,000 meters = 1 kilometer

Write the length of each line.

1. **9 cm**

cm 1 2 3 4 5 6 7 8 9 10 11 12 13

2. **11 cm**

cm 1 2 3 4 5 6 7 8 9 10 11 12 13

Tell which unit would be best to measure the following. Use *cm, dm, m,* or *km.*

3. your foot **cm**
4. a pink eraser **cm**
5. your vacation trip **km**
6. your classroom **m**
7. a paper clip **cm**
8. your desk **dm**

Use with Grade 3, text pages 152–155.

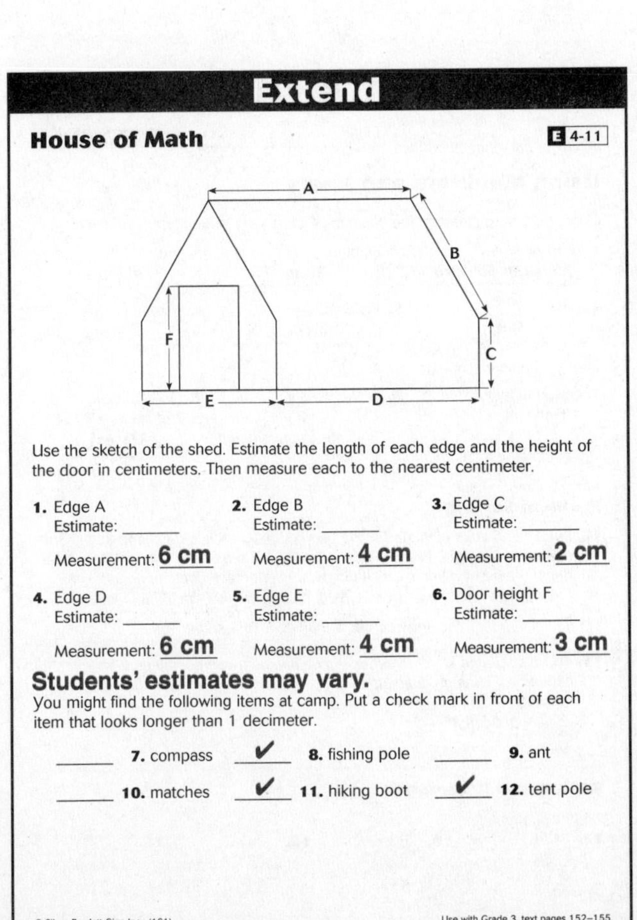

Extend

House of Math

E 4-11

A B C D E F

Use the sketch of the shed. Estimate the length of each edge and the height of the door in centimeters. Then measure each to the nearest centimeter.

1. Edge A
Estimate: ____
Measurement: **6 cm**
2. Edge B
Estimate: ____
Measurement: **4 cm**
3. Edge C
Estimate: ____
Measurement: **2 cm**
4. Edge D
Estimate: ____
Measurement: **6 cm**
5. Edge E
Estimate: ____
Measurement: **4 cm**
6. Door height F
Estimate: ____
Measurement: **3 cm**

Students' estimates may vary.

You might find the following items at camp. Put a check mark in front of each item that looks longer than 1 decimeter.

____ 7. compass
✔ 8. fishing pole
____ 9. ant
____ 10. matches
✔ 11. hiking boot
✔ 12. tent pole

Use with Grade 3, text pages 152–155.

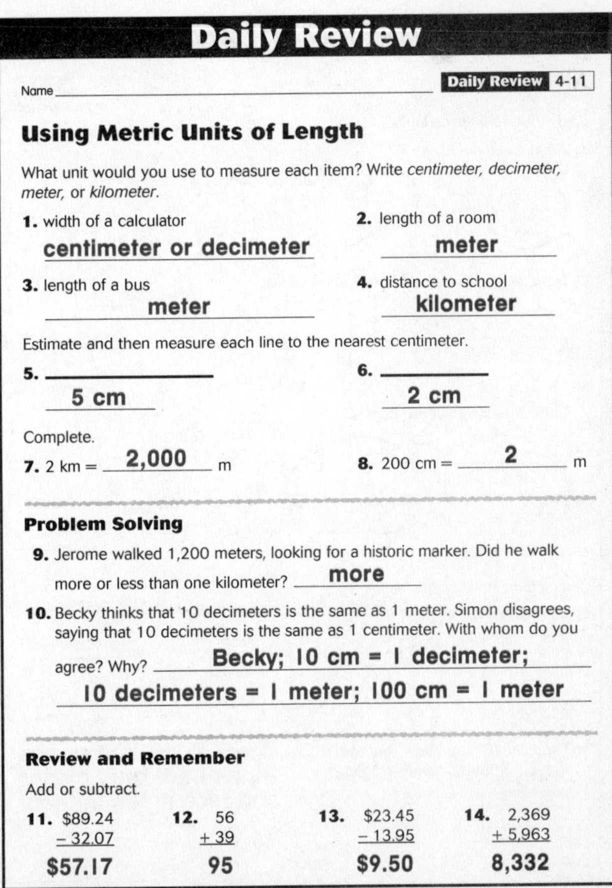

Daily Review

Name ____________________

Daily Review 4-11

Using Metric Units of Length

What unit would you use to measure each item? Write *centimeter, decimeter, meter,* or *kilometer.*

1. width of a calculator **centimeter or decimeter**
2. length of a room **meter**
3. length of a bus **meter**
4. distance to school **kilometer**

Estimate and then measure each line to the nearest centimeter.

5. ________ **5 cm**
6. ________ **2 cm**

Complete.

7. 2 km = **2,000** m
8. 200 cm = **2** m

Problem Solving

9. Jerome walked 1,200 meters, looking for a historic marker. Did he walk more or less than one kilometer? **more**
10. Becky thinks that 10 decimeters is the same as 1 meter. Simon disagrees, saying that 10 decimeters is the same as 1 centimeter. With whom do you agree? Why? **Becky; 10 cm = 1 decimeter; 10 decimeters = 1 meter; 100 cm = 1 meter**

Review and Remember

Add or subtract.

11. $89.24 − 32.07 = **$57.17**
12. 56 + 39 = **95**
13. $23.45 − 13.95 = **$9.50**
14. 2,369 + 5,963 = **8,332**

Chapter 4 • Lesson 12

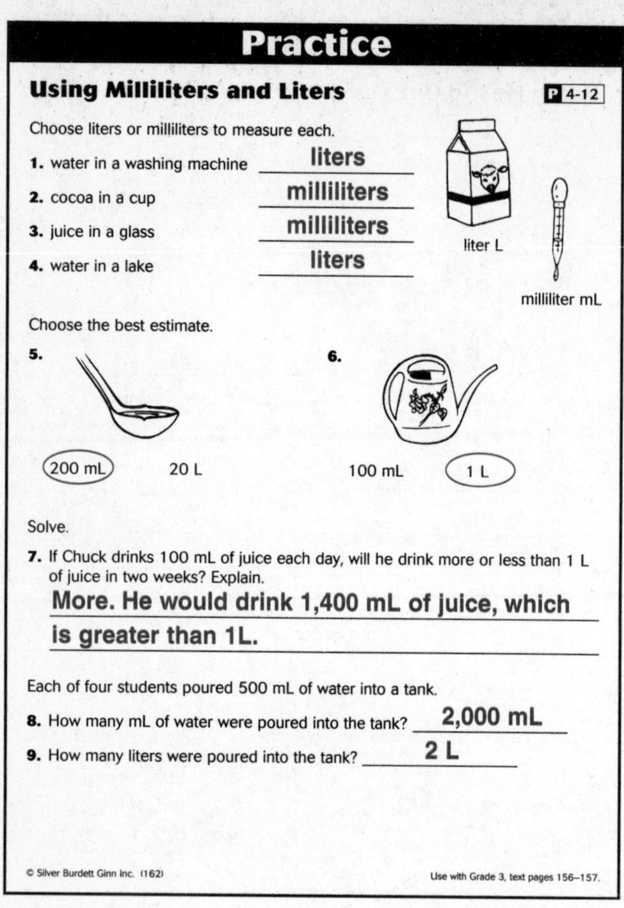

Practice

Using Milliliters and Liters

P 4-12

Choose liters or milliliters to measure each.

1. water in a washing machine **liters**
2. cocoa in a cup **milliliters**
3. juice in a glass **milliliters**
4. water in a lake **liters**

Choose the best estimate.

5. (200 mL) 20 L
6. 100 mL (1 L)

Solve.

7. If Chuck drinks 100 mL of juice each day, will he drink more or less than 1 L of juice in two weeks? Explain.
   More. He would drink 1,400 mL of juice, which is greater than 1L.

Each of four students poured 500 mL of water into a tank.

8. How many mL of water were poured into the tank? **2,000 mL**
9. How many liters were poured into the tank? **2 L**

Use with Grade 3, text pages 156–157.

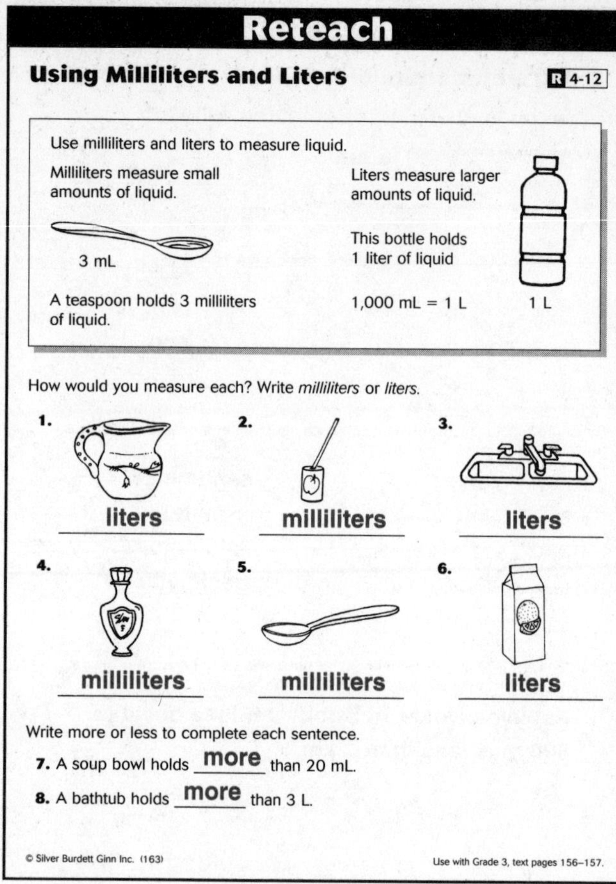

Reteach

Using Milliliters and Liters

R 4-12

Use milliliters and liters to measure liquid.

Milliliters measure small amounts of liquid.

3 mL

A teaspoon holds 3 milliliters of liquid.

Liters measure larger amounts of liquid.

This bottle holds 1 liter of liquid

1,000 mL = 1 L

1 L

How would you measure each? Write *milliliters* or *liters.*

1. **liters**
2. **milliliters**
3. **liters**
4. **milliliters**
5. **milliliters**
6. **liters**

Write more or less to complete each sentence.

7. A soup bowl holds **more** than 20 mL.
8. A bathtub holds **more** than 3 L.

Use with Grade 3, text pages 156–157.

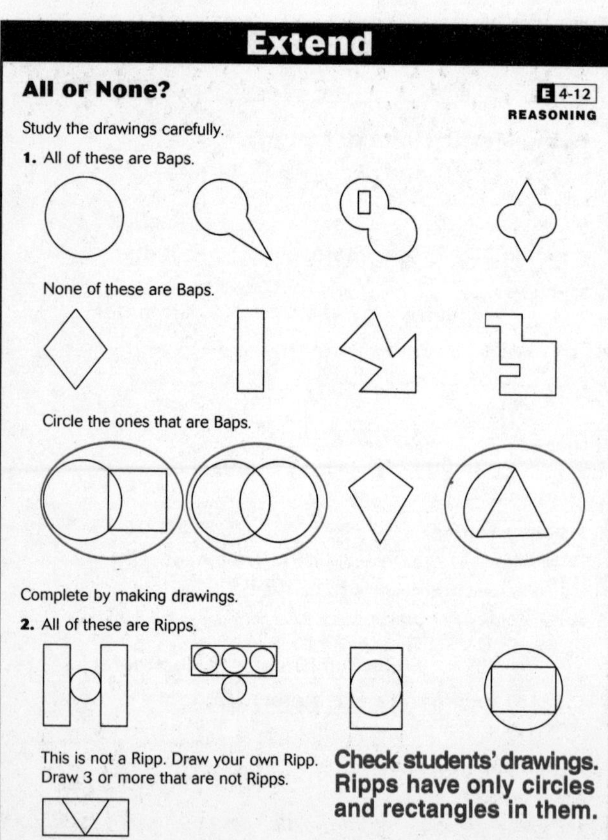

Extend

All or None?

E 4-12

REASONING

Study the drawings carefully.

1. All of these are Baps.

None of these are Baps.

Circle the ones that are Baps.

Complete by making drawings.

2. All of these are Ripps.

This is not a Ripp. Draw your own Ripp. Draw 3 or more that are not Ripps.

Check students' drawings. Ripps have only circles and rectangles in them.

Use with Grade 3, text pages 156–157.

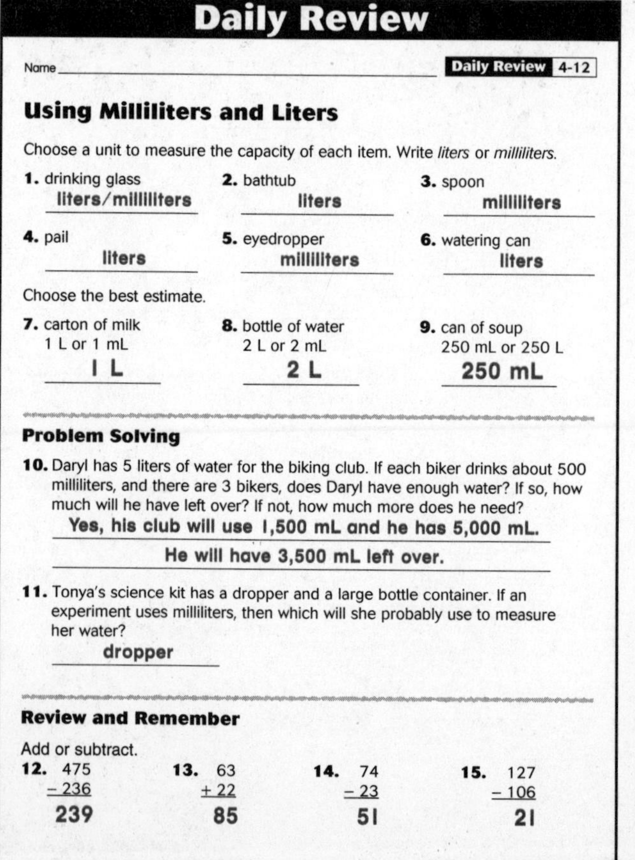

Daily Review

Name ______________________

Daily Review 4-12

Using Milliliters and Liters

Choose a unit to measure the capacity of each item. Write *liters* or *milliliters.*

1. drinking glass **liters/milliliters**
2. bathtub **liters**
3. spoon **milliliters**
4. pail **liters**
5. eyedropper **milliliters**
6. watering can **liters**

Choose the best estimate.

7. carton of milk 1 L or 1 mL **1 L**
8. bottle of water 2 L or 2 mL **2 L**
9. can of soup 250 mL or 250 L **250 mL**

Problem Solving

10. Daryl has 5 liters of water for the biking club. If each biker drinks about 500 milliliters, and there are 3 bikers, does Daryl have enough water? If so, how much will he have left over? If not, how much more does he need?
    Yes, his club will use 1,500 mL and he has 5,000 mL. He will have 3,500 mL left over.
11. Tonya's science kit has a dropper and a large bottle container. If an experiment uses milliliters, then which will she probably use to measure her water?
    dropper

Review and Remember

Add or subtract.

12. $475 - 236 =$ **239**
13. $63 + 22 =$ **85**
14. $74 - 23 =$ **51**
15. $127 - 106 =$ **21**

Practice

Using Grams and Kilograms

P 4-13

1. Read the words in each rectangle. Color the rectangle if you would use kilograms to find its weight. Leave the rectangle uncolored if you would use grams to find its weight.

piece of toast	chair	large bag of onions	lawnmower	napkin
whistle	strand of hair	small stuffed animal	baseball bat	cup
hat	scarf	steel beam	book shelves	name tag
pocket mirror	flower petal	piece of paper	television	egg
balloon	microwave oven	refrigerator	dog	ten pieces of popcorn

2. What number do you see in the colored shape? 3

 Use with Grade 3, text pages 158–159.

Reteach

Using Grams and Kilograms

R 4-13

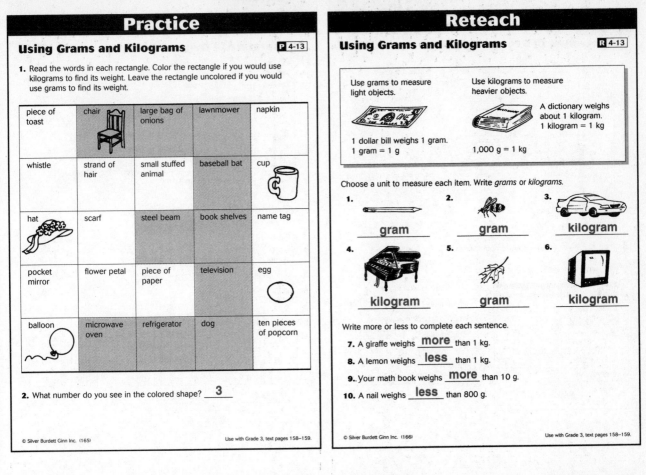

Use grams to measure light objects.

1 dollar bill weighs 1 gram.
1 gram = 1 g

Use kilograms to measure heavier objects.

A dictionary weighs about 1 kilogram.
1 kilogram = 1 kg

1,000 g = 1 kg

Choose a unit to measure each item. Write *grams* or *kilograms*.

1. 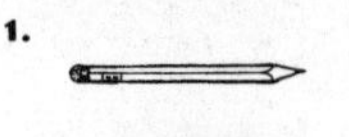 gram
2.  gram
3.  kilogram
4.  kilogram
5.  gram
6.  kilogram

Write more or less to complete each sentence.

7. A giraffe weighs more than 1 kg.
8. A lemon weighs less than 1 kg.
9. Your math book weighs more than 10 g.
10. A nail weighs less than 800 g.

 Use with Grade 3, text pages 158–159.

Extend

Boxes, Bottles, and Mugs

E 4-13
ALGEBRA

How many mugs will balance the last scale in each set?

HINT: Replace each box with mugs.

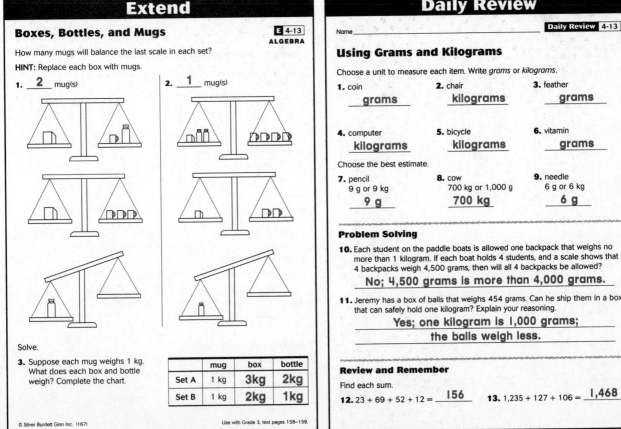

1. 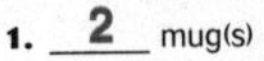 2 mug(s)

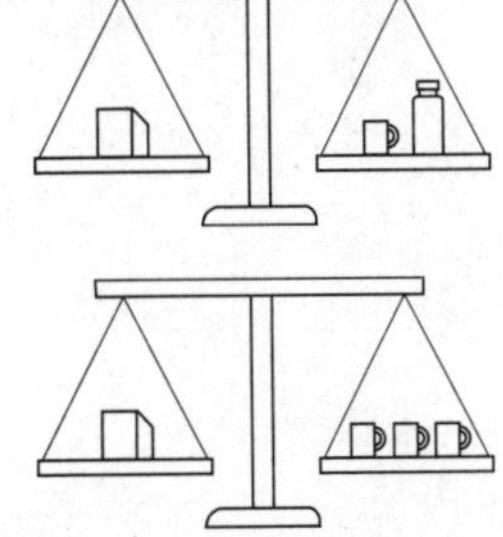

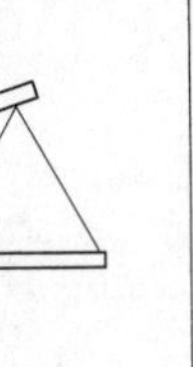

2. 1 mug(s)

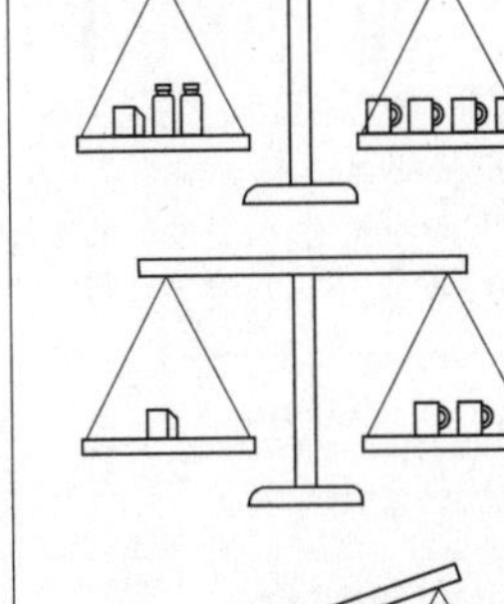

Solve.

3. Suppose each mug weighs 1 kg. What does each box and bottle weigh? Complete the chart.

	mug	box	bottle
Set A	1 kg	3kg	2kg
Set B	1 kg	2kg	1kg

 Use with Grade 3, text pages 158–159.

Daily Review

Name ____________________

Daily Review 4-13

Using Grams and Kilograms

Choose a unit to measure each item. Write *grams* or *kilograms*.

1. coin grams
2. chair kilograms
3. feather grams
4. computer kilograms
5. bicycle kilograms
6. vitamin grams

Choose the best estimate.

7. pencil 9 g or 9 kg — 9 g
8. cow 700 kg or 1,000 g — 700 kg
9. needle 6 g or 6 kg — 6 g

Problem Solving

10. Each student on the paddle boats is allowed one backpack that weighs no more than 1 kilogram. If each boat holds 4 students, and a scale shows that 4 backpacks weigh 4,500 grams, then will all 4 backpacks be allowed?
No; 4,500 grams is more than 4,000 grams.

11. Jeremy has a box of balls that weighs 454 grams. Can he ship them in a box that can safely hold one kilogram? Explain your reasoning.
Yes; one kilogram is 1,000 grams; the balls weigh less.

Review and Remember

Find each sum.

12. 23 + 69 + 52 + 12 = 156
13. 1,235 + 127 + 106 = 1,468

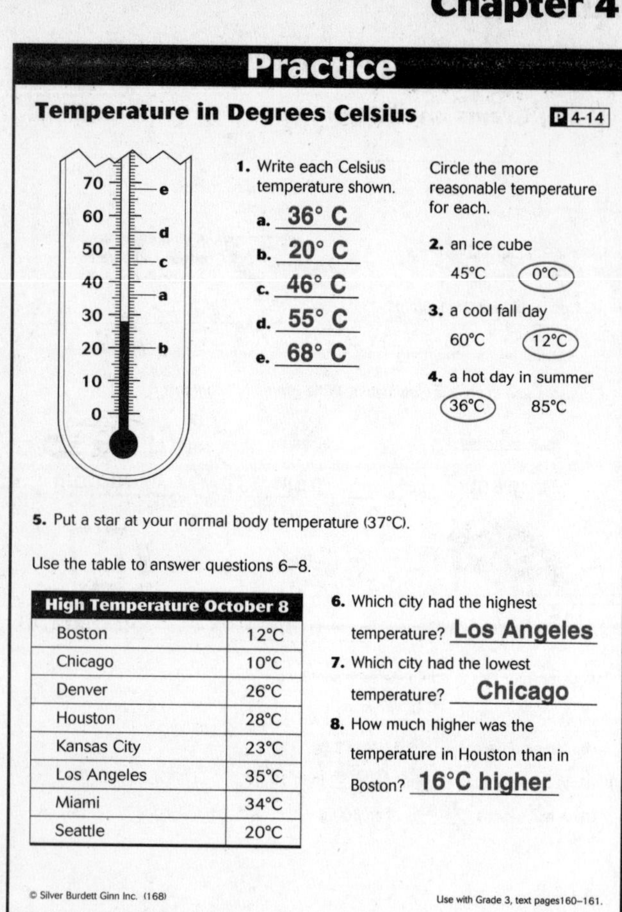

Practice

Temperature in Degrees Celsius

P 4-14

1. Write each Celsius temperature shown.
   a. 36° C
   b. 20° C
   c. 46° C
   d. 55° C
   e. 68° C

Circle the more reasonable temperature for each.

2. an ice cube
   45°C (0°C)
3. a cool fall day
   60°C (12°C)
4. a hot day in summer
   (36°C) 85°C

5. Put a star at your normal body temperature (37°C).

Use the table to answer questions 6–8.

High Temperature October 8	
Boston	12°C
Chicago	10°C
Denver	26°C
Houston	28°C
Kansas City	23°C
Los Angeles	35°C
Miami	34°C
Seattle	20°C

6. Which city had the highest temperature? Los Angeles
7. Which city had the lowest temperature? Chicago
8. How much higher was the temperature in Houston than in Boston? 16°C higher

 Use with Grade 3, text pages160–161.

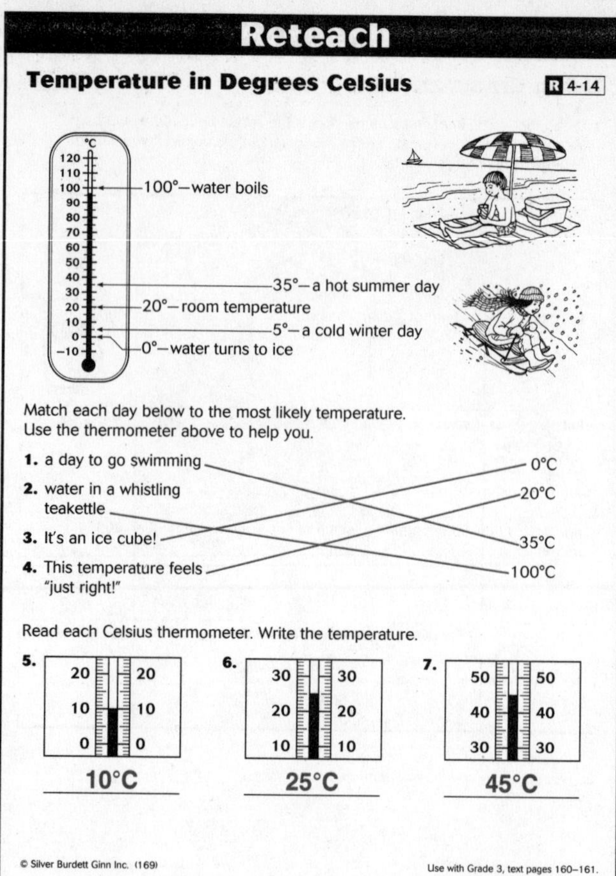

Reteach

Temperature in Degrees Celsius

R 4-14

Match each day below to the most likely temperature. Use the thermometer above to help you.

1. a day to go swimming — 35°C
2. water in a whistling teakettle — 100°C
3. It's an ice cube! — 0°C
4. This temperature feels "just right!" — 20°C

Read each Celsius thermometer. Write the temperature.

5. 10°C
6. 25°C
7. 45°C

 Use with Grade 3, text pages 160–161.

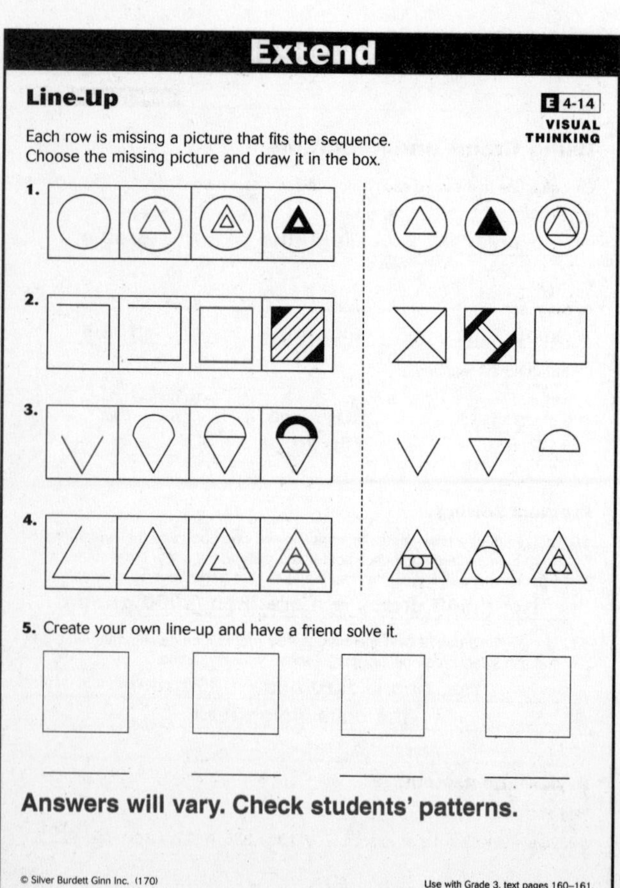

Extend

Line-Up

E 4-14
VISUAL THINKING

Each row is missing a picture that fits the sequence. Choose the missing picture and draw it in the box.

1.

2.

3.

4.

5. Create your own line-up and have a friend solve it.

Answers will vary. Check students' patterns.

 Use with Grade 3, text pages 160–161.

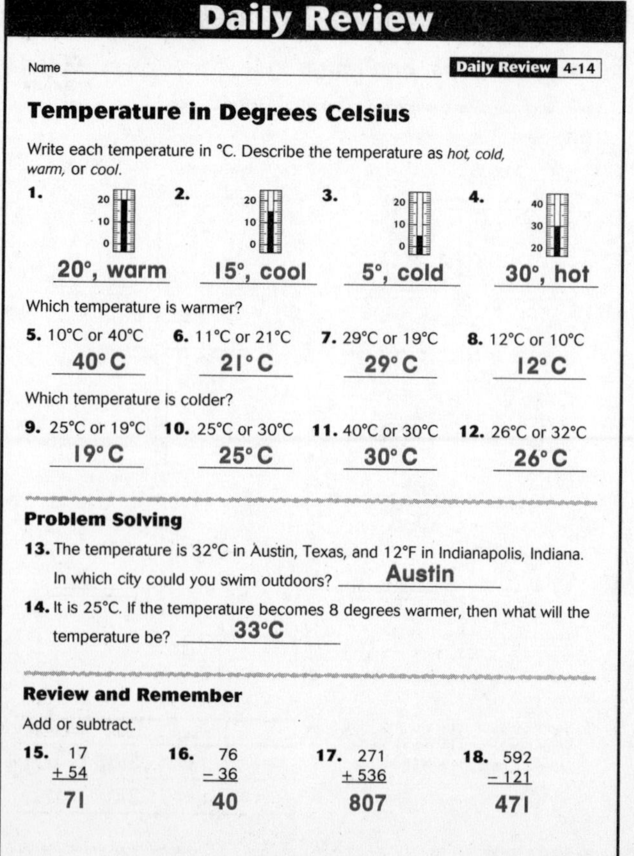

Daily Review

Name ____________ Daily Review 4-14

Temperature in Degrees Celsius

Write each temperature in °C. Describe the temperature as *hot, cold, warm,* or *cool.*

1. 20°, warm
2. 15°, cool
3. 5°, cold
4. 30°, hot

Which temperature is warmer?

5. 10°C or 40°C — 40° C
6. 11°C or 21°C — 21° C
7. 29°C or 19°C — 29° C
8. 12°C or 10°C — 12° C

Which temperature is colder?

9. 25°C or 19°C — 19° C
10. 25°C or 30°C — 25° C
11. 40°C or 30°C — 30° C
12. 26°C or 32°C — 26° C

Problem Solving

13. The temperature is 32°C in Austin, Texas, and 12°F in Indianapolis, Indiana. In which city could you swim outdoors? Austin
14. It is 25°C. If the temperature becomes 8 degrees warmer, then what will the temperature be? 33°C

Review and Remember

Add or subtract.

15. 17 + 54 = 71
16. 76 − 36 = 40
17. 271 + 536 = 807
18. 592 − 121 = 471

Practice

Problem Solving P 4-15

Using Measurement

Use measurement to answer each question.

1. When Jesse got to work, it was 65° Fahrenheit. The temperature rose 9° by noon, then became 3° hotter by 3:00. What was the temperature at 3:00?
   77° Fahrenheit

2. Jesse cut a piece of wood 3 feet, and 3 inches long. The remaining piece was 3 feet, 9 inches long. How long was the piece of wood before it was cut?
   7 feet long

3. Jesse bought a container of paint mix. He mixed it with 3 quarts of water to make a gallon. How much paint was in the container before it was mixed?
   1 quart

4. Jesse's day ended at 3:15. He had worked for 5 hours and took 1 hour off for lunch. At what time did Jesse's work day begin?
   9:15

Use the chart to answer questions 5-7.

Area Rugs

Rug	Length	Width
A	8 feet	5 feet
B	10 feet	7 feet
C	12 feet	3 feet

5. Which rug has the greatest length? **Rug C**
6. Which rug has the greatest width? **Rug B**
7. Suppose each rug has a binding ribbon around the outside edge. Which rug would need the greatest length of ribbon? Explain.
   Rug B–34 feet around. Rug A is only 26 feet; Rug C is only 30 feet.

 Use with Grade 3, text pages 162–163.

Reteach

Problem Solving R 4-15

Using Measurement

You can use measurement to solve real-life problems.

The school blacktop is 50 meters wide and 100 meters long. How many meters will Ray run if he runs around the outside of the blacktop once?

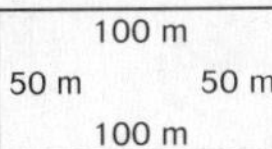

1. How can you find the total distance around the blacktop?

Understand You need to find the distance around, or length of, all four sides of the blacktop.

Plan You can list the lengths of each side. Then you can add them to find the total.

Solve 50 + 100 + 50 + 100 = **300**

So, Ray will run 300 meters if he runs around the blacktop once.

Look Back Check your work by adding the numbers in a different order.

100 + **100** + **50** + **50** = **300** ✓

Use what you know about measurement to solve each problem.

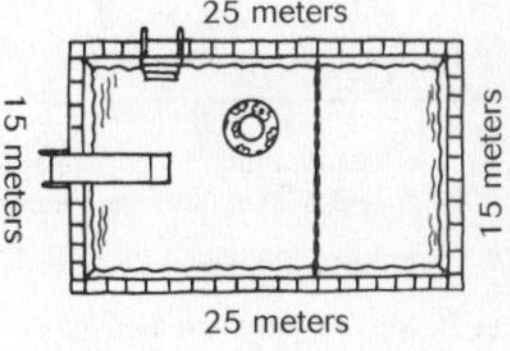

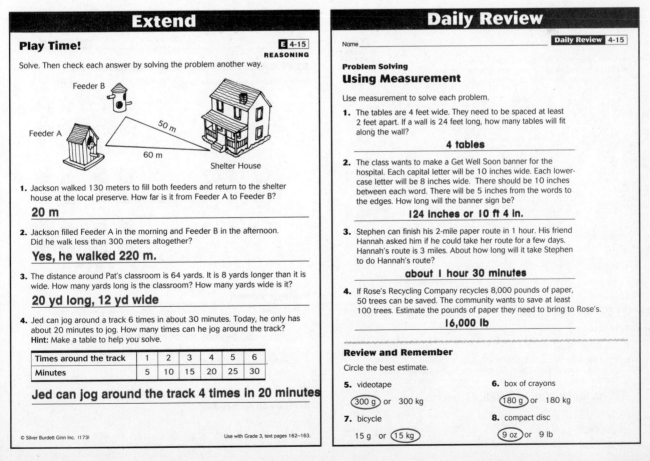

2. Kim swam around each side of the pool. How many meters did Kim swim?
   80 meters
3. How far would Kim swim if she circled the sides of the pool 3 times?
   240 meters

 Use with Grade 3, text pages 162–163.

Extend

Play Time!

E 4-15 REASONING

Solve. Then check each answer by solving the problem another way.

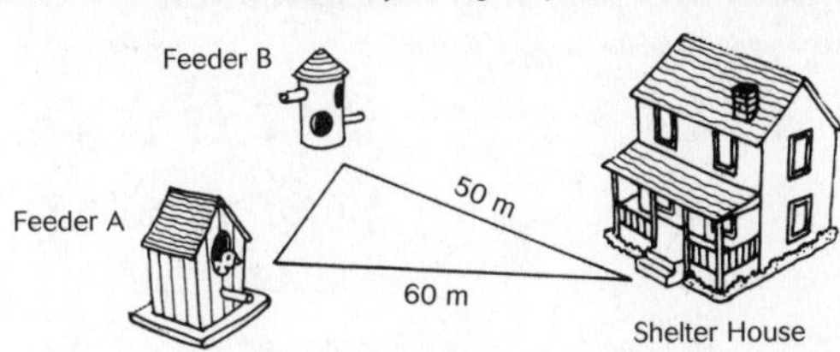

1. Jackson walked 130 meters to fill both feeders and return to the shelter house at the local preserve. How far is it from Feeder A to Feeder B?
   20 m
2. Jackson filled Feeder A in the morning and Feeder B in the afternoon. Did he walk less than 300 meters altogether?
   Yes, he walked 220 m.
3. The distance around Pat's classroom is 64 yards. It is 8 yards longer than it is wide. How many yards long is the classroom? How many yards wide is it?
   20 yd long, 12 yd wide
4. Jed can jog around a track 6 times in about 30 minutes. Today, he only has about 20 minutes to jog. How many times can he jog around the track?
   Hint: Make a table to help you solve.

Times around the track	1	2	3	4	5	6
Minutes	5	10	15	20	25	30

Jed can jog around the track 4 times in 20 minutes

 Use with Grade 3, text pages 162–163.

Daily Review

Name ____________

Daily Review 4-15

Problem Solving

Using Measurement

Use measurement to solve each problem.

1. The tables are 4 feet wide. They need to be spaced at least 2 feet apart. If a wall is 24 feet long, how many tables will fit along the wall?
   4 tables
2. The class wants to make a Get Well Soon banner for the hospital. Each capital letter will be 10 inches wide. Each lower-case letter will be 8 inches wide. There should be 10 inches between each word. There will be 5 inches from the words to the edges. How long will the banner sign be?
   124 inches or 10 ft 4 in.
3. Stephen can finish his 2-mile paper route in 1 hour. His friend Hannah asked him if he could take her route for a few days. Hannah's route is 3 miles. About how long will it take Stephen to do Hannah's route?
   about 1 hour 30 minutes
4. If Rose's Recycling Company recycles 8,000 pounds of paper, 50 trees can be saved. The community wants to save at least 100 trees. Estimate the pounds of paper they need to bring to Rose's.
   16,000 lb

Review and Remember

Circle the best estimate.

5. videotape
   (300 g) or 300 kg
6. box of crayons
   (180 g) or 180 kg
7. bicycle
   15 g or (15 kg)
8. compact disc
   (9 oz) or 9 lb

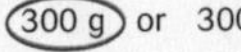

Practice

Explore: Understanding Multiplication

P 5-1

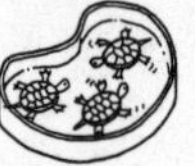

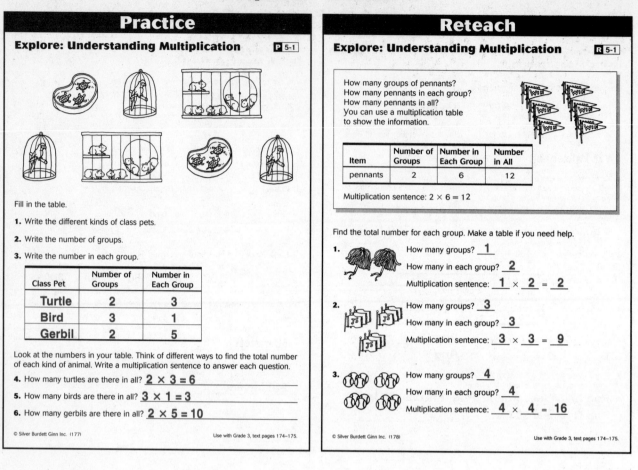

Fill in the table.

1. Write the different kinds of class pets.
2. Write the number of groups.
3. Write the number in each group.

Class Pet	Number of Groups	Number in Each Group
Turtle	2	3
Bird	3	1
Gerbil	2	5

Look at the numbers in your table. Think of different ways to find the total number of each kind of animal. Write a multiplication sentence to answer each question.

4. How many turtles are there in all? $2 \times 3 = 6$
5. How many birds are there in all? $3 \times 1 = 3$
6. How many gerbils are there in all? $2 \times 5 = 10$

Use with Grade 3, text pages 174–175.

Reteach

Explore: Understanding Multiplication

R 5-1

How many groups of pennants?
How many pennants in each group?
How many pennants in all?
You can use a multiplication table to show the information.

Item	Number of Groups	Number in Each Group	Number in All
pennants	2	6	12

Multiplication sentence: $2 \times 6 = 12$

Find the total number for each group. Make a table if you need help.

1. 
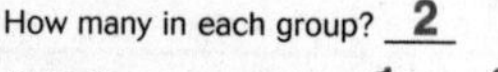
How many groups? 1
How many in each group? 2
Multiplication sentence: 1 × 2 = 2

2. 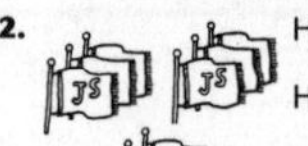
How many groups? 3
How many in each group? 3
Multiplication sentence: 3 × 3 = 9

3. 
How many groups? 4
How many in each group? 4
Multiplication sentence: 4 × 4 = 16

Use with Grade 3, text pages 174–175.

Extend

Playing Ball

E 5-1

NUMBER SENSE

Help the sports director count the sports equipment. Circle like groups of equipment. Draw a line to connect them, then write the missing numbers. One has been started for you.

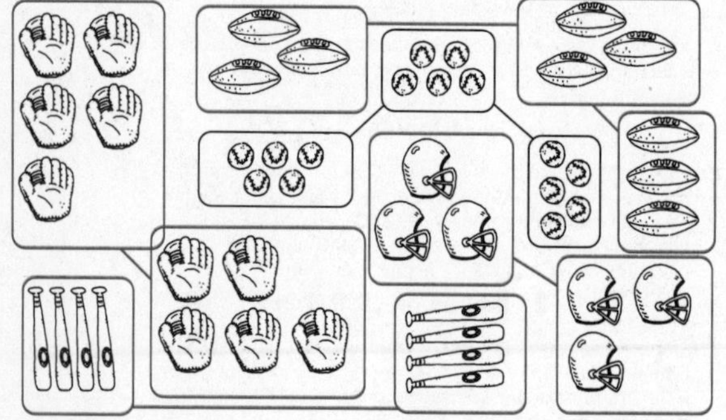

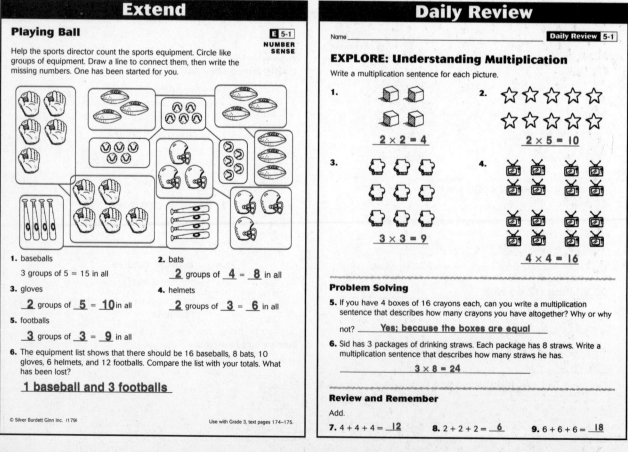

1. baseballs
3 groups of 5 = 15 in all
2. bats
2 groups of 4 = 8 in all
3. gloves
2 groups of 5 = 10 in all
4. helmets
2 groups of 3 = 6 in all
5. footballs
3 groups of 3 = 9 in all
6. The equipment list shows that there should be 16 baseballs, 8 bats, 10 gloves, 6 helmets, and 12 footballs. Compare the list with your totals. What has been lost?
1 baseball and 3 footballs

Use with Grade 3, text pages 174–175.

Daily Review

Name ____________________

Daily Review 5-1

EXPLORE: Understanding Multiplication

Write a multiplication sentence for each picture.

1. 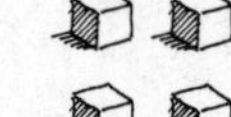
$2 \times 2 = 4$

2. $2 \times 5 = 10$

3. $3 \times 3 = 9$

4. $4 \times 4 = 16$

Problem Solving

5. If you have 4 boxes of 16 crayons each, can you write a multiplication sentence that describes how many crayons you have altogether? Why or why not? Yes; because the boxes are equal
6. Sid has 3 packages of drinking straws. Each package has 8 straws. Write a multiplication sentence that describes how many straws he has.
$3 \times 8 = 24$

Review and Remember

Add.

7. $4 + 4 + 4 =$ 12
8. $2 + 2 + 2 =$ 6
9. $6 + 6 + 6 =$ 18

Practice

Relating Multiplication and Addition

P 5-2

Write an addition sentence and a multiplication sentence for each picture.

1. □□□□□□□
□□□□□□□
7 + 7 = 14
2 × 7 = 14

2. △△△△△
△△△△△
△△△△△
5 + 5 + 5 = 15
3 × 5 = 15

Write a multiplication sentence. Find each product.

3. 4 + 4 + 4 + 4
4 × 4 = 16

4. 3 + 3 + 3 + 3 + 3 + 3
6 × 3 = 18

Use the chart for Problems 5-8.

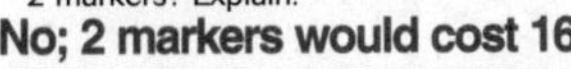
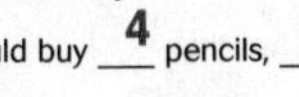
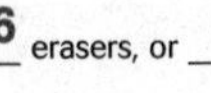

5. How much do 3 pencils cost? 18¢

6. How much do 5 erasers cost? 20¢

7. Suppose you have 15¢. Can you buy 2 markers? Explain.
No; 2 markers would cost 16¢

8. Suppose you have 24¢. Complete the sentence to tell how many of each item you could buy.

I could buy 4 pencils, 6 erasers, or 3 markers.

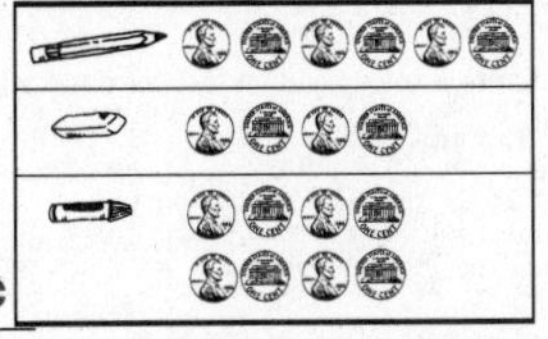

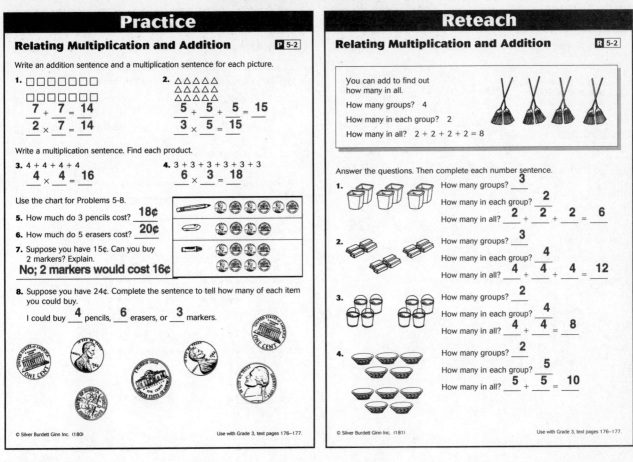

 Use with Grade 3, text pages 176–177.

Reteach

Relating Multiplication and Addition

R 5-2

You can add to find out how many in all.
How many groups? 4
How many in each group? 2
How many in all? 2 + 2 + 2 + 2 = 8

Answer the questions. Then complete each number sentence.

1. 
How many groups? 3
How many in each group? 2
How many in all? 2 + 2 + 2 = 6

2. 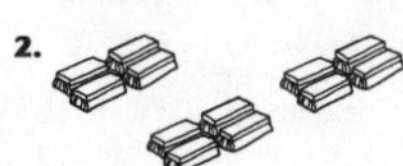
How many groups? 3
How many in each group? 4
How many in all? 4 + 4 + 4 = 12

3.  
How many groups? 2
How many in each group? 4
How many in all? 4 + 4 = 8

4.  
How many groups? 2
How many in each group? 5
How many in all? 5 + 5 = 10

 Use with Grade 3, text pages 176–177.

Extend

Shape Up!

E 5-2 VISUAL THINKING

Look at the rectangle below. It is made up of rectangles.

Can you find 9 rectangles in the picture? Try it.

Hint: Two rectangles can make one larger rectangle. Don't forget to count the largest rectangle.

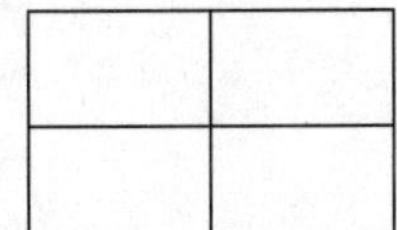

Now look at the next shape. Count all the rectangles. Remember to use the hint above.

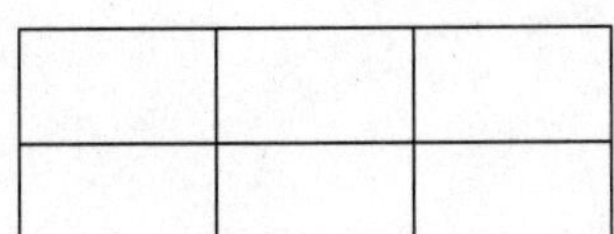

How many rectangles do you see in all? Write the number 18

WRECKEDTANGLE

 Use with Grade 3, text pages 176–177.

Daily Review

Name ______________________ Daily Review 5-2

Relating Multiplication and Addition

Write a multiplication sentence for each addition sentence.

1. 4 + 4 + 4 + 4 = 16
4 × 4 = 16

2. 6 + 6 = 12
6 × 2 = 12

3. 3 + 3 + 3 = 9
3 × 3 = 9

4. 7 + 7 = 14
7 × 2 = 14

5. 9 + 9 + 9 = 27
9 × 3 = 27

6. 8 + 8 + 8 + 8 + 8 = 40
8 × 5 = 40

Write an addition sentence and a multiplication sentence for each set of pictures.

7. 3 + 3 + 3 = 9
3 × 3 = 9

8. 8 + 8 = 16
8 × 2 = 16

Problem Solving

9. How much do three Pony rides cost? $15

10. Which costs less, 3 rides on the Ferris Wheel or 4 rides on the Spinner?
4 rides on the Spinner

Carnival Rides	
Pony	$5
Spinner	$1
Ferris Wheel	$2

Review and Remember

Add or subtract.

11. 114 + 222 = 336

12. 26 − 19 = 7

13. 636 + 118 = 754

14. 2,365 − 639 = 1,726

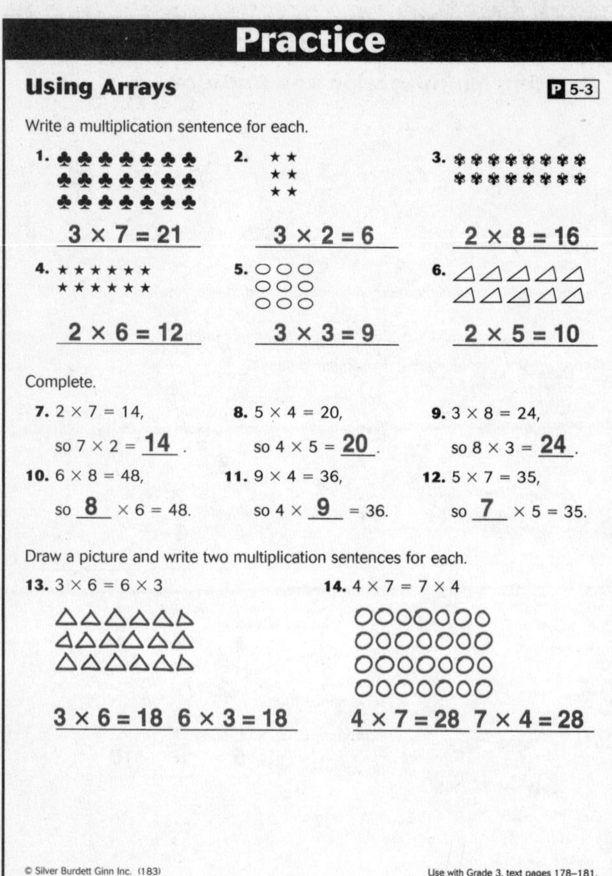

Practice

Using Arrays

P 5-3

Write a multiplication sentence for each.

1. ♣♣♣♣♣♣♣ / ♣♣♣♣♣♣♣ / ♣♣♣♣♣♣♣ **3 × 7 = 21**
2. ★★ / ★★ / ★★ **3 × 2 = 6**
3. ✽✽✽✽✽✽✽✽ / ✽✽✽✽✽✽✽✽ **2 × 8 = 16**
4. ★★★★★★ / ★★★★★★ **2 × 6 = 12**
5. ○○○ / ○○○ / ○○○ **3 × 3 = 9**
6. △△△△△ / △△△△△ **2 × 5 = 10**

Complete.

7. 2 × 7 = 14, so 7 × 2 = **14**.
8. 5 × 4 = 20, so 4 × 5 = **20**.
9. 3 × 8 = 24, so 8 × 3 = **24**.
10. 6 × 8 = 48, so **8** × 6 = 48.
11. 9 × 4 = 36, so 4 × **9** = 36.
12. 5 × 7 = 35, so **7** × 5 = 35.

Draw a picture and write two multiplication sentences for each.

13. 3 × 6 = 6 × 3 — **3 × 6 = 18** **6 × 3 = 18**
14. 4 × 7 = 7 × 4 — **4 × 7 = 28** **7 × 4 = 28**

© Silver Burdett Ginn Inc. (183) Use with Grade 3, text pages 178–181.

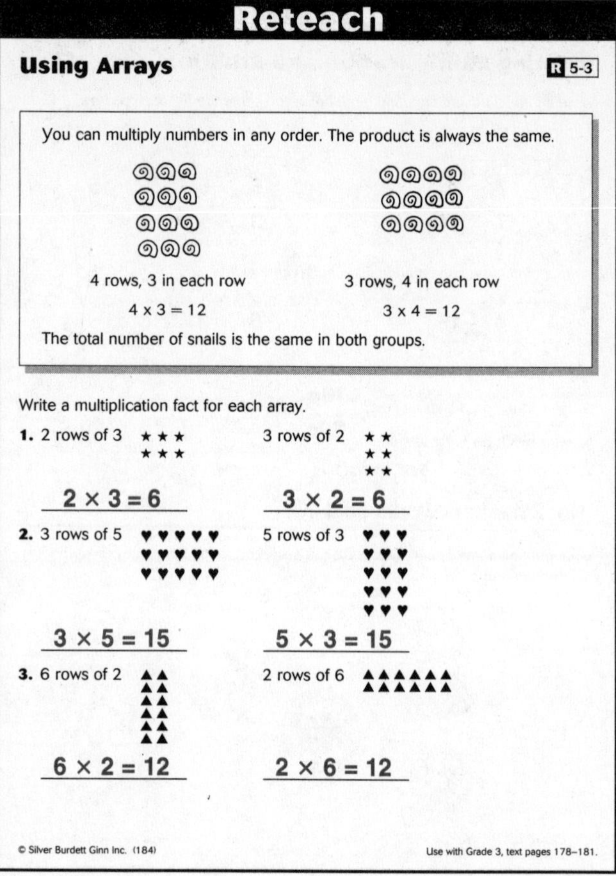

Reteach

Using Arrays

R 5-3

You can multiply numbers in any order. The product is always the same.

4 rows, 3 in each row
4 x 3 = 12

3 rows, 4 in each row
3 x 4 = 12

The total number of snails is the same in both groups.

Write a multiplication fact for each array.

1. 2 rows of 3 ★★★ / ★★★ **2 × 3 = 6** 3 rows of 2 ★★ / ★★ / ★★ **3 × 2 = 6**
2. 3 rows of 5 ♥♥♥♥♥ **3 × 5 = 15** 5 rows of 3 ♥♥♥ **5 × 3 = 15**
3. 6 rows of 2 ▲▲ **6 × 2 = 12** 2 rows of 6 ▲▲▲▲▲▲ **2 × 6 = 12**

© Silver Burdett Ginn Inc. (184) Use with Grade 3, text pages 178–181.

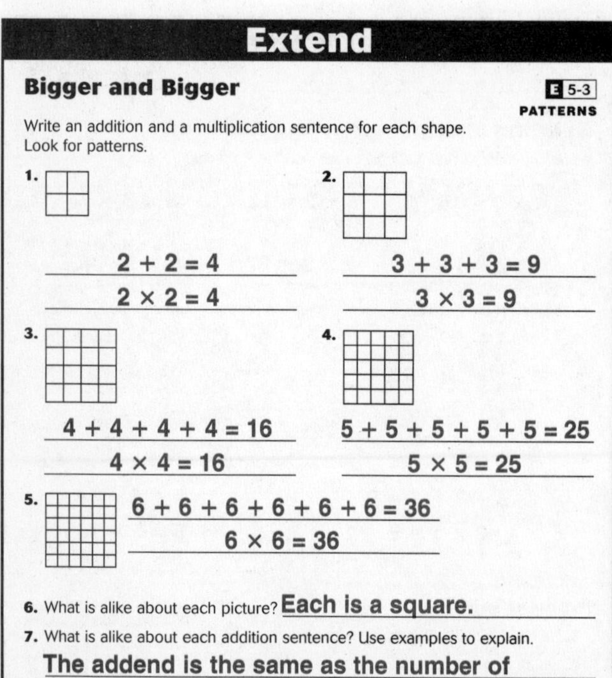

Extend

Bigger and Bigger

E 5-3
PATTERNS

Write an addition and a multiplication sentence for each shape. Look for patterns.

1. **2 + 2 = 4** **2 × 2 = 4**
2. **3 + 3 + 3 = 9** **3 × 3 = 9**
3. **4 + 4 + 4 + 4 = 16** **4 × 4 = 16**
4. **5 + 5 + 5 + 5 + 5 = 25** **5 × 5 = 25**
5. **6 + 6 + 6 + 6 + 6 + 6 = 36** **6 × 6 = 36**
6. What is alike about each picture? **Each is a square.**
7. What is alike about each addition sentence? Use examples to explain. **The addend is the same as the number of addends. There are 4 fours, 5 fives, and so on.**
8. How many tiles would be in a 7-tile square? Tell how you found your answer. **49 tiles; added 7 seven times, or multiplied 7 x 7.**

© Silver Burdett Ginn Inc. (185) Use with Grade 3, text pages 178–181.

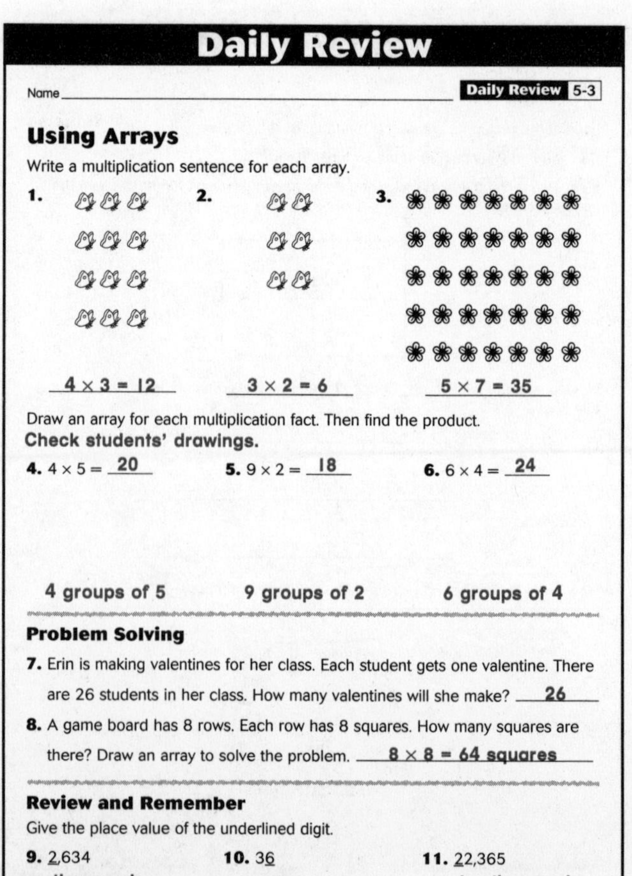

Daily Review

Name ______

Daily Review 5-3

Using Arrays

Write a multiplication sentence for each array.

1. **4 x 3 = 12**
2. **3 x 2 = 6**
3. **5 x 7 = 35**

Draw an array for each multiplication fact. Then find the product.
Check students' drawings.

4. 4 x 5 = **20**
5. 9 x 2 = **18**
6. 6 x 4 = **24**

4 groups of 5 **9 groups of 2** **6 groups of 4**

Problem Solving

7. Erin is making valentines for her class. Each student gets one valentine. There are 26 students in her class. How many valentines will she make? **26**
8. A game board has 8 rows. Each row has 8 squares. How many squares are there? Draw an array to solve the problem. **8 x 8 = 64 squares**

Review and Remember

Give the place value of the underlined digit.

9. 2,634 **thousands**
10. 36 **ones**
11. 22,365 **ten thousands**

Practice

Problem Solving P 5-4

Reasonable Answers

Circle the best choice for each question.

The students of Bayview School want to make their school more beautiful. They plant 6 rows of tulips in a flower bed. Each row has 8 tulips. Five of the tulips in each row are yellow.

1. What could you do to find the number of tulips in a row that are not yellow?
   a. Add 6 to the total number of tulips.
   (b.) Subtract 5 from 8.
   c. Add 6 to 5.

2. If someone wanted to know how many tulips are not yellow, would 25 be a reasonable answer?
   a. Yes; 25 is a reasonable answer.
   (b.) No; 25 is too high.
   c. No; 25 is too low.

There are now 4 tulip gardens and a daffodil garden at Bayview School. Students offer public tours through the garden. Tours through each tulip garden last 5 minutes and the daffodil garden tour takes 12 minutes. Is it reasonable to think that it would take 21 minutes to tour all of the gardens?

3. What could you do to find the total number of minutes it would take to go on all of the tours?
   a. Find 5 + 12. Then multiply by 4.
   (b.) Find 4 x 5. Then add 12.
   c. Find 5 x 12. Then add 4.

4. Explain. Do you need to find the total number of minutes it takes to go on all the tours to decide if 21 minutes is reasonable? Explain.
   No; 4 tours at 5 minutes each is 20 minutes, and daffodil tour takes longer than 1 minute.

 Use with Grade 3, text pages 182–183.

Reteach

Problem Solving R 5-4

Reasonable Answers

It is important to decide if the answer to a question is reasonable. Read the question again. Think, *Is my answer possible? Does it make sense? Does it use all the information given?*

Greg keeps his video tapes on shelves. There are 7 tapes on each of 3 shelves and 2 tapes on the fourth shelf. How many video tapes does Greg have?

- An answer of 7 would not be reasonable because Greg has 7 video tapes on each of 3 different shelves. So, 7 is too low.
- An answer of *more than 20 tapes* would be reasonable because Greg has 3 shelves, each with 7 tapes.

1. Is it reasonable to say that Greg has about 100 video tapes? Explain.
   No; there are only 3 shelves of 7 plus 2 more tapes.
2. How many tapes does Greg have? Is 21 a reasonable answer?
   No; Greg has 23 tapes.
3. How can you tell if your answer is reasonable?
   Reread the problem. Ask if the answer makes sense and uses all the information.
4. Greg's friend offers to build him a bookcase that holds 22 video tapes. Will there be enough room to hold all of Greg's video tapes?
   No; he needs room for 1 more tape.
5. Greg's friend builds the bookcase. A shelf will hold 28 video tapes. There are 3 shelves. About how many tapes does the bookcase hold? How do you know your answer is reasonable?
   About 90 tapes; 28 is about 30, and 30 × 3 = 90.

 Use with Grade 3, text pages 182–183.

Extend

Butler's Orchard

E 5-4 NUMBER SENSE

Butler's Orchard sells packages of apples containing 3, 6, or 8 apples. Monday, Butler's sells 50 packages of 3 apples, 40 packages of 6 apples, and 40 packages of 8 apples.

1. Make a table to show how many apples were sold of each kind of package.

Kind of Package	Number of Apples Sold
3 to a package	150
6 to a package	240
8 to a package	320
Total Apples Sold	710

2. Would it be reasonable to say that Butler's sold about twice as many apples 8 to a package as they sold 3 to a package? Explain.
   Yes; 150 + 150 = 300, about the same as 320.
3. Would it be reasonable to say that Butler's will sell about 2,000 apples Monday through Friday? Explain.
   No; if they continue at the same rate they will sell that amount by the end of Wednesday.
4. If Butler's sells apples Monday through Friday, is it reasonable to say that they will sell about 14,000 apples in a month? Explain.
   Yes; 700 apples a day = 3,500 apples a week = 14,000 apples for 4 weeks.

 Use with Grade 3, text pages 182–183.

Daily Review

Name________________ Daily Review 5-4

Problem Solving

Reasonable Answers

Read each story. Then answer each question.

Marty had a party for his 29 classmates. He needed to buy paper plates and cups. The plates he wanted came in packages of 10. The cups came in stacks of 6.

1. Would it be reasonable for Marty to buy 3 packages of plates and 3 packages of cups? Why or why not?
   No, there would not be enough cups.
2. Explain how you could decide how many cups Marty needs for his party.
   Find the total number of people at the party: Marty + 29 = 30.

Holly has a cake recipe that calls for 3 cups of flour, 5 sticks of butter, and 2 cups of sugar. She plans to make 3 cakes for the bake sale. Each cake must bake for 2 hours. Only 1 cake will fit into the oven at a time.

3. Write a number sentence that tells the number of sticks of butter that Holly needs.
   3 × 5 = 15 sticks
4. Holly needs time to mix and bake the cakes. Is it reasonable for her to plan for 6 hours to do the cakes? Why or why not?
   No, it would not allow time for preparing and mixing.
5. Find the total number of cups of flour and sugar that Holly needs.
   9 cups flour, 6 cups sugar

Review and Remember

Add.

6. 23 + 17 = **40** 7. 51 + 18 = **69** 8. 27 + 34 = **61** 9. 24 + 62 = **86**

Practice

Multiplying by 2

P 5-5

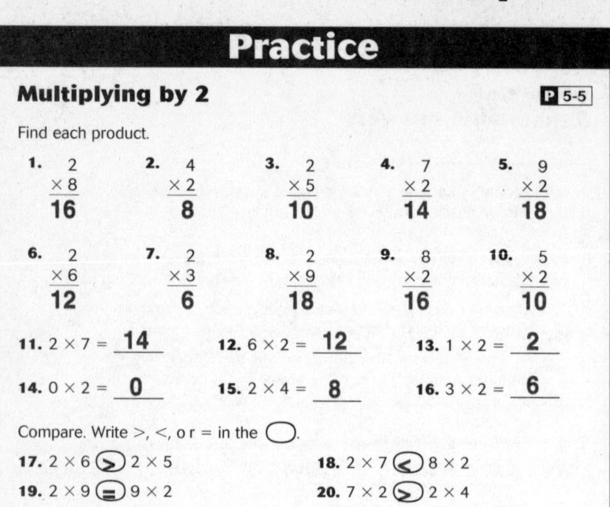

Find each product.

1. $2 \times 8 = 16$
2. $4 \times 2 = 8$
3. $2 \times 5 = 10$
4. $7 \times 2 = 14$
5. $9 \times 2 = 18$
6. $2 \times 6 = 12$
7. $2 \times 3 = 6$
8. $2 \times 9 = 18$
9. $8 \times 2 = 16$
10. $5 \times 2 = 10$

11. $2 \times 7 =$ **14**
12. $6 \times 2 =$ **12**
13. $1 \times 2 =$ **2**
14. $0 \times 2 =$ **0**
15. $2 \times 4 =$ **8**
16. $3 \times 2 =$ **6**

Compare. Write >, <, or = in the ◯.

17. 2×6 (>) 2×5
18. 2×7 (<) 8×2
19. 2×9 (=) 9×2
20. 7×2 (>) 2×4

Solve.

21. At a basketball game, the girls' team scored 7 two-point baskets. How many points did they score?

14 points

22. Ms. Young's class made team banners. They sold 9 banners for $2 each. How much did the class earn?

$18

 Use with Grade 3, text pages 184–185.

Reteach

Multiplying by 2

R 5-5

Here are 4 pairs of running shoes. How many shoes are there in all?

You can skip count by 2s. If it helps, say the other numbers mentally.

$2 + 2 + 2 + 2 = 8$
or
$4 \times 2 = 8$

Write an addition fact and a multiplication fact for each picture.

1. **2 + 2 + 2 + 2 + 2** = **10**
5 × **2** = **10**

2. **2 + 2 + 2 + 2 + 2 + 2 + 2 + 2** = **16**
8 × **2** = **16**

3. **2 + 2 + 2** = **6**
3 × **2** = **6**

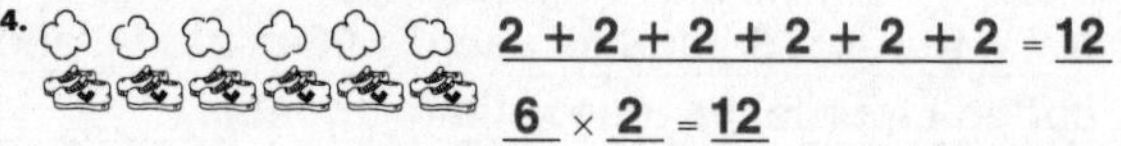

4. **2 + 2 + 2 + 2 + 2 + 2** = **12**
6 × **2** = **12**

 Use with Grade 3, text pages 184–185.

Extend

A Picture Tells....Three Facts

E 5-5 VISUAL THINKING

Write three facts for each picture. The first one is done for you.

1. $4 \times 2 = 8$ (white circles) $2 \times 2 = 4$ (shaded circles)
$6 \times 2 = 12$ (all circles)

2. **5 × 2 = 10** (white stars) **3 × 2 = 6** (shaded stars)
8 × 2 = 16 (all stars)

3. **5 × 2 = 10** (white squares) **2 × 2 = 4** (shaded squares)
7 × 2 = 14 (all squares)

4. **4 × 2 = 8** (white triangles) **3 × 2 = 6** (shaded triangles)
7 × 2 = 14 (all triangles)

Shade the same number of shapes in each row.
Write multiplication sentences to describe what you did.

5. **Answers will vary.** (white squares) (shaded squares)
9 × 2 = 18 (all squares)

6. **Answers will vary.** (white squares) (shaded circles)
10 × 2 = 20 (all circles)

Write three multiplication sentences for the pictures.

7. **5 × 2 = 10** (white balloons) **2 × 2 = 4** (shaded balloons)
7 × 2 = 14 (all balloons)

 Use with Grade 3, text pages 184–185.

Daily Review

Name ______________________ Daily Review 5-5

Multiplying by 2

Complete each multiplication sentence.

1. $2 \times 4 =$ **8**
2. $2 \times 6 =$ **12**
3. $3 \times 6 =$ **18**

Multiply.

4. $2 \times 6 = 12$
5. $2 \times 3 = 6$
6. $2 \times 1 = 2$
7. $2 \times 2 = 4$
8. $4 \times 2 = 8$
9. $2 \times 4 = 8$
10. $2 \times 5 = 10$
11. $2 \times 8 = 16$
12. $2 \times 9 = 18$
13. $8 \times 2 = 16$

14. $2 \times 6 =$ **12**
15. $2 \times 7 =$ **14**
16. $2 \times 2 =$ **4**
17. $6 \times 2 =$ **12**

Problem Solving

18. Seats on the band's minibus are arranged in rows. There are 5 rows with 2 seats in each row. How many seats are there altogether?

10

19. Used music books cost $2. Is $20 enough to buy 9 books?

Yes ($2 × 9 = $18)

Review and Remember

Estimate. Then use a calculator to find each sum or difference.

20. $184 + 296 =$ **480**
21. $604 - 325 =$ **279**
22. $821 - 105 =$ **716**

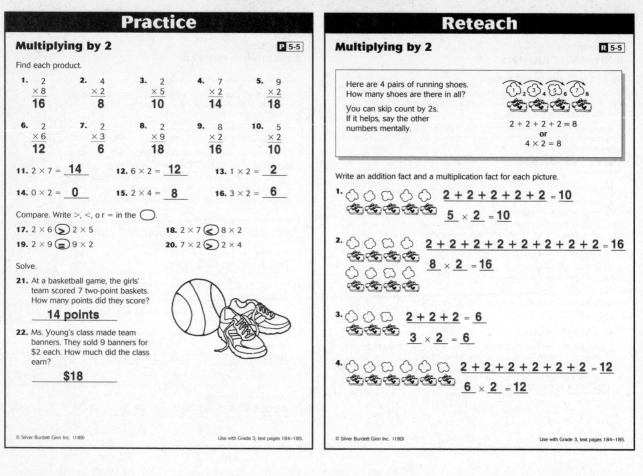

Practice

Multiplying by 5

P 5-6

Find each product.

1. $\begin{array}{r}5\\ \times 4\\ \hline 20\end{array}$ 2. $\begin{array}{r}5\\ \times 6\\ \hline 30\end{array}$ 3. $\begin{array}{r}5\\ \times 7\\ \hline 35\end{array}$ 4. $\begin{array}{r}2\\ \times 5\\ \hline 10\end{array}$ 5. $\begin{array}{r}1\\ \times 5\\ \hline 5\end{array}$

6. $\begin{array}{r}5\\ \times 5\\ \hline 25\end{array}$ 7. $\begin{array}{r}3\\ \times 5\\ \hline 15\end{array}$ 8. $\begin{array}{r}9\\ \times 5\\ \hline 45\end{array}$ 9. $\begin{array}{r}0\\ \times 5\\ \hline 0\end{array}$ 10. $\begin{array}{r}8\\ \times 5\\ \hline 40\end{array}$

11. $4 \times 5 =$ 20 12. $5 \times 2 =$ 10 13. $5 \times 8 =$ 40

14. $0 \times 5 =$ 0 15. $5 \times 9 =$ 45 16. $7 \times 5 =$ 35

Complete the table.

17.

Number of hands	0	1	2	3	4	5	6	7	8	9
Number of fingers	0	5	10	15	20	25	30	35	40	45

Solve.

18. If you skip count by 5 six times, you will get me. What is my number?
30

19. If you subtract 5 from the product of 3 x 5, you will get me. What is my number?
10

20. Hannah makes a bead pattern with 5 beads. If she repeats the pattern 9 times, how many beads will she need?
45 beads

21. Ginger bought 5 boxes of crayons. There are 8 crayons in each pack. How many crayons did Ginger buy?
40 crayons

 Use with Grade 3, text pages 186–187.

Reteach

Multiplying by 5

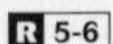

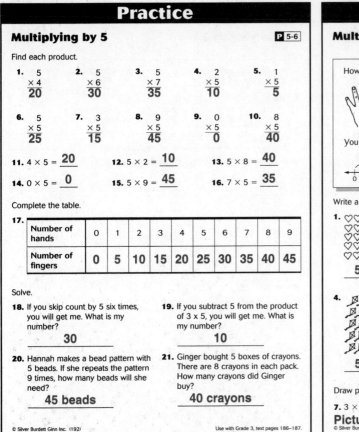

How many fingers?

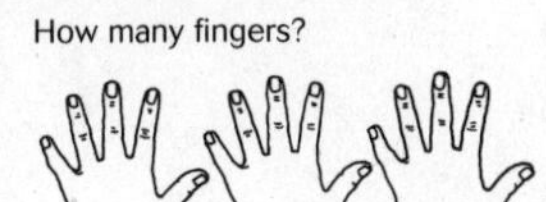

5 fingers on each hand 5
3 hands × 3
15 fingers in all 3

$3 \times 5 = 15$

You can also skip-count to find the product.

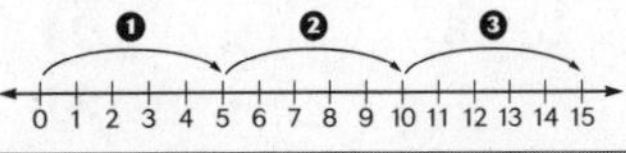

3 jumps of 5 = 15

Write a multiplication fact for each array.

1. $5 \times 5 = 25$

2. 
$4 \times 5 = 20$

3. 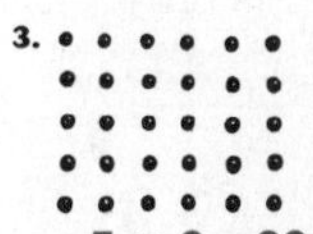
$5 \times 6 = 30$

4. $5 \times 2 = 10$

5. $5 \times 7 = 35$

6. 
$5 \times 1 = 5$

Draw pictures to help you find the products. Then write the product.

7. $3 \times 5 =$ 15 8. $5 \times 9 =$ 45

Pictures will vary. Check students' work.

 Use with Grade 3, text pages 186–187.

Extend

Mystery Cards

E 5-6
ALGEBRA

Your friend is holding some cards to a game.
Here are the backs of the cards.

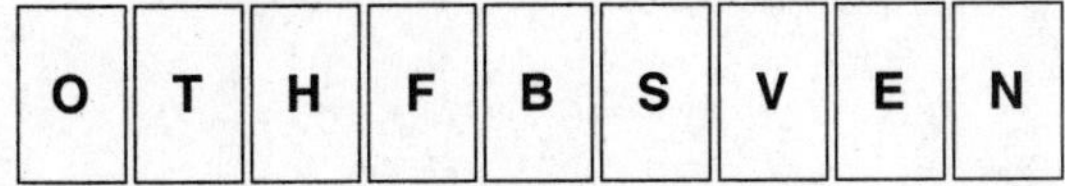

You have to guess what numbers are on the other side.
Here are some clues to help you:

1. B × B = 25
B + B = 10
B = 5

2. O × B = 5
O + B = 6
O = 1

3. B × T = 10
B + T = 7
T = 2

4. B × F = 20
B − F = 1
F = 4

5. B × E = 40
E − B = 3
E = 8

6. B × S = 30
S − B = 1
S = 6

7. H × B = OB
H + B = E
H = 3

8. B × V = HB
V − B = T
V = 7

9. N × B = FB
N − B = F
N = 9

Write the numbers beneath the letters.

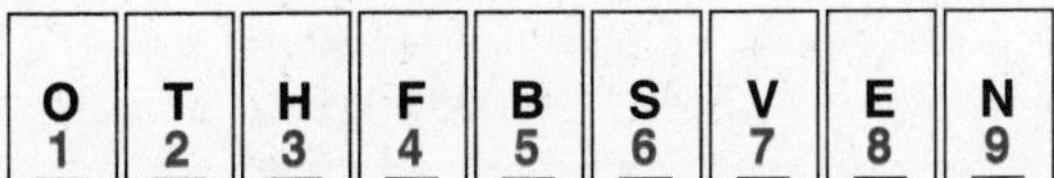

 Use with Grade 3, text pages 186–187.

Daily Review

Name__________ Daily Review 5-6

Multiplying by 5

Draw a picture for each multiplication fact. Check students' drawings.

1. 5×6 2. 4×5 3. 5×2 4. 3×5

5 groups of 6 4 groups of 5 5 groups of 2 3 groups of 5

Multiply.

5. $\begin{array}{r}5\\ \times 6\\ \hline 30\end{array}$ 6. $\begin{array}{r}5\\ \times 3\\ \hline 15\end{array}$ 7. $\begin{array}{r}5\\ \times 1\\ \hline 5\end{array}$ 8. $\begin{array}{r}5\\ \times 4\\ \hline 20\end{array}$ 9. $\begin{array}{r}5\\ \times 2\\ \hline 10\end{array}$

10. $\begin{array}{r}5\\ \times 4\\ \hline 20\end{array}$ 11. $\begin{array}{r}5\\ \times 5\\ \hline 25\end{array}$ 12. $\begin{array}{r}5\\ \times 8\\ \hline 40\end{array}$ 13. $\begin{array}{r}5\\ \times 9\\ \hline 45\end{array}$ 14. $\begin{array}{r}5\\ \times 7\\ \hline 35\end{array}$

15. $5 \times 6 =$ 30 16. $5 \times 7 =$ 35 17. $5 \times 1 =$ 5

Problem Solving

18. Jeremy has 5 nickels. Does he have enough money to buy a granola bar that costs 45¢?
No ($0.05 × 5 = $0.25)

19. Posterboard is sold in packages of 5 sheets. If Suki buys 6 packages, will she have more than or less than 40 sheets?
Less than 40 sheets (5 × 6 = 30 sheets)

Review and Remember

Estimate each answer by rounding to the nearest hundred.

20. 384 + 496 = 900 21. 514 − 125 = 400 22. 221 + 465 = 700

Chapter 5 • Lesson 7

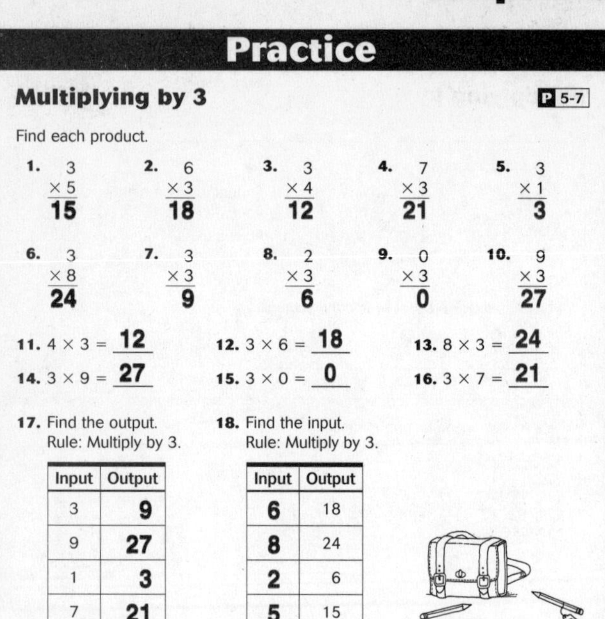

Practice

Multiplying by 3

P 5-7

Find each product.

1. 3 × 5 = **15**
2. 6 × 3 = **18**
3. 3 × 4 = **12**
4. 7 × 3 = **21**
5. 3 × 1 = **3**
6. 3 × 8 = **24**
7. 3 × 3 = **9**
8. 2 × 3 = **6**
9. 0 × 3 = **0**
10. 9 × 3 = **27**

11. 4 × 3 = **12**
12. 3 × 6 = **18**
13. 8 × 3 = **24**
14. 3 × 9 = **27**
15. 3 × 0 = **0**
16. 3 × 7 = **21**

17. Find the output. Rule: Multiply by 3.

Input	Output
3	**9**
9	**27**
1	**3**
7	**21**

18. Find the input. Rule: Multiply by 3.

Input	Output
6	18
8	24
2	6
5	15

Solve.

19. There are 8 rows of bookbags for sale, 3 bookbags in each row. How many bookbags are for sale? **24 bookbags**

20. How much would 3 pencils cost? **15¢**

 Use with Grade 3, text pages 190–191.

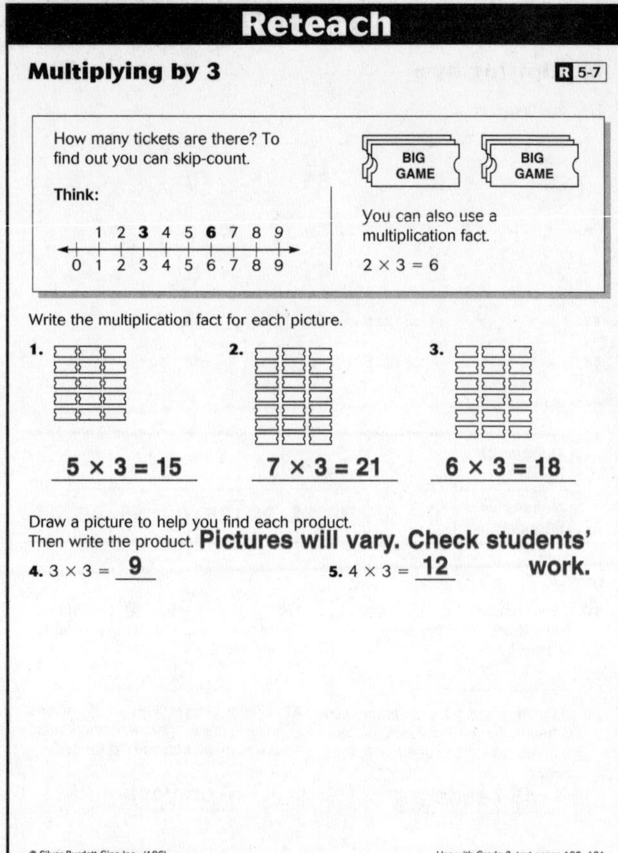

Reteach

Multiplying by 3

R 5-7

How many tickets are there? To find out you can skip-count.

Think:

1 2 **3** 4 5 **6** 7 8 9

0 1 2 3 4 5 6 7 8 9

BIG GAME BIG GAME

You can also use a multiplication fact.

2 × 3 = 6

Write the multiplication fact for each picture.

1. **5 × 3 = 15**
2. **7 × 3 = 21**
3. **6 × 3 = 18**

Draw a picture to help you find each product.
Then write the product. **Pictures will vary. Check students' work.**

4. 3 × 3 = **9**
5. 4 × 3 = **12**

 Use with Grade 3, text pages 190–191.

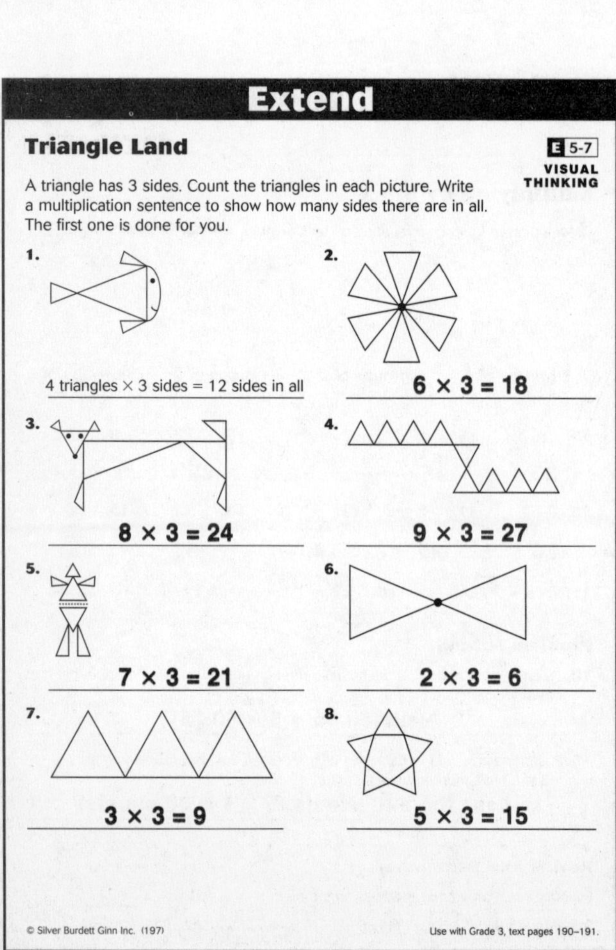

Extend

Triangle Land

E 5-7 VISUAL THINKING

A triangle has 3 sides. Count the triangles in each picture. Write a multiplication sentence to show how many sides there are in all. The first one is done for you.

1. 4 triangles × 3 sides = 12 sides in all
2. **6 × 3 = 18**
3. **8 × 3 = 24**
4. **9 × 3 = 27**
5. **7 × 3 = 21**
6. **2 × 3 = 6**
7. **3 × 3 = 9**
8. **5 × 3 = 15**

 Use with Grade 3, text pages 190–191.

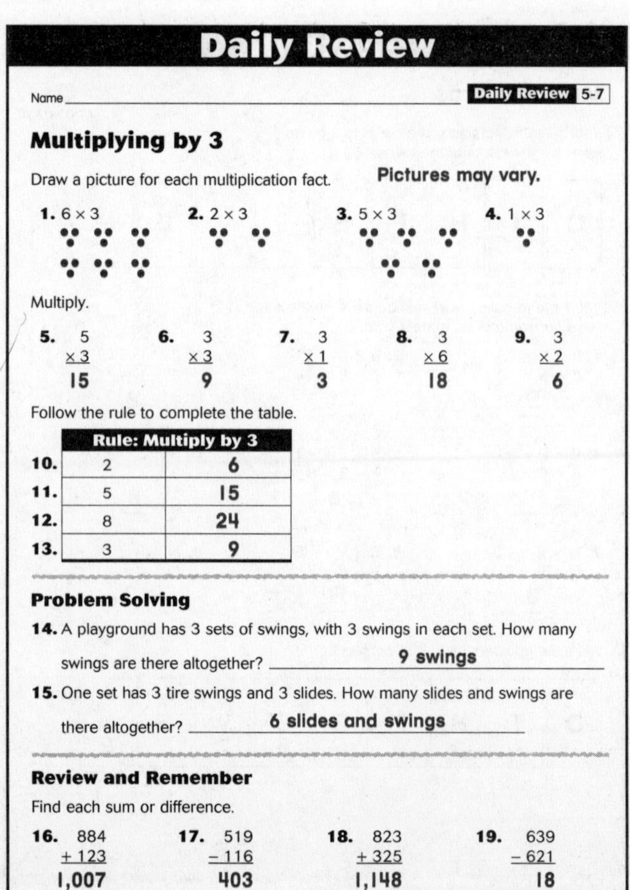

Daily Review

Name ______________________

Daily Review 5-7

Multiplying by 3

Draw a picture for each multiplication fact. **Pictures may vary.**

1. 6 × 3
2. 2 × 3
3. 5 × 3
4. 1 × 3

Multiply.

5. 5 × 3 = **15**
6. 3 × 3 = **9**
7. 3 × 1 = **3**
8. 3 × 6 = **18**
9. 3 × 2 = **6**

Follow the rule to complete the table.

	Rule: Multiply by 3	
10.	2	**6**
11.	5	**15**
12.	8	**24**
13.	3	**9**

Problem Solving

14. A playground has 3 sets of swings, with 3 swings in each set. How many swings are there altogether? **9 swings**

15. One set has 3 tire swings and 3 slides. How many slides and swings are there altogether? **6 slides and swings**

Review and Remember

Find each sum or difference.

16. 884 + 123 = **1,007**
17. 519 − 116 = **403**
18. 823 + 325 = **1,148**
19. 639 − 621 = **18**

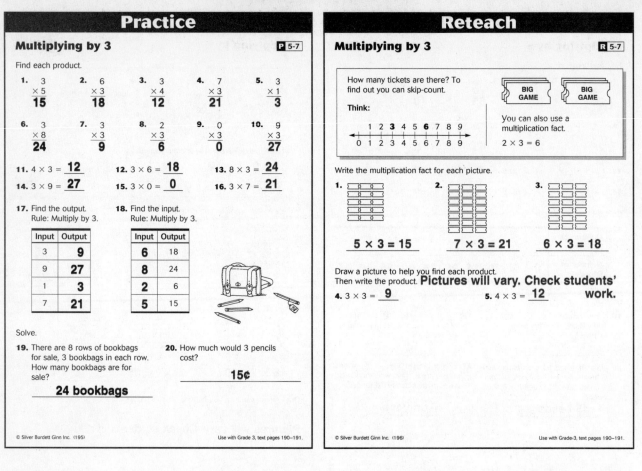

Practice

Multiplying by 4

P 5-8

Find each product. Shade a box that matches your answer. You may need to shade a number more than once.

1. 3 × 4 = **12** **2.** 1 × 4 = **4** **3.** 4 × 7 = **28** **4.** 4 × 2 = **8** **5.** 0 × 4 = **0**

6. 4 × 5 = **20** **7.** 6 × 4 = **24** **8.** 4 × 4 = **16** **9.** 9 × 4 = **36** **10.** 8 × 4 = **32**

11. 4 × 3 = **12** **12.** 4 × 7 = **28** **13.** 4 × 6 = **24**

14. 4 × 8 = **32** **15.** 5 × 4 = **20** **16.** 4 × 9 = **36**

36	43	32	3	4
24	15	12	21	28
20	27	9	45	8
32	16	0	13	20
28	36	12	7	24

17. Look at the shape of the squares you did not shade. What number do they form? **the number 4**

Solve.

18. One floppy computer disk can save the work of four students. Ms. Dyer has 7 floppy computer disks. Ms. Dyer can save the work of how many students? **7 × 4 = 28 students**

 Use with Grade 3, text pages 192–193.

Reteach

Multiplying by 4

R 5-8

How many corners in 5 squares?
You can draw a picture to help you multiply.

5 squares.
4 corners in each square.

5 groups of 4 = 20 5 × 4 = 20 So, 5 squares have 20 corners.

Write a multiplication fact for each picture.

1. **3 × 4 = 12**

2. 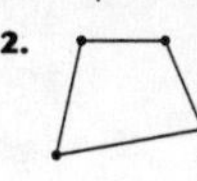 **1 × 4 = 4**

3. 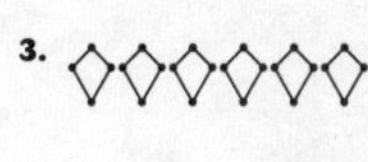 **6 × 4 = 24**

4. **7 × 4 = 28**

5. **8 × 4 = 32**

6. 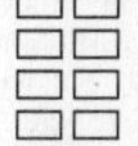 **2 × 4 = 8**

Draw a picture to help you find each product.
Then write the product. **Pictures will vary. Check students' work.**

7. 6 × 4 = **24** **8.** 9 × 4 = **36**

 Use with Grade 3, text pages 192–193.

Extend

Drive-In Multiplication

E 5-8 NUMBER SENSE

Here is an auto mechanic's list of cars scheduled to have their tires changed in one week. Each car needs 4 new tires.

Day	Number of Cars
Monday	2
Tuesday	7
Wednesday	3
Thursday	5
Friday	4
Saturday	6

1. How many tires will the mechanic change on Monday? **2 × 4 = 8 tires**

2. How many tires will he change on Friday? **4 × 4 = 16 tires**

3. How many tires will he change on Saturday? **6 × 4 = 24 tires**

4. How many more tires will the mechanic change on Tuesday than on Monday? **28 − 8 = 20 tires**

5. How many tires will the mechanic change on Wednesday and Thursday? **12 + 20 = 32 tires**

6. How many tires in all will the mechanic change from Monday through Wednesday? **8 + 28 + 12 = 48 tires**

Solve.

7. On Sunday two mechanics changed tires at the county fair racetrack. One changed all the tires on 5 cars. The other changed all the tires on 4 cars. How many tires did they use in all? **20 + 16 = 36 in all**

 Use with Grade 3, text pages 192–193.

Daily Review

Name ____________________ Daily Review 5-8

Multiplying by 4

Multiply. Tell how you found the product. **Methods may vary.**

1. 3 × 4 = **12** **2.** 2 × 4 = **8** **3.** 5 × 4 = **20** **4.** 1 × 4 = **4**

Find each product.

5. 4 × 3 = **12** **6.** 4 × 4 = **16** **7.** 4 × 8 = **32** **8.** 4 × 6 = **24** **9.** 4 × 2 = **8**

10. 5 × 4 = **20** **11.** 4 × 3 = **12** **12.** 4 × 1 = **4** **13.** 4 × 9 = **36** **14.** 4 × 7 = **28**

Problem Solving

15. Groups of 4 students work together in math class. There are 5 groups. How many students are there altogether? **20**

16. There are 3 groups of 4 students in social studies. If one person from each group takes notes, how many students take notes? **3**

Review and Remember

Find each sum or difference.

17. 362 + 615 = **977** **18.** 569 − 429 = **140** **19.** 841 + 326 = **1,167** **20.** 658 − 611 = **47**

21. 407 + 329 = **736** **22.** 716 − 592 = **124** **23.** 297 + 538 = **835** **24.** 890 − 197 = **693**

Practice

Problem Solving P 5-9

Make a List

Make a list to solve.

1. Troy has white bread, rye bread, and a roll. He has roast beef and ham. How many different ways can Troy make a sandwich?

   roast beef, white
   roast beef, rye
   roast beef, roll
   ham, white
   ham, rye
   ham, roll

   6 different sandwiches

2. Gil orders a sandwich. How many different ways can the sandwich-maker arrange turkey, bacon, and cheese on the roll?

   turkey, bacon, cheese
   turkey, cheese, bacon
   bacon, cheese, turkey
   bacon, turkey, cheese
   cheese, turkey, bacon
   cheese, bacon, turkey

   6 different ways

3. Wanda can buy chips, pretzels, or nuts. She can buy juice or milk. How many different ways can Wanda buy a snack and a drink?

   chips, juice
   chips, milk
   pretzels, juice
   pretzels, milk
   nuts, juice
   nuts, milk

   6 different ways

4. Jared plays the piano and the organ. Kacey plays the trombone and the trumpet. In how many different ways can they play their instruments?

   piano, trombone
   piano, trumpet
   organ, trombone
   organ, trumpet

   4 different ways

 Use with Grade 3, text pages 194–195.

Reteach

Problem Solving R 5-9

Make a List

A class banner has wide stripes in red, green, and blue. In how many ways can the stripes be ordered on the banner?

Red	Blue	Green

1. How can you find all the ways the stripes can be ordered?

Understand You need to make a list to show the ways.

Plan There are 3 different color stripes. Each color can be the first stripe.

Solve List all the ways you can make the banner.

• red, blue, green • red, green, blue	• green, red, blue • green, blue, red	• blue, green, red • blue, red, green

3 groups of 2 ways each = 6 ways.

Look Back The list includes all the possible ways, so the answer makes sense.

Make a list to solve.

2. Ricky has a sweatshirt and a T-shirt. He has a pair of black jeans and a pair of blue jeans. How many different outfits can he wear?

   sweatshirt, black jeans
   sweatshirt, blue jeans
   T-shirt, black jeans
   T-shirt, blue jeans

   4 different outfits

3. Martha can see a play on Friday, Saturday, or Sunday. She can go at 5:00 or 8:00. How many choices does she have?

   Friday, 5:00
   Friday, 8:00
   Saturday, 5:00
   Saturday, 8:00
   Sunday, 5:00
   Sunday, 8:00

   6 choices

 Use with Grade 3, text pages 194–195.

Extend

Costume Choices

E 5-9 **PROBABILITY**

Del, Mel, Belle, Nell, and Stella are wearing costumes for the big party. Their choices are shown below.

neckwear	headwear	footwear	outerwear
red bow tie polka dot scarf	cowboy hat wig baseball cap	shoes boots slippers	cape jacket

1. Del wants to wear something on his head and something around his neck. How many combinations can he make? 6 combinations
2. Mel wants to wear a cape and special shoes. How many combinations can he make? 3 combinations
3. Belle wants to wear something special on her head and something special on her feet. How many combinations can she make? 9 combinations
4. Stella thinks that she should wear the red bow tie, a wig, and some special footwear. How many different ways can she do this? 3 different ways
5. Nell wants to wear something on her head, her feet, and her neck. How many different combinations can Nell wear? You can make a table like this one on another piece of paper. 18 combinations

Headwear	Footwear	Neckwear
cowboy hat	boots	bow tie
cowboy hat	boots	scarf

6. Suppose you want to wear a cape, slippers, something around your neck, and something on your head. How many different ways could you do this? 6 different ways

 Use with Grade 3, text pages 194–195.

Daily Review

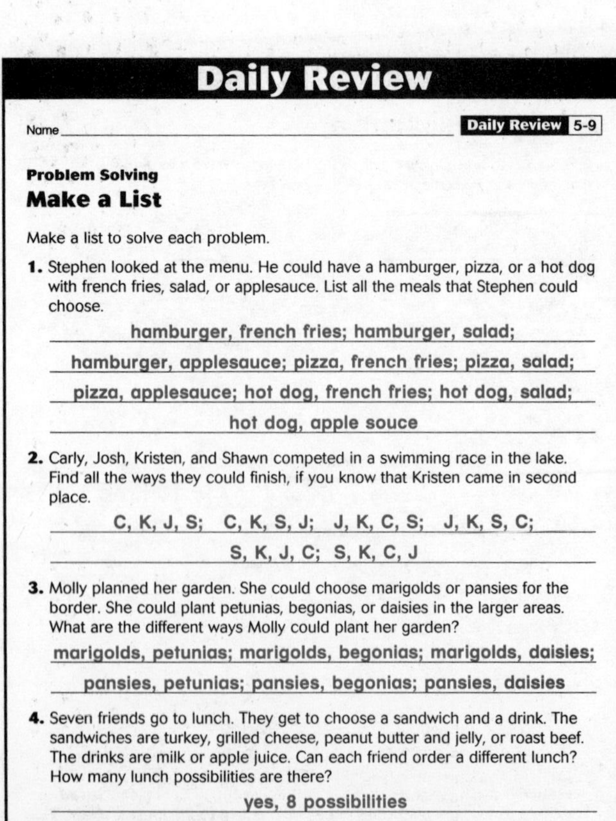

Name ____________________ Daily Review 5-9

Problem Solving

Make a List

Make a list to solve each problem.

1. Stephen looked at the menu. He could have a hamburger, pizza, or a hot dog with french fries, salad, or applesauce. List all the meals that Stephen could choose.

   hamburger, french fries; hamburger, salad; hamburger, applesauce; pizza, french fries; pizza, salad; pizza, applesauce; hot dog, french fries; hot dog, salad; hot dog, apple souce

2. Carly, Josh, Kristen, and Shawn competed in a swimming race in the lake. Find all the ways they could finish, if you know that Kristen came in second place.

   C, K, J, S; C, K, S, J; J, K, C, S; J, K, S, C; S, K, J, C; S, K, C, J

3. Molly planned her garden. She could choose marigolds or pansies for the border. She could plant petunias, begonias, or daisies in the larger areas. What are the different ways Molly could plant her garden?

   marigolds, petunias; marigolds, begonias; marigolds, daisies; pansies, petunias; pansies, begonias; pansies, daisies

4. Seven friends go to lunch. They get to choose a sandwich and a drink. The sandwiches are turkey, grilled cheese, peanut butter and jelly, or roast beef. The drinks are milk or apple juice. Can each friend order a different lunch? How many lunch possibilities are there?

   yes, 8 possibilities

Review and Remember

Round to the nearest hundred.

5. 683 700 **6.** 2,841 2,800 **7.** 1,567 1,600 **8.** 515 500

Practice

Multiplying by 1 or 0

P 5-10

Find the product.

1.	2.	3.	4.	5.
3 × 1 = **3**	1 × 4 = **4**	0 × 7 = **0**	5 × 0 = **0**	1 × 9 = **9**

6.	7.	8.	9.	10.
8 × 0 = **0**	1 × 6 = **6**	7 × 1 = **7**	1 × 8 = **8**	5 × 1 = **5**

11. 4 × 1 = **4** **12.** 1 × 5 = **5** **13.** 0 × 6 = **0**

14. 1 × 0 = **0** **15.** 7 × 0 = **0** **16.** 0 × 9 = **0**

Complete each sentence.

17. When 1 is a factor, the product is always **the same as the other factor.**

18. When 0 is a factor, the product is always **0.**

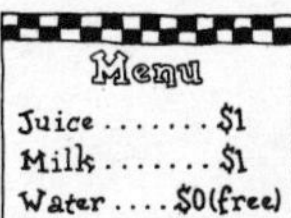

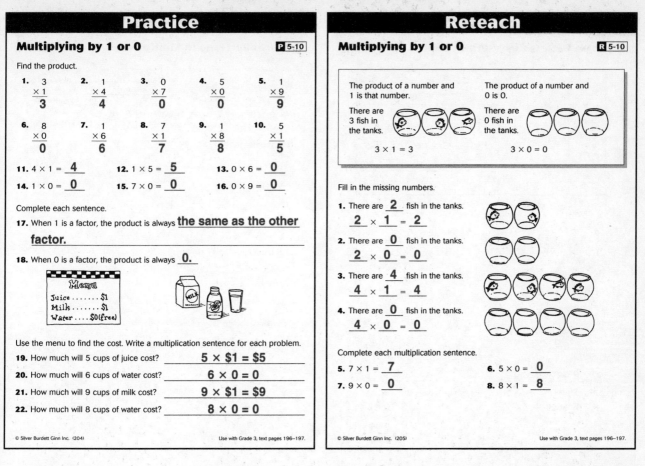

Use the menu to find the cost. Write a multiplication sentence for each problem.

19. How much will 5 cups of juice cost? **5 × $1 = $5**

20. How much will 6 cups of water cost? **6 × 0 = 0**

21. How much will 9 cups of milk cost? **9 × $1 = $9**

22. How much will 8 cups of water cost? **8 × 0 = 0**

 Use with Grade 3, text pages 196–197.

Reteach

Multiplying by 1 or 0

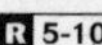
R 5-10

The product of a number and 1 is that number.

There are 3 fish in the tanks.

3 × 1 = 3

The product of a number and 0 is 0.

There are 0 fish in the tanks.

3 × 0 = 0

Fill in the missing numbers.

1. There are **2** fish in the tanks.
2 × **1** = **2**

2. There are **0** fish in the tanks.
2 × **0** = **0**

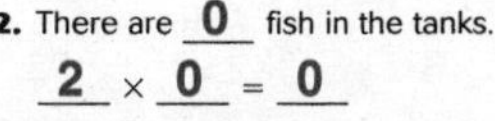

3. There are **4** fish in the tanks.
4 × **1** = **4**

4. There are **0** fish in the tanks.
4 × **0** = **0**

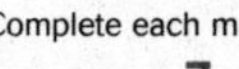

Complete each multiplication sentence.

5. 7 × 1 = **7** **6.** 5 × 0 = **0**

7. 9 × 0 = **0** **8.** 8 × 1 = **8**

 Use with Grade 3, text pages 196–197.

Extend

The Bee and the Flower

E 5-10
MENTAL MATH

Find each product. Then take the bee to the flower. The bee can go across or down, but it can only move to a smaller product.

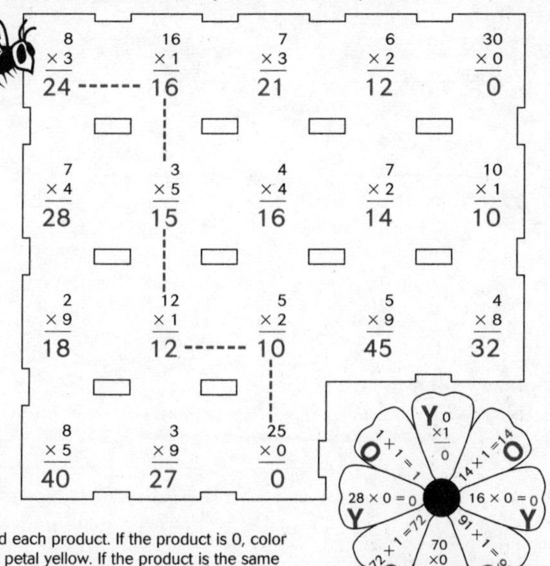

Find each product. If the product is 0, color the petal yellow. If the product is the same as one of the factors, color the petal orange.

 Use with Grade 3, text pages 196–197.

Daily Review

Name ____________________

Daily Review 5-10

Multiplying by 1 and 0

Multiply. Use rules for 1 and 0.

1. 3 × 0 = **0** **2.** 1 × 4 = **4** **3.** 5 × 0 = **0** **4.** 1 × 1 = **1**

5. 0 × 1 = **0** **6.** 0 × 8 = **0** **7.** 0 × 6 = **0** **8.** 1 × 2 = **2**

Find each product.

9.	10.	11.	12.	13.
5 × 1 = **5**	0 × 3 = **0**	4 × 1 = **4**	1 × 9 = **9**	4 × 0 = **0**

14.	15.	16.	17.	18.
6 × 1 = **6**	0 × 6 = **0**	3 × 1 = **3**	1 × 5 = **5**	9 × 0 = **0**

Problem Solving

Snacks	
Popcorn	5 tickets
Fruit Bar	2 tickets
Cookie	3 tickets
Juice	1 ticket

19. How many tickets do you need to buy 6 cups of juice? **6**

20. You don't buy any cookies. How many tickets do you use for cookies? **None**

Review and Remember

Compare. Use >, <, or = for each.

21. 5 + 5 **>** 7 + 2 **22.** 12 − 9 **<** 11 − 2 **23.** 8 + 4 **=** 6 + 6

24. 3 + 4 **=** 9 − 2 **25.** 6 − 0 **<** 5 + 3 **26.** 8 − 2 **>** 9 − 5

27. 4 + 0 **<** 9 − 3 **28.** 8 + 3 **=** 6 + 5 **29.** 14 − 7 **=** 7 + 0

Practice

Explore: Patterns in Multiplication

P 5-11

X	0	1	2	3	4	5
0	0	0	0	0	0	0
1	0	1	2	3	4	5
2	0	2	4	6	8	10
3	0	3	6	9	12	15
4	0	4	8	12	16	20
5	0	5	10	15	20	25
6	0	6	12	18	24	30
7	0	7	14	21	28	35
8	0	8	16	24	32	40
9	0	9	18	27	36	45

Use the patterns in the table to find the products.

1. 4 × 5 = **20**
2. 4 × 6 = **24**
3. 4 × 7 = **28**
4. 6 × 6 = **36**
5. 6 × 7 = **42**
6. 6 × 8 = **48**

Which answers are odd and which are even?

They are all even.

Use the multiplication table. Find all the facts in the table that:

7. have a product of 27. **9 × 3**
8. have a product of 12. **3 × 4; 4 × 3; 6 × 2**
9. have a product of 16. **8 × 2; 4 × 4**
10. have a product of 36. **9 × 4**
11. have a product of 10. **5 × 2; 2 × 5**
12. have a product of 15. **5 × 3; 3 × 5**

 Use with Grade 3, text pages 198–199.

Reteach

Explore: Patterns in Multiplication

R 5-11

The numbers in a multiplication table follow patterns.

Read the numbers in the 2 row. →

Each number is 2 more than the number before it.

Count.
0, 2, 4, 6, 8, 10.

X	0	1	2	3	4	5
0	0	0	0	0	0	0
1	0	1	2	3	4	5
2	0	2	4	6	8	10
3	0	3	6	9	12	15
4	0	4	8	12	16	20
5	0	5	10	15	20	25
6	0	6	12	18	24	30
7	0	7	14	21	28	35
8	0	8	16	24	32	40
9	0	9	18	27	36	45

Use the multiplication table. Look for patterns to help you answer.

1. Study the 3 row on the table.
   Each number is **3** more than the number before it.
2. Study the 5 row on the table.
   Each number is **5** more than the number before it.

Use the patterns in the table to find the products.

3. 3 × 3 = **9**; 3 × 4 = **12**; 3 × 5 = **15**; 3 × 6 = **18**; 3 × 7 = **21**; 3 × 8 = **24**; 3 × 9 = **27**
4. 5 × 3 = **15**; 5 × 4 = **20**; 5 × 5 = **25**; 5 × 6 = **30**; 5 × 7 = **35**; 5 × 8 = **40**; 5 × 9 = **45**

 Use with Grade 3, text pages 198–199.

Extend

Finding a Way

E 5-11 MENTAL MATH

Use mental math to find each missing product, sum, or difference.

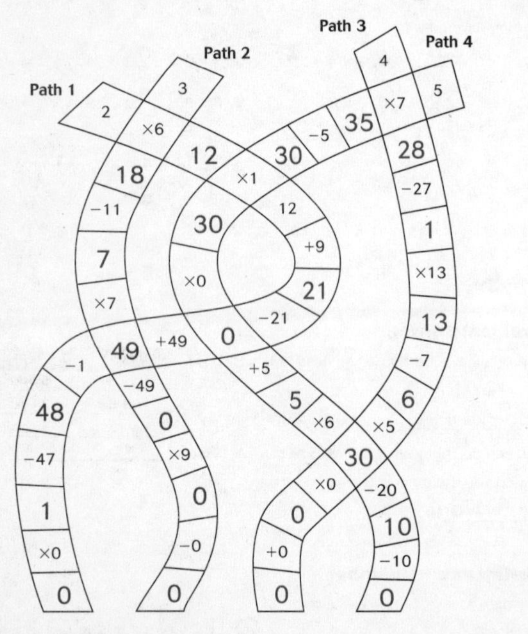

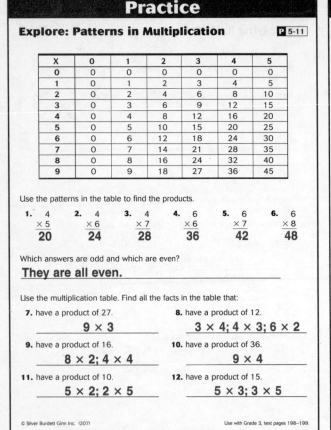

What do you notice about each path?

They all end in zero.

 Use with Grade 3, text pages 198–199.

Daily Review

Name ____________ Daily Review 5-11

EXPLORE: Patterns in Multiplication

Multiply. Follow each rule to complete the tables.

Rule: Multiply by 3

	Input	Output
1.	2	6
2.	4	12
3.	8	24
4.	5	15

Rule: Multiply by 5

	Input	Output
5.	5	25
6.	2	10
7.	4	20
8.	6	30

Continue each pattern.

9. 4, 8, 12, **16**, **20**
10. 6, 9, **12**, **15**
11. 2, 4, **6**, **8**, 10

Multiply.

12. 5 × 2 = **10**
13. 4 × 3 = **12**
14. 3 × 1 = **3**
15. 2 × 5 = **10**
16. 4 × 4 = **16**

Problem Solving

17. A quilt pattern uses 4 green squares, 4 red squares, and 4 blue squares. How many squares are in the pattern?
    12
18. Dog treats cost $1 each. How many can you buy with $9?
    9

Review and Remember

Compare. Use >, <, or = for each.

19. 46 < 54
20. 192 > 97
21. 8,186 = 8,186
22. 97 > 79
23. 187 = 187
24. 9,019 < 9,109

Chapter 5 • Lesson 12

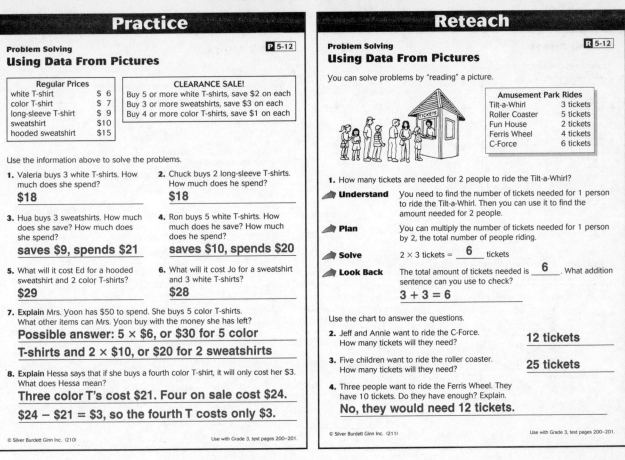

Practice

Problem Solving P 5-12

Using Data From Pictures

Regular Prices	
white T-shirt	$ 6
color T-shirt	$ 7
long-sleeve T-shirt	$ 9
sweatshirt	$10
hooded sweatshirt	$15

CLEARANCE SALE!
Buy 5 or more white T-shirts, save $2 on each
Buy 3 or more sweatshirts, save $3 on each
Buy 4 or more color T-shirts, save $1 on each

Use the information above to solve the problems.

1. Valeria buys 3 white T-shirts. How much does she spend?
$18

2. Chuck buys 2 long-sleeve T-shirts. How much does he spend?
$18

3. Hua buys 3 sweatshirts. How much does she save? How much does she spend?
saves $9, spends $21

4. Ron buys 5 white T-shirts. How much does he save? How much does he spend?
saves $10, spends $20

5. What will it cost Ed for a hooded sweatshirt and 2 color T-shirts?
$29

6. What will it cost Jo for a sweatshirt and 3 white T-shirts?
$28

7. **Explain** Mrs. Yoon has $50 to spend. She buys 5 color T-shirts. What other items can Mrs. Yoon buy with the money she has left?
Possible answer: 5 × $6, or $30 for 5 color T-shirts and 2 × $10, or $20 for 2 sweatshirts

8. **Explain** Hessa says that if she buys a fourth color T-shirt, it will only cost her $3. What does Hessa mean?
Three color T's cost $21. Four on sale cost $24. $24 − $21 = $3, so the fourth T costs only $3.

 Use with Grade 3, text pages 200–201.

Reteach

Problem Solving R 5-12

Using Data From Pictures

You can solve problems by "reading" a picture.

Amusement Park Rides	
Tilt-a-Whirl	3 tickets
Roller Coaster	5 tickets
Fun House	2 tickets
Ferris Wheel	4 tickets
C-Force	6 tickets

1. How many tickets are needed for 2 people to ride the Tilt-a-Whirl?

Understand You need to find the number of tickets needed for 1 person to ride the Tilt-a-Whirl. Then you can use it to find the amount needed for 2 people.

Plan You can multiply the number of tickets needed for 1 person by 2, the total number of people riding.

Solve 2 × 3 tickets = **6** tickets

Look Back The total amount of tickets needed is **6**. What addition sentence can you use to check?
3 + 3 = 6

Use the chart to answer the questions.

2. Jeff and Annie want to ride the C-Force. How many tickets will they need? **12 tickets**

3. Five children want to ride the roller coaster. How many tickets will they need? **25 tickets**

4. Three people want to ride the Ferris Wheel. They have 10 tickets. Do they have enough? Explain.
No, they would need 12 tickets.

 Use with Grade 3, text pages 200–201.

Extend

Shopping Detective

E 5-12 DATA

You are the shopping detective. You know how much money each shopper had and how much each shopper has left. Decide what was on their shopping list.

SPECIAL PURCHASES

1. Mrs. Stanley had $25, got $4 change, and bought 7 of the same thing. What did she buy?
7 loaves of bread

2. Mr. Black had $10, got $2 change, and bought 4 of the same thing. What did he buy?
4 cartons of milk

3. Ms. Winters had $20, got no change, and bought 5 of the same thing. What did she buy?
5 pieces of watermelon

4. Mr. Sampson had $30, got $5 change and bought 5 of the same thing. What did he buy?
5 bags of apples

5. Mr. Waverly had $10 and got $1 change. He bought 2 of one thing and 1 of another. What did he buy?
2 cartons of milk
1 bag of apples

6. Ms. Calloway had $20 and got $2 change. She bought 3 of one thing and 2 of another. What did she buy?
3 pieces of watermelon
2 loaves of bread

7. Suppose you have $30 to spend. Decide what you would like to buy. Buy at least two of each item you choose. Find out how much you spent.
Answers will vary. Check that 2 items of each are purchased. Check totals.

 Use with Grade 3, text pages 200–201.

Daily Review

Name ______________________ Daily Review 5-12

Problem Solving

Using Data From Pictures

Use the information below to answer the questions.

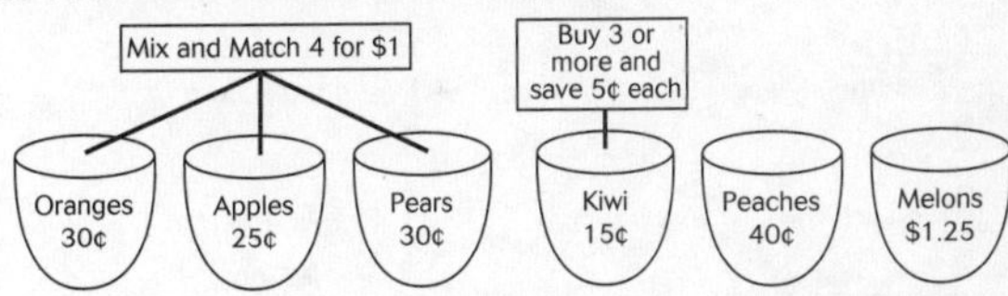

1. Mark buys 3 apples, 1 pear, 2 peaches, and 1 melon. How much money does he spend?
$3.05

2. If Jennifer buys 2 oranges, 2 apples, and 4 kiwi fruit, how much money will she save by using the special prices?
She saves 30¢.

3. Which costs more, 1 melon or 3 oranges and 1 kiwi?
1 melon

4. Jason needed to buy 2 peaches, 2 kiwis, and 2 pears. Which additional piece of fruit could he take home for the same amount of money?
A kiwi; 2 or 3 kiwis cost 30¢.

Review and Remember

Put in order from lowest to highest number.

5. 543 968 230
230 543 968

6. 1,044 3,986 3,865
1,044 3,865 3,986

7. 853 785 382
382 785 853

Chapter 6 • Lesson 1

Practice

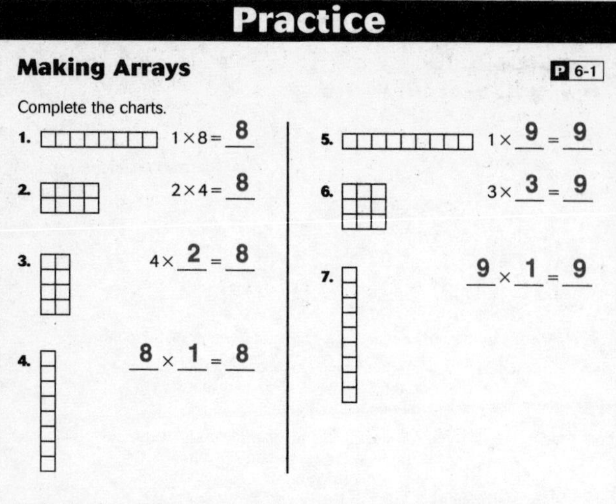

Making Arrays

P 6-1

Complete the charts.

1. 1 × 8 = 8
2. 2 × 4 = 8
3. 4 × 2 = 8
4. 8 × 1 = 8
5. 1 × 9 = 9
6. 3 × 3 = 9
7. 9 × 1 = 9

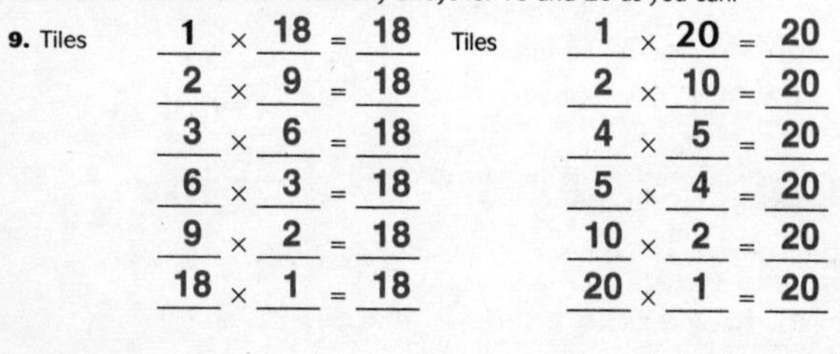

8. Which of the above answers is a square number? Tell how you know.
   9; one array is shaped like a square.

Use tiles or counters. Make as many arrays for 18 and 20 as you can.

9. Tiles

1	×	18	=	18	Tiles 1	× 20	=	20
2	×	9	=	18	2	× 10	=	20
3	×	6	=	18	4	× 5	=	20
6	×	3	=	18	5	× 4	=	20
9	×	2	=	18	10	× 2	=	20
18	×	1	=	18	20	× 1	=	20

Use with Grade 3, text pages 212–215.

Reteach

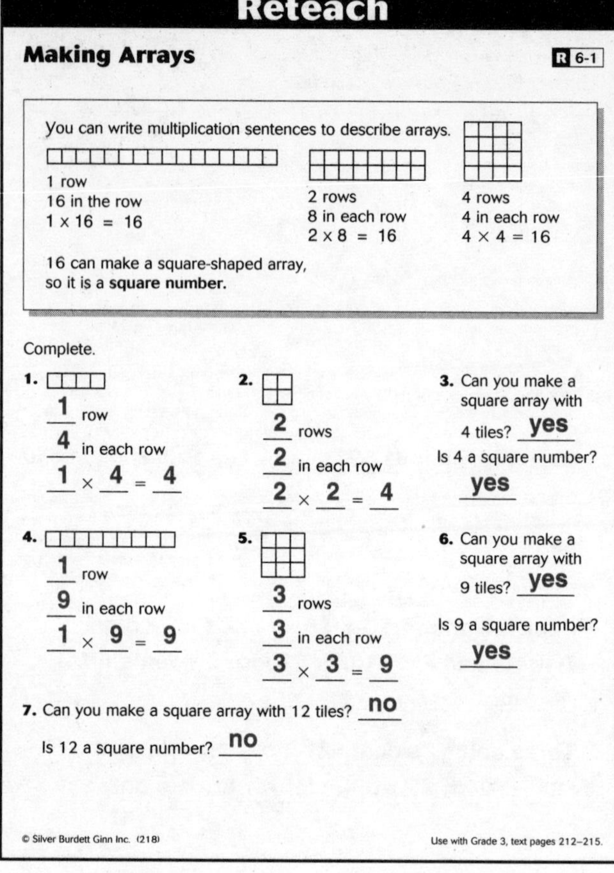

Making Arrays

R 6-1

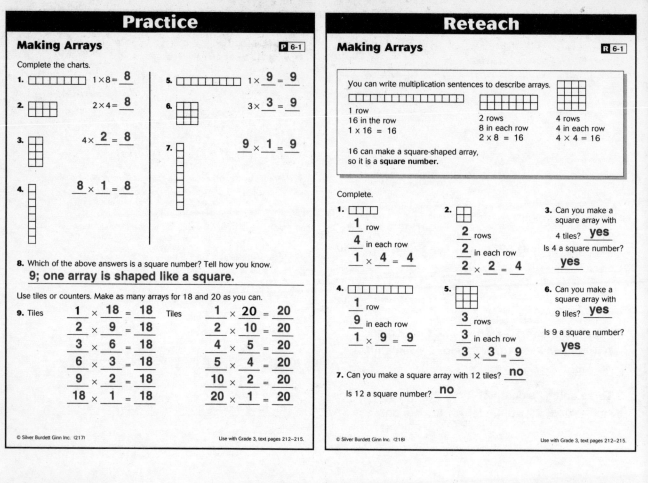

You can write multiplication sentences to describe arrays.

1 row
16 in the row
1 × 16 = 16

2 rows
8 in each row
2 × 8 = 16

4 rows
4 in each row
4 × 4 = 16

16 can make a square-shaped array, so it is a **square number.**

Complete.

1. 1 row, 4 in each row, 1 × 4 = 4
2. 2 rows, 2 in each row, 2 × 2 = 4
3. Can you make a square array with 4 tiles? **yes** Is 4 a square number? **yes**
4. 1 row, 9 in each row, 1 × 9 = 9
5. 3 rows, 3 in each row, 3 × 3 = 9
6. Can you make a square array with 9 tiles? **yes** Is 9 a square number? **yes**
7. Can you make a square array with 12 tiles? **no** Is 12 a square number? **no**

Use with Grade 3, text pages 212–215.

Extend

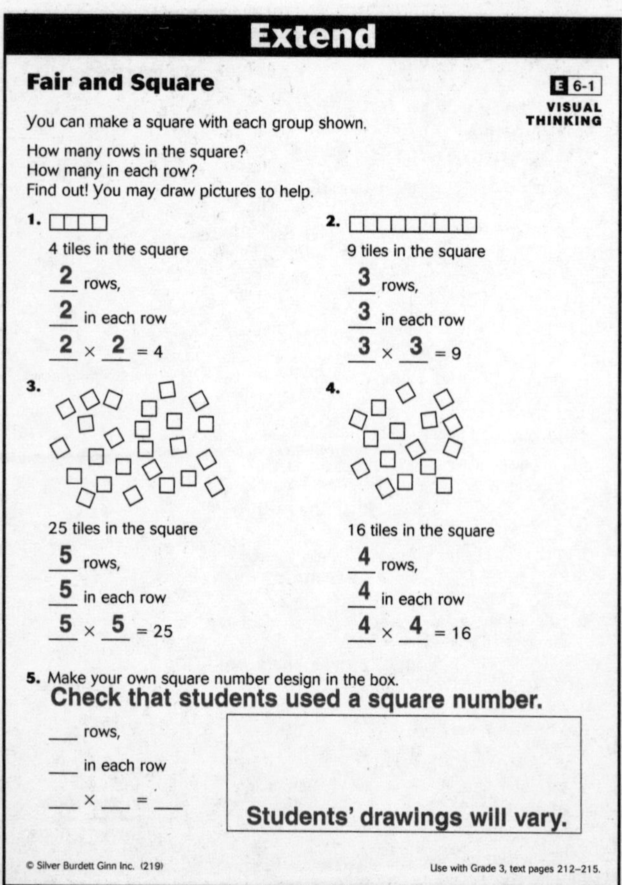

Fair and Square

E 6-1 VISUAL THINKING

You can make a square with each group shown.
How many rows in the square?
How many in each row?
Find out! You may draw pictures to help.

1. 4 tiles in the square: 2 rows, 2 in each row, 2 × 2 = 4
2. 9 tiles in the square: 3 rows, 3 in each row, 3 × 3 = 9
3. 25 tiles in the square: 5 rows, 5 in each row, 5 × 5 = 25
4. 16 tiles in the square: 4 rows, 4 in each row, 4 × 4 = 16
5. Make your own square number design in the box.
   Check that students used a square number.
   ___ rows,
   ___ in each row
   ___ × ___ = ___
   Students' drawings will vary.

Use with Grade 3, text pages 212–215.

Daily Review

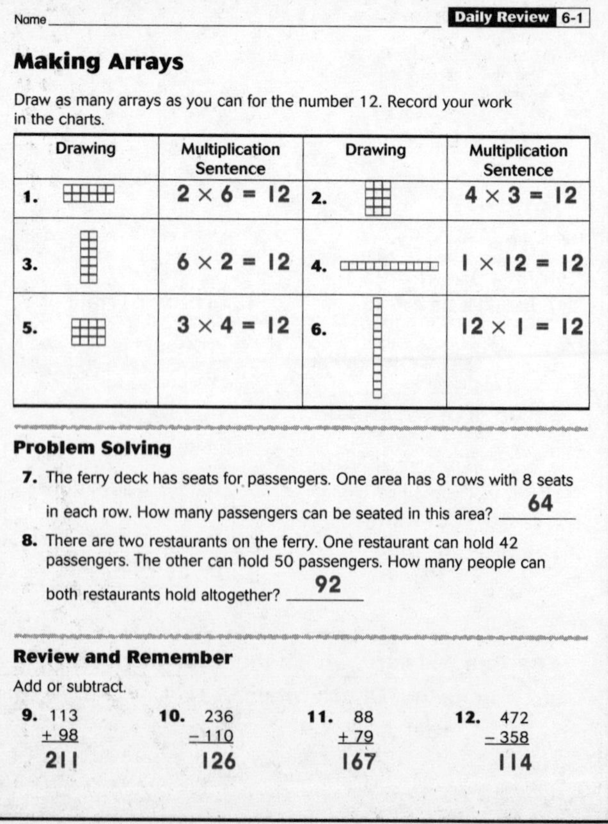

Name ____________

Daily Review 6-1

Making Arrays

Draw as many arrays as you can for the number 12. Record your work in the charts.

	Drawing	Multiplication Sentence		Drawing	Multiplication Sentence
1.		2 × 6 = 12	2.		4 × 3 = 12
3.		6 × 2 = 12	4.		1 × 12 = 12
5.		3 × 4 = 12	6.		12 × 1 = 12

Problem Solving

7. The ferry deck has seats for passengers. One area has 8 rows with 8 seats in each row. How many passengers can be seated in this area? **64**
8. There are two restaurants on the ferry. One restaurant can hold 42 passengers. The other can hold 50 passengers. How many people can both restaurants hold altogether? **92**

Review and Remember

Add or subtract.

9. 113 + 98 = **211**
10. 236 − 110 = **126**
11. 88 + 79 = **167**
12. 472 − 358 = **114**

Practice

Explore: Doubling Patterns

P 6-2

Find each product. Match each fact on the left with its double on the right. Write the letter of the matching double fact. Read the letters from top to bottom to complete the definition for doubles.

1. T	4 × 4 = 16	A	5 × 8 = 40
2. W	3 × 3 = 9	W	3 × 6 = 18
3. I	6 × 3 = 18	T	4 × 8 = 32
4. C	8 × 4 = 32	C	8 × 8 = 64
5. E	3 × 4 = 12	E	3 × 8 = 24
6. A	5 × 4 = 20	I	9 × 6 = 54
7. S	7 × 3 = 21	E	7 × 8 = 56
8. N	6 × 4 = 24	I	6 × 6 = 36
9. I	9 × 3 = 27	C	9 × 8 = 72
10. C	9 × 4 = 36	N	6 × 8 = 48
11. E	7 × 4 = 28	S	7 × 6 = 42

Doubles are T W I C E A S N I C E.

Solve.

12. A toy shop sells glow markers in packs of 4. They sold 3 packs of markers on Friday, and doubled their sales on Saturday. How many markers did they sell each day?

12 Friday,
24 Saturday

13. Train car A has 8 rows of seats with 4 seats in each row. Train car B has twice as many seats in each row as train car A. How many seats in each car?

Train car A: 32 seats
Train car B: 64 seats

 Use with Grade 3, text pages 216–217.

Reteach

Explore: Doubling Patterns

R 6-2

Doubling patterns can help you find products.

You can use: 2 × 4 = 8 to find 2 × 8 = ?

OOOO
OOOO

OOOO OOOO
OOOO OOOO

So, 2 × 8 = 16

Write the first product. Use your answer and doubling patterns to find the second product. Draw pictures to help you.

1. 2 × 2 = 4   2 × 4 = 8
2. 3 × 2 = 6   3 × 4 = 12
3. 3 × 3 = 9   3 × 6 = 18
4. 4 × 2 = 8   4 × 4 = 16
5. 4 × 3 = 12   4 × 6 = 24
6. 5 × 4 = 20   5 × 8 = 40

 Use with Grade 3, text pages 216–217.

Extend

Seeing Double

E 6-2 VISUAL THINKING

Shade the boxes on the grids to show each product.

Take the facts in Exercises 1 through 6 and double them for Exercises 7 through 12.

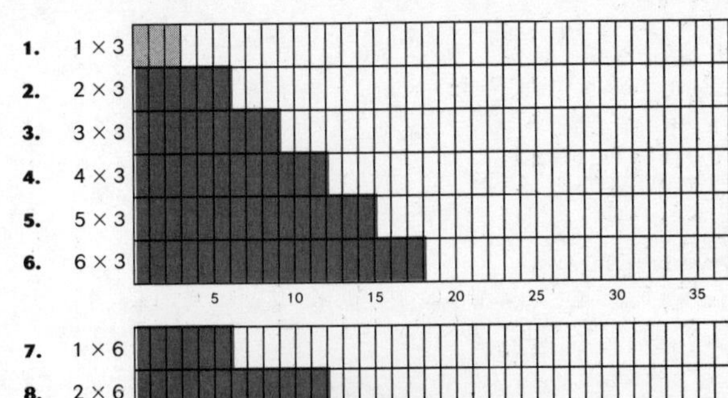

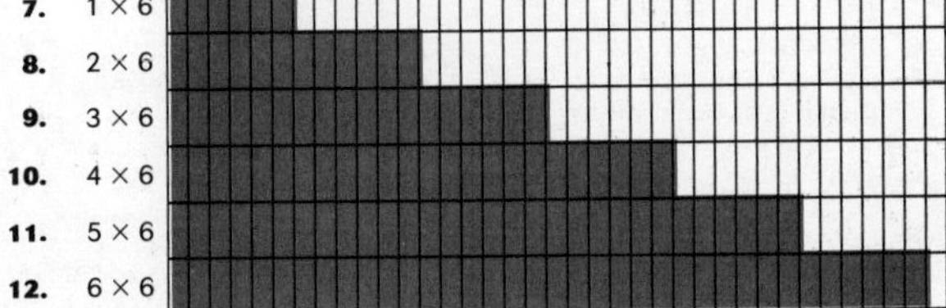

13. How are the grids alike? How are they different?

Both stairstep patterns; rows in second graph increase by 6.

14. Predict the next three lines of the grid for Exercises 7–12. Write the multiplication sentences and products.

7 × 6 = 42; 8 × 6 = 48; 9 × 6 = 54

 Use with Grade 3, text pages 216–217.

Daily Review

Name ______

Daily Review 6-2

EXPLORE: Doubling Patterns

Use the first fact to help you multiply the second fact.

1. 3 × 3 = 9; 3 × 6 = 18
2. 6 × 4 = 24; 6 × 8 = 48
3. 7 × 4 = 28; 7 × 8 = 56
4. 5 × 4 = 20; 5 × 8 = 40
5. 8 × 4 = 32; 8 × 8 = 64
6. 8 × 3 = 24; 8 × 6 = 48
7. 5 × 3 = 15; 5 × 6 = 30
8. 7 × 3 = 21; 7 × 6 = 42
9. 9 × 4 = 36; 9 × 8 = 72

Problem Solving

10. Seats for a baseball game sell for $5 or $10. Troy calculates that the price for 8 of the $5 tickets is $40. How much would 8 of the $10 tickets cost?

$80

11. Baseball caps sell for $8 each. Brenna wants to buy 6 caps, one for each person in her family. What basic fact can she use to find the total cost of the 6 caps?

$8 × 6 = $48

Review and Remember

Add or subtract.

12. $100 + 44 = $144
13. $38 − 12 = $26
14. $56 + 98 = $154
15. $123 − 76 = $47
16. $126 + 27 = $153
17. $48 − 32 = $16

Practice

Multiplying by 3 and 6

P 6-3

Find each product.

1.	2.	3.	4.	5.
3 × 7 = **21**	6 × 7 = **42**	4 × 3 = **12**	8 × 6 = **48**	4 × 6 = **24**

6.	7.	8.	9.	10.
4 × 8 = **32**	0 × 6 = **0**	6 × 9 = **54**	9 × 3 = **27**	5 × 6 = **30**

11. 3 × 6 = **18** 12. 6 × 6 = **36** 13. 7 × 6 = **42**

Complete. Write the rule.

14.

Input	Output
1	3
2	6
3	9
4	**12**
5	**15**
6	**18**

Rule: Multiply by **3**.

15.

Input	Output
1	6
2	12
3	18
4	**24**
5	**30**
6	**36**

Rule: Multiply by **6**.

Solve.

16. Juice boxes can be bought in 3-packs. At a bulk food store, Jen found nine 3-packs of juice packaged in a carton. How many juice boxes were in the carton?

27 juice boxes

17. Amy waits about 6 minutes for each person ahead of her to take a hot-air balloon ride. If there are 8 people ahead of her, about how long will Amy wait for her turn?

about 48 minutes

 Use with Grade 3, text pages 218–219.

Reteach

Multiplying by 3 and 6

R 6-3

6 × 3 = ? Use doubles to help you.

6 groups of 3 = 3 groups of 3 + 3 groups of 3

Use doubles to help you.

Think: 3 × 3 = 9
So: 6 × 3 = 9 + 9
6 × 3 = 18

To find 6 times each number, find 3 times the number. Then double the product.

1. *Think:* 3 × 2 = 6
So: 6 × 2 = **6** + **6**
6 × 2 = **12**

2. *Think:* 3 × 7 = 21
So: 6 × 7 = **21** + **21**
6 × 7 = **42**

3. *Think:* 3 × 6 = 18
So: 6 × 6 = **18** + **18**
6 × 6 = **36**

4. *Think:* 3 × 5 = 15
So: 6 × 5 = **15** + **15**
6 × 5 = **30**

 Use with Grade 3, text pages 218–219.

Extend

Put It Together

E 6-3 VISUAL THINKING

Each of the numbered designs can be made from some of the blocks below. On the blank grids, copy the blocks that make up the design. You can cut out the blocks below to help you.

1.

1	3	1
1	4	1
1	3	1

2.

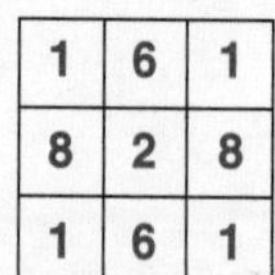

1	6	1
8	2	8
1	6	1

3.

1	6	6	1
6	7	7	6
6	7	7	6
1	6	6	1

HINT: A block can be turned in any direction and used again and again.

 Use with Grade 3, text pages 218–219.

Daily Review

Name ____________________

Daily Review 6-3

Multiplying by 3 and 6

Multiply.

1.	2.	3.	4.	5.
4 × 3 = **12**	5 × 3 = **15**	6 × 7 = **42**	3 × 3 = **9**	3 × 6 = **18**

6.	7.	8.	9.	10.
8 × 3 = **24**	2 × 3 = **6**	3 × 6 = **18**	6 × 5 = **30**	8 × 6 = **48**

Problem Solving

11. A hot-air balloon gives 6 rides each day. On each ride, the balloon takes 8 passengers. How many passengers in all does the balloon take in one day?

48 passengers

12. Last year 8 hot-air balloons took part in a race. There were 3 people in each balloon. This year 9 balloons are in the race, but there are 6 people in each balloon. A race official said that the number of people in the race this year has more than doubled over last year. Is this true? Why or why not?

This year 6 × 9 = 54; this is more than double.

Review and Remember

Estimate to the nearest hundred first. Then use a calculator to solve.

13. 382 + 316 **700; 698**
14. 468 + 421 **900; 889**
15. 892 − 298 **600; 594**
16. 789 − 276 **500; 513**
17. 532 + 225 **700; 757**
18. 629 − 215 **400; 414**

Practice

Multiplying by 4 and 8

P 6-4

Find each product.

1. $3 \times 8 = 24$ 2. $8 \times 1 = 8$ 3. $8 \times 6 = 48$ 4. $4 \times 3 = 12$ 5. $4 \times 6 = 24$

6. $0 \times 8 = 0$ 7. $2 \times 4 = 8$ 8. $4 \times 4 = 16$ 9. $8 \times 8 = 64$ 10. $7 \times 8 = 56$

11. $5 \times 4 =$ **20** 12. $9 \times 8 =$ **72** 13. $5 \times 8 =$ **40**

14. $6 \times 8 =$ **48** 15. $4 \times 9 =$ **36** 16. $8 \times 4 =$ **32**

Compare. Use >, <, or = for ◯.

17. 9×4 (<) 40 18. 8×6 (=) 48

19. 4×4 (>) 12 20. 1×8 (<) 9

Use the pictures to solve the problems.

$8.00 $4.00

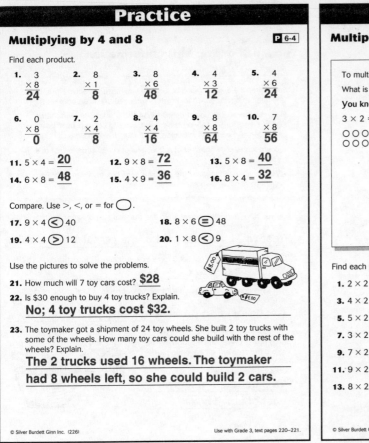

21. How much will 7 toy cars cost? **$28**

22. Is $30 enough to buy 4 toy trucks? Explain. **No; 4 toy trucks cost $32.**

23. The toymaker got a shipment of 24 toy wheels. She built 2 toy trucks with some of the wheels. How many toy cars could she build with the rest of the wheels? Explain. **The 2 trucks used 16 wheels. The toymaker had 8 wheels left, so she could build 2 cars.**

 Use with Grade 3, text pages 220–221.

Reteach

Multiplying by 4 and 8

R 6-4

To multiply by 4 and 8, use facts you already know.

What is 3×4? What is 3×8?

You know:	Double it.	Double again.
$3 \times 2 = 6$?	If 3×2 is	If 3×4 is
○○○ ○○○	○○○ ○○○	○○○ ○○○ ○○○ ○○○
	Then 3×4 is double 3×2	Then 3×8 is double 3×4
	○○○ ○○○ ○○○ ○○○	○○○ ○○○ ○○○ ○○○ ○○○ ○○○ ○○○ ○○○
	So, $3 \times 4 = 12$	So, $3 \times 8 = 24$

Find each product. Use doubling or repeated addition to help you.

1. $2 \times 2 = 4$, so $2 \times 4 =$ **8** 2. $2 \times 4 =$ **8**, so $2 \times 8 =$ **16**

3. $4 \times 2 =$ **8**, so $4 \times 4 =$ **16** 4. $4 \times 4 =$ **16**, so $4 \times 8 =$ **32**

5. $5 \times 2 =$ **10**, so $5 \times 4 =$ **20** 6. $5 \times 4 =$ **20**, so $5 \times 8 =$ **40**

7. $3 \times 2 =$ **6**, so $3 \times 4 =$ **12** 8. $3 \times 4 =$ **12**, so $3 \times 8 =$ **24**

9. $7 \times 2 =$ **14**, so $7 \times 4 =$ **28** 10. $7 \times 4 =$ **28**, so $7 \times 8 =$ **56**

11. $9 \times 2 =$ **18**, so $9 \times 4 =$ **36** 12. $9 \times 4 =$ **36**, so $9 \times 8 =$ **72**

13. $8 \times 2 =$ **16**, so $8 \times 4 =$ **32** 14. $8 \times 4 =$ **32**, so $8 \times 8 =$ **64**

 Use with Grade 3, text pages 220–221.

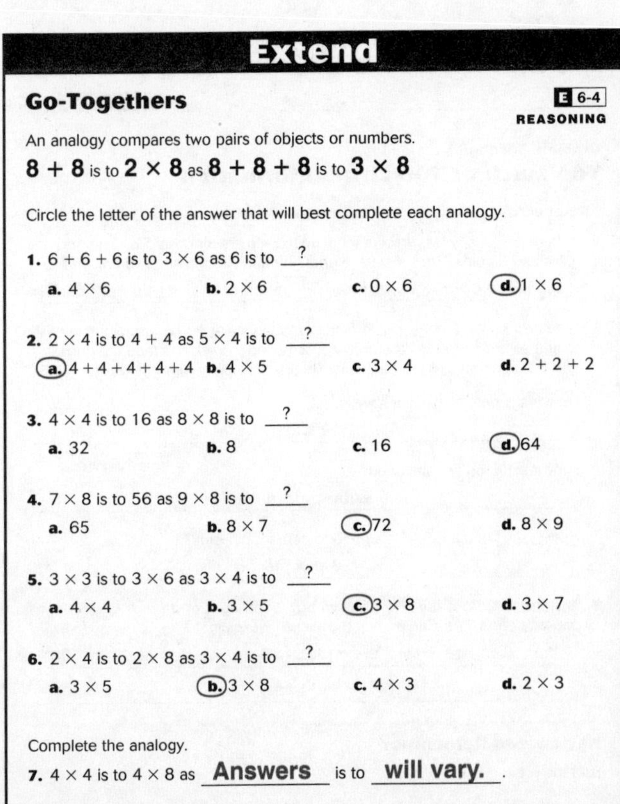

Extend

Go-Togethers

E 6-4 REASONING

An analogy compares two pairs of objects or numbers.

8 + 8 is to **2 × 8** as **8 + 8 + 8** is to **3 × 8**

Circle the letter of the answer that will best complete each analogy.

1. $6 + 6 + 6$ is to 3×6 as 6 is to ___?___
   a. 4×6 b. 2×6 c. 0×6 **(d.)** 1×6

2. 2×4 is to $4 + 4$ as 5×4 is to ___?___
   (a.) $4 + 4 + 4 + 4 + 4$ b. 4×5 c. 3×4 d. $2 + 2 + 2$

3. 4×4 is to 16 as 8×8 is to ___?___
   a. 32 b. 8 c. 16 **(d.)** 64

4. 7×8 is to 56 as 9×8 is to ___?___
   a. 65 b. 8×7 **(c.)** 72 d. 8×9

5. 3×3 is to 3×6 as 3×4 is to ___?___
   a. 4×4 b. 3×5 **(c.)** 3×8 d. 3×7

6. 2×4 is to 2×8 as 3×4 is to ___?___
   a. 3×5 **(b.)** 3×8 c. 4×3 d. 2×3

Complete the analogy.

7. 4×4 is to 4×8 as **Answers** is to **will vary.**

 Use with Grade 3, text pages 220–221.

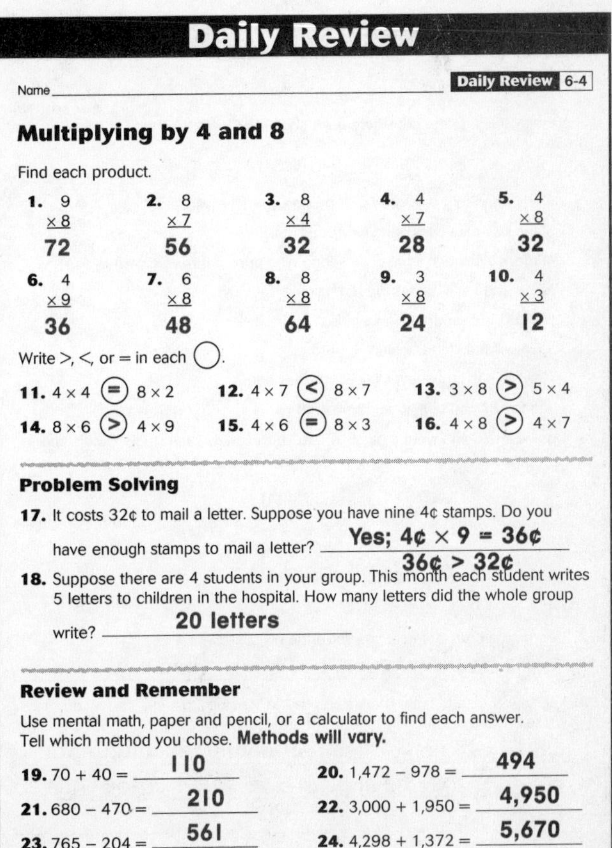

Daily Review

Name ______________________ Daily Review 6-4

Multiplying by 4 and 8

Find each product.

1. $9 \times 8 = 72$ 2. $8 \times 7 = 56$ 3. $8 \times 4 = 32$ 4. $4 \times 7 = 28$ 5. $4 \times 8 = 32$

6. $4 \times 9 = 36$ 7. $6 \times 8 = 48$ 8. $8 \times 8 = 64$ 9. $3 \times 8 = 24$ 10. $4 \times 3 = 12$

Write >, <, or = in each ◯.

11. 4×4 (=) 8×2 12. 4×7 (<) 8×7 13. 3×8 (>) 5×4

14. 8×6 (>) 4×9 15. 4×6 (=) 8×3 16. 4×8 (>) 4×7

Problem Solving

17. It costs 32¢ to mail a letter. Suppose you have nine 4¢ stamps. Do you have enough stamps to mail a letter? **Yes; 4¢ × 9 = 36¢ 36¢ > 32¢**

18. Suppose there are 4 students in your group. This month each student writes 5 letters to children in the hospital. How many letters did the whole group write? **20 letters**

Review and Remember

Use mental math, paper and pencil, or a calculator to find each answer. Tell which method you chose. **Methods will vary.**

19. $70 + 40 =$ **110** 20. $1,472 - 978 =$ **494**

21. $680 - 470 =$ **210** 22. $3,000 + 1,950 =$ **4,950**

23. $765 - 204 =$ **561** 24. $4,298 + 1,372 =$ **5,670**

Practice

Problem Solving P 6-5

Too Much or Too Little Information

Circle the correct answer or answers to each question.

Tanya practices the piano for one hour each day, starting at 4:00 P.M. She takes a lesson on Monday. Lessons cost $9 each. How much will it cost for Tanya to take four lessons?

1. What information do you need to solve the problem?
   a. how often Tanya takes a lesson
   (b.) the cost of a piano lesson
   c. the time Tanya starts to practice piano each day

2. What else do you need to know to solve the problem?
   a. how long Tanya practices each day
   b. the day of Tanya's lesson
   (c.) the number of lessons Tanya takes

3. Which number sentence would tell you the cost of four lessons?
   (a.) $4 \times \$9 = \square$
   b. $4 + \$9 = \square$
   c. $\$9 + \$9 = \square$

Mrs. Gidge gave each student in her class a piece of fruit for lunch. She passed out 6 apples, 4 oranges, and 8 plums. She paid the clerk 39¢ for each piece of fruit. How many students were in Mrs. Gidge's class?

4. Is there enough information to answer the question? Explain. What information is not needed?
   Yes; you add the amounts of fruit, to find total number of students. You do not need to know the cost of each piece of fruit.

5. Is there enough information to find out how much change Mrs. Gidge got back from paying for the fruit? Explain.
   No; you do not know how much she gave clerk.

 Use with Grade 3, text pages 222–223.

Reteach

Problem Solving R 6-5

Too Much or Too Little Information

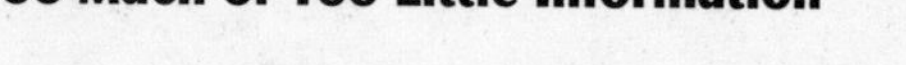

Sometimes there is *too much or too little information* to solve a problem. You need to decide which information you need to find an answer.

Ryan can buy a large box of cereal for $4 and a small box of the same kind of cereal for $3. Milk costs $1. Ryan wants to buy two small boxes of cereal and one carton of milk. How much does Ryan owe the clerk?

- You need to know the cost of a small box of cereal and the cost of a carton of milk.
- You do not need to know the cost of a large box of cereal since Ryan is not buying a large box of cereal.

1. Do you have enough information to find the total cost of Ryan's purchases? Why or why not?
   Yes; you know the cost of the cereal and the milk.
2. Can Ryan find the total cost of 3 large boxes of cereal? If so, how?
   Yes; he can add $4 + $4 + $4.
3. Can Ryan find the total cost of a jumbo box of cereal and a carton of milk? Why or why not?
   No; there is no price given for a jumbo box.
4. Suppose Ryan wants to find the cost of a large box of cereal and a carton of milk. Would the problem still have too much information? If so, which information would not be needed?
   Yes; no need to know cost of small box.

 Use with Grade 3, text pages 222–223.

Extend

Group Picture

E 6-5 **REASONING**

Use these clues to find out where each student will stand for the group picture.

Clues:

- Marie and Emily will stand side by side.
- Marie has blue eyes, but Emily does not.
- Marie will stand in front of someone who does not have brown eyes.
- Marie and Emily both have red hair.
- Howard will stand behind a girl.
- John will not stand behind Howard.
- Howard has brown eyes but John does not.
- John will stand behind a girl with red hair.

1. Draw a circle and write a name in it to show where each student will stand.

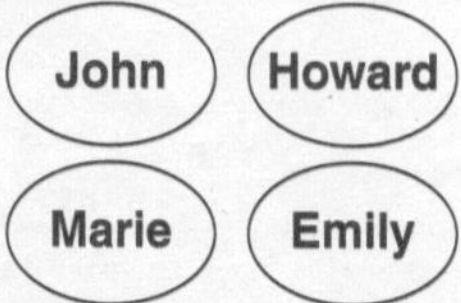

2. Which clue does not help you solve the problem?
   Marie has blue eyes, but Emily does not.
3. Keisha wants to get into the picture, too. Write clues that you could add that will tell where Keisha will stand. Then draw her in.
   Clues will vary. Check students' reasoning and whether they have given too much or too little information.

 Use with Grade 3, text pages 222–223.

Daily Review

Name ____________________ Daily Review 6-5

Problem Solving

Too Much or Too Little Information

Answer each question if enough information is available.

1. Pam needs to buy two erasers for school. Each eraser costs 52¢. Pam has 1 bill and 6 coins. Does she have enough money to buy the two erasers?
   Yes, she would have at least $1.06, and she needs only $1.04.
2. Gina has 3 cats, 2 dogs, and 4 goldfish. When she goes on vacation she has to find someone to feed the goldfish, someone to walk and feed the dogs, and someone else to feed the cats. She plans to be gone for 2 weeks.
   How many pets does Gina have?
   9 pets
   How much food will she need?
   Not enough information
   How many people does Gina need to care for her pets?
   3 people
3. Paul has some quarters. He wants to buy 2 packages of stickers. Each package costs 18¢. Can he buy the stickers? Explain.
   Yes, some quarters are at least 2. So he has at least 50¢ and needs only 36¢.

Review and Remember

Find the products.

4. $3 \times 7 =$ **21**
5. $4 \times 8 =$ **32**
6. $9 \times 4 =$ **36**
7. $3 \times 6 =$ **18**
8. $8 \times 8 =$ **64**
9. $5 \times 3 =$ **15**
10. $9 \times 6 =$ **54**
11. $7 \times 5 =$ **35**

Practice

Multiplying by 7

P 6-6

Find each product. Use the letters from your answers to solve the riddle, "What goes up when the rain comes down?"

1. 3 × 7 = **21** A
2. 7 × 1 = **7** E
3. 7 × 6 = **42** U
4. 2 × 7 = **14** A
5. 4 × 7 = **28** B
6. 0 × 7 = **0** M
7. 7 × 5 = **35** N
8. 7 × 7 = **49** R
9. 9 × 7 = **63** L
10. 7 × 8 = **56** L

A	**N**		**U**	**M**	**B**	**R**	**E**	**L**	**L**	**A**
21	35		42	0	28	49	7	63	56	14

Solve.

11. Complete the table.

Weeks	1	2	3	4	5	6
Days	**7**	**14**	**21**	**28**	**35**	**42**

12. It rained for two weeks in November. For how many days did it rain?
14 days

13. Manny is going to camp for 35 days. Is that more or less than 6 weeks?
less

14. December is 31 days long. Is this more or less than 4 weeks?
more

15. Summer vacation is about 9 weeks long. How many days is this?
63 days

Reteach

Multiplying by 7

R 6-6

You can use a number line to find products.

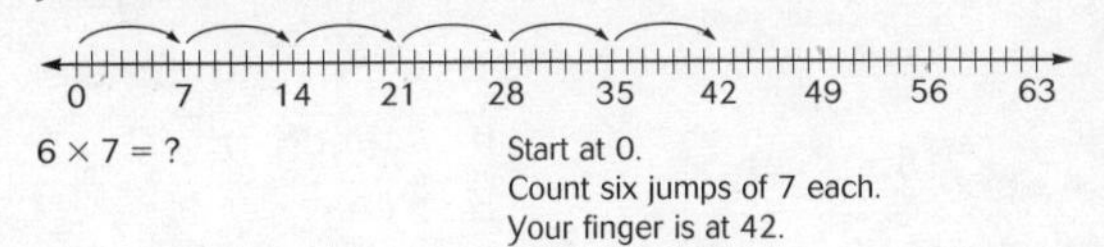

6 × 7 = ?

Start at 0.
Count six jumps of 7 each.
Your finger is at 42.
So, 6 × 7 = 42.

Use the number line to help you find each product.

0 7 14 21 28 35 42 49 56 63

1. Start at 0. Count 3 jumps. 3 × 7 = **21**
2. Start at 0. Count 2 jumps. 2 × 7 = **14**
3. Start at 0. Count 5 jumps. 5 × 7 = **35**
4. Start at 0. Count 1 jump. 1 × 7 = **7**
5. Start at 0. Count 7 jumps. 7 × 7 = **49**
6. Start at 0. Count 9 jumps. 9 × 7 = **63**
7. Start at 0. Count 0 jumps. 0 × 7 = **0**
8. Start at 0. Count 8 jumps. 8 × 7 = **56**
9. Start at 0. Count 4 jumps. 4 × 7 = **28**

10. 7 × 5 = **35**
11. 1 × 7 = **7**
12. 7 × 6 = **42**
13. 7 × 8 = **56**
14. 9 × 7 = **63**

Extend

A-Mazing Facts

E 6-6 NUMBER SENSE

Skip-count by sevens to find multiples of 7.
7, **14**, **21**, **28**, **35**, **42**, **49**, **56**, **63**

Help the mouse reach the cheese. First, multiply. Then follow the path where the product is a multiple of 7.

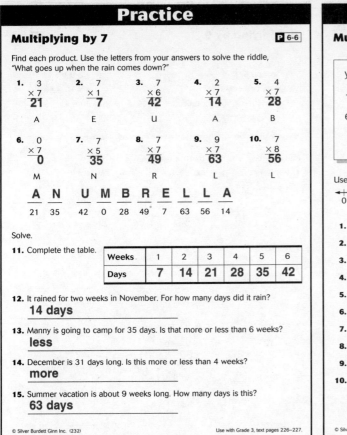

2 × 3 = **6**	5 × 7 = **35**	8 × 4 = **32**	5 × 5 = **25**	
7 × 4 = **28**	4 × 9 = **36**	2 × 7 = **14**	8 × 2 = **16**	Start
7 × 9 = **63**	8 × 3 = **24**	0 × 5 = **0**	7 × 3 = **21**	1 × 7 = **7**
9 × 2 = **18**	3 × 7 = **21**	4 × 5 = **20**	5 × 6 = **30**	2 × 4 = **8**
4 × 4 = **16**	8 × 8 = **64**	7 × 8 = **56**	6 × 7 = **42**	4 × 8 = **32**
9 × 5 = **45**	8 × 4 = **32**	6 × 8 = **48**	4 × 5 = **20**	7 × 9 = **63**
		3 × 3 = **9**	9 × 5 = **45**	7 × 7 = **49**
End		1 × 7 = **7**	8 × 7 = **56**	4 × 6 = **24**

What number is part of every fact on your path? **7**

Daily Review

Name ______________________

Daily Review 6-6

Multiplying by 7

Multiply.

1. 7 × 0 = **0**
2. 7 × 2 = **14**
3. 4 × 7 = **28**
4. 5 × 7 = **35**
5. 6 × 7 = **42**
6. 7 × 6 = **42**
7. 8 × 7 = **56**
8. 3 × 7 = **21**
9. 1 × 7 = **7**
10. 7 × 8 = **56**
11. 7 × 9 = **63**
12. 7 × 4 = **28**
13. 7 × 7 = **49**
14. 7 × 5 = **35**
15. 0 × 7 = **0**

Problem Solving

16. A boat crew spends 7 weeks exploring islands in the Pacific Ocean. How many days long is their trip? **49 days**

17. A boat dock is 63 feet long. A captain wants to tie 3 boats to the side of the dock. The boats are 16, 20, and 18 feet long. Is the dock long enough? Why or why not? **Yes; the boats' total length is 54 feet.**

Review and Remember

Find each answer. Use mental math.

18. 70 − 40 = **30**
19. $4,000 + $3,000 = **$7,000**
20. 950 − 20 = **930**
21. 125 + 50 = **175**
22. 600 − 120 = **480**
23. 8,000 − 5,000 = **3,000**
24. 360 − 130 = **230**
25. 560 − 20 = **540**
26. 9,700 − 3,700 = **6,000**
27. 710 + 330 = **1,040**

Chapter 6 • Lesson 7

Practice

Multiplying by 9

P 6-7

Complete the table.

	Fact	Product	Sum of digits in product
1.	1 × 9	9	9
2.	2 × 9	18	9
3.	3 × 9	27	9
4.	4 × 9	36	9
5.	5 × 9	45	9
6.	6 × 9	54	9
7.	7 × 9	63	9
8.	8 × 9	72	9
9.	9 × 9	81	9

Use the table to answer the questions.

10. What patterns do you see in the tens digits and in the ones digits in the list of products?
Tens digits increase by 1; ones digits decrease by 1.

11. Describe the pattern in the sums of the digits.
The sum of the digits is always 9.

Solve.

12. How many puppies are there if 9 dogs each have 9 puppies?
81 puppies

13. Jorge must travel 9 miles to get to school and back each day. How many miles does he travel in a 5-day week?
45 miles

Use with Grade 3, text pages 228–229.

Reteach

Multiplying by 9

R 6-7

To multiply by 9:	4 × 9 = ?
First multiply 4 by 10.	4 × 10 = 40
Then subtract 4 from the product.	40 − 4 = 36
	So, 4 × 9 = 36

Find the products. Multiply by 10 to help you.

1. 2 × 9 = ?
2 × 10 = 20
20 − 2 = 18
So, 2 × 9 = 18

2. 5 × 9 = ?
5 × 10 = 50
50 − 5 = 45
So, 5 × 9 = 45

3. 4 × 9 = ?
4 × 10 = 40
40 − 4 = 36
So, 4 × 9 = 36

4. 7 × 9 = ?
7 × 10 = 70
70 − 7 = 63
So, 7 × 9 = 63

5. 3 × 9 = ?
3 × 10 = 30
30 − 3 = 27
So, 3 × 9 = 27

6. 6 × 9 = ?
6 × 10 = 60
60 − 6 = 54
So, 6 × 9 = 54

7. 8 × 9 = ?
8 × 10 = 80
80 − 8 = 72
So, 8 × 9 = 72

8. 9 × 9 = ?
9 × 10 = 90
90 − 9 = 81
So, 9 × 9 = 81

Use with Grade 3, text pages 228–229.

Extend

Finger Fun

E 6-7

VISUAL THINKING

You can use your fingers to find products with 9!

Hold your hands out with palms facing out. Mentally number your fingers as shown.

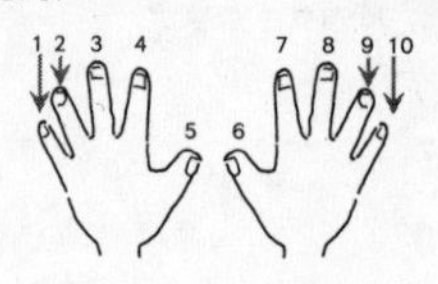

To find the product of 9 × 4, bend your fourth finger. Fingers to the left of the bent finger tell how many tens in the product. Fingers to the right of the bent finger tell how many ones in the product.

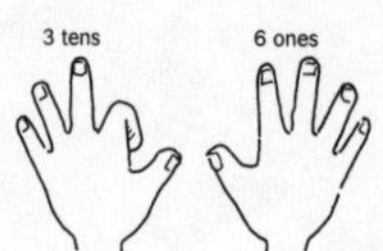

Use the finger method to find the products.

1. 9 × 1 = 9
2. 9 × 2 = 18
3. 9 × 3 = 27
4. 9 × 4 = 36
5. 9 × 5 = 45
6. 9 × 8 = 72
7. 9 × 9 = 81
8. 9 × 7 = 63
9. 9 × 6 = 54
10. 8 × 9 = 72

11. Describe another pattern to help find products that have 9 as a factor.
Digit in tens place always 1 less than factor multiplied by 9; digit in ones place is difference between 9 and digit in tens place; sum of the digits in tens and ones places always 9.

Use with Grade 3, text pages 228–229.

Daily Review

Name ____________________

Daily Review 6-7

Multiplying by 9

Find the product.

1. 1 × 9 = 9
2. 9 × 0 = 0
3. 6 × 9 = 54
4. 3 × 9 = 27
5. 9 × 8 = 72
6. 9 × 5 = 45
7. 9 × 9 = 81
8. 9 × 2 = 18
9. 4 × 9 = 36
10. 7 × 9 = 63

Follow each rule to complete each table.

Rule: Multiply by 6

	Input	Output
11.	5	30
12.	9	54

Rule: Multiply by 9

	Input	Output
13.	3	27
14.	5	45

Rule: Multiply by 8

	Input	Output
15.	7	56
16.	9	72

Problem Solving

17. There are 9 stops on a train route. This route is run 8 times a day. How many total stops are on this route in one day? 72 stops

18. A school bus driver has 2 routes. One route is 9 miles long and the other is 7 miles long. The driver takes each route once in the morning and once in the afternoon. How many miles does the driver travel in a day on these routes? 32 miles

Review and Remember

Find the total amount of each.

19. 3 pennies, 6 nickels, 2 quarters — $0.83
20. 8 nickels, 2 dimes, 3 dollars — $3.60
21. 4 pennies, 6 dimes, 3 quarters — $1.39
22. 4 dimes, 2 quarters, 4 dollars — $4.90

Chapter 6 • Lesson 8

Practice

Using Multiplication Strategies

P 6-8

Find each product. Color the box red if the product is even. Color the box yellow if the product is odd.

1. 3 × 7 = 21	**2.** 4 × 6 = 24	**3.** 6 × 7 = 42	**4.** 8 × 8 = 64	**5.** 7 × 7 = 49
6. 2 × 8 = 16	**7.** 9 × 7 = 63	**8.** 6 × 6 = 36	**9.** 5 × 7 = 35	**10.** 2 × 6 = 12
11. 6 × 8 = 48	**12.** 9 × 2 = 18	**13.** 9 × 3 = 27	**14.** 4 × 7 = 28	**15.** 4 × 8 = 32
16. 4 × 9 = 36	**17.** 9 × 5 = 45	**18.** 4 × 4 = 16	**19.** 1 × 7 = 7	**20.** 8 × 7 = 56
21. 7 × 5 = 35	**22.** 7 × 8 = 56	**23.** 9 × 8 = 72	**24.** 8 × 6 = 48	**25.** 3 × 9 = 27

26. What shape do you see in the box? multiplication sign, x

Reteach

Using Multiplication Strategies

R 6-8

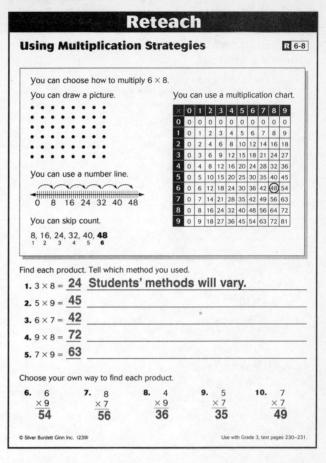

You can choose how to multiply 6 × 8.

You can draw a picture.

● ● ● ● ● ● ● ●
● ● ● ● ● ● ● ●
● ● ● ● ● ● ● ●
● ● ● ● ● ● ● ●
● ● ● ● ● ● ● ●
● ● ● ● ● ● ● ●

You can use a number line.

0 8 16 24 32 40 48

You can skip count.

8, 16, 24, 32, 40, **48**
1 2 3 4 5 **6**

You can use a multiplication chart.

×	0	1	2	3	4	5	6	7	8	9
0	0	0	0	0	0	0	0	0	0	0
1	0	1	2	3	4	5	6	7	8	9
2	0	2	4	6	8	10	12	14	16	18
3	0	3	6	9	12	15	18	21	24	27
4	0	4	8	12	16	20	24	28	32	36
5	0	5	10	15	20	25	30	35	40	45
6	0	6	12	18	24	30	36	42	(48)	54
7	0	7	14	21	28	35	42	49	56	63
8	0	8	16	24	32	40	48	56	64	72
9	0	9	18	27	36	45	54	63	72	81

Find each product. Tell which method you used.

1. 3 × 8 = 24 Students' methods will vary.
2. 5 × 9 = 45
3. 6 × 7 = 42
4. 9 × 8 = 72
5. 7 × 9 = 63

Choose your own way to find each product.

6. 6 × 9 = 54 **7.** 8 × 7 = 56 **8.** 4 × 9 = 36 **9.** 5 × 7 = 35 **10.** 7 × 7 = 49

Extend

Shopping Spree

E 6-8
REASONING

Carrie is shopping for new school clothes. She wants to make as many outfits as she can from the new jeans and tops she buys.

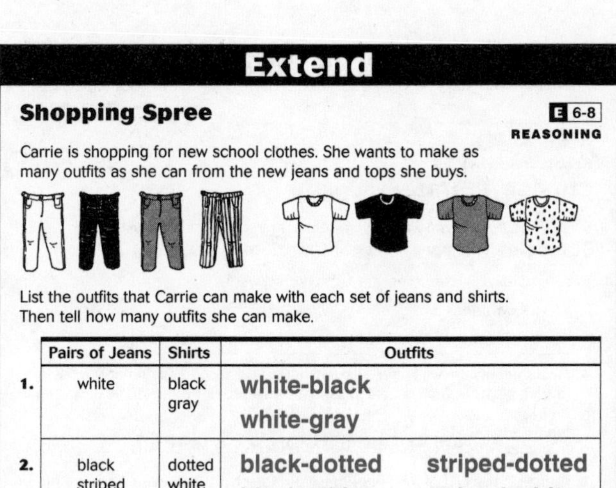

List the outfits that Carrie can make with each set of jeans and shirts. Then tell how many outfits she can make.

	Pairs of Jeans	Shirts	Outfits
1.	white	black gray	white-black white-gray
2.	black striped	dotted white	black-dotted, striped-dotted black-white, striped-white
3.	striped gray white	gray white	striped-gray, gray-white striped-white, white-gray gray-gray, white-white

4. Look at your table. What pattern do you see?
Number of total outfits is product of number of pairs of jeans and number of shirts.

5. How many outfits could Carrie make with 3 pairs of jeans and 4 shirts? 12

6. Tell how many pairs of jeans and how many shirts Carrie might buy if she wanted to have a total of 8 outfits.
2 pairs of jeans, 4 shirts; 4 pairs of jeans, 2 shirts

Daily Review

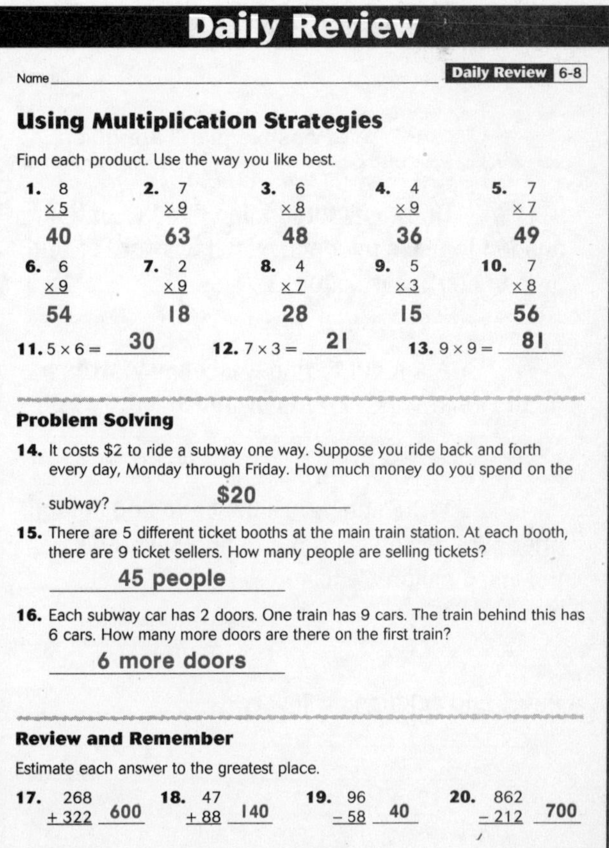

Name ____________

Daily Review 6-8

Using Multiplication Strategies

Find each product. Use the way you like best.

1. 8 × 5 = 40 **2.** 7 × 9 = 63 **3.** 6 × 8 = 48 **4.** 4 × 9 = 36 **5.** 7 × 7 = 49

6. 6 × 9 = 54 **7.** 2 × 9 = 18 **8.** 4 × 7 = 28 **9.** 5 × 3 = 15 **10.** 7 × 8 = 56

11. 5 × 6 = 30 **12.** 7 × 3 = 21 **13.** 9 × 9 = 81

Problem Solving

14. It costs $2 to ride a subway one way. Suppose you ride back and forth every day, Monday through Friday. How much money do you spend on the subway? $20

15. There are 5 different ticket booths at the main train station. At each booth, there are 9 ticket sellers. How many people are selling tickets?
45 people

16. Each subway car has 2 doors. One train has 9 cars. The train behind this has 6 cars. How many more doors are there on the first train?
6 more doors

Review and Remember

Estimate each answer to the greatest place.

17. 268 + 322 600 **18.** 47 + 88 140 **19.** 96 − 58 40 **20.** 862 − 212 700

Practice

Problem Solving P 6-9

Choose a Strategy

Choose a strategy to solve these problems. Tell which strategy you will use. Then solve. **Possible strategies are given.**

- Use Logical Reasoning
- Make a Table
- Make a List
- Work Backwards
- Act It Out
- Draw a Picture

1. Ivan buys six tickets to a school play. Each ticket costs $3. How much does Ivan spend for tickets?

   Strategy: **Make a Table**

   Solution: **$18**

2. The classroom is set up for a play. There are 4 rows with 8 seats in each row. How many seats are set up?

   Strategy: **Draw a Picture**

   Solution: **32 seats**

3. It takes 5 minutes to seat people for the play, which lasts 35 minutes. It takes 5 minutes for people to leave. At 2:00 the play is over and the room empty. What time were people first seated?

   Strategy: **Work Backward**

   Solution: **1:15**

4. There were 30 people seated in the classroom. Six people left, then 4 people came. Then 10 more people left, and 14 people came. How many people are in the classroom now?

   Strategy: **Make a Table**

   Solution: **32 people**

5. The copy machine can copy 20 programs for the play in one minute. How long will it take the machine to copy 100 programs?

   Strategy: **Make a Table**

   Solution: **5 minutes**

6. The actors in the play take a bow. Jim bows before Roy. Ben bows after Didi. Didi bows between Jim and Roy. In what order do the actors bow?

   Strategy: **Act It Out**

   Solution: **Jim, Didi, Roy, Ben**

 Use with Grade 3, text pages 232–233.

Reteach

Problem Solving R 6-9

Choose a Strategy

Jessica has 4 cans of tennis balls with 3 balls in each can.

1. How many tennis balls does Jessica have?

Understand You need to find the total number of tennis balls. You need to know you can use different strategies.

Plan You have a choice of plans.

- You can *draw a picture.*
- You can *act it out.*
- You can *make a table.*
- You can write a *number sentence.*

What is *your* plan? **Answers will vary.**

Solve Use the strategy you chose to solve the problem.

What is your solution? **12 tennis balls**

Look Back To check your work, try to solve the problem using a different plan. Your solution should be the same.

Choose a strategy to solve these problems. Tell which strategy you choose. Then solve. **Possible strategies are given.**

- Use Logical Reasoning
- Make a Table
- Make a List
- Work Backward
- Act It Out
- Draw a Picture

2. Mae's class goes on a trip. There are 7 people in a van. Two vans go. How many people are on the trip?

   Strategy: **Draw a Picture**

   Solution: **14 people**

3. Jack buys 5 passes to go roller skating. Each pass costs $2. How much does he spend?

   Strategy: **Act It Out**

   Solution: **$10**

4. A ticket to the skating rink is $3. Dan wants to know how much it would cost to take 2, 3, 4, and 5 children.

   Strategy: **Make a List**

   Solution: **$6, $9, $12, $15**

 Use with Grade 3, text pages 232–233.

Extend

What a Plan!

E 6-9 NUMBER SENSE

Make a plan to solve each problem. Your plan may involve more than one strategy! Then solve. **Possible plans are given.**

1. Hank is making 6 puppets for a show. He can make 2 puppets in 1 hour. If all of the puppets must be finished by 5:00, when should Hank start to work?

   Here's my plan: **Draw a picture to find number of hours needed to make puppets; work backward to find time to start; start 2:00.**

2. Jan has 9 pennies and 3 nickels. How much money will she have left if she buys a marker for 17¢?

   Here's my plan: **Act it out to find total money; write a number sentence to find how much left; 7¢ left.**

3. Mr. Jones has $20. Tickets to a ball game are $5 for adults and $3 for children. Mr. Jones buys a ticket for himself and spends the rest for children's tickets. How many children's tickets does he buy?

   Here's my plan: **Write number sentence to find amount after adult ticket; act it out to find children's tickets; 5 children's tickets.**

4. Write your own problem using the information in the sign. Ask a classmate to write a plan and solve.

   Softball game tournament
   Each game: 1 hour, 30 minutes
   Tournament ends: 5:00

   Plans and solutions will vary.

 Use with Grade 3, text pages 232–233.

Daily Review

Name ____________________ Daily Review 6-9

Problem Solving

Choose a Strategy

Solve these problems using these or other strategies you have learned. **Strategies will vary. Possible strategies are given.**

Use Logical Reasoning	Work Backwards
Make a Table	Act It Out
Make a List	Write a Number Sentence

1. Four students are waiting to buy lunch. Drew is second on line and Jeff is in front of Drew. Beth is behind Jane. In what order are the students waiting on line?

   Act It Out; Jeff, Drew, Jane, Beth

2. Nathan is thinking of a number between 35 and 51. It is even. The sum of the digits is more than 10, and less than 12. There is no digit 4. What is the number?

   Use Logical Reasoning; 38

3. At the cookie factory, a machine makes 200 cookies in 3 minutes. How many cookies can the machine make in a half an hour?

   Make a Table; 2,000 cookies

4. Julie bought balloons for her mother's birthday. She wants to make a bunch of balloons for each guest. If there are 9 guests, how many balloons would she need to make bunches of 3 balloons for each guest?

   Write a Number Sentence; 9 × 3 = 27

Review and Remember

Calculate the change from a $10.00 bill.

5. $4.45 **$5.55**
6. $8.15 **$1.85**
7. $0.74 **$9.26**
8. $5.99 **$4.01**
9. $6.88 **$3.12**
10. $1.09 **$8.91**

Practice

Multiplying Three Numbers

P 6-10

Multiply in any order.

1. 1 × 3 × 3 = 9
2. 2 × 4 × 5 = 40
3. 2 × 3 × 4 = 24
4. 3 × 2 × 1 = 6
5. 4 × 2 × 1 = 8
6. 3 × 3 × 3 = 27
7. 3 × 2 × 2 = 12
8. 2 × 5 × 4 = 40
9. 2 × 1 × 6 = 12
10. 3 × 5 × 2 = 30
11. 7 × 2 × 2 = 28
12. 3 × 4 × 3 = 36
13. 8 × 7 × 0 = 0
14. 4 × 6 × 2 = 48
15. 3 × 3 × 7 = 63
16. 2 × 4 × 8 = 64
17. 5 × 3 × 3 = 45
18. 1 × 9 × 9 = 81

Compare. Use <, >, or = in the ◯.

19. 4 × 2 × 5 (>) 3 × 3 × 4
20. 2 × 3 × 3 (<) 4 × 2 × 3
21. 5 × 1 × 6 (=) 2 × 3 × 5
22. 4 × 9 × 2 (>) 7 × 4 × 2
23. 8 × 4 × 1 (=) 2 × 2 × 8
24. 7 × 3 × 3 (<) 8 × 4 × 2

Solve.

25. Kamisha put 2 shoes in each box. She put 4 boxes of shoes on each shelf. She filled 3 shelves with shoes. How many shoes were on the shelf?

24 shoes

26. Sean needs 3 yards of 2 fabric colors for each school flag. He is making 8 flags. How many yards of fabric does Sean need?

48 yards

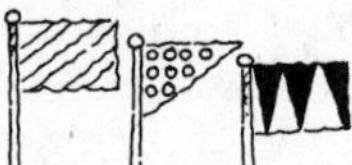

 Use with Grade 3, text pages 234–235.

Reteach

Multiplying Three Numbers

R 6-10

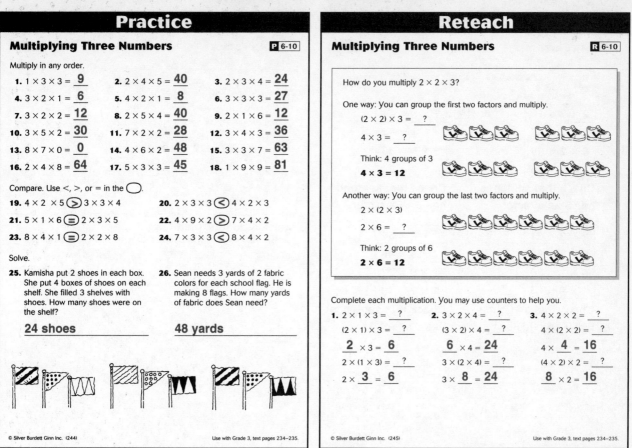

How do you multiply 2 × 2 × 3?

One way: You can group the first two factors and multiply.

(2 × 2) × 3 = ?

4 × 3 = ?

Think: 4 groups of 3

4 × 3 = 12

Another way: You can group the last two factors and multiply.

2 × (2 × 3)

2 × 6 = ?

Think: 2 groups of 6

2 × 6 = 12

Complete each multiplication. You may use counters to help you.

1. 2 × 1 × 3 = ?
   (2 × 1) × 3 = ?
   2 × 3 = 6
   2 × (1 × 3) = ?
   2 × 3 = 6
2. 3 × 2 × 4 = ?
   (3 × 2) × 4 = ?
   6 × 4 = 24
   3 × (2 × 4) = ?
   3 × 8 = 24
3. 4 × 2 × 2 = ?
   4 × (2 × 2) = ?
   4 × 4 = 16
   (4 × 2) × 2 = ?
   8 × 2 = 16

 Use with Grade 3, text pages 234–235.

Extend

Bull's Eye

E 6-10 NUMBER SENSE

You want to travel to the center of the maze from Start. You can cross into the next circle only at a problem that has the same product as the problem at Start. Draw your route. Write the product in the center. The first maze has been started for you.

1.

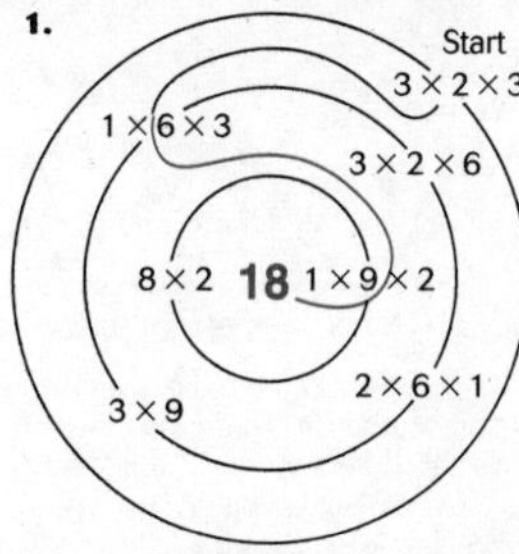

2.

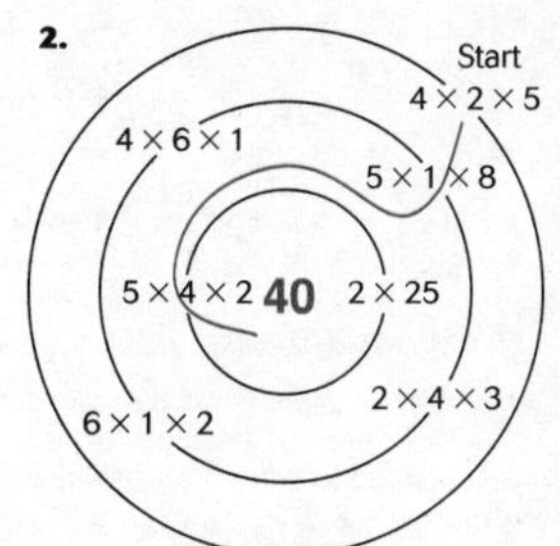

3.

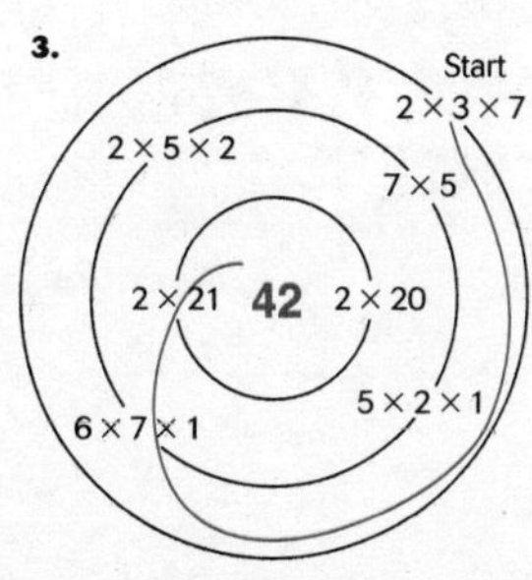

4.

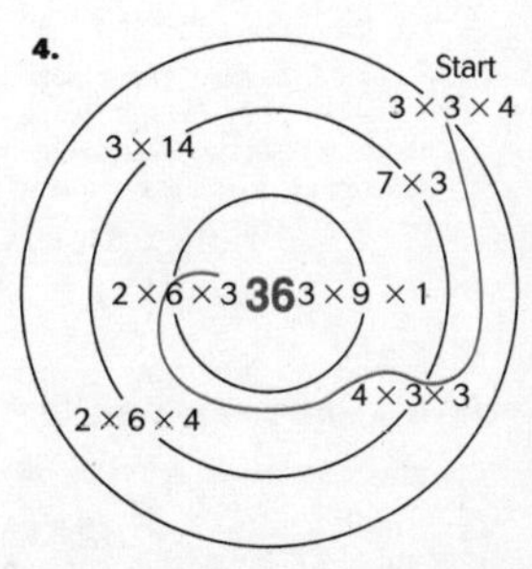

 Use with Grade 3, text pages 234–235.

Daily Review

Name ______

Daily Review 6-10

Multiplying Three Numbers

Find each product.

1. 4 × (1 × 7) = 28
2. (2 × 4) × 5 = 40
3. (9 × 3) × 1 = 27
4. 5 × (0 × 7) = 0
5. 2 × (2 × 8) = 32
6. (2 × 3) × 6 = 36
7. 7 × (2 × 1) = 14
8. (3 × 3) × 4 = 36
9. 6 × (1 × 7) = 42
10. (4 × 2) × 7 = 56
11. (1 × 9) × 9 = 81
12. (3 × 2) × 8 = 48
13. (2 × 2) × 9 = 36
14. 7 × (1 × 8) = 56
15. (8 × 8) × 0 = 0

Problem Solving

16. A skate path is 6 miles long. A skater skates the length of the path and back, then half the length and back. How many miles did the skater go? 18 miles
17. A skating team replaces all of their wheels. There are 4 wheels on each skate. There are 8 people on the team. How many wheels are replaced? 64 wheels
18. Public skating costs $3 for each person. How much would it cost for a group of 7 people to go skating? $21
19. You pay $47.99 for a pair of skates. How much change do you get back from $50? $2.01

Review and Remember.

Write *inches, feet,* or *miles.*

20. The height of your skate boot might be 7 inches.
21. The length of a bike path might be 8 miles.
22. At a show, a skater might jump 3 feet high.
23. Your elbow pads might be 4 inches wide.

Chapter 6 • Lesson 11

Practice

Missing Factors

P 6-11

Cut out the missing factor sentence strips below. Paste them next to the correct missing factor number. When you are done, add a missing factor multiplication sentence under each group.

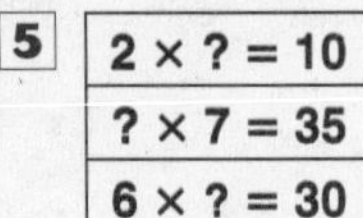

5

2 × ? = 10
? × 7 = 35
6 × ? = 30
? × 9 = 45

Check that sentence has 5 as a factor.

6

? × 3 = 18
7 × ? = 42
? × 6 = 36
4 × ? = 24

Check that sentence has 6 as a factor.

7

? × 3 = 21
8 × ? = 56
4 × ? = 28
? × 9 = 63

Check that sentence has 7 as a factor.

8

? × 8 = 64
? × 6 = 48
? × 9 = 72
5 × ? = 40

Check that sentence has 8 as a factor.

7 × ? = 42	? × 3 = 18	2 × ? = 10	? × 9 = 63
? × 8 = 64	? × 3 = 21	? × 7 = 35	4 × ? = 24
8 × ? = 56	? × 6 = 36	6 × ? = 30	? × 9 = 45
5 × ? = 40	? × 9 = 72	? × 6 = 48	4 × ? = 28

 Use with Grade 3, text pages 236–237.

Reteach

Missing Factors

R 6-11

You can use what you know about multiplication facts to help you find a missing factor.

4 × ? = 20

Count and draw groups of 4 until you reach 20.

4 × 1 = 4 OOOO
4 × 2 = 8 OOOO OOOO
4 × 3 = 12 OOOO OOOO OOOO
4 × 4 = 16 OOOO OOOO OOOO OOOO
4 × 5 = 20 OOOO OOOO OOOO OOOO OOOO

So, 4 × **5** = 20

Check students' pictures.

Find each missing factor. Draw pictures to help. The first one is done for you.

1. 3 × 2 = 6 OOO OOO
2. 1 × 5 = 5
3. 2 × 4 = 8
4. 3 × 5 = 15
5. 4 × 3 = 12
6. 3 × 6 = 18
7. 6 × 4 = 24
8. 4 × 5 = 20
9. 7 × 2 = 14
10. 9 × 3 = 27
11. 9 × 2 = 18
12. 3 × 8 = 24
13. 7 × 4 = 28
14. 6 × 5 = 30

 Use with Grade 3, text pages 236–237.

Extend

Cross Out!

E 6-11
REASONING

Look at the number grid. One number in the grid is the secret number. To find out the secret number, you must play Cross Out!

26	27	28	29	30
31	32	33	34	35
36	37	38	39	40
41	42	43	44	45
46	47	48	49	50

A **factor** is one of two numbers that are multiplied together to get a product. For example, 4 and 3 are each factors of 12.

Secret number is 41.

To play Cross Out!, read and follow each direction in order.

1. Put an × on numbers that have 7 as a factor.
2. Put an × on numbers that have 5 as a factor.
3. Put an × on numbers that have 3 as a digit.
4. Put an × on numbers where the sum of the digits is 10 or more.
5. Put an × on the remaining numbers for which the product of the digits is more than 10.
6. What number is left? 41
7. Check yourself. Look at your answer to 6. The sum of the digits should be 5. The product of the digits should be 4.

Create Your Own

Make your own game of Cross Out! on another sheet of paper. Use these numbers. Write directions for crossing out all but one number. The first direction is done for you.

55	56	57	58	59
60	61	62	63	64
65	66	67	68	69

(1) Put an × on numbers that have 6 as one of the digits.

 Use with Grade 3, text pages 236–237.

Daily Review

Name ____________________

Daily Review 6-11

Missing Factors

Find each missing factor.

1. 3 × 7 = 21
2. 4 × 6 = 24
3. 4 × 8 = 32
4. 6 × 8 = 48
5. 7 × 6 = 42
6. 9 × 4 = 36
7. 8 × 8 = 64
8. 6 × 0 = 0
9. 8 × 9 = 72
10. 7 × 7 = 49
11. 9 × 5 = 45
12. 3 × 6 = 18

Problem Solving

13. A small plane holds 8 passengers. How many of these planes are needed to carry 32 passengers? 4 planes

14. There are 5 people in a helicopter rescue crew. There are always 6 helicopters on duty. How many people are on duty? 30 people

15. A company's helicopters make 36 flights each day. Each helicopter makes 6 flights a day. How many helicopters does the company have? 6 helicopters

16. On a helicopter ride, 8 passengers go up at a time. The helicopter makes 9 trips each day. If the helicopter is full for each ride, how many passengers does it take in a day? 72 passengers

Review and Remember

Estimate each answer to the nearest 10.

17. 88 − 22 → 70
18. 91 − 36 → 50
19. 59 + 57 → 120
20. 39 + 59 → 100
21. 87 − 32 → 60
22. 75 + 37 → 120

Chapter 6 • Lesson 12

Practice

Problem Solving P 6-12

Using a Pictograph

Use the pictograph to solve each problem.

Our Rock Collections

Student	Number of Rocks in Collection
Boris	○○○○○○○○
Devi	○○○
Kaitlin	○○○○○○
Ann	○○○○○

Key: Each ○ stands for 5 rocks.

1. Who has the greatest number of rocks? **Boris**
2. Who has the least number of rocks? **Devi**
3. Kaitlin has her rocks on a table. How many rocks are on the table? **30 rocks**
4. Who has collected half as many rocks as Kaitlin? **Devi**
5. **Explain** Ann wants to show her rocks on another table. Will she have more, fewer, or the same number of rocks on as Kaitlin?
   fewer; Kaitlin, 30 rocks; Ann, 25 rocks
6. Boris puts 8 rocks on a small sheet of construction paper. How many sheets of construction paper does he need to display all his rocks? Explain.
   5 sheets × 8 rocks a sheet = 40 rocks
7. On the back of this page, write your own problem using the information in the pictograph. Give your problem to a classmate to solve.
   Check students' work.

 Use with Grade 3, text pages 238–239.

Reteach

Problem Solving R 6-12

Using a Pictograph

The data in this pictograph can help you solve problems.

Books We Like Best

Book Title	Number of Students
Stuart Little	●●●●
Charlotte's Web	●●●●●
Ramona Quimby, Age 8	●●●●●●
Shoeshine Girl	●●●●●●●●●

Key: Each ● stands for 2 students.

1. How many students voted for each book?

Understand You need to find the number of votes for each book. You need to know that each ● stands for 2 students.

Plan To find the total number of votes, you can
• count ● by twos. • multiply the number of ● by 2.

Solve
Stuart Little 4 × 2 = **8**
Charlotte's Web 5 × 2 = **10**
Ramona Quimby, Age 8 6 × 2 = **12**
Shoeshine Girl 9 × 2 = **18**

Look Back *Shoeshine Girl* got the most votes (18). That makes sense because it has the most ●'s.

Use the pictograph to solve.

2. Which book had the fewest votes? ***Stuart Little***
3. Suppose *Ramona Quimby, Age 8,* has 7 ●'s. How many votes would it have? **14 votes**

 Use with Grade 3, text pages 238–239.

Extend

School Fair

E 6-12 DATA

Rosemont School students are selling raffle tickets for the school fair. The pictograph shows how many tickets each class has sold.

Raffle Ticket Sales

Teacher of Class	Number of Tickets Sold
Ms. West	❑❑❑❑❑❑❑❑
Mrs. Midgley	❑❑❑❑❑▯
Mr. Johnson	❑❑❑❑▯
Ms. Jordan	❑❑❑❑❑❑
Mrs. Hsu	❑❑❑❑❑❑❑▯

Key: Each ❑ stands for 8 tickets.

1. How many tickets did Ms. Jordan's class sell? **48 tickets**
2. How many tickets did Mrs. West's class sell? **64 tickets**
3. If Mr. Johnson's class sold 36 tickets, what does ▯ stand for? **4 tickets**
4. How many tickets did Ms. Midgley's class sell? **44 tickets**
5. Mrs. Nancy's class sold 20 tickets. How could that amount be shown?
   Use 2 whole tickets and one-half ticket.
6. Add Mrs. Hsu's class to the pictograph. They sold 60 tickets.
7. Mr. Coach's class sold 50 tickets. He can draw whole pictures to show 48 tickets. What would you do to show the last two tickets?
   Possible answer: Draw $\frac{1}{4}$ of a ticket.
8. Add a class and the number of tickets sold to the pictograph. Write the number of tickets you showed. **Answers will vary.**

 Use with Grade 3, text pages 238–239.

Daily Review

Name__________ Daily Review 6-12

Problem Solving

Using a Pictograph

Use the pictograph to solve the problems.

Fish Counted

Grouper Tank	🐟🐟🐟
Flounder Tank	🐟🐟🐟🐟
Flashlight Tank	🐟🐟🐟🐟🐟
Mudskipper Tank	🐟🐟🐟
Lionfish Tank	🐟🐟

Key: Each 🐟 stands for 4 fish

1. Which tank has the most fish? Which tank has the least number of fish?
   most **flashlight tank** least **lionfish tank**
2. All but 5 of the mudskippers will be moved to another display area.
   How many will be moved? **7 mudskippers**
3. How many more flounder are there than lionfish? **8 more flounder**
4. The grouper tank has a maximum capacity of 20 fish. Can the aquarium provide space for 8 more grouper fish? **yes**
5. How many fish were counted in all? **68 fish**

Review and Remember

Find each sum.

6. 777 + 222 = **999** 7. 369 + 84 = **453** 8. 529 + 274 = **803**

9. 545 + 225 = **770** 10. 439 + 38 = **477** 11. 931 + 78 = **1,009**

Practice

Explore: Collect and Organize Data

P 7-1

The students voted on their favorite birds. Use the list the class made. Complete the tally chart.

Our Favorite Birds	
Annie	bluebird
Phil	hawk
Sarah	eagle
Jim	hawk
Chloe	eagle
Ed	bluebird
Luis	hawk
Ming	bluebird
Reyna	robin
Tess	eagle
Ben	hawk

Birds	Tallies	Totals
bluebird	|||	3
hawk	||||	4
eagle	|||	3
robin			1

Use your tally chart to answer the questions.

1. How many different birds did the students name? **4**
2. How many students like bluebirds best? **3**
3. How many students took part in the survey? **11**
4. List the birds in order from the most popular to the least popular.
   hawk, eagle, or bluebird, robin

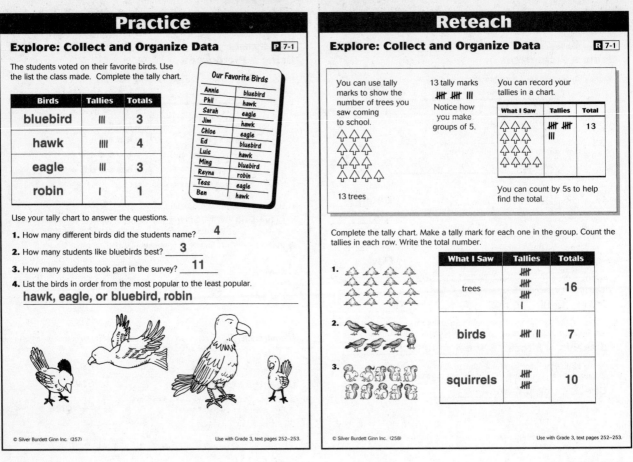

 Use with Grade 3, text pages 252–253.

Reteach

Explore: Collect and Organize Data

R 7-1

You can use tally marks to show the number of trees you saw coming to school.

13 trees

13 tally marks

卌 卌 |||

Notice how you make groups of 5.

You can record your tallies in a chart.

What I Saw	Tallies	Total
(trees)	卌 卌 |||	13

You can count by 5s to help find the total.

Complete the tally chart. Make a tally mark for each one in the group. Count the tallies in each row. Write the total number.

1. 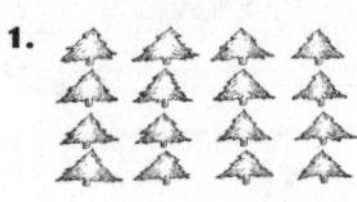
2. 
3. 

What I Saw	Tallies	Totals
trees	卌 卌 卌		16
birds	卌 ||	**7**
squirrels	卌 卌	**10**

 Use with Grade 3, text pages 252–253.

Extend

Tile Teasers

E 7-1 VISUAL THINKING

You can make each design by using some of the tiles below. Write the numbers of the blocks that make up the design in each empty square. Then copy the design.

HINT: A tile can be turned in any direction and used again and again.

1 2 3 4 5 6 7 8

1. 
2. 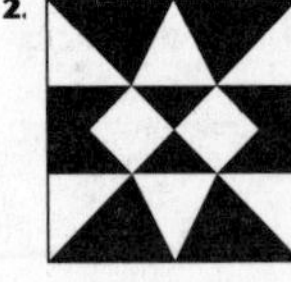
3. 

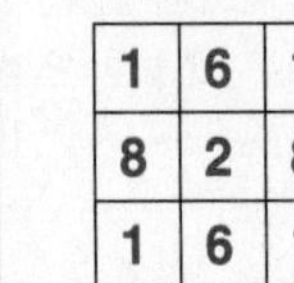

1.

1	3	1
1	4	1
1	3	1

2.

1	6	1
8	2	8
1	6	1

3.

1	6	6	1
6	7	7	6
6	7	7	6
1	6	6	1

 Use with Grade 3, text pages 252–253.

Daily Review

Name ______________________ Daily Review 7-1

Explore: Collect and Organize Data

Our Class's Favorite Vacation Spots	
Name	**Vacation Spot**
Shani	ocean
Erin	mountains
Kent	ocean
Jay	lake
Ariel	mountains
Louis	ocean
Yolanda	lake
Ping	ocean
Madison	ocean

1. Make a tally chart to record the information shown at left.

Our Class's Favorite Vacation Spots	
Vacation Spot	**Votes**
Ocean	卌
Mountains	||
Lake	||

2. Use the number of tallies in your tally chart to make a table.

Our Class's Favorite Vacation Spots	
Vacation Spot	**Votes**
Ocean	5
Mountains	2
Lake	2

Problem Solving

3. What do the tally chart and table tell you about the class's favorite vacation spots? **The ocean got the most votes. The mountains and the lake got the same number of votes.**
4. Write a word problem that can be answered using the data in your table. Write the answer to the word problem. **Answers will vary.**

Review and Remember

Write the value of the underlined digit.

5. 6<u>4</u>9 **40**
6. <u>1</u>,395 **1,000**
7. 2<u>8</u> **8**
8. <u>1</u>27 **100**
9. 2,<u>9</u>04 **900**

Practice

Problem Solving P 7-2

Is an Estimate Enough?

The Steen School sells buttons that read, "Keep Steen Green."

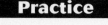

- They sell the buttons for 50 cents each.
- They buy them for 10 cents each.
- When they sell about 50 buttons, they buy a baby tree.

Use the information above to answer the questions.

1. How much money does the school collect when it sells 2 buttons?
$1

2. For each $1 that the school collects, how much can it keep and how much must it pay the button company?
keep 80¢; pay 20¢

3. Steen sells 46, 52, 41, 53, and 49 buttons. The school estimates it sold 250 buttons and can buy 5 trees. Is the school correct. Explain.
No; the estimate is high; the school can plant only 4 trees.

4. The school must pay for each button it sells. Can it estimate to find the amount it owes to the button company? Explain.
No; an exact payment is needed.

5. The school wants to plant about 50 trees. Over the last 5 months, it has planted 3, 12, 11, 9, and 4 trees. Estimate to find how many more trees the school needs to plant.
about 10 more trees

6. At most, the school has room for 60 new trees. When the school estimates about 45 trees planted, can it continue to estimate how many trees it still needs? Explain.
No; exact numbers needed to ensure school does not exceed 60 trees.

 Use with Grade 3, text pages 254–255.

Reteach

Problem Solving R 7-2

Is an Estimate Enough?

If you are asked *if an amount is enough,* you can usually use an *estimate* to solve the problem.

- There are 29 students in each third grade classroom at Rosemont School.
- There are 3 third grade classrooms.
- A new school rock garden has enough benches to seat about 100 students.

Is there enough room for all the third grade students to sit on the benches in the rock garden at the same time?

You need to find out if there is enough room. So, you can estimate to answer the question.

1. Is there enough room for the students to sit in the rock garden? Explain.
Yes; 29 is about 30; 30 + 30 + 30 = 90.

2. Mrs. Greene has 50 small rocks to place in the rock garden. Does Mrs. Greene have enough rocks to give one to each student? Explain.
No; she would need about 90 rocks to have one for each student.

3. On another day, the second grade students want to sit in the rock garden. There are 4 second grade classes. Each class has 31 students. Will there be enough room? Explain.
Possible answer: No; 31 is about 30; 30 + 30 + 30 + 30 = 120; 120 > 100.

 Use with Grade 3, text pages 254–255.

Extend

Clownin' Around

E 7-2 ESTIMATION

Amy is helping her teacher with the class play. Decide whether Amy needs to find an exact answer or an estimate. Then write an estimated or an exact amount in the table.

Estimate	Exact Amount
1. —	1. 24 yards
2. 200-inch roll	2. —
3. 4 spools	3. —
4. 5 batches	4. —

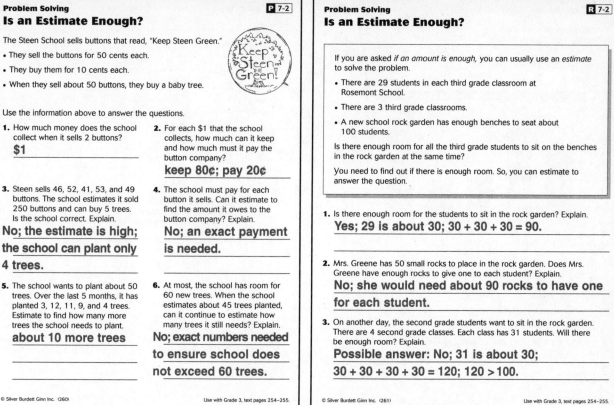

1. Amy needs fabric for 8 clown costumes. Each is cut to order and uses 3 yards of fabric. How many yards are needed?
2. One clown in the play will hold 5 balloons on strings about 28 inches long. String comes in rolls of 100 inches or 200 inches. Which roll should Amy get?
3. Amy needs ribbon for the 8 clown costumes. Each ribbon is 23 inches long. Ribbon comes in 50-inch spools. How many spools are needed?
4. Amy makes cookies for the play. She thinks 49 students will come and eat about 2 cookies each. Each batch of cookie mix makes 20 cookies. How many batches does Amy need?

Use a strategy of your choice to solve each of the following.

5. Amy will sew buttons on the soldiers' costumes. There will be 2 rows of 6 buttons each on a costume. How many buttons are on each costume?
12

6. There are 5 soldiers in the play. How many buttons does Amy need altogether? If she estimates the amount based on 10 buttons per costume, will she have enough?
60; no, she would be 10 short.

 Use with Grade 3, text pages 254–255.

Daily Review

Name __________ Daily Review 7-2

Problem Solving

Is an Estimate Enough?

Read each story. Answer each question.

1. Amanda's third-grade class collected 38 bundles of newspaper for recycling. The fourth-grade class collected 52 bundles. Which expression would you use to estimate about how many bundles were collected in all?
(a.) 40 + 50 **b.** 30 + 60 **c.** 52 – 38

2. Hillary's class collected 3,256 pounds of paper for recycling. The average class collection at her school was 1,973 pounds.
Which expression would you use to find exactly how many more pounds of paper Hillary's class collected than the average amount?
a. 3,000 – 2,000 **b.** 3,256 + 1,973 **(c.)** 3,256 – 1,973

3. Each song the chorus will sing takes about 4 minutes. There are 11 songs in the program, and a 10-minute intermission. The concert begins at 7:30. About what time will the concert end?
Is an estimate enough to solve the problem? How do you know?
Yes, an estimate is enough. The songs will take about 40 minutes. Add a 10-minute break and you get about 50 minutes, which is close to the calculated time of 54 minutes; the concert will end about 8:30.

Review and Remember

Subtract.

4. 705 – 314 = **391**
5. 430 – 215 = **215**
6. 740 – 605 = **135**
7. 510 – 76 = **434**
8. 304 – 298 = **6**
9. 600 – 189 = **411**

Practice

Bar Graphs

P 7-3

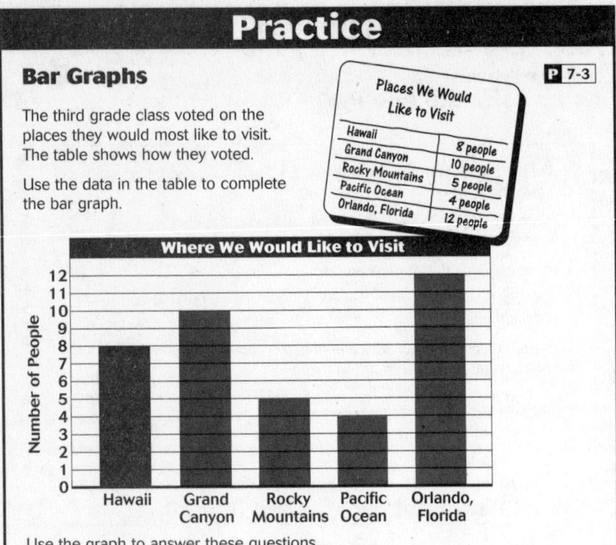

The third grade class voted on the places they would most like to visit. The table shows how they voted.

Use the data in the table to complete the bar graph.

Places We Would Like to Visit	
Hawaii	8 people
Grand Canyon	10 people
Rocky Mountains	5 people
Pacific Ocean	4 people
Orlando, Florida	12 people

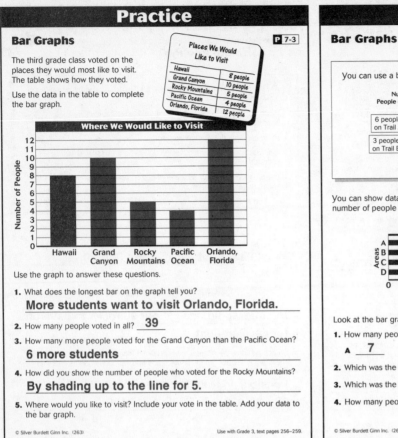

Use the graph to answer these questions.

1. What does the longest bar on the graph tell you? **More students want to visit Orlando, Florida.**
2. How many people voted in all? **39**
3. How many more people voted for the Grand Canyon than the Pacific Ocean? **6 more students**
4. How did you show the number of people who voted for the Rocky Mountains? **By shading up to the line for 5.**
5. Where would you like to visit? Include your vote in the table. Add your data to the bar graph.

 Use with Grade 3, text pages 256–259.

Reteach

Bar Graphs

R 7-3

You can use a bar graph to read data.

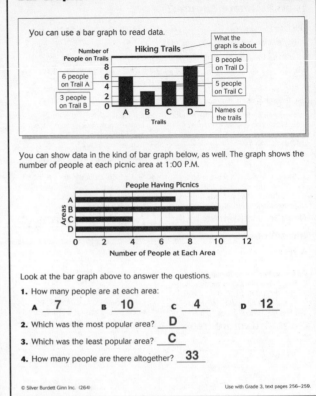

Hiking Trails — What the graph is about

Number of People on Trails: 0, 2, 4, 6, 8

6 people on Trail A; 3 people on Trail B; 5 people on Trail C; 8 people on Trail D

Trails: A B C D — Names of the trails

You can show data in the kind of bar graph below, as well. The graph shows the number of people at each picnic area at 1:00 P.M.

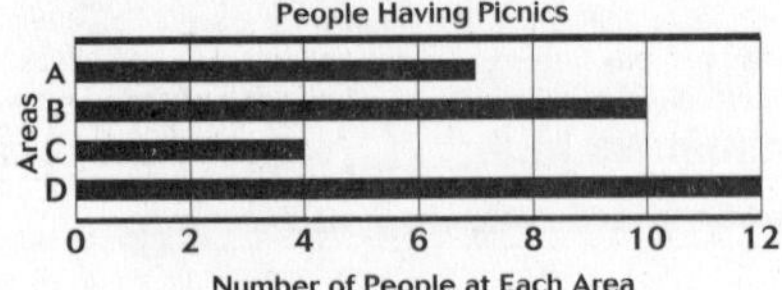

Look at the bar graph above to answer the questions.

1. How many people are at each area:
   A **7** B **10** C **4** D **12**
2. Which was the most popular area? **D**
3. Which was the least popular area? **C**
4. How many people are there altogether? **33**

 Use with Grade 3, text pages 256–259.

Extend

Checkers Challenge

E 7-3

REASONING

Chad and his parents had a checkers tournament. They made a table to show who won each game. Use the information to finish the table for Game 4.

- Each person played four games with each opponent.
- Mom won 3 games.
- Dad won 5 games.
- Chad won 4 games.

Winners	Game 1	Game 2	Game 3	Game 4	Game 5
Mom and Chad	Chad	Mom	Chad	**Chad**	**Chad**
Dad and Chad	Dad	Dad	Chad	**Dad**	**Chad**
Mom and Dad	Mom	Dad	Mom	**Dad**	**Mom**

Use the table to answer the questions.

1. Who won more games when Mom played Chad? **Chad**
2. After Chad played Dad twice, who was ahead? **Dad**
3. How many games against Chad did Dad win? **3**
4. How many games against Mom did Dad win? **2**
5. Which player won $\frac{1}{3}$ of the games in the first two columns? **Mom**
6. Chad, Mom, and Dad each played one more game against each other. Chad beat Dad, Chad beat Mom, and Mom beat Dad. Show the winners in the column for Game 5.

 Use with Grade 3, text pages 256–259.

Daily Review

Name ______________________

Daily Review 7-3

Bar Graphs

1. The table shows the number of campsites in five different parts of a park. Make a bar graph to show the data. Then use the graph to answer the problems. The graph has been started for you.

Sites in Silver Lake Campground	
Area 1	25 sites
Area 2	20 sites
Area 3	50 sites
Area 4	20 sites
Area 5	35 sites

Sites in Silver Lake Campground

Number of Campsites: 0 5 10 15 20 25 30 35 40 45 50

Area 1, Area 2, Area 3, Area 4, Area 5 — Park Campgrounds

2. Which area has the most sites? **Area 3**
3. How many more sites are there in Area 5 than in Area 4? **15 more sites**
4. Which areas have the same number of sites? **Area 2 and Area 4**

Problem Solving

5. Make a list of five activities you like to do when you are on vacation. Ask your classmates to vote for their favorites. Then make a bar graph to show your results. **Answers will vary.**

Review and Remember

Find each answer.

6. $32 + 49 = $ **81**
7. $9 \times 5 = $ **45**
8. $97 - 36 = $ **61**
9. $62 - 18 = $ **44**
10. $8 \times 7 = $ **56**
11. $77 + 78 = $ **155**
12. $80 - 28 = $ **52**

Practice

Pictographs

P 7-4

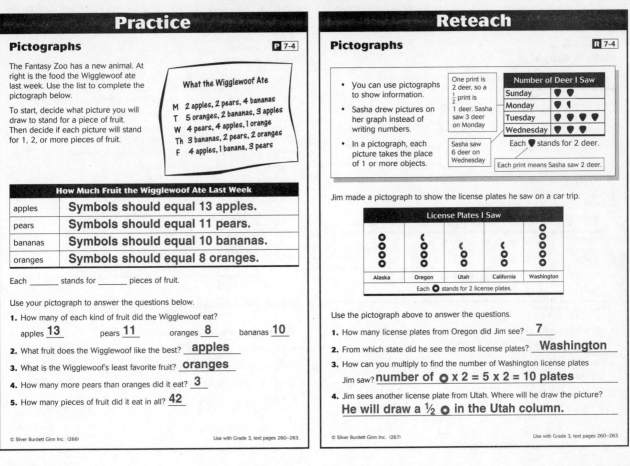

The Fantasy Zoo has a new animal. At right is the food the Wigglewoof ate last week. Use the list to complete the pictograph below.

To start, decide what picture you will draw to stand for a piece of fruit. Then decide if each picture will stand for 1, 2, or more pieces of fruit.

What the Wigglewoof Ate

M 2 apples, 2 pears, 4 bananas
T 5 oranges, 2 bananas, 3 apples
W 4 pears, 4 apples, 1 orange
Th 3 bananas, 2 pears, 2 oranges
F 4 apples, 1 banana, 3 pears

How Much Fruit the Wigglewoof Ate Last Week	
apples	**Symbols should equal 13 apples.**
pears	**Symbols should equal 11 pears.**
bananas	**Symbols should equal 10 bananas.**
oranges	**Symbols should equal 8 oranges.**

Each ______ stands for ______ pieces of fruit.

Use your pictograph to answer the questions below.

1. How many of each kind of fruit did the Wigglewoof eat?
   apples **13** pears **11** oranges **8** bananas **10**
2. What fruit does the Wigglewoof like the best? **apples**
3. What is the Wigglewoof's least favorite fruit? **oranges**
4. How many more pears than oranges did it eat? **3**
5. How many pieces of fruit did it eat in all? **42**

 Use with Grade 3, text pages 260–263.

Reteach

Pictographs

R 7-4

- You can use pictographs to show information.
- Sasha drew pictures on her graph instead of writing numbers.
- In a pictograph, each picture takes the place of 1 or more objects.

One print is 2 deer, so a $\frac{1}{2}$ print is 1 deer. Sasha saw 3 deer on Monday

Sasha saw 6 deer on Wednesday

Number of Deer I Saw	
Sunday	♥ ♥
Monday	♥ (
Tuesday	♥ ♥ ♥ ♥
Wednesday	♥ ♥ ♥

Each ♥ stands for 2 deer.

Each print means Sasha saw 2 deer.

Jim made a pictograph to show the license plates he saw on a car trip.

License Plates I Saw				
O O O O	(O O O	(O O	(O O	O O O O O
Alaska	Oregon	Utah	California	Washington

Each O stands for 2 license plates.

Use the pictograph above to answer the questions.

1. How many license plates from Oregon did Jim see? **7**
2. From which state did he see the most license plates? **Washington**
3. How can you multiply to find the number of Washington license plates Jim saw? **number of O x 2 = 5 x 2 = 10 plates**
4. Jim sees another license plate from Utah. Where will he draw the picture?
   He will draw a ½ O in the Utah column.

 Use with Grade 3, text pages 260–263.

Extend

Sock System

E 7-4
REASONING

Kim has 7 kinds of hiking socks.

He has red socks, black socks, and green socks.
He also has striped stocks.
Some socks have stripes in 2 colors.
Some socks have stripes in 3 colors.

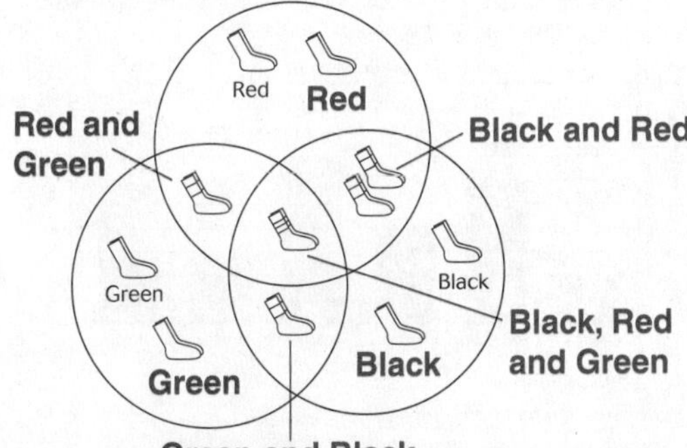

Use your diagram to answer the questions.

1. How many pairs of socks does Kim have that are one color only? **6**
2. How many pairs of socks have red and green stripes? **2**
3. How many pairs of socks have black and red stripes? **3**
4. How many pairs of socks have red, black, and green stripes? **1**

 Use with Grade 3, text pages 260–263.

Daily Review

Name ______________________

Daily Review 7-4

Pictographs

1. This table shows the sizes (in inches) of some kinds of owls. Make a pictograph to show the sizes of the owls. The graph has been started for you. **Check students' graphs.**

Sizes of Owls	
Barn Owl	14 inches
Burrowing Owl	10 inches
Eagle Owl	30 inches
Snowy Owl	26 inches
Tawny Owl	16 inches

Sizes of Owls	
Barn Owl	H H H H H H H
Burrowing Owl	H H H H H
Eagle Owl	H H H H H H H H H H H H H H H
Snowy Owl	H H H H H H H H H H H H H
Tawny Owl	H H H H H H H H

H = 2 inches

Problem Solving

Use the data in the pictograph above to answer the problems.

2. Which owl is the largest? **Eagle Owl**
3. Which owl is the smallest? **Burrowing Owl**
4. Which owl is closest in size to the tawny owl? **Barn Owl**
5. The snowy owl is about 10 inches larger than what kind of owl?
   Tawny Owl

Review and Remember

Solve.

6.	7.	8.	9.	10.
643	452	$8.15	4,628	$85.37
− 212	+ 334	+ 7.32	− 1,345	− 28.19
431	**786**	**$15.47**	**3,283**	**$57.18**

Chapter 7 • Lesson 5

Practice

Problem Solving

Make a Graph

P 7-5

Judy's school has a small farm. Students volunteer time to help run it.

Animals	Number
cats	𝍸 IIII
dogs	III
cows	𝍸 𝍸 III
horses	II

1. Judy made a tally chart to record the animals students were taking care of on the farm. Make a pictograph to organize the data.

Animals on the School Farm

cats	● ● ● ● ● ● ● ● ●
dogs	● ● ●
cows	● ● ● ● ● ● ● ● ● ● ● ● ●
horses	● ●

Key: 1 ● = 1 animal

2. Which animal is the greatest in number? the least?
cows, greatest; horses, least

3. How many more cats are there than dogs?
6 more cats than dogs

4. How many more cows does the school need in order to have 20 cows?
7 more cows

 Use with Grade 3, text pages 264–265.

Reteach

Problem Solving

Make a Graph

R 7-5

A different lunch is served to Sandy's class each day for students who do not bring lunch. On Monday students buy 5 lunches, 3 on Tuesday, 4 on Wednesday, 6 on Thursday, and 10 on Friday. On which day is the most popular lunch served?

1. How can you find the most popular lunch?

Understand You need to find the number of lunches bought each day. Then you can compare the numbers.

Plan You can make a graph to compare amounts.

Solve Complete the pictograph.

Day of the Week	Number of Lunches Bought
Monday	○○○○○
Tuesday	○○○
Wednesday	○○○○
Thursday	○○○○○○
Friday	○○○○○○○○○○

Key: 1 ○ = 1 lunch

Look Back There are more pictures beside Friday, so the greatest number of lunches were sold on Friday.

Use the graph to answer the questions.

2. On which day did 5 students buy lunch? **Monday**
3. How many students bought lunch on Thursday? **6 students**
4. On which day were the fewest lunches sold? **Tuesday**
5. If Sandy makes a bar graph showing the data, which bar will be longest? **Friday**

 Use with Grade 3, text pages 264–265.

Extend

Showing Favorites

E 7-5 DATA

The tally chart shows data collected from 65 students who voted for their favorite fruit.

Favorite Fruits

Orange	𝍸 𝍸
Apple	𝍸 𝍸 𝍸
Watermelon	𝍸 𝍸 𝍸 𝍸 𝍸
Peach	𝍸
Plum	𝍸 𝍸

1. Maya is making a pictograph using this data. She thinks 1 circle should show 2 votes. Do you agree? If not, what would you suggest?
No; 2 votes would mean too many half-circles.
Possible answer: one circle could show 5 votes.

2. Your school is buying one kind of fruit for all the students to eat at a spring picnic. You need to choose which fruit to buy. How can this graph help you? Which fruit will you choose?
Possible answer: Graph shows most popular fruit, watermelon. You would probably buy watermelon.

Use a strategy of your choice to solve.

3. Jerry, Sally, Fabian, and Patricia work one of the food tables at the picnic. Jerry serves the first customer, Sally the next, then Fabian, then Patricia, and then Jerry again. Who serves the 25th customer?
Jerry

4. One class at the picnic measured an ivy plant at 8 inches. Two weeks later, the plant is 24 inches high. How much did it grow in the two week period?
16 inches

 Use with Grade 3, text pages 264–265.

Daily Review

Name__________ Daily Review 7-5

Problem Solving

Make a Graph

Read the story and make a graph. Then answer the questions.

Chris asked his classmates what career they want to have. He found out that there are 2 future artists, 6 scientists, 4 lawyers, 7 teachers, 3 doctors, and 6 nurses. Make a graph that shows Chris's data.

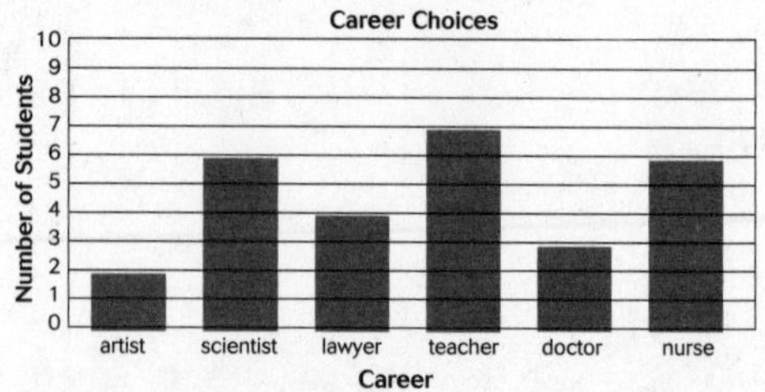

1. How many students are there in the class? **28 students**
2. What career do most students want? **Teacher**
3. How many students are interested in medical careers? **9 students**
4. How many more students want to be scientists than artists? **4 students**
5. Of the girls in the class, 3 want to be nurses, 1 wants to be a doctor, 3 want to be teachers, 2 want to be lawyers, and 3 want to be scientists. How many boys are in the class? **16 boys**

Review and Remember

Choose >, <, or = for each.

6. 4 kg (>) 4 g 7. 47° (<) 62° 8. 300 (<) 3,000 9. 16 oz (=) 1 lb

Chapter 7 • Lesson 6

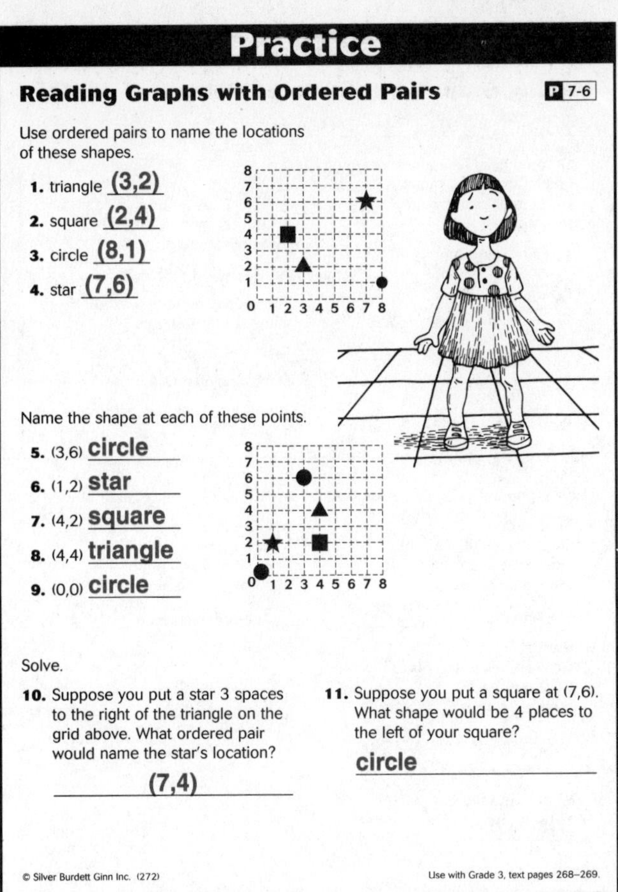

Practice

Reading Graphs with Ordered Pairs

P 7-6

Use ordered pairs to name the locations of these shapes.

1. triangle **(3,2)**
2. square **(2,4)**
3. circle **(8,1)**
4. star **(7,6)**

Name the shape at each of these points.

5. (3,6) **circle**
6. (1,2) **star**
7. (4,2) **square**
8. (4,4) **triangle**
9. (0,0) **circle**

Solve.

10. Suppose you put a star 3 spaces to the right of the triangle on the grid above. What ordered pair would name the star's location? **(7,4)**

11. Suppose you put a square at (7,6). What shape would be 4 places to the left of your square? **circle**

Use with Grade 3, text pages 268–269.

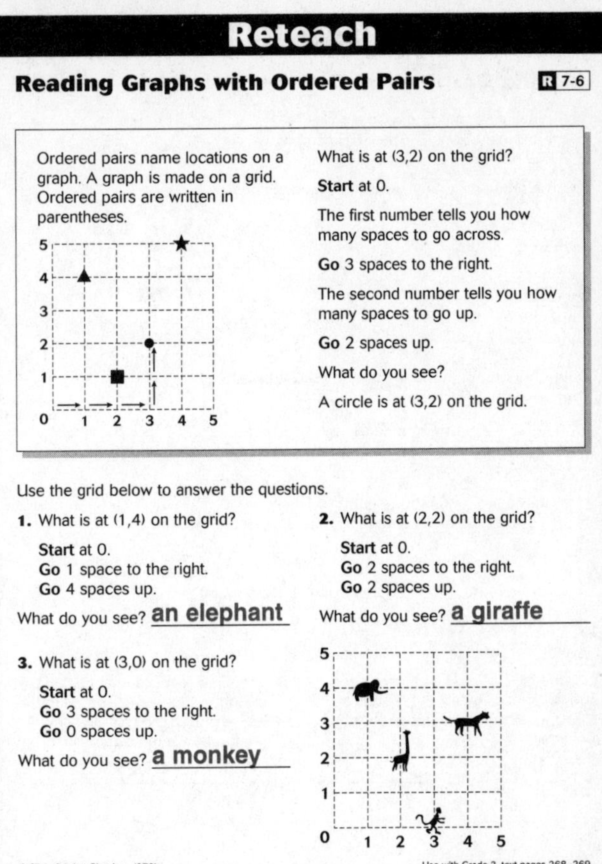

Reteach

Reading Graphs with Ordered Pairs

R 7-6

Ordered pairs name locations on a graph. A graph is made on a grid. Ordered pairs are written in parentheses.

What is at (3,2) on the grid?

Start at 0.

The first number tells you how many spaces to go across.

Go 3 spaces to the right.

The second number tells you how many spaces to go up.

Go 2 spaces up.

What do you see?

A circle is at (3,2) on the grid.

Use the grid below to answer the questions.

1. What is at (1,4) on the grid?
   Start at 0.
   Go 1 space to the right.
   Go 4 spaces up.
   What do you see? **an elephant**

2. What is at (2,2) on the grid?
   Start at 0.
   Go 2 spaces to the right.
   Go 2 spaces up.
   What do you see? **a giraffe**

3. What is at (3,0) on the grid?
   Start at 0.
   Go 3 spaces to the right.
   Go 0 spaces up.
   What do you see? **a monkey**

Use with Grade 3, text pages 268–269.

Extend

Picture Hunt

E 7-6

DATA

Draw a dot for each ordered pair. Label it with the letter. The first one is done for you. Then connect the dots in letter order. Finish the picture. Name the object.

a. (2,1)
b. (5,3)
c. (8,1)
d. (7,5)
e. (9,7)
f. (6,7)
g. (5,10)
h. (4,7)
i. (1,7)
j. (3,5)

1. I have drawn a **star**.

a. (1,3)
b. (2,1)
c. (8,1)
d. (9,3)
e. (6,3)
f. (6,7)
g. (3,4)
h. (6,4)

2. I have drawn a **sailboat**.

Use with Grade 3, text pages 268–269.

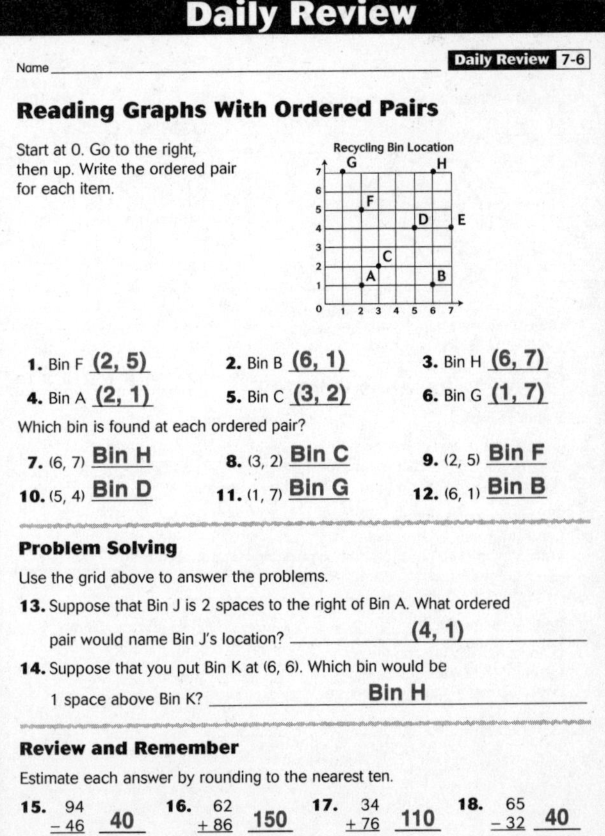

Daily Review

Daily Review 7-6

Name ______

Reading Graphs With Ordered Pairs

Start at 0. Go to the right, then up. Write the ordered pair for each item.

1. Bin F **(2, 5)**
2. Bin B **(6, 1)**
3. Bin H **(6, 7)**
4. Bin A **(2, 1)**
5. Bin C **(3, 2)**
6. Bin G **(1, 7)**

Which bin is found at each ordered pair?

7. (6, 7) **Bin H**
8. (3, 2) **Bin C**
9. (2, 5) **Bin F**
10. (5, 4) **Bin D**
11. (1, 7) **Bin G**
12. (6, 1) **Bin B**

Problem Solving

Use the grid above to answer the problems.

13. Suppose that Bin J is 2 spaces to the right of Bin A. What ordered pair would name Bin J's location? **(4, 1)**

14. Suppose that you put Bin K at (6, 6). Which bin would be 1 space above Bin K? **Bin H**

Review and Remember

Estimate each answer by rounding to the nearest ten.

15. 94 − 46 **40**
16. 62 + 86 **150**
17. 34 + 76 **110**
18. 65 − 32 **40**

Practice

Making Graphs with Ordered Pairs

P 7-7

You can make a grid to show the points of interest in the park. The park has gardens, ponds, food stands, and a forest.

Use the ordered pairs. Draw each item on the grid.

1.  (5,8)
2. (3,1)
3. (2,3)
4. (7,4)
5. (8,2)
6. EXIT (1,6)

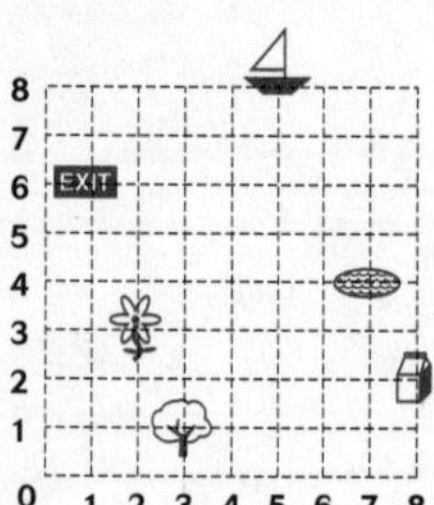

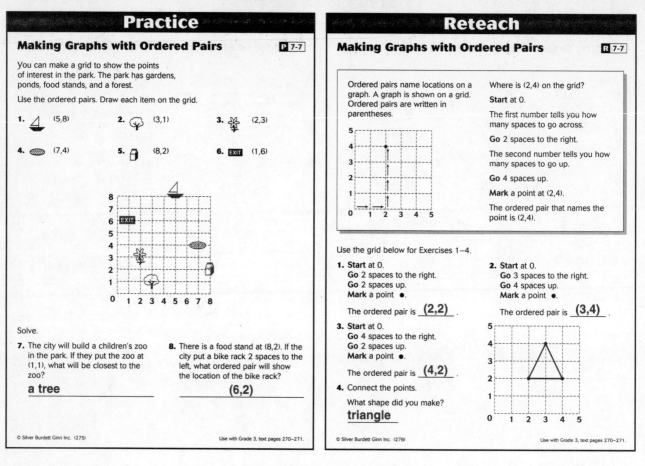

Solve.

7. The city will build a children's zoo in the park. If they put the zoo at (1,1), what will be closest to the zoo? **a tree**

8. There is a food stand at (8,2). If the city put a bike rack 2 spaces to the left, what ordered pair will show the location of the bike rack? **(6,2)**

Reteach

Making Graphs with Ordered Pairs

R 7-7

Ordered pairs name locations on a graph. A graph is shown on a grid. Ordered pairs are written in parentheses.

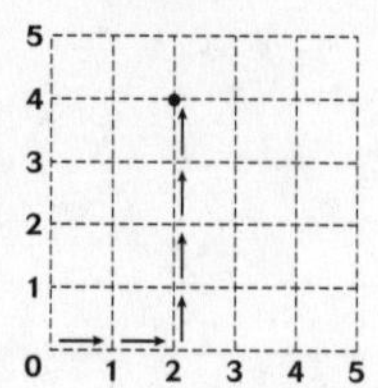

Where is (2,4) on the grid?

Start at 0.

The first number tells you how many spaces to go across.

Go 2 spaces to the right.

The second number tells you how many spaces to go up.

Go 4 spaces up.

Mark a point at (2,4).

The ordered pair that names the point is (2,4).

Use the grid below for Exercises 1–4.

1. **Start** at 0.
   Go 2 spaces to the right.
   Go 2 spaces up.
   Mark a point •.
   The ordered pair is **(2,2)**.

2. **Start** at 0.
   Go 3 spaces to the right.
   Go 4 spaces up.
   Mark a point •.
   The ordered pair is **(3,4)**.

3. **Start** at 0.
   Go 4 spaces to the right.
   Go 2 spaces up.
   Mark a point •.
   The ordered pair is **(4,2)**.

4. Connect the points.
   What shape did you make?
   triangle

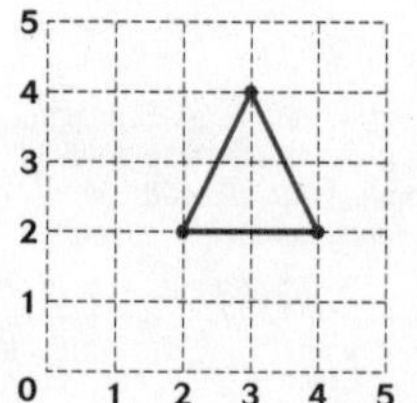

Extend

Map Town

E 7-7

VISUAL THINKING

Help plan a map of a new vacation spot.

Wild West City

1. Draw the buildings below on the grid. Label the buildings. Write the ordered pair for each building. **Drawings will vary.**

   Sheriff's Office: ________ General Store: ________

   Blacksmith: ________ Stable: ________

   Pony Express: ________ May's Restaurant: ________

2. The mayor wants to build some roads. Draw two roads on the graph. Write the ordered pairs for the beginning and end of each road.

   Road 1 Beginning: ________ End: ________

   Road 2 Beginning: ________ End: ________

3. Draw other buildings on the graph. Label these buildings. Write the name and the ordered pair for each building.

   ________ : ________ ________ : ________

   ________ : ________ ________ : ________

Daily Review

Name ________

Daily Review 7-7

Making Graphs With Ordered Pairs

Draw each of these shapes on the grid at the coordinate given.
Check students' graphs.

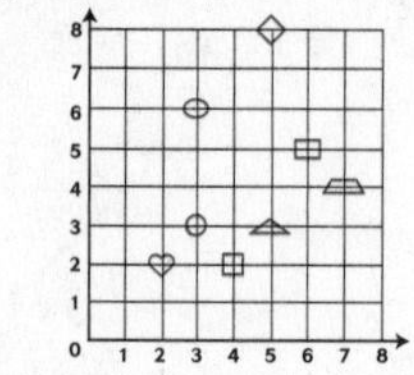

1. ○ (3, 3)
2. □ (4, 2)
3. △ (5, 3)
4. ▭ (6, 5)
5. ⏢ (7, 4)
6. ◇ (5, 8)
7. ♡ (2, 2)
8. ⬭ (3, 6)

Problem Solving

9. Make a grid map to show these plants in the Plant Place. Mark points and letters for each ordered pair.
   Check students' graphs.
   a. An azalea is at (5, 1).
   b. A yew is 2 spaces above the azalea.
   c. A burning bush is at (3, 4).
   d. A juniper is 2 spaces to the left of the burning bush.

The Plant Place

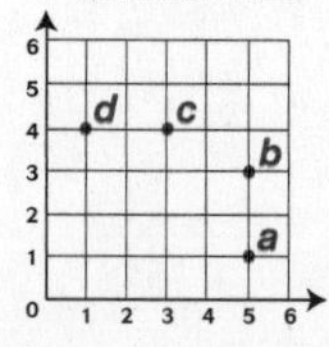

Review and Remember

Find each answer.

10. 20 + 80 = **100**
11. $52.15 − 40.07 = **$12.08**
12. 500 + 500 = **1,000**
13. $88.75 + 14.44 = **$103.19**
14. 210 − 99 = **111**

Chapter 7 • Lesson 8

Practice

Explore: Understanding Probability

P 7-8

Use 4 red counters, 2 blue counters, and a paper bag.

Predict the chance of picking one color.
Try it. Tally the results. Circle the answer.

1. Put 4 red and 1 blue in a bag.
Pick 1 counter at a time. Tally.
Put the counter back. Pick 10 times.

	Tally	Total
Red		
Blue		

The chance of picking red is equally likely (more likely)

Why? **There are more red counters than blue counters in the bag.**

2. Put 2 red and 2 blue in a bag.
Pick 1 counter at a time. Tally.
Put the counter back. Pick 10 times.

	Tally	Total
Red		
Blue		

The chance of picking blue is less likely (equally likely)

Why? **There are the same number of blue counters as red counters in the bag.**

3. Put 4 red in a bag.
Pick 1 counter at a time. Tally.
Put the counter back. Pick 10 times.

	Tally	Total
Red		
Blue		

The chance of picking blue is certain (impossible)

Why? **There are no blue counters in the bag.**

 Use with Grade 3, text pages 272–273.

Reteach

Explore: Understanding Probability

R 7-8

Use 8 unit blocks and a paper bag.

Put a ● on 4 blocks and a ■ on 4 blocks.

What is the chance you will pick a circle or a square from a paper bag?

For each experiment, fill the bag as shown.
Take turns. You pick. Put the block back. Pick again.
Your partner tallies each pick.
Use your results to circle the answers below. **Results will vary.**

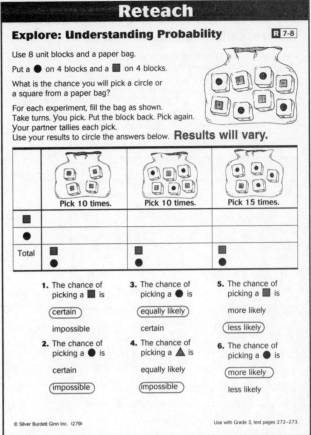

	Pick 10 times.	Pick 10 times.	Pick 15 times.
■			
●			
Total	■ ●	■ ●	■ ●

1. The chance of picking a ■ is (certain) impossible

2. The chance of picking a ● is certain (impossible)

3. The chance of picking a ● is (equally likely) certain

4. The chance of picking a ▲ is equally likely (impossible)

5. The chance of picking a ■ is more likely (less likely)

6. The chance of picking a ● is (more likely) less likely

 Use with Grade 3, text pages 272–273.

Extend

Heads or Tails?

E 7-8
PROBABILITY

Experiment with two pennies.
Toss the coins at the same time 30 times.
Each time make a tally to show the result of the toss.
The possible results are: both heads, both tails, or one head and one tail.

1. Before you begin, predict how many times out of 30 you will get: **Predictions will vary.**

both heads ____ both tails ____ a head and a tail ____

2. Toss the coins at the same time 30 times. Tally your results. Write the total.

Result	Tally	Total
Both heads		
Both tails		
One head and one tail		

Tallies will vary.

3. Which result did you get most often? **one head and one tail**

Least often? **either both heads or both tails**

4. Look at your predictions in Exercise 1. What was your closest prediction? **Predictions will vary.**

5. Usually in this experiment the result of one head and one tail occurs most often. Why? **HINT:** The possible results are H-H, H-T, T-H, T-T.
Possible answer: One head and one tail can occur in more ways (2) than either both heads (1) or both tails (1). The answers given are the most likely. Individual results may vary.

 Use with Grade 3, text pages 272–273.

Daily Review

Name ____________ Daily Review 7-8

Explore: Understanding Probability

A bag contains 4 squares. Write *certain* or *impossible* for each question.

1. Is picking a square certain or impossible? **certain**

2. Is picking a triangle certain or impossible? **impossible**

Write *more likely*, *less likely*, or *equally likely* to tell how likely it would be to pick an item from a bag containing 4 triangles, 4 squares, and 6 circles.

3. How likely would it be to pick a triangle rather than a square? **equally likely**

4. How likely would it be to pick a square rather than a circle? **less likely**

5. How likely would it be to pick a circle rather than a triangle? **more likely**

Problem Solving

6. Suppose you have a number cube, each side labeled with a different number, 1 through 6. Write a statement that tells how likely it is to roll any of these numbers.
Example: It would be equally likely to roll any of the numbers 1–6.

7. A board game has a deck of cards with 14 winning cards and 10 losing cards. Write a statement that tells how likely it is to pick a certain kind of card.
Example: It would be more likely to pick a winning card than a losing card.

Review and Remember

Multiply.

8. 5 × 4 = **20** **9.** 7 × 9 = **63** **10.** 8 × 6 = **48**

11. 5 × 9 = **45** **12.** 6 × 5 = **30** **13.** 3 × 7 = **21**

Chapter 7 • Lesson 9

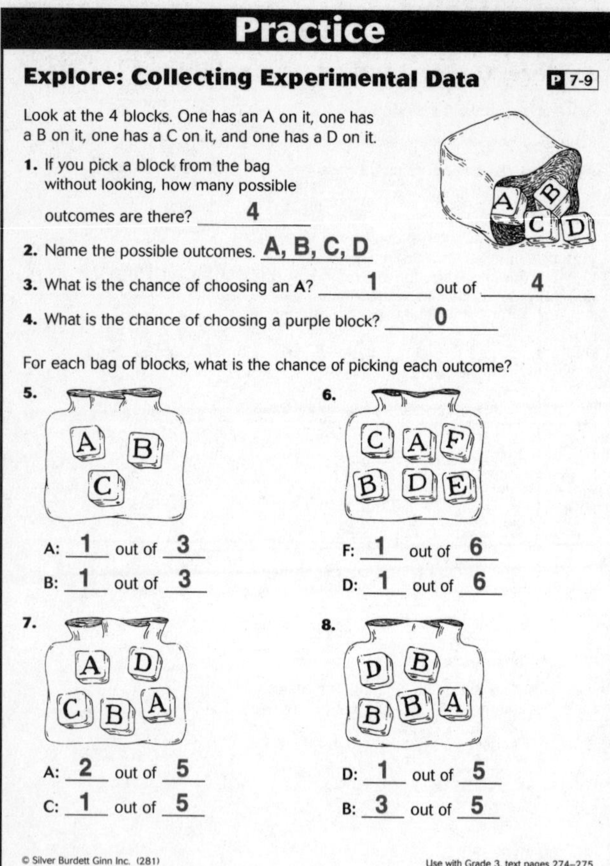

Practice

Explore: Collecting Experimental Data

P 7-9

Look at the 4 blocks. One has an A on it, one has a B on it, one has a C on it, and one has a D on it.

1. If you pick a block from the bag without looking, how many possible outcomes are there? **4**
2. Name the possible outcomes. **A, B, C, D**
3. What is the chance of choosing an A? **1** out of **4**
4. What is the chance of choosing a purple block? **0**

For each bag of blocks, what is the chance of picking each outcome?

5. A: **1** out of **3**
   B: **1** out of **3**
6. F: **1** out of **6**
   D: **1** out of **6**
7. A: **2** out of **5**
   C: **1** out of **5**
8. D: **1** out of **5**
   B: **3** out of **5**

Use with Grade 3, text pages 274–275.

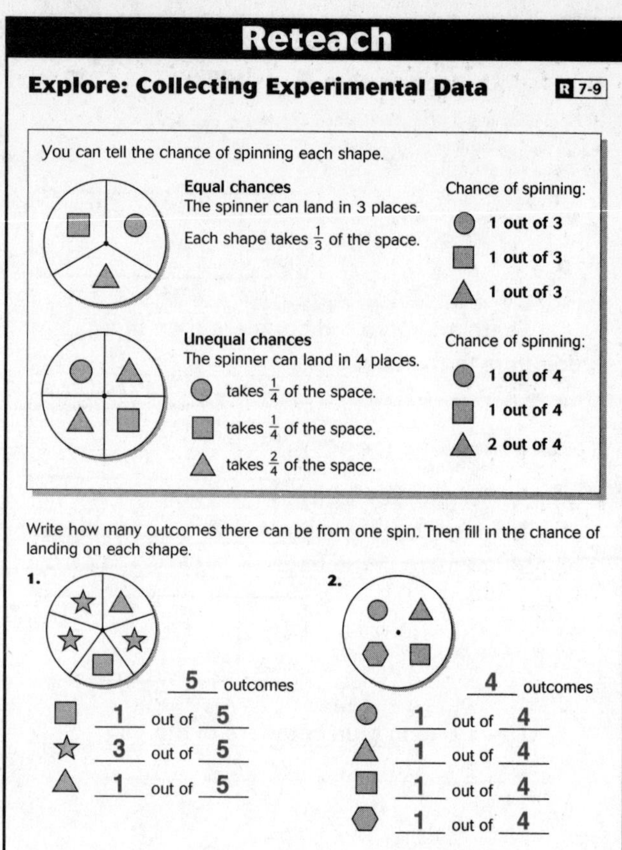

Reteach

Explore: Collecting Experimental Data

R 7-9

You can tell the chance of spinning each shape.

Equal chances
The spinner can land in 3 places.
Each shape takes $\frac{1}{3}$ of the space.

Chance of spinning:
● **1 out of 3**
■ **1 out of 3**
▲ **1 out of 3**

Unequal chances
The spinner can land in 4 places.
● takes $\frac{1}{4}$ of the space.
■ takes $\frac{1}{4}$ of the space.
▲ takes $\frac{2}{4}$ of the space.

Chance of spinning:
● **1 out of 4**
■ **1 out of 4**
▲ **2 out of 4**

Write how many outcomes there can be from one spin. Then fill in the chance of landing on each shape.

1. **5** outcomes
   ■ **1** out of **5**
   ☆ **3** out of **5**
   ▲ **1** out of **5**
2. **4** outcomes
   ● **1** out of **4**
   ▲ **1** out of **4**
   ■ **1** out of **4**
   ⬢ **1** out of **4**

Use with Grade 3, text pages 274–275.

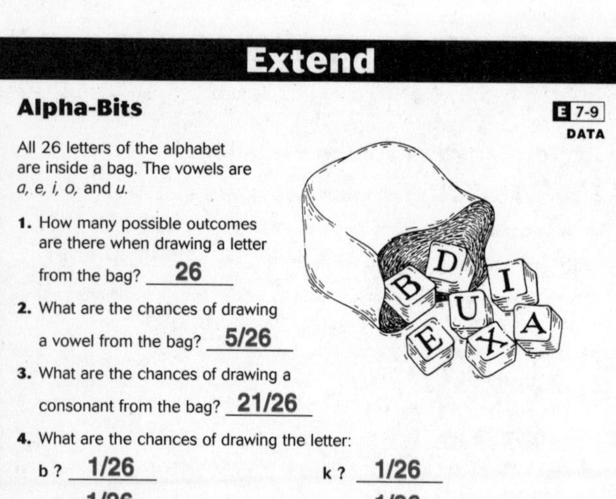

Extend

Alpha-Bits

E 7-9
DATA

All 26 letters of the alphabet are inside a bag. The vowels are *a, e, i, o,* and *u.*

1. How many possible outcomes are there when drawing a letter from the bag? **26**
2. What are the chances of drawing a vowel from the bag? **5/26**
3. What are the chances of drawing a consonant from the bag? **21/26**
4. What are the chances of drawing the letter:
   b ? **1/26** k ? **1/26**
   z ? **1/26** a ? **1/26**

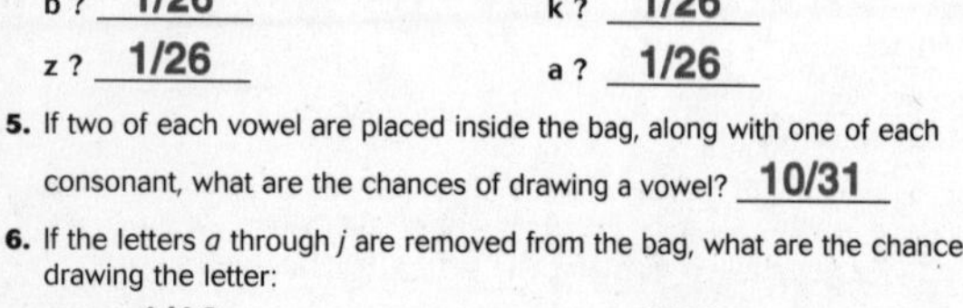

5. If two of each vowel are placed inside the bag, along with one of each consonant, what are the chances of drawing a vowel? **10/31**
6. If the letters *a* through *j* are removed from the bag, what are the chances of drawing the letter:
   m ? **1/16** u ? **1/16**
7. If all the vowels are removed from the bag, what are the chances of drawing a consonant? **1**
8. If the blocks for the numbers 1–9 are combined with the 26 letter blocks, what are the chances of drawing:
   a number? **9/35** a letter? **26/35**
   a vowel? **5/35 (or 1/7)** a consonant? **21/35 (or 3/5)**

Use with Grade 3, text pages 274–275.

Daily Review

Name ____________________

Daily Review 7-9

Explore: Collecting Experimental Data

1. For each spinner, name the possible outcomes of a spin. Then write the chance of spinning each outcome.

Spinner	Possible Outcomes	Chance for Each Outcome
1, 2, 3	1 2 3	1 out of 3 1 out of 3 1 out of 3
yellow, blue, yellow, red, yellow, red	blue red yellow	1 out of 6 2 out of 6 3 out of 6

Problem Solving

2. Cut out 20 small square pieces of paper. On five squares, write the number 1. On five squares, write the number 2. On ten squares, write the number 3. Put the squares in a bag and shake. Pick 1 square at a time. Put back the square after each pick. Do this 40 times. How many times do you think each number will be picked? Write your predictions in the table. Then do the experiment and write the actual outcome. **Outcomes will vary.**

Number	Prediction	Outcome
1	10	
2	10	
3	20	

Review and Remember

Find the answer. Use mental math.

3. 300 + 288 = **588**
4. 32 + 18 = **50**
5. 540 − 240 = **300**

Chapter 7 • Lesson 10

Practice

Problem Solving P 7-10

Fair and Unfair Games

Nan, Dan, and Fran use different spinners to play games. The player whose name appears on the spinner gets a point.

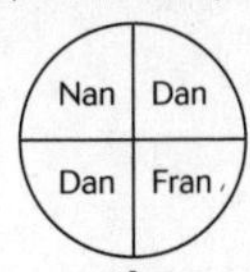

A

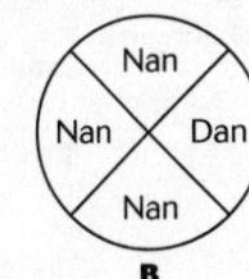

B

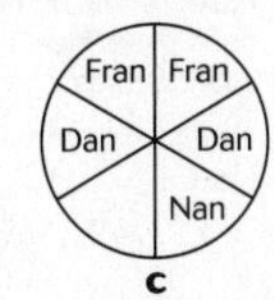

C

1. When Spinner A is used to play the game, who is most likely to win? Is this a fair spinner to use?
   Dan; not fair
2. Nan wants to use Spinner B to play the game, but Fran doesn't. Can you explain Fran's thinking?
   Possible answer: Fran cannot win the game; her name is not on the spinner.
3. Adding which name on Spinner C will make the spinner fair? Explain.
   Nan; then each player will have two sections.

Create Your Own

4. Make two spinners for Dan, Nan, and Fran to use. Make one spinner fair. Make the other spinner unfair.

This spinner is fair.

This spinner is unfair.

_______ will most likely win.

Check students' work.

Reteach

Problem Solving R 7-10

Fair and Unfair Games

Suppose you play a game with your friend, Pat. You take turns spinning the spinner. You get a point if you spin a ○. Pat gets a point if she spins a △. Is the game fair? If not, who is most likely to win?

1. How can you decide if the game is fair?

Understand You need to find out if the number of sections with ○ and with △ are equal. If they are, the game is fair. If they are not, the game is not fair.

Plan You can count the number of sections with ○ and △.

Solve There is **1** section(s) with ○.

There are **3** sections with △.

The game is not fair. Pat will probably win, since she gets a point when the spinner lands on △.

Look Back Look at the spinner again. There are more sections with △, so the answer makes sense.

2. Suppose you use the spinner below. Is the game fair? If not, which player is most likely to win?

Possible wording: fair; equal number of sections have ○ and △.

3. Suppose you use the spinner below. Is the game fair? If not, which player is most likely to win?

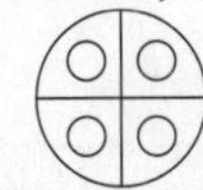

Possible wording: not fair; impossible for △ to win since all sections have ○.

Extend

Fair Play

E 7-10 PROBABILITY

Use the spinner to answer the question.

1. Sara's class spins 18 times. How many times do you think they spun a vowel? Why?
   About 6 times; 18 ÷ 6 = 3; 3 x 2 = 6

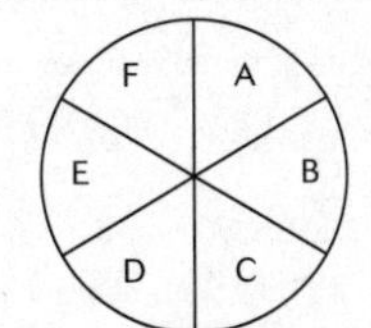

Play this game with a partner and 2 number cubes. One of you choose *even* and one of you choose *odd*. Each of you throw down a number cube, then multiply the 2 numbers that come up. If the product is *even*, the player with *even* gets a point. If *odd*, the player with *odd* gets the point.

2. Roll 20 times and keep track of your *even* and *odd* products with this tally table.

Even	Odd

3. and 4. Answers will vary but will probably show more even than odd products.

3. How many even products did you spin? ________
4. How many odd products did you spin? ________
5. Is this game fair? Explain. **No; only about ¼ of the products are odd. The player with odd stands almost no chance of winning.**

Daily Review

Name ________________________ Daily Review 7-10

Problem Solving

Fair and Unfair Games

Read and answer each question.

1. Lynn's number cube has odd numbers on four sides, and even numbers on the other two sides. When she rolls the cube, is it more likely or less likely that she will roll an even number?
   Less likely
2. Lauren's parents told her that if she picked a blue marble from a bag, they would go to the beach for their family vacation. If she picked a red marble, they would go to the theme park. A green marble would mean a trip to a lake. The bag has 4 blue marbles, 4 red marbles and 5 green marbles. Where is Lauren's family most likely to go on vacation?
   The lake
3. Your cube has six sides numbered 1, 2, 3, 4, 5, and 6. Which number are you most likely to roll and why?
   All numbers are equally likely because there is a 1 in 6 chance for each number.
4. A board game has a spinner with 4 different colors—red, blue, green, and orange. It has eight sections. There is an equal chance of spinning any color. Draw the spinner.
   Accept any spinner that has eight equal sections and two sections representing each color.

Review and Remember

Add.

5. 145 + 235 = **380**
6. 371 + 189 = **560**
7. 508 + 99 = **607**
8. 685 + 105 = **790**
9. 456 + 789 = **1,245**
10. 289 + 82 = **371**

Practice

Explore: Investigating Division

P 8-1

Use the pictures to answer the questions.

1. a. How many in all? 8
   b. How many groups? 2
   c. How many in each group? 4
   d. 8 ÷ 2 = 4

2. a. How many in all? 9
   b. How many groups? 3
   c. How many in each group? 3
   d. 9 ÷ 3 = 3

3. a. How many in all? 12
   b. How many groups? 4
   c. How many in each group? 3
   d. 12 ÷ 4 = 3

Solve. Then write a division sentence.

4. Subi wants to divide the merry-go-round tickets equally between herself and her brother.

   How many merry-go-round tickets can each person have?

   5 merry-go-round tickets 10 ÷ 2 = 5

5. The Cardoza's food stand has 12 pieces of bread left. It takes 2 pieces to make a sandwich.

   How many sandwiches can be made?

   6 sandwiches
   12 ÷ 2 = 6

 Use with Grade 3, text pages 288–289.

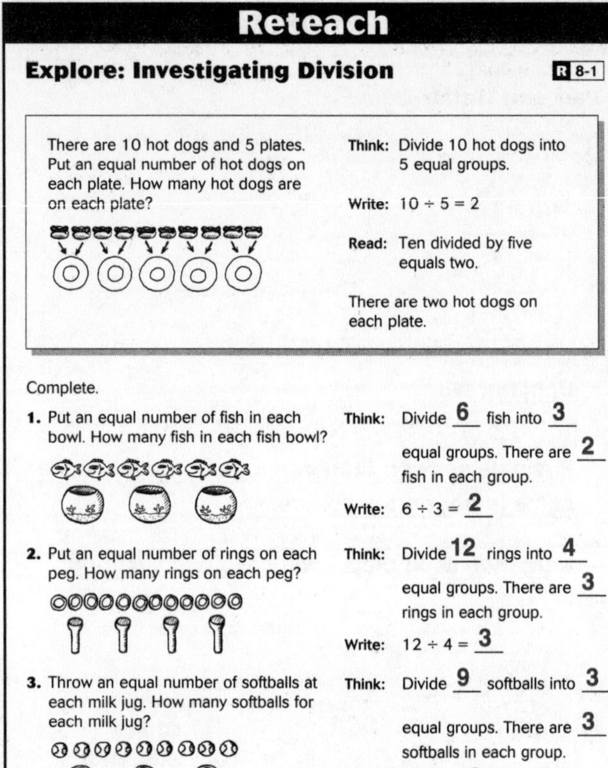

Reteach

Explore: Investigating Division

R 8-1

There are 10 hot dogs and 5 plates. Put an equal number of hot dogs on each plate. How many hot dogs are on each plate?

Think: Divide 10 hot dogs into 5 equal groups.

Write: 10 ÷ 5 = 2

Read: Ten divided by five equals two.

There are two hot dogs on each plate.

Complete.

1. Put an equal number of fish in each bowl. How many fish in each fish bowl?

   Think: Divide 6 fish into 3 equal groups. There are 2 fish in each group.

   Write: 6 ÷ 3 = 2

2. Put an equal number of rings on each peg. How many rings on each peg?

   Think: Divide 12 rings into 4 equal groups. There are 3 rings in each group.

   Write: 12 ÷ 4 = 3

3. Throw an equal number of softballs at each milk jug. How many softballs for each milk jug?

   Think: Divide 9 softballs into 3 equal groups. There are 3 softballs in each group.

   Write: 9 ÷ 3 = 3

 Use with Grade 3, text pages 288–289.

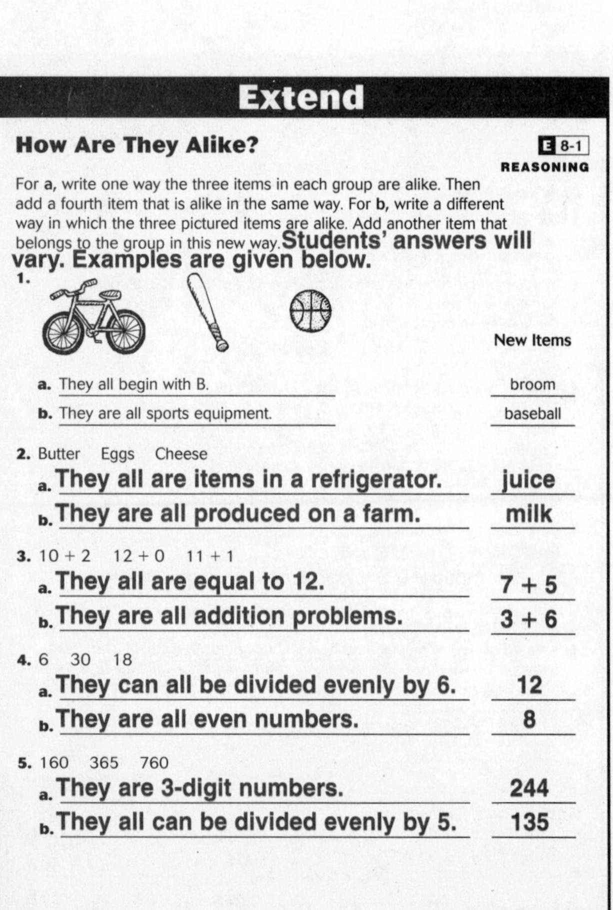

Extend

How Are They Alike?

E 8-1
REASONING

For **a**, write one way the three items in each group are alike. Then add a fourth item that is alike in the same way. For **b**, write a different way in which the three pictured items are alike. Add another item that belongs to the group in this new way. Students' answers will vary. Examples are given below.

1. New Items
   a. They all begin with B. — broom
   b. They are all sports equipment. — baseball

2. Butter Eggs Cheese
   a. They all are items in a refrigerator. — juice
   b. They are all produced on a farm. — milk

3. 10 + 2 12 + 0 11 + 1
   a. They all are equal to 12. — 7 + 5
   b. They are all addition problems. — 3 + 6

4. 6 30 18
   a. They can all be divided evenly by 6. — 12
   b. They are all even numbers. — 8

5. 160 365 760
   a. They are 3-digit numbers. — 244
   b. They all can be divided evenly by 5. — 135

 Use with Grade 3, text pages 288–289.

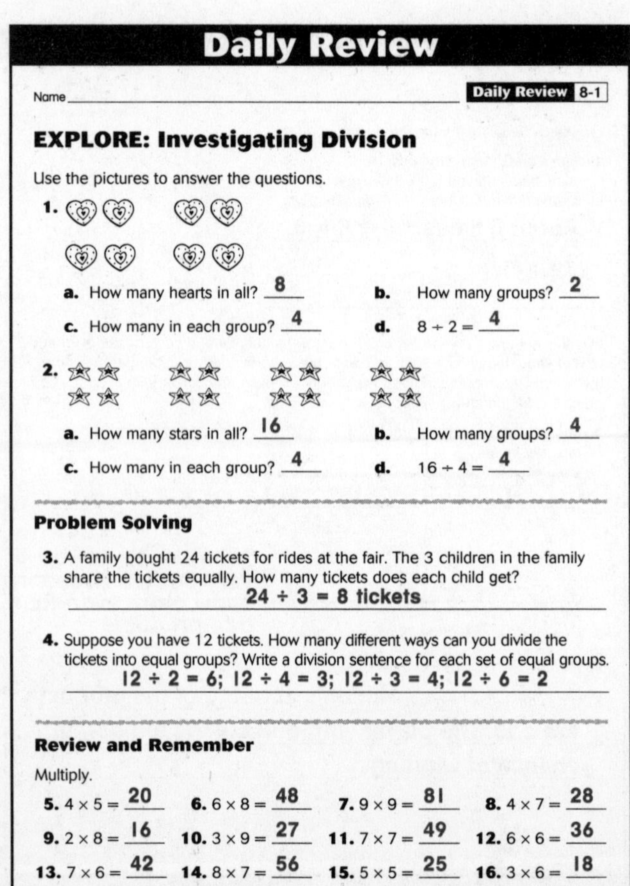

Daily Review

Name__________ Daily Review 8-1

EXPLORE: Investigating Division

Use the pictures to answer the questions.

1. a. How many hearts in all? 8
   b. How many groups? 2
   c. How many in each group? 4
   d. 8 ÷ 2 = 4

2. a. How many stars in all? 16
   b. How many groups? 4
   c. How many in each group? 4
   d. 16 ÷ 4 = 4

Problem Solving

3. A family bought 24 tickets for rides at the fair. The 3 children in the family share the tickets equally. How many tickets does each child get?
   24 ÷ 3 = 8 tickets

4. Suppose you have 12 tickets. How many different ways can you divide the tickets into equal groups? Write a division sentence for each set of equal groups.
   12 ÷ 2 = 6; 12 ÷ 4 = 3; 12 ÷ 3 = 4; 12 ÷ 6 = 2

Review and Remember

Multiply.

5. 4 × 5 = 20 6. 6 × 8 = 48 7. 9 × 9 = 81 8. 4 × 7 = 28
9. 2 × 8 = 16 10. 3 × 9 = 27 11. 7 × 7 = 49 12. 6 × 6 = 36
13. 7 × 6 = 42 14. 8 × 7 = 56 15. 5 × 5 = 25 16. 3 × 6 = 18

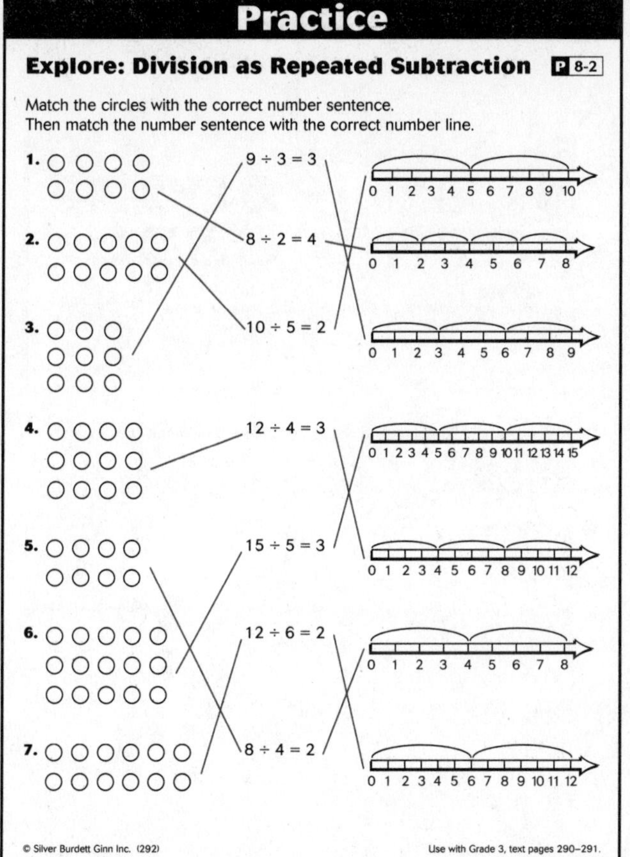

Practice

Explore: Division as Repeated Subtraction P 8-2

Match the circles with the correct number sentence.
Then match the number sentence with the correct number line.

1. ○○○○ ○○○○ — 9 ÷ 3 = 3
2. ○○○○○ ○○○○○ — 8 ÷ 2 = 4
3. ○○○ ○○○ ○○○ — 10 ÷ 5 = 2
4. ○○○○ ○○○○ ○○○○ — 12 ÷ 4 = 3
5. ○○○○ ○○○○ — 15 ÷ 5 = 3
6. ○○○○○ ○○○○○ ○○○○○ — 12 ÷ 6 = 2
7. ○○○○○○ ○○○○○○ — 8 ÷ 4 = 2

 Use with Grade 3, text pages 290–291.

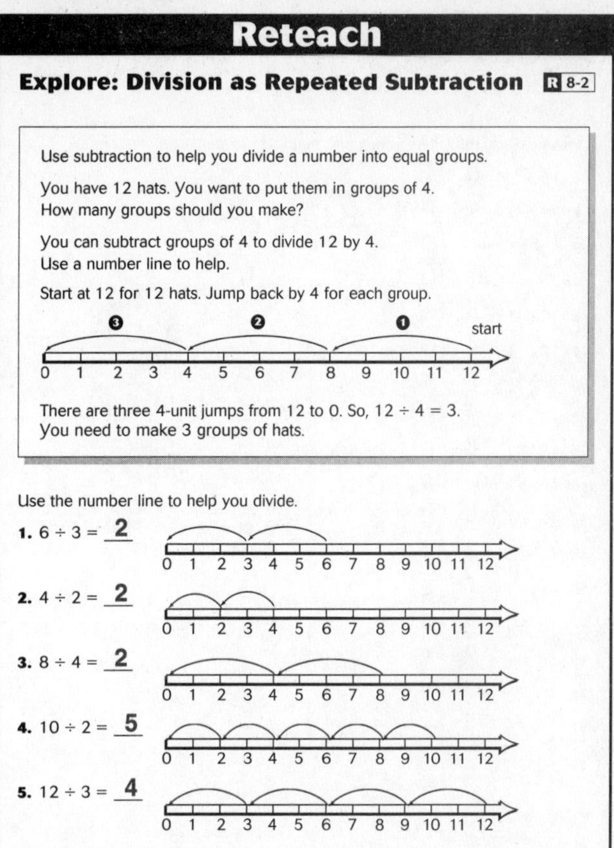

Reteach

Explore: Division as Repeated Subtraction R 8-2

Use subtraction to help you divide a number into equal groups.

You have 12 hats. You want to put them in groups of 4.
How many groups should you make?

You can subtract groups of 4 to divide 12 by 4.
Use a number line to help.

Start at 12 for 12 hats. Jump back by 4 for each group.

There are three 4-unit jumps from 12 to 0. So, 12 ÷ 4 = 3.
You need to make 3 groups of hats.

Use the number line to help you divide.

1. 6 ÷ 3 = **2**
2. 4 ÷ 2 = **2**
3. 8 ÷ 4 = **2**
4. 10 ÷ 2 = **5**
5. 12 ÷ 3 = **4**

 Use with Grade 3, text pages 290–291.

Extend

Add a Sign E 8-2 NUMBER SENSE

Write a plus sign or a minus sign somewhere in each problem to get the answer shown. One is done for you.

1. 4 3 − 2 1 = 22
2. 1 2 + 3 4 = 46
3. 5 5 5 + 5 = 560
4. 9 9 9 − 9 9 = 900
5. 6 7 8 − 9 = 669
6. 3 + 4 3 4 3 = 4,346
7. 7 6 5 − 4 3 = 722
8. 9 1 9 1 − 9 = 9,182
9. 3 3 3 + 3 3 = 366
10. 8 8 8 + 8 8 8 = 1,776

SIGNS FOR SALE

Create Your Own Check students' equations.

Use the numbers below to create your own add-a-sign problems. Write a sum or difference after each equal sign and give your problems to a classmate to solve.

11. 4 4 4 4 = ______
12. 6 5 4 3 2 1 = ______
13. 9 8 9 8 9 = ______
14. 3 2 1 1 2 3 = ______

 Use with Grade 3, text pages 290–291.

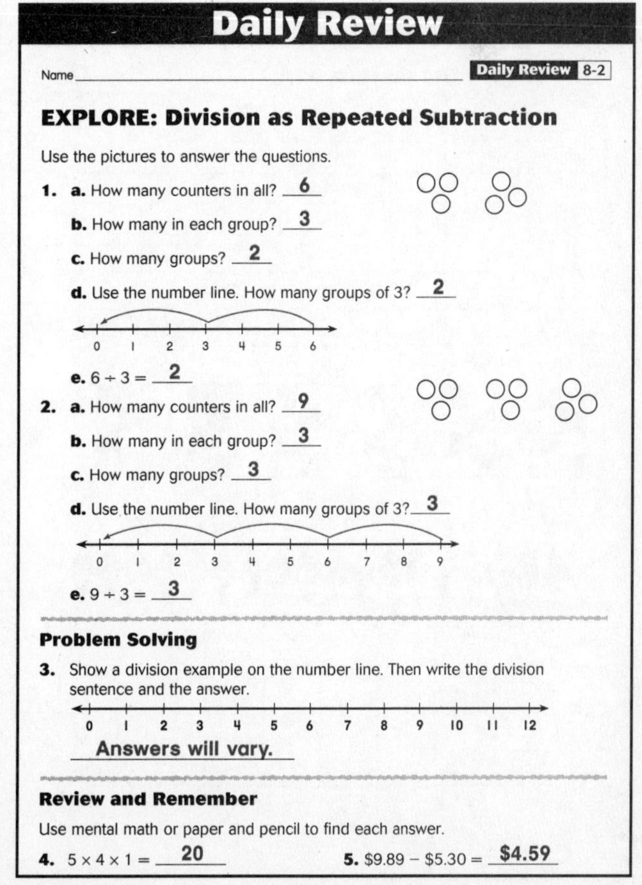

Daily Review

Name ______ Daily Review 8-2

EXPLORE: Division as Repeated Subtraction

Use the pictures to answer the questions.

1. a. How many counters in all? **6**
   b. How many in each group? **3**
   c. How many groups? **2**
   d. Use the number line. How many groups of 3? **2**
   e. 6 ÷ 3 = **2**
2. a. How many counters in all? **9**
   b. How many in each group? **3**
   c. How many groups? **3**
   d. Use the number line. How many groups of 3? **3**
   e. 9 ÷ 3 = **3**

Problem Solving

3. Show a division example on the number line. Then write the division sentence and the answer.
   Answers will vary.

Review and Remember

Use mental math or paper and pencil to find each answer.

4. 5 × 4 × 1 = **20**
5. \$9.89 − \$5.30 = **\$4.59**

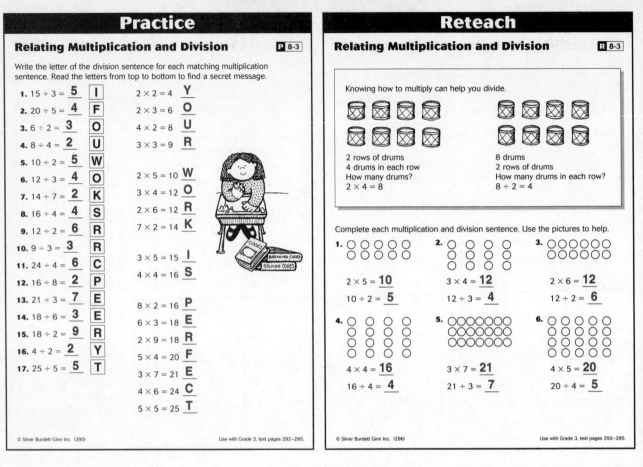

Chapter 8 • Lesson 3

Practice

Relating Multiplication and Division — P 8-3

Write the letter of the division sentence for each matching multiplication sentence. Read the letters from top to bottom to find a secret message.

1. 15 ÷ 3 =	5	I
2. 20 ÷ 5 =	4	F
3. 6 ÷ 2 =	3	O
4. 8 ÷ 4 =	2	U
5. 10 ÷ 2 =	5	W
6. 12 ÷ 3 =	4	O
7. 14 ÷ 7 =	2	K
8. 16 ÷ 4 =	4	S
9. 12 ÷ 2 =	6	R
10. 9 ÷ 3 =	3	R
11. 24 ÷ 4 =	6	C
12. 16 ÷ 8 =	2	P
13. 21 ÷ 3 =	7	E
14. 18 ÷ 6 =	3	E
15. 18 ÷ 2 =	9	R
16. 4 ÷ 2 =	2	Y
17. 25 ÷ 5 =	5	T

2 × 2 = 4 Y
2 × 3 = 6 O
4 × 2 = 8 U
3 × 3 = 9 R

2 × 5 = 10 W
3 × 4 = 12 O
2 × 6 = 12 R
7 × 2 = 14 K

3 × 5 = 15 I
4 × 4 = 16 S

8 × 2 = 16 P
6 × 3 = 18 E
2 × 9 = 18 R
5 × 4 = 20 F
3 × 7 = 21 E
4 × 6 = 24 C
5 × 5 = 25 T

BREAKING CODES
SOLVING CODES
CODES

Use with Grade 3, text pages 292–295.

Reteach

Relating Multiplication and Division — R 8-3

Knowing how to multiply can help you divide.

2 rows of drums
4 drums in each row
How many drums?
2 × 4 = 8

8 drums
2 rows of drums
How many drums in each row?
8 ÷ 2 = 4

Complete each multiplication and division sentence. Use the pictures to help.

1. 2 × 5 = **10**; 10 ÷ 2 = **5**
2. 3 × 4 = **12**; 12 ÷ 3 = **4**
3. 2 × 6 = **12**; 12 ÷ 2 = **6**
4. 4 × 4 = **16**; 16 ÷ 4 = **4**
5. 3 × 7 = **21**; 21 ÷ 3 = **7**
6. 4 × 5 = **20**; 20 ÷ 4 = **5**

Use with Grade 3, text pages 292–295.

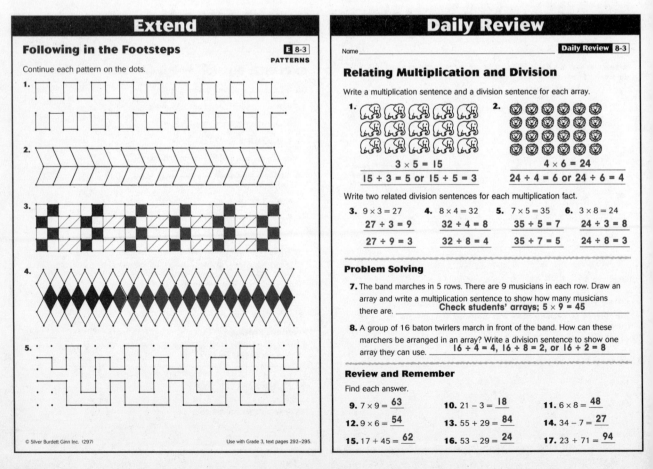

Extend

Following in the Footsteps — E 8-3

PATTERNS

Continue each pattern on the dots.

1.

2.

3.

4.

5.

Use with Grade 3, text pages 292–295.

Daily Review

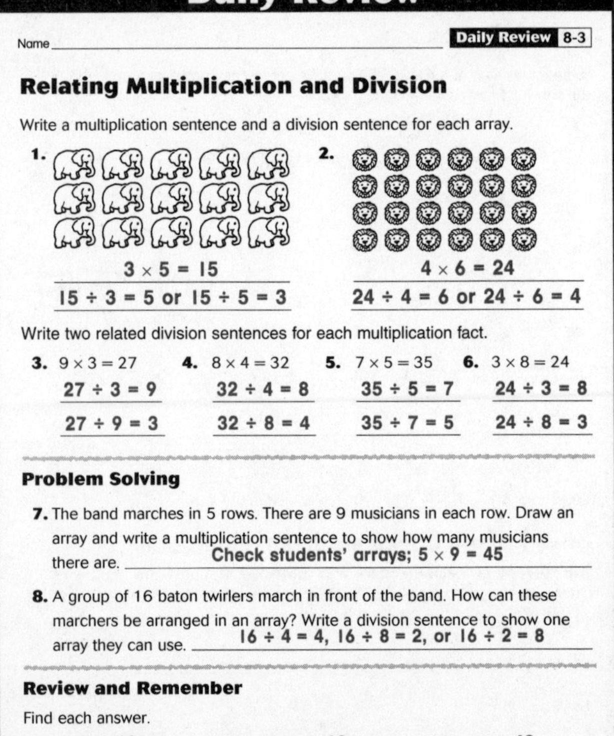

Name ____________ Daily Review 8-3

Relating Multiplication and Division

Write a multiplication sentence and a division sentence for each array.

1. **3 × 5 = 15**
15 ÷ 3 = 5 or 15 ÷ 5 = 3
2. **4 × 6 = 24**
24 ÷ 4 = 6 or 24 ÷ 6 = 4

Write two related division sentences for each multiplication fact.

3. 9 × 3 = 27 — **27 ÷ 3 = 9**; **27 ÷ 9 = 3**
4. 8 × 4 = 32 — **32 ÷ 4 = 8**; **32 ÷ 8 = 4**
5. 7 × 5 = 35 — **35 ÷ 5 = 7**; **35 ÷ 7 = 5**
6. 3 × 8 = 24 — **24 ÷ 3 = 8**; **24 ÷ 8 = 3**

Problem Solving

7. The band marches in 5 rows. There are 9 musicians in each row. Draw an array and write a multiplication sentence to show how many musicians there are. **Check students' arrays; 5 × 9 = 45**
8. A group of 16 baton twirlers march in front of the band. How can these marchers be arranged in an array? Write a division sentence to show one array they can use. **16 ÷ 4 = 4, 16 ÷ 8 = 2, or 16 ÷ 2 = 8**

Review and Remember

Find each answer.

9. 7 × 9 = **63**	10. 21 − 3 = **18**	11. 6 × 8 = **48**
12. 9 × 6 = **54**	13. 55 + 29 = **84**	14. 34 − 7 = **27**
15. 17 + 45 = **62**	16. 53 − 29 = **24**	17. 23 + 71 = **94**

Practice

Dividing by 2

P 8-4

Use the picture to find the quotient.

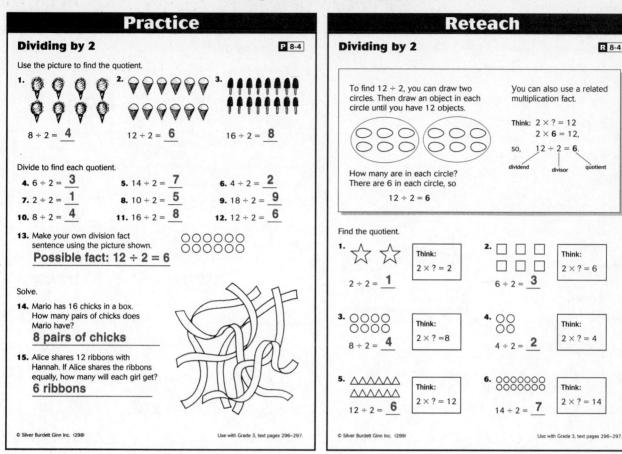

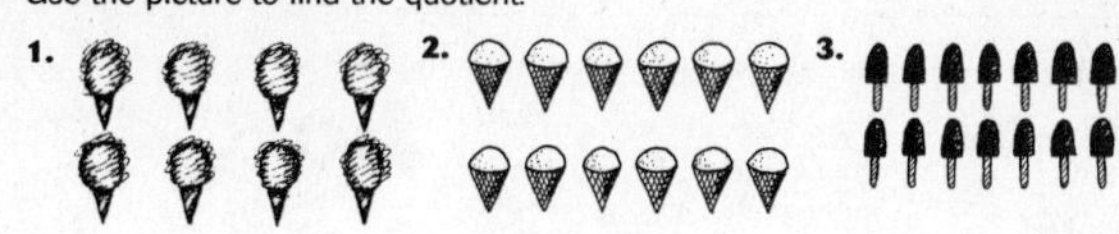

1. 8 ÷ 2 = 4
2. 12 ÷ 2 = 6
3. 16 ÷ 2 = 8

Divide to find each quotient.

4. 6 ÷ 2 = 3
5. 14 ÷ 2 = 7
6. 4 ÷ 2 = 2
7. 2 ÷ 2 = 1
8. 10 ÷ 2 = 5
9. 18 ÷ 2 = 9
10. 8 ÷ 2 = 4
11. 16 ÷ 2 = 8
12. 12 ÷ 2 = 6
13. Make your own division fact sentence using the picture shown. ○○○○○○ ○○○○○○
Possible fact: 12 ÷ 2 = 6

Solve.

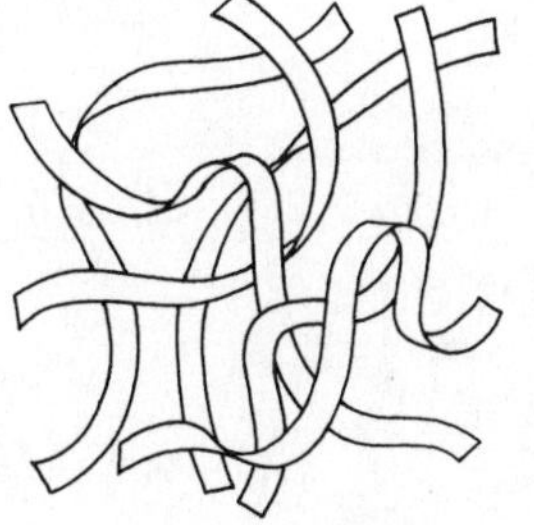

14. Mario has 16 chicks in a box. How many pairs of chicks does Mario have?
8 pairs of chicks
15. Alice shares 12 ribbons with Hannah. If Alice shares the ribbons equally, how many will each girl get?
6 ribbons

Use with Grade 3, text pages 296–297.

Reteach

Dividing by 2

R 8-4

To find 12 ÷ 2, you can draw two circles. Then draw an object in each circle until you have 12 objects.

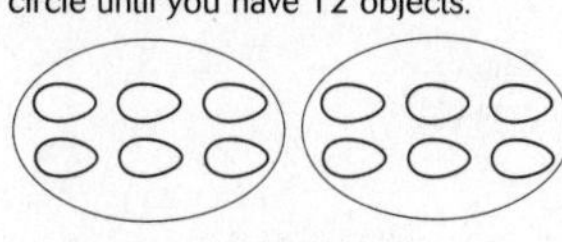

How many are in each circle?
There are 6 in each circle, so

12 ÷ 2 = **6**

You can also use a related multiplication fact.

Think: 2 × ? = 12
2 × **6** = 12,
so, 12 ÷ 2 = **6**.

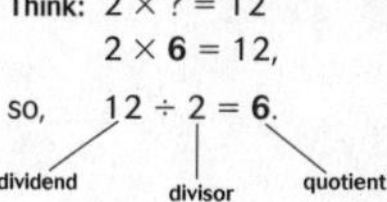

Find the quotient.

1. 
2 ÷ 2 = 1 — Think: 2 × ? = 2
2. 6 ÷ 2 = 3 — Think: 2 × ? = 6
3. 8 ÷ 2 = 4 — Think: 2 × ? = 8
4. 4 ÷ 2 = 2 — Think: 2 × ? = 4
5. 12 ÷ 2 = 6 — Think: 2 × ? = 12
6. 14 ÷ 2 = 7 — Think: 2 × ? = 14

Use with Grade 3, text pages 296–297.

Extend

Number Puzzlers

E 8-4
REASONING

Find the pair of numbers for each puzzler. Write the pair of numbers next to the puzzler. Then write the letter for the pair of numbers in the blank at the bottom of the page. When you are done, you will solve this riddle:

"How does Samantha know whether to subtract or divide?"

1. Sum is 4, quotient is 1. — 2, 2 — D
2. Difference is 2, quotient is 2. — 4, 2 — F
3. Difference is 4, quotient is 3. — 6, 2 — H
4. Sum is 10, quotient is 9. — 9, 1 — I
5. Difference is 6, quotient is 4. — 8, 2 — S
6. Sum is 5, product is 6. — 2, 3 — K
7. Sum is 7, product is 10. — 2, 5 — O
8. Difference is 8, quotient is 5. — 10, 2 — E
9. Sum is 9, product is 14. — 2, 7 — W
10. Sum is 20, quotient is 9. — 18, 2 — N
11. Difference is 14, quotient is 8. — 16, 2 — T
12. Difference is 12, quotient is 7. — 14, 2 — R
13. Sum is 14, quotient is 6. — 12, 2 — C

S	H	E		K	N	O	W	S		T	H	E
8,2	6,2	10,2		2,3	18,2	2,5	2,7	8,2		16,2	6,2	10,2

D	I	F	F	E	R	E	N	C	E
2,2	9,1	4,2	4,2	10,2	14,2	10,2	18,2	12,2	10,2

Use with Grade 3, text pages 296–297.

Daily Review

Name ____________________

Daily Review 8-4

Dividing by 2

Use the multiplication fact to find each quotient.

1. 2 × 5 = 10; 10 ÷ 2 = 5
2. 2 × 3 = 6; 6 ÷ 2 = 3
3. 2 × 7 = 14; 14 ÷ 2 = 7
4. 2 × 4 = 8; 8 ÷ 2 = 4

Find each quotient.

5. 4 ÷ 2 = 2
6. 18 ÷ 2 = 9
7. 8 ÷ 2 = 4
8. 16 ÷ 2 = 8
9. 14 ÷ 2 = 7
10. 12 ÷ 2 = 6
11. 6 ÷ 2 = 3
12. 10 ÷ 2 = 5
13. 16 ÷ 2 = 8
14. 2 ÷ 2 = 1
15. 14 ÷ 2 = 7
16. 12 ÷ 2 = 6

Problem Solving

17. In the relay race, each of 6 people on a team have to run 2 laps. If Bill's team has run 8 laps, how many people have not yet run? **2 people**
18. Twenty people won prizes at the fair. Ten of these people won stuffed animals. Half of the remaining people won gift certificates. How many people won gift certificates? **5 people**

Review and Remember

Use the pictograph to solve.

19. The band has the most of which kind of instrument?
woodwind
20. How many percussion instruments are in the band?
10 percussion
21. How many more woodwind are there than brass instruments?
5 more

Instruments in the Band

Kind of Instrument	Number
Brass	◎ ◎ ◎
Woodwind	◎ ◎ ◎ ◎
Percussion	◎ ◎

Each ◎ stands for 5 instruments

Chapter 8 • Lesson 5

Practice

Dividing by 3

P 8-5

Find the missing factor. Use it to help you divide.

1. 3 × **4** = 12　12 ÷ 3 = **4**
2. 3 × **8** = 24　24 ÷ 3 = **8**
3. 3 × **6** = 18　18 ÷ 3 = **6**

Find the quotient.

4. 3 ÷ 3 = **1**
5. 9 ÷ 3 = **3**
6. 12 ÷ 2 = **6**
7. 6 ÷ 3 = **2**
8. 15 ÷ 3 = **5**
9. 21 ÷ 3 = **7**
10. 18 ÷ 2 = **9**
11. 6 ÷ 2 = **3**
12. 27 ÷ 3 = **9**

Solve.
Use the sign for problems 13–15.

13. How many times can Will ride the ferris wheel if he has 14 tickets?
7 rides

14. Mr. Ramos wants to ride the roller coaster. He has 15 tickets. How many rides can he take?
5 rides

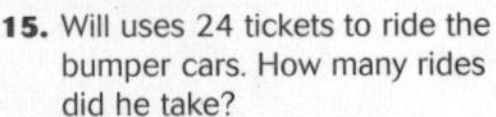

FUN RIDES
Ferris wheel 2 tickets per ride
Roller coaster 3 tickets per ride
Bumper cars 3 tickets per ride

15. Will uses 24 tickets to ride the bumper cars. How many rides did he take?
8 rides

16. Make your own word problem for the division fact 18 ÷ 3 = ? Then solve.
Problems will vary. 18 ÷ 3 = 6

 Use with Grade 3, text pages 298–299.

Reteach

Dividing by 3

R 8-5

You can use objects or repeated subtraction to divide by 3.

15 ÷ 3 = ?　Draw a dot in one circle, then in the next circle, then in the next, until you have drawn 15 dots.

There are 5 dots in each circle. So, 15 ÷ 3 = 5.

Find the quotient. Use the pictures to help you.

1. 6 ÷ 3 = **2**
2. 12 ÷ 3 = **4**

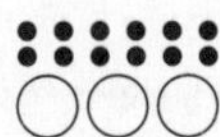

3. 9 ÷ 3 = **3**

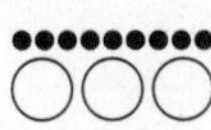

4. 3 ÷ 3 = **1**

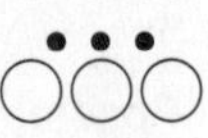

5. 15 ÷ 3 = **5**

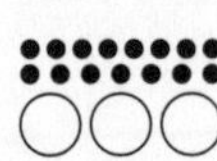

6. 18 ÷ 3 = **6**

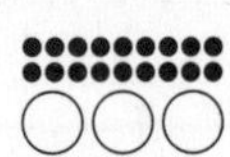

Find the quotient.

7. 6 ÷ 3 = **2**
8. 15 ÷ 3 = **5**
9. 21 ÷ 3 = **7**
10. 18 ÷ 2 = **9**
11. 6 ÷ 2 = **3**
12. 27 ÷ 3 = **9**

 Use with Grade 3, text pages 298–299.

Extend

Back to the Beginning

E 8-5
PATTERNS

Complete the first 4 rows. Can you fill in the rest of the table by following the patterns?

27 ÷ 3 = **9**	× 2 = **18**	÷ 2 = **9**	× 3 = **27**
24 ÷ 3 = **8**	× 2 = **16**	÷ 2 = **8**	× 3 = **24**
21 ÷ 3 = **7**	× 2 = **14**	÷ 2 = **7**	× 3 = **21**
18 ÷ 3 = **6**	× 2 = **12**	÷ 2 = **6**	× 3 = **18**
15 ÷ 3 = **5**	× 2 = **10**	÷ 2 = **5**	× 3 = **15**
12 ÷ 3 = **4**	× 2 = **8**	÷ 2 = **4**	× 3 = **12**
9 ÷ 3 = **3**	× 2 = **6**	÷ 2 = **3**	× 3 = **9**
6 ÷ 3 = **2**	× 2 = **4**	÷ 2 = **2**	× 3 = **6**
3 ÷ 3 = **1**	× 2 = **2**	÷ 2 = **1**	× 3 = **3**

Describe the patterns in the table.

Answers will vary. Possible patterns: the first column is the numbers from 9 to 1; the second column begins at 18 and counts down by two; the third column is the same as the second; the final column is the same as the original numbers.

 Use with Grade 3, text pages 298–299.

Daily Review

Name ______________________

Daily Review 8-5

Dividing by 3

Find the missing factor. Use it to help you divide.

1. 3 × **4** = 12　12 ÷ 3 = **4**
2. 3 × **5** = 15　15 ÷ 3 = **5**
3. 3 × **2** = 6　6 ÷ 3 = **2**
4. 3 × **7** = 21　21 ÷ 3 = **7**

Find the quotient.

5. 9 ÷ 3 = **3**
6. 18 ÷ 3 = **6**
7. 12 ÷ 3 = **4**
8. 21 ÷ 3 = **7**
9. 24 ÷ 3 = **8**
10. 3 ÷ 3 = **1**
11. 27 ÷ 3 = **9**
12. 6 ÷ 3 = **2**
13. 12 ÷ 3 = **4**
14. 21 ÷ 3 = **7**
15. 18 ÷ 3 = **6**
16. 15 ÷ 3 = **5**

Problem Solving

17. A dollmaker has 24 pieces of fabric. Each doll needs a piece of fabric for the head, a piece of fabric for the torso, and a piece of fabric for the legs. How many dolls can the dollmaker make? **24 ÷ 3 = 8 dolls**

18. Handmade ornaments are placed in rows in boxes. There can be 18 ornaments in a box. How can the ornaments be arranged in rows in a box? Write division sentences to show the rows.
18 ÷ 2 = 9; 18 ÷ 3 = 6; 18 ÷ 6 = 3

Review and Remember

Round to the nearest ten to estimate each answer.

19. 45 + 18 **70**
20. 82 − 29 **50**
21. 93 − 47 **40**
22. 64 + 22 **80**
23. 84 − 36 **40**
24. 57 + 18 **80**
25. 61 − 29 **30**
26. 43 + 34 **70**

Chapter 8 • Lesson 6

Practice

Problem Solving P 8-6

Multistep Problems

Circle the best choice for each question.

Rachel has 2 trays of 7 mum plants each. Then she buys 4 trays of zinnias with 6 plants in each tray. How many more zinnia plants than mum plants does Rachel have?

1. How can you find the total number of zinnia plants?

a. add 2 + 7 + 4 + 6

b. multiply 4 × 6 (circled)

c. multiply 2 × 4

2. How can you find the total number of mum plants?

a. add 2 + 7

b. multiply 7 × 6

c. multiply 2 × 7 (circled)

3. How can you solve the problem?

a. add the number of mum plants and zinnia plants

b. subtract the number of zinnia plants from mum plants

c. subtract the number of mum plants from zinnia plants (circled)

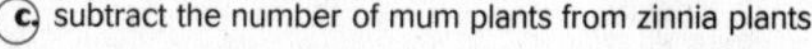

Wade can buy mulch for $4 per bag. If he buys 10 bags or more, the cost is $3 per bag. Wade needs 9 bags of mulch. How much money can Wade save by buying 10 bags of mulch?

4. How can you find the total cost for 9 bags of mulch?

a. multiply $4 × 9 (circled)

b. multiply $3 × 9

c. multiply $3 × 10

5. What number sentence tells the cost of 10 bags of mulch?

a. multiply $4 × 9 = $36

b. multiply $4 × 10 = $40

c. multiply $3 × 10 = $30 (circled)

6. Show the steps you would take to solve the problem.

9 bags x $4 = $36; 10 bags x $3 = $30;
$36 – $30 = $6 saving

Use with Grade 3, text pages 300–301.

Reteach

Problem Solving R 8-6

Multistep Problems

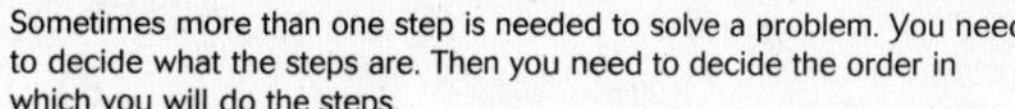

Sometimes more than one step is needed to solve a problem. You need to decide what the steps are. Then you need to decide the order in which you will do the steps.

Maria bought 4 azalea bushes for $7 each. She gave the clerk $30. How much change should Maria get?

Step 1 Find the total cost of 4 azalea bushes.
4 azalea bushes for $7 each = 4 × $7 = $28

Step 2 Find the difference between the cost of the azalea bushes and the amount Marie gave the clerk.

$30 – $28 = $2
(money to clerk) (cost of bushes) (change)

Maria plants a total of 15 bushes. She has 3 rose bushes and 7 azalea bushes. The rest are juniper bushes. How many juniper bushes does she have?

1. How many rose and azalea bushes does Maria plant? 10 bushes

2. How many juniper bushes does Maria plant? 5 bushes

3. How many steps did you need to solve the problem? 2 steps

4. Explain the steps in the order that you completed them.

a. Find the sum of the azalea and rose bushes.

b. Find the difference between the sum of the rose and azalea bushes and total number of bushes.

Use with Grade 3, text pages 300–301.

Extend

Video Viewers

E 8-6 **REASONING**

Solve.

1. Damien wants to watch three 6-minute cartoon videos and play some 3-minute video games. He has 30 minutes. How many video games can he play?

4 video games

2. If it takes 1 minute to load a video game and 5 minutes to play, how many different video games can be played in 60 minutes?

10 video games

3. Jack, Jill, Jennie, Josh, and Jonah each watched a different kind of video at the video store. The schedule for showing videos is shown.

12:00 – Mystery	2:00 – Travel	4:00 – History
6:00 – Comedy	8:00 – Adventure	

Which video did each person see? Use the clues below. Write *yes* or *no* in every box you can. Use one clue to help with another clue.

Hint: There is only one *yes* in every row and every column.

Clue A: Jack did not watch the mystery or the travel video.
Clue B: Jill can only watch a video after 6:30.
Clue C: Jennie and Josh did not see the history or the travel video.
Clue D: Josh could not watch a video after 2:00.

	Jack	Jill	Jennie	Josh	Jonah
12:00 Mystery	no	no	no	yes	no
2:00 Travel	no	no	no	no	yes
4:00 History	yes	no	no	no	no
6:00 Comedy	no	no	yes	no	no
8:00 Adventure	no	yes	no	no	no

Use with Grade 3, text pages 300–301.

Daily Review

Name______________________ Daily Review 8-6

Problem Solving

Multistep Problems

Answer each question.

1. Kristin wants to buy 8 balloons. Each one costs $1.50. She has a ten-dollar bill, a one-dollar bill and 5 quarters. Will she have enough money to buy the balloons?

What would you do to first solve the problem?

Find how much money 8 balloons cost.

What is the final step you need to do to solve the problem?

Compare the amount of money Kristin has to the cost of the balloons.

2. Marty has a 23-hour project to do. He has already worked on it for 5 hours. If Marty works 2 hours every day, how many days will it take him to complete the project?

9 days

3. Susan wants to send 3 greeting cards. She needs a special 42¢ stamp on each card. She gives the clerk a $5 bill. Will she get change back? If so, how much?

Yes; $3.74

Review and Remember

Add.

4. 43 + 18 = 61

5. 36 + 56 = 92

6. 57 + 24 = 81

7. 61 + 30 = 91

8. 504 + 102 = 606 **9.** 713 + 192 = 905 **10.** 56 + 381 = 437

Practice

Dividing by 4

P 8-7

Divide.

1. $4\overline{)12}$ 3
2. $4\overline{)8}$ 2
3. $3\overline{)18}$ 6
4. $4\overline{)4}$ 1
5. $4\overline{)28}$ 7
6. $2\overline{)16}$ 8
7. $4\overline{)16}$ 4
8. $4\overline{)24}$ 6
9. $3\overline{)15}$ 5
10. $4\overline{)20}$ 5
11. $4\overline{)32}$ 8
12. $4\overline{)36}$ 9
13. 16 ÷ 4 = 4
14. 8 ÷ 4 = 2
15. 12 ÷ 4 = 3
16. 24 ÷ 4 = 6
17. 32 ÷ 4 = 8
18. 28 ÷ 4 = 7
19. 36 ÷ 4 = 9
20. 4 ÷ 4 = 1
21. 20 ÷ 4 = 5

22. Complete the table.

Number of cows	1	2	3	4	5	6	7	8	9
Number of legs	4	8	12	16	20	24	28	32	36

Solve.

23. Rochelle has 24 tickets. She wants to ride the Ferris wheel. Each ride costs 4 tickets. How many rides can she take?
Rochelle can take 6 rides.

24. There are 4 hot dog buns in a package. If the hot dog vendor needs 12 buns, how many packages should he buy?
3 packages

Use with Grade 3, text pages 304–305.

Reteach

Dividing by 4

R 8-7

You can use objects or repeated subtraction to divide by 4.

20 ÷ 4 = ? Draw a dot in one circle. Then draw in the next circle, then in the next, until you have drawn 20 dots.

There are 5 dots in each circle. So, 20 ÷ 4 = 5.

Find the quotient. Use the pictures to help you.

1. 12 ÷ 4 = 3
2. 16 ÷ 4 = 4
3. 8 ÷ 4 = 2
4. 24 ÷ 4 = 6

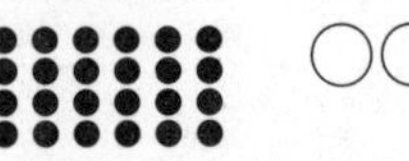

Find the quotient.

5. 28 ÷ 4 = 7
6. 4 ÷ 4 = 1
7. 36 ÷ 4 = 9
8. $4\overline{)16}$ 4
9. $4\overline{)20}$ 5
10. $4\overline{)8}$ 2
11. $4\overline{)32}$ 8

Use with Grade 3, text pages 304–305.

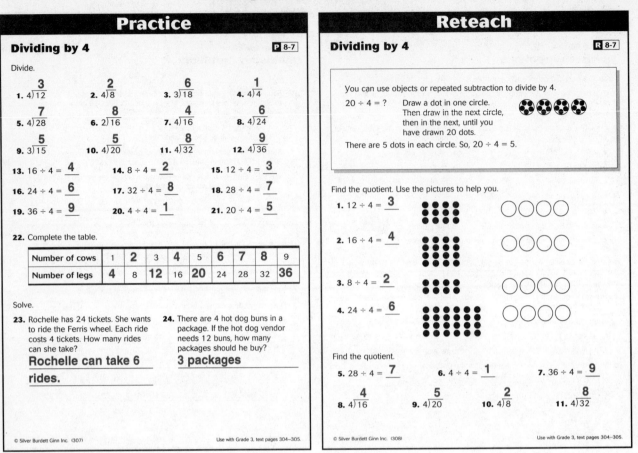

Extend

Who Lives Where?

E 8-7
REASONING

Meg, Linda, Ruth, Jake, Kevin, and Fred live in a row of six houses. Use the clues below to help you figure out who lives in which house. Then write the name of the person on the correct line.

- Fred's house has 2 chimneys, but it is not on the end.
- Meg lives next door to Fred.
- Ruth lives in an end house with no chimneys.
- Kevin's house is the tallest.
- Linda does not live next door to Meg.

Linda Kevin Jake Meg Fred Ruth

Use with Grade 3, text pages 304–305.

Daily Review

Name ____________

Daily Review 8-7

Dividing by 4

Draw an array to help you complete the related facts.

1. 4 × 5 = 20
20 ÷ 4 = 5
2. 4 × 8 = 32
32 ÷ 4 = 8
3. 4 × 4 = 16
16 ÷ 4 = 4

Divide.

4. $4\overline{)36}$ 9
5. $4\overline{)4}$ 1
6. $4\overline{)20}$ 5
7. $4\overline{)24}$ 6
8. $4\overline{)8}$ 2
9. $4\overline{)28}$ 7
10. $4\overline{)36}$ 9
11. $4\overline{)12}$ 3
12. $4\overline{)16}$ 4
13. $3\overline{)18}$ 6
14. 8 ÷ 2 = 4
15. 20 ÷ 4 = 5
16. 36 ÷ 9 = 4
17. 21 ÷ 3 = 7

Problem Solving

18. Four clowns at the fair are putting on a show. A group of 32 children watch the show. The children break up into equal groups to watch each clown. How many children are in each group? 32 ÷ 4 = 8 children

19. The 4 clowns do a juggling act. There are 16 balls to juggle. Two clowns each have 2 more balls than the other 2 clowns. How many balls does each clown have? 2 clowns have 5 balls each. 2 clowns have 3 balls each.

Review and Remember

Solve.

20. 6 × 9 = 54
21. 292 + 302 = 594
22. 7 × 5 = 35
23. 364 − 128 = 236
24. 5 × 4 = 20

Chapter 8 • Lesson 8

Practice

Dividing by 5

P 8-8

Divide.

1. 20 ÷ 4 = **5**
2. 30 ÷ 5 = **6**
3. 45 ÷ 5 = **9**
4. 5 ÷ 5 = **1**
5. 15 ÷ 5 = **3**
6. 20 ÷ 5 = **4**
7. 25 ÷ 5 = **5**
8. 32 ÷ 4 = **8**
9. 40 ÷ 5 = **8**
10. 5)10 **2**
11. 5)5 **1**
12. 5)20 **4**
13. 4)12 **3**
14. 5)25 **5**
15. 4)24 **6**
16. 3)18 **6**
17. 5)35 **7**
18. 5)40 **8**
19. 4)36 **9**
20. 2)18 **9**
21. 5)45 **9**

Follow each rule to complete the table.

22. Rule: Divide by 2

Input	Output
18	9
12	**6**
8	**4**
16	**8**

23. Rule: Divide by 3

Input	Output
12	4
9	**3**
15	**5**
27	**9**

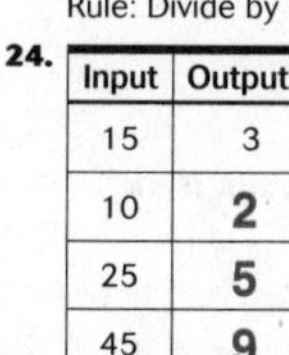

24. Rule: Divide by 5

Input	Output
15	3
10	**2**
25	**5**
45	**9**

Solve.

25. Thirty students sit at 5 lunch tables every day. How many students are at one table, if the same number of students sit at each table?

There are 6 students at each table.

Reteach

Dividing by 5

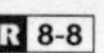

R 8-8

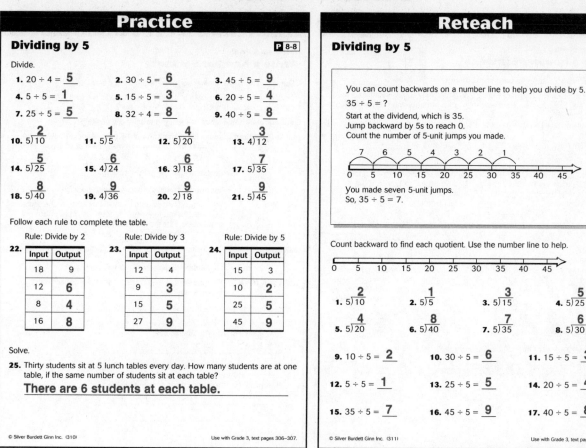

You can count backwards on a number line to help you divide by 5.

35 ÷ 5 = ?

Start at the dividend, which is 35.
Jump backward by 5s to reach 0.
Count the number of 5-unit jumps you made.

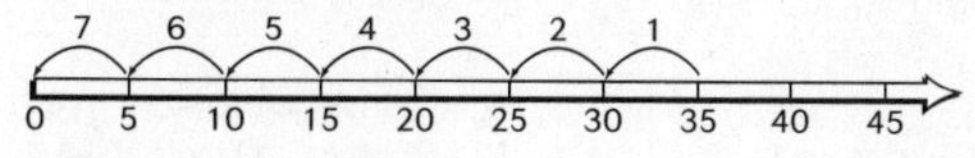

You made seven 5-unit jumps.
So, 35 ÷ 5 = 7.

Count backward to find each quotient. Use the number line to help.

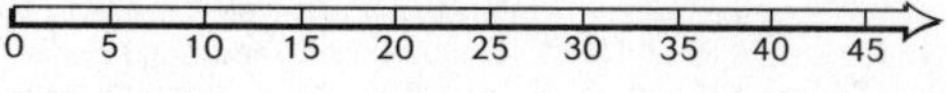

1. 5)10 **2**
2. 5)5 **1**
3. 5)15 **3**
4. 5)25 **5**
5. 5)20 **4**
6. 5)40 **8**
7. 5)35 **7**
8. 5)30 **6**
9. 10 ÷ 5 = **2**
10. 30 ÷ 5 = **6**
11. 15 ÷ 5 = **3**
12. 5 ÷ 5 = **1**
13. 25 ÷ 5 = **5**
14. 20 ÷ 5 = **4**
15. 35 ÷ 5 = **7**
16. 45 ÷ 5 = **9**
17. 40 ÷ 5 = **8**

Extend

Number Crunchers

E 8-8

ALGEBRA

Use the numbers in the IN box to feed the Number Cruncher. Use one number at a time. Do what each sign tells you to do. Write the answers in the OUT box.

1.

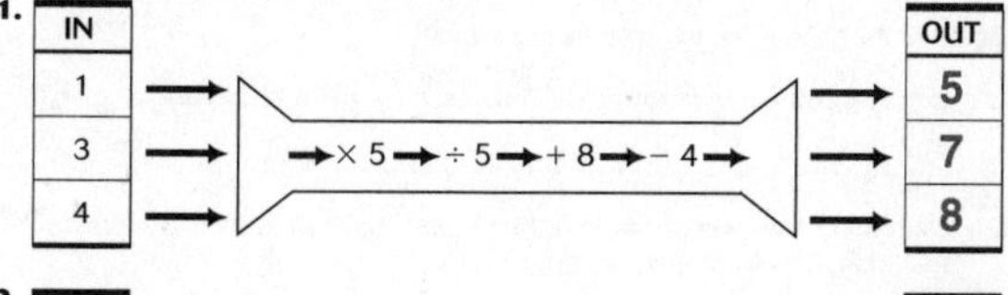

IN	OUT
1	**5**
3	**7**
4	**8**

2.

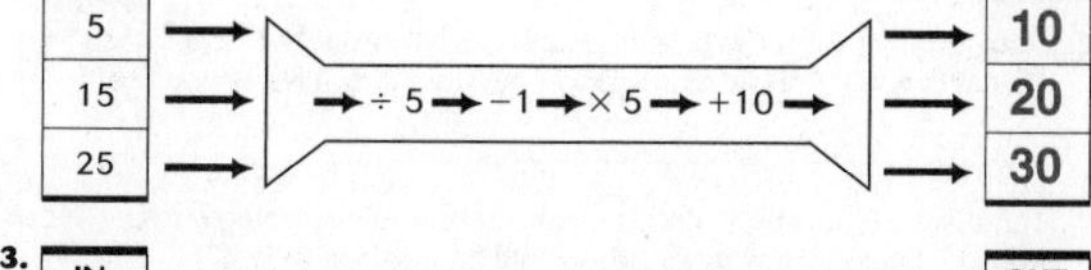

IN	OUT
5	**10**
15	**20**
25	**30**

3.

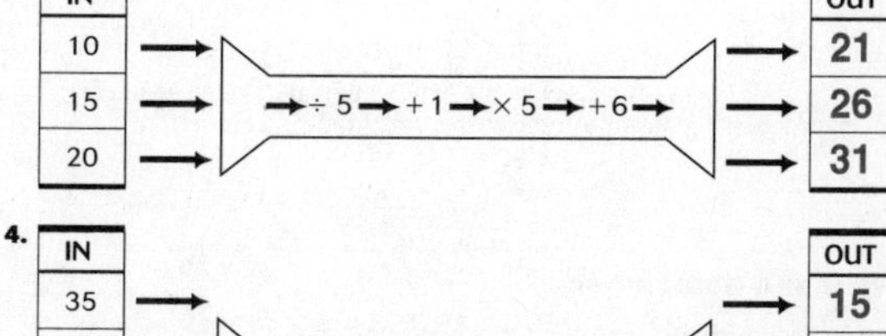

IN	OUT
10	**21**
15	**26**
20	**31**

4.

→ ÷ 5 → − 5 → × 5 → + 5 →

IN	OUT
35	**15**
40	**20**
45	**25**
50	**30**

Daily Review

Name ______________________

Daily Review 8-8

Dividing by 5

Find each quotient.

1. 5)30 **6**
2. 5)15 **3**
3. 5)35 **7**
4. 5)45 **9**
5. 5)25 **5**
6. 5)20 **4**
7. 5)5 **1**
8. 5)10 **2**
9. 5)40 **8**
10. 4)36 **9**
11. 3)24 **8**
12. 4)32 **8**
13. 3)27 **9**
14. 4)16 **4**
15. 3)21 **7**

Follow each rule to complete each table.

	Rule: Divide by 3	
	Input	Output
16.	15	**5**
17.	27	**9**
18.	9	**3**

	Rule: Divide by 4	
	Input	Output
19.	20	**5**
20.	24	**6**
21.	36	**9**

	Rule: Divide by 5	
	Input	Output
22.	25	**5**
23.	45	**9**
24.	40	**8**

Problem Solving

25. There are 30 boots at the firehouse. If each firefighter has 5 pairs of boots, how many firefighters work at the firehouse?

30 ÷ 5 = 6 ÷ 2 = 3 firefighters

26. Twenty-five firefighters on trucks are in the parade. Each truck will carry the same number of firefighters. How many firefighters will ride on each truck? How many trucks will there be?

5 firefighters per truck; 5 trucks

Review and Remember

Look at each pair of times. How much time has passed?

27. 8:30 A.M. and 10:00 A.M. **1 hour 30 minutes**
28. 7:10 P.M. and 7:32 P.M. **22 minutes**
29. 5:52 P.M. and 8:52 P.M. **3 hours**

Practice

Problem Solving

Write a Number Sentence

P 8-9

Write a number sentence to solve each problem.

1. Angie puts books on shelves for a book fair. She puts 8 books on each shelf. She fills 4 shelves with books. How many books does Angie put on the shelves?
   8 x 4 = 32 books

2. Angie puts books in cartons. She has 24 books and 4 cartons. Each carton holds the same amount. How many books will she put in each carton?
   24 ÷ 4 = 6 books

3. Angie's school sells 60 animal books and 19 puzzle books. How many more animal books than puzzle books are sold?
   60 − 19 = 41 more animal books

4. Angie collects $15 for 5 books. The cost of each book is the same. How much does each book cost?
   $15 ÷ 5 = $3 a book

5. Soni buys a book with 32 pages. Raul buys a book with 15 more pages than Soni's. How many pages does Raul's book have?
   32 + 15 = 47 pages

6. There are 21 students waiting in line to buy a book. There are 3 clerks collecting money. Each clerk helps the same number of students. How many students does each clerk help?
   21 ÷ 3 = 7 students

Create Your Own

7. Write your own problem for the number sentence 20 ÷ 5 = 4.
   Problems will vary. Check student's logic.

Reteach

Problem Solving

Write a Number Sentence

R 8-9

Sometimes writing a number sentence helps you find a solution.

Robbie needs to buy 12 pairs of socks for camp. Socks are sold 3 pairs to a package. How many packages should Robbie buy?

1. What number sentence can be used to solve the problem?

Understand You need to know how many pairs of socks Robbie needs. You also need to know how many pairs of socks are in each package.

Robbie needs 12 pairs of socks.

There are 3 pairs of socks in each package.

Plan Write a number sentence to show how to solve the problem. You need to find how many packages of 3 pairs each will give Robbie 12 pairs of socks. You can write a division sentence to find out.

Solve 12 pairs ÷ 3-pairs of socks per package = 4 packages

So, Robbie should buy 4 3-pair packages.

Look Back Four 3-pair packages make 12 pairs. So, the answer makes sense.

Write a number sentence to solve.

2. There are 3 T-shirts in a pack. Robbie buys 6 packs. How many T-shirts does Robbie buy?
   3 x 6 = 18 T-shirts

3. Robbie dyes his T-shirts. He dyes half of the shirts one color and the second half another color. How many T-shirts of each color does Robbie have?
   18 ÷ 2 = 9 T-shirts in each color

Extend

Summer Packing

E 8-9

Write 4 problems with the information below. You do not have to use all the information. Write problems that can be solved by using addition, subtraction, multiplication, and division. Write the number sentences to solve your problems.

> Mr. Johnson is putting away school supplies for the summer. There are 8 math books, 5 boxes of blocks, 7 boxes of fraction pieces, and 9 dictionaries. Each math book costs the school $9. Each dictionary weighs 6 pounds. The combined weight of the boxes of blocks is 40 pounds.

1. Check students' work.
2.
3.
4.

Try Working Backwards to solve these problems.

5. Mr. Johnson needs 2 weeks to pack. He wants to finish by June 10. When should he start packing? May 27
6. Mr. Johnson packs for 2 hours and 30 minutes. When he is done, it is 5:30. When did he begin? 3:00

Daily Review

Name ______

Daily Review 8-9

Problem Solving

Write a Number Sentence

Write a number sentence to solve each problem.

1. Each of the 3 parks in town has 2 slides. How many slides are in town?
   3 × 2 = 6
2. Matt puts 32 markers back into their boxes. Each box holds 8 markers. How many boxes of markers does he have?
   32 ÷ 8 = 4
3. Abby brought 2 soccer balls to practice, Emily brought 1, and Coach Mason brought 5. How many soccer balls did they have at practice?
   2 + 1 + 5 = 8
4. There are 29 houses in Tyler's neighborhood. He collected recyclable cans from 17 houses. How many houses did he have left to visit?
   29 − 17 = 12
5. Each of Brendan's 5 cousins wrote him 3 letters during the year. How many letters did Brendan receive this year from his cousins?
   5 × 3 = 15

Review and Remember

Continue each pattern.

6. 201, 301, 401, 501
7. 784, 764, 744, 724
8. 557, 559, 561, 563, 565, 567
9. 1, 3, 6, 10, 15, 21, 28
10. 1; 11; 111; 1,111; 11,111
11. 95, 85, 75, 65, 55

Practice

0 and 1 Division

P 8-10

Divide. Color each section according to your answer.

0: yellow 1: red 2 through 9: blue

1. 5 ÷ 5 = 1; red	2. 8 ÷ 1 = 8; blue	3. 7 ÷ 7 = 1; red
4. 2 ÷ 2 = 1; red	5. 0 ÷ 8 = 0; yellow	6. 1 ÷ 1 = 1; red
7. 6 ÷ 1 = 6; blue	8. 0 ÷ 4 = 0; yellow	9. 3 ÷ 1 = 3; blue
10. 4 ÷ 1 = 4; blue	11. 0 ÷ 7 = 0; yellow	12. 2 ÷ 1 = 2; blue
13. 5 ÷ 1 = 5; blue	14. 0 ÷ 2 = 0; yellow	15. 7 ÷ 1 = 7; blue
16. 3 ÷ 3 = 1; red	17. 0 ÷ 9 = 0; yellow	18. 4 ÷ 4 = 1; red
19. 9 ÷ 9 = 1; red	20. 9 ÷ 1 = 9; blue	21. 8 ÷ 8 = 1; red

22. Make up your own problem for 6 ÷ 6 = ? Then solve.
Problems will vary. Check students' work.

 Use with Grade 3, text pages 310–311.

Reteach

0 and 1 Division

R 8-10

Follow the rules for zero and one.
Divide with them for lots of fun!

Rule 1	Rule 2	Rule 3	Rule 4
Divide *any* number by 1. The quotient is *always* that number.	Divide *any* number by itself. The quotient is *always* 1.	Divide 0 by *any* number. The answer is *always* 0.	You *cannot* divide *any* number by 0.
5 ÷ 1 = 5	2 ÷ 2 = 1	0 ÷ 4 = 0	3 ~~÷~~ 0 =

Divide. Write the number of the rule that helped you find the quotient.

1. 3 ÷ 1 = 3 Rule: 1
2. 6 ÷ 6 = 1 Rule: 2
3. 5 ~~÷~~ 0 = ___ Rule: 4
4. 0 ÷ 2 = 0 Rule: 3
5. 4 ÷ 4 = 1 Rule: 2
6. 9 ÷ 1 = 9 Rule: 1
7. 0 ÷ 6 = 0 Rule: 3
8. 8 ÷ 8 = 1 Rule: 2
9. 0 ÷ 9 = 0 Rule: 3
10. 5 ÷ 1 = 5 Rule: 1
11. 1 ~~÷~~ 0 = ___ Rule: 4
12. 0 ÷ 1 = 0 Rule: 3
13. 9 ÷ 9 = 1 Rule: 2
14. 7 ÷ 1 = 7 Rule: 1
15. 6 ÷ 1 = 6 Rule: 1
16. 6 ~~÷~~ 0 = ___ Rule: 4

 Use with Grade 3, text pages 310–311.

Extend

Carloads of Rules

E 8-10 NUMBER SENSE

Decide where each division sentence belongs. Write it in its car. Find the quotients. Fill the cars with your own division sentences that belong.

2 ÷ 2 = ?	0 ÷ 10 = ?	6 ÷ 1 = ?	3 ÷ 0 = ?
95 ÷ 1 = ?	13 ÷ 0 = ?	0 ÷ 72 = ?	442 ÷ 442 = ?
816 ÷ 0 = ?	0 ÷ 341 = ?	87 ÷ 87 = ?	215 ÷ 1 = ?

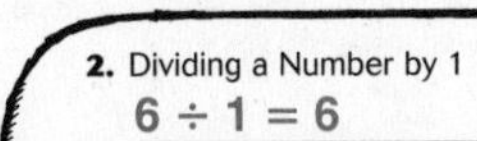

1. Dividing a Number by Itself
2 ÷ 2 = 1 442 ÷ 442 = 1
87 ÷ 87 = 1 Answers will vary.

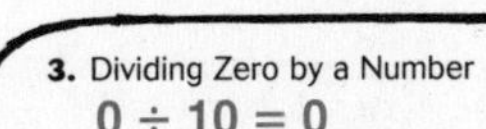

2. Dividing a Number by 1
6 ÷ 1 = 6 95 ÷ 1 = 95
215 ÷ 1 = 215 Answers will vary.

3. Dividing Zero by a Number
0 ÷ 10 = 0 0 ÷ 72 = 0
0 ÷ 341 = 0 Answers will vary.

4. Dividing a Number by Zero
816 ÷ 0, 13 ÷ 0, and 3 ÷ 0
cannot be divided.

 Use with Grade 3, text pages 310–311.

Daily Review

Name ____________

Daily Review 8-10

0 and 1 in Division

Find each quotient.

1. 0 ÷ 3 = 0 2. 8 ÷ 1 = 8 3. 0 ÷ 5 = 0 4. 5 ÷ 5 = 1
5. 0 ÷ 7 = 0 6. 6 ÷ 1 = 6 7. 4 ÷ 4 = 1 8. 6 ÷ 6 = 1

Find each quotient.

9. 1)4 → 4 10. 6)0 → 0 11. 5)5 → 1 12. 1)9 → 9 13. 3)3 → 1
14. 8)0 → 0 15. 5)0 → 0 16. 1)7 → 7 17. 9)9 → 1 18. 1)5 → 5

Problem Solving

19. I am a number. If you divide me by 1, you get the same number.
What number am I? Any number

20. Prizes are given for 3 different relay races. A first-, second-, and third-place prize is given for each race. How many prizes are there in all for the 3 races? 9 prizes

Review and Remember

Use the bar graph to answer Problems 21–23.

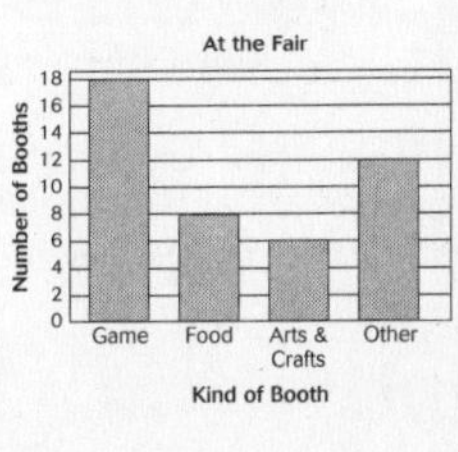

21. How many food booths are at the fair?
8 food booths

22. The fair has the most of what kind of booth?
game booths

23. How many more game booths are there than arts and crafts booths?
12 more booths

Chapter 8 • Lesson 11

Practice

Problem Solving

Using Money

P 8-11

Solve.

1. The softball team at Wootton School is playing in the finals. Tickets cost $3.00 each. How much will it cost for 6 tickets? **$18.00**
2. At the team spirit booth, T-shirts are sold for $8 and sweatshirts are sold for $12. How much more will it cost for a family of four to buy sweatshirts than T-shirts? **$16 more**
3. Gigi buys two visors for $3 each and a team banner for $2.00. How much change will she get from $10? **$2.00**
4. A team tote bag costs $6.00. How many tote bags can Jon buy for $20? **3 bags**
5. Mr. Fuentes has $20 to spend. He buys a tote bag for $6.00, and would like to buy as many visors as he can at $3 each. How many visors can Mr. Fuentes buy? **4 visors**
6. Ivan spends $18 on 6 team cups. If each one costs the same amount, how much does each team cup cost? **$3**
7. Roy buys 5 banners for $15. Kim says she bought 6 banners that sold at 2 banners for $4. Who spent less for each banner? Explain.
   Kim; $4 ÷ 2 = $2 a banner; $15 ÷ 5 = $3 a banner; Kim spent less.

 Use with Grade 3, text pages 312–313.

Reteach

Problem Solving

Using Money

R 8-11

Holly and Greg are buying a game that costs $12. They both plan to play the game. They are going to split the cost equally. How much money will each person spend?

1. How can you find the cost for one person?

Understand You need to know the cost of the game. You also need to know how many people are sharing the cost equally.

The game costs **$12**.

2 people are sharing the cost equally.

Plan You can divide the cost of the game by the number of people sharing it. Write a number sentence to help you.

Solve **$12** ÷ **2** = **$6**.

Holly and Greg will each spend **$6**

Look Back Together, will Greg and Holly spend a total of $12? If so, the answer makes sense.

2. Holly finds a set of 5 stuffed animals. The set cost $20. What is the cost of each animal? **$4**
3. Greg spent $9 in a video store to play a game for 3 hours. How much did he spend per hour? **$3 per hour**
4. Holly has $25 to spend. She buys a jigsaw puzzle for $12 and a game of jacks for $7. How much money does Holly have left? **$6 left**

 Use with Grade 3, text pages 312–313.

Extend

Buy It!

E 8-11

Solve.

Price List	
Small beads	$6 bottle
Large beads	$7 bottle
Chains: long	$5
Chains: short	$3
Decorated beads	$1 each

1. Kari spends $10 on jewelry crafts and Drew spends $6. They decide to put their supplies together and share the total cost equally. Who owes money? How much? **Drew owes Kari $2.**
2. Jesse wants 2 bottles of small beads, 4 short chains, and 6 decorated beads. Is $20 enough for what he wants? If not, how much more does he need? **No; he needs $10 more.**
3. Tina looks at her watch and finds that she has been at the crafts store for 1 hour and 15 minutes. It is now 4:30. What time did Tina arrive at the store? **3:15**
4. Mrs. Askin buys 1 bottle of small beads, 5 decorated beads, and 5 long chains. She makes 5 necklaces, which she plans to sell. How much should Mrs. Askin charge for each necklace so that she earns a total of $14? Explain. **Her cost, $36 + $14 = $50; $50 ÷ 5 = $10 a necklace**
5. Patricia makes the following bead pattern:

   large, small, decorated, small, large, small, decorated, small, large

   What are the next three beads in the pattern? **small, decorated, small**

 Use with Grade 3, text pages 312–313.

Daily Review

Name ______________________ Daily Review 8-11

Problem Solving

Using Money

Solve each problem.

1. Ryan earns $6 a week delivering groceries. He has $6 now. If he saves his money, when can he buy a new computer game for $36? **in five weeks**
2. Amy has $29 to spend on souvenirs during her vacation. If she spends $6 a day, how much will she have left after 4 days? **$5 left**
3. Kevin earns 75¢ each time he brings in Mrs. Malone's mail and newspaper. He did this for 3 days. How much money did he earn? **$2.25**
4. Julia wants to buy 60¢ postcards for her friends. How many postcards can she buy for $3.00? **5 postcards**

Review and Remember

Subtract.

5. 24 − 5 = **19**
6. 62 − 3 = **59**
7. 18 − 8 = **10**
8. 72 − 5 = **67**

Find the product.

9. 8 × 9 = **72**
10. 7 × 7 = **49**
11. 6 × 4 = **24**
12. 5 × 8 = **40**

Practice

Fact Families

P 9-1

Complete each fact family.

1. 8 × 7 = 56
7 × 8 = 56
56 ÷ 7 = 8
56 ÷ 8 = 7

2. 8 + 7 = 15
7 + 8 = 15
15 − 7 = 8
15 − 8 = 7

3. 5 × 6 = 30
6 × 5 = 30
30 ÷ 5 = 6
30 ÷ 6 = 5

4. 5 + 6 = 11
6 + 5 = 11
11 − 5 = 6
11 − 6 = 5

Give the other facts in each family.

5. 40 ÷ 8 = 5
40 ÷ 5 = 8
8 × 5 = 40
5 × 8 = 40

6. 3 × 6 = 18
18 ÷ 3 = 6
6 × 3 = 18
18 ÷ 6 = 3

7. 2 + 7 = 9
7 + 2 = 9
9 − 2 = 7
9 − 7 = 2

8. 21 ÷ 3 = 7
21 ÷ 7 = 3
3 × 7 = 21
7 × 3 = 21

9. 9 × 6 = 54
54 ÷ 9 = 6
6 × 9 = 54
54 ÷ 6 = 9

10. 72 ÷ 9 = 8
72 ÷ 8 = 9
9 × 8 = 72
8 × 9 = 72

Write a multiplication and division fact family for each group.

11. 6, 7, 42
42 ÷ 7 = 6
42 ÷ 6 = 7
6 × 7 = 42
7 × 6 = 42

12. 4, 28, 7
28 ÷ 7 = 4
28 ÷ 4 = 7
4 × 7 = 28
7 × 4 = 28

 Use with Grade 3, text pages 324–327.

Reteach

Fact Families

R 9-1

Multiplication and division facts that all have the same numbers are part of a fact family.

Use multiplication to put the groups together. 5 × 3 = 15, 3 × 5 = 15

Use division to share all the tickets evenly. 15 ÷ 3 = 5, 15 ÷ 5 = 3

The fact family contains the numbers 3, 5, and 15.

Complete each fact family.

1. 
3 × 7 = 21
7 × 3 = 21
21 ÷ 7 = 3
21 ÷ 3 = 7

2. 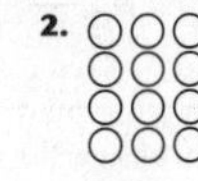
4 × 3 = 12
3 × 4 = 12
12 ÷ 3 = 4
12 ÷ 4 = 3

3. 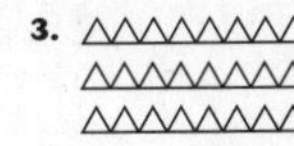
3 × 8 = 24
8 × 3 = 24
24 ÷ 3 = 8
24 ÷ 8 = 3

4. 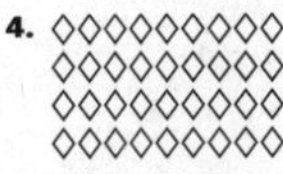
4 × 9 = 36
9 × 4 = 36
36 ÷ 9 = 4
36 ÷ 4 = 9

5. 
3 × 6 = 18
6 × 3 = 18
18 ÷ 6 = 3
18 ÷ 3 = 6

6. ★★★★★ ★★★★★ ★★★★★ ★★★★★
4 × 5 = 20
5 × 4 = 20
20 ÷ 4 = 5
20 ÷ 5 = 4

 Use with Grade 3, text pages 324–327.

Extend

Changing Times

E 9-1 VISUAL THINKING

Look at the first two pictures in each row. Decide how the first picture has been changed to make the second. Then look at the third picture. Circle the picture that shows what the third picture would look like if it were changed in the same way.

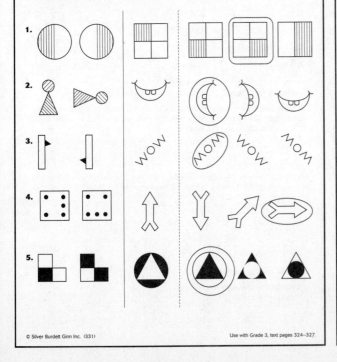

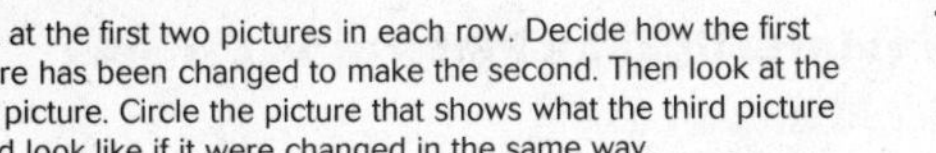

1. 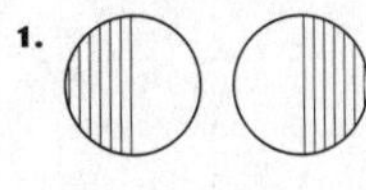

2.  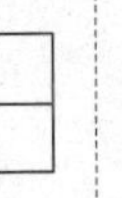 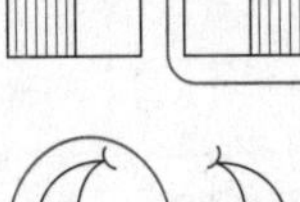

3. 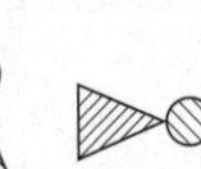 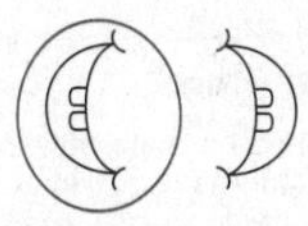

4.  

5. 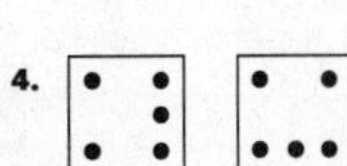  

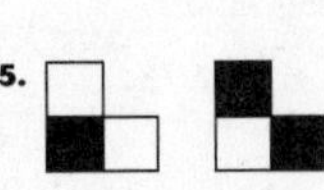    

 Use with Grade 3, text pages 324–327.

Daily Review

Name ______________________

Daily Review 9-1

Fact Families

Complete each fact family.

1. 3 × 4 = 12
4 × 3 = 12
12 ÷ 3 = 4
12 ÷ 4 = 3

2. 6 × 5 = 30
5 × 6 = 30
30 ÷ 6 = 5
30 ÷ 5 = 6

3. 9 × 7 = 63
7 × 9 = 63
63 ÷ 9 = 7
63 ÷ 7 = 9

Write the fact family for each set of numbers.

4. 2, 8, 16
2 × 8 = 16
8 × 2 = 16
16 ÷ 2 = 8
16 ÷ 8 = 2

5. 5, 9, 45
5 × 9 = 45
9 × 5 = 45
45 ÷ 5 = 9
45 ÷ 9 = 5

6. 3, 7, 21
3 × 7 = 21
7 × 3 = 21
21 ÷ 3 = 7
21 ÷ 7 = 3

Problem Solving

7. There are 24 dance students planning a recital. For part of their act, the dancers form equal groups. What are four different ways they can form these groups? 2 groups, 12 in each group; 3 groups, 8 in each group; 4 groups, 6 in each group; 6 groups, 4 in each group; 8 groups, 3 in each group; 12 groups, 2 in each group

8. Three rows of 6 dancers move around the stage. They then form 2 rows. How many dancers are in each of the 2 rows? 9 dancers

Review and Remember

Estimate each answer by rounding to the nearest hundred.

9. 378 + 241 600 **10.** 718 − 532 200 **11.** 889 − 465 400

Practice

Explore: Investigating Patterns in Division P 9-2

×	0	1	2	3	4	5
0	0	0	0	0	0	0
1	0	1	2	3	4	5
2	0	2	4	6	8	10
3	0	3	6	9	12	15
4	0	4	8	12	16	20
5	0	5	10	15	20	25

Use the multiplication table to answer the questions.

Remember: 12 ÷ 3 = 4
dividend — divisor — quotient

1. Find 5 at the side of the table. How do you find the quotient of 20 ÷ 5?
   Move across the 5 row to 20. Move to the top of the column to find the quotient 4.
2. Look at the numbers in the zero column. What is the rule about dividing with 0?
   The quotient of 0 and a number is always zero.
3. The 4 row has all even numbers. Can 25 be divided by 4? Explain.
   No; 25 is not an even number.
4. Write about another pattern you see in the multiplication table.
   Answers will vary. Students may refer to the properties involving dividing a number by itself.

Write the division fact.

5. Point to the row for the divisor 4. Move across the row until you come to the dividend 8. Move to the quotient at the top of the column. 8 ÷ 4 = 2
6. Point to the row for the divisor 5. Move across the row until you come to the dividend 25. Move to the quotient at the top of the column. 25 ÷ 5 = 5

 Use with Grade 3, text pages 328–329.

Reteach

Explore: Investigating Patterns in Division R 9-2

A multiplication table can help you learn division facts. 6 ÷ 3 = ?

×	0	1	2	3	4
0	0	0	0	0	0
1	0	1	2	3	4
2	0	2	4	6	8
3	0	3	6	9	12
4	0	4	8	12	16

Step 1 Put your finger on the 3 row; 3 is your divisor.

Step 2 Move your finger right until you reach 6; 6 is your dividend.

Step 3 From 6, move your finger up to the top of the chart.

Step 4 Your finger is on 2, so the quotient is 2.

6 ÷ 3 = 2

Follow the directions to find each quotient. Use the multiplication table to help.

1. 8 ÷ 2 = ?
   Start at the 2 row.
   Move across to 8.
   Move up from 8.
   The quotient is 4.
2. 12 ÷ 4 = ?
   Start at the 4 row.
   Move across to 12.
   Move up from 12
   The quotient is 3.
3. 4 ÷ 4 = ?
   Start at the 4 row.
   Move across to 4.
   Move to the top.
   The quotient is 1.
4. 3 ÷ 1 = ?
   Start at the 1 row.
   Move across to 3.
   Move to the top.
   The quotient is 3.
5. 12 ÷ 3 = ?
   Start at the 3 row.
   Move across to 12.
   Move to the top.
   The quotient is 4.
6. 16 ÷ 4 = ?
   Start at the 4 row.
   Move across to 16.
   Move to the top.
   The quotient is 4.

 Use with Grade 3, text pages 328–329.

Extend

Finding the Facts

E 9-2 REASONING

The Venn diagram shows the favorite activities of three students. Find the spaces where the shapes overlap. The activities listed in these overlapping spaces are enjoyed by two or more students.

Study the diagram. Complete each sentence.

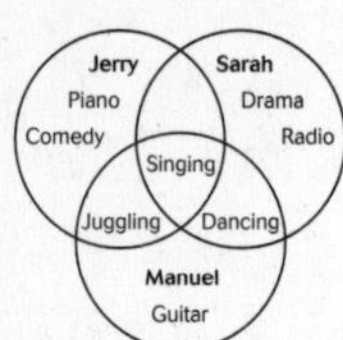

1. All three students enjoy singing as an activity.
2. Only Jerry and Manuel enjoy juggling as an activity.
3. Only Sarah and Manuel enjoy dancing as an activity.
4. The following activities are the favorites of only one student each. Write their name.
   guitar Manuel piano Jerry
   comedy Jerry drama Sarah

Create Your Own

Work with two other classmates. Make a Venn diagram to show your favorite activities. If two or all three of you have the same favorite activity, be sure that your diagram shows that activity in a special place.

 Use with Grade 3, text pages 328–329.

Daily Review

Name ____________ Daily Review 9-2

Explore: Investigating Patterns in Division

Use the multiplication table to help you answer the questions.

	0	1	2	3	4	5
0	0	0	0	0	0	0
1	0	1	2	3	4	5
2	0	2	4	6	8	10
3	0	3	6	9	12	15
4	0	4	8	12	16	20
5	0	5	10	15	20	25

1. 15 ÷ 3 = 5
2. 8 ÷ 4 = 2
3. 9 ÷ 3 = 3
4. 16 ÷ 2 = 8
5. 12 ÷ 3 = 4
6. 10 ÷ 2 = 5
7. 6 ÷ 6 = 1
8. 4 ÷ 1 = 4

Problem Solving

9. Look at the rows in the table that begin with the numbers 2 and 4. Are the numbers in these rows odd or even? Do you get an odd or even number when you divide an even number by two?
   Even; when you divide an even number by two, you may get an even number or an odd number.
10. Look at the row that begins with the number 3. Do you get an odd number or even number when you divide an odd number in the row by 3? What do you get when you divide an even number in the row by 3?
   When you divide an odd number in the row by 3, you get an odd number. When you divide an even number in the row by 3, you get an even number.

Review and Remember

Write the value of the underlined digit.

11. 6,<u>5</u>03 500
12. 7<u>6</u>2 60
13. 9<u>8</u> 8
14. <u>3</u>,472 3,000
15. 9<u>1</u>8 10
16. 2,57<u>9</u> 9

Chapter 9 • Lesson 3

Practice

Dividing by 6

P 9-3

Write a related division fact for each division sentence.

1. 12 ÷ 2 = 6 — 12 ÷ 6 = 2
2. 24 ÷ 4 = 6 — 24 ÷ 6 = 4
3. 30 ÷ 5 = 6 — 30 ÷ 6 = 5
4. 18 ÷ 3 = 6 — 18 ÷ 6 = 3
5. 6 ÷ 1 = 6 — 6 ÷ 6 = 1
6. 42 ÷ 7 = 6 — 42 ÷ 6 = 7

Divide.

7. 6)12 — 2
8. 6)18 — 3
9. 5)30 — 6
10. 6)42 — 7
11. 6)30 — 5
12. 6)54 — 9
13. 4)24 — 6
14. 6)48 — 8
15. 6)6 — 1
16. 6)24 — 4
17. 6)36 — 6
18. 2)18 — 9

Solve.

19. Dina spends $30 on 6 juggling balls. How much does each ball cost?
Each ball costs $5.

20. A box of guitar strings contains 24 strings. How many sets of 6 strings come in one box?

4 sets of 6 strings

21. Mindy has 54 guitar picks. She wants to place them in boxes, with 6 picks to a box. How many boxes does she need?
9 boxes

 Use with Grade 3, text pages 330–331.

Reteach

Dividing by 6

24 ÷ 6 = ?

You can use counters to divide.

Step 1 Make 6 groups. ○○○○○○

Step 2 Add counters to each group until you have 24 counters.

Step 3 There are 4 counters in each group, so 24 ÷ 6 = 4.

You can think of a related division fact to divide.

Step 1 If you know 24 ÷ 4 = 6, then you know 24 ÷ 6 = 4.

Step 2 If you know 6 × 4 = 24, then you know 24 ÷ 6 = 4.

Complete the division fact for each picture.

1. 
36 ÷ 6 = 6
2. 24 ÷ 6 = 4
3. 30 ÷ 6 = 5
4. 18 ÷ 6 = 3
5. 42 ÷ 6 = 7
6. 12 ÷ 6 = 2

Use the related facts to help you divide.

7. 12 ÷ 6 = 2
8. 36 ÷ 6 = 6
9. 24 ÷ 6 = 4
10. 48 ÷ 6 = 8
11. 42 ÷ 6 = 7
12. 54 ÷ 6 = 9
13. 6 ÷ 6 = 1
14. 18 ÷ 6 = 3
15. 30 ÷ 6 = 5

 Use with Grade 3, text pages 330–331.

Extend

Fact Finding

E 9-3
NUMBER SENSE

Twenty addition, subtraction, multiplication, and division facts are hidden in the puzzle below. Every fact uses the number 6. The facts go → or ↓.

Find every number 6. Write +, −, × or ÷, and an = sign to make a fact. Circle the fact. One is done for you.

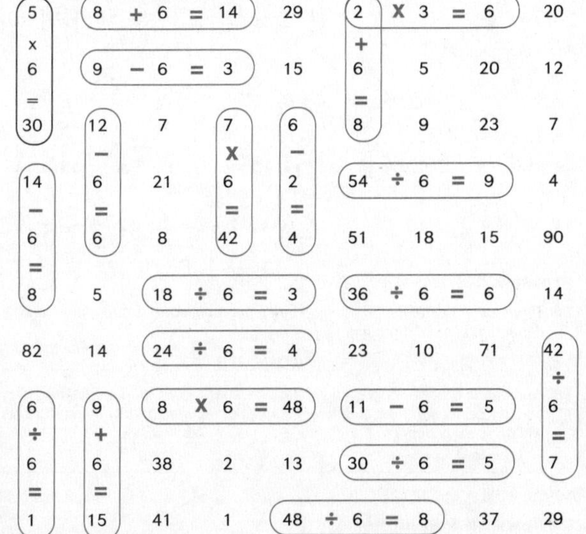

5		8	+	6	=	14		29		2	X	3	=	6		20
x										+						
6		9	−	6	=	3		15		6		5		20		12
=										=						
30		12		7		7		6		8		9		23		7
		−				X		−								
14		6		21		6		2		54	÷	6	=	9		4
−		=				=		=								
6		6		8		42		4		51		18		15		90
=																
8		5		18	÷	6	=	3		36	÷	6	=	6		14
82		14		24	÷	6	=	4		23		10		71		42
																÷
6		9		8	X	6	=	48		11	−	6	=	5		6
÷		+														=
6		6		38		2		13		30	÷	6	=	5		7
=		=														
1		15		41		1		48	÷	6	=	8		37		29

 Use with Grade 3, text pages 330–331.

Daily Review

Name_______________________________ Daily Review 9-3

Dividing by 6

Write the division fact for each picture.

1. 18 ÷ 6 = 3
2. 30 ÷ 6 = 5

Divide.

3. 6)42 — 7
4. 6)48 — 8
5. 6)24 — 4
6. 6)30 — 5
7. 6)36 — 6
8. 6 ÷ 6 = 1
9. 54 ÷ 6 = 9
10. 12 ÷ 6 = 2
11. 18 ÷ 6 = 3

Problem Solving

12. During a concert a band plays 12 songs. The band plays the same number of songs in 2 sets. How many songs do they play in each set? 6 songs
13. There are 36 members in a band. The members form 6 groups with an equal number of people in each group. Draw a picture and write a division sentence to show this. Check students' drawings for accuracy; division sentence: 36 ÷ 6 = 6

Review and Remember

Write the missing numbers.

14. 24, 28, 32, 36, 40, 44
15. 620, 615, 610, 605, 600, 595
16. 24, 36, 48, 60, 72, 84
17. 286, 284, 282, 280, 278, 276
18. 328, 318, 308, 298, 288, 278
19. 410, 510, 610, 710, 810, 910

Practice

Dividing by 7

P 9-4

Find the missing factor. Use it to find the quotient.

1. 7 × **4** = 28
28 ÷ 7 = **4**

2. 7 × **6** = 42
42 ÷ 7 = **6**

3. 7 × **3** = 21
21 ÷ 7 = **3**

4. 7 × **8** = 56
56 ÷ 7 = **8**

5. 7 × **5** = 35
35 ÷ 7 = **5**

6. 7 × **7** = 49
49 ÷ 7 = **7**

Divide.

7. 7)7 **1** **8.** 7)28 **4** **9.** 7)35 **5** **10.** 6)42 **7**

11. 4)28 **7** **12.** 7)21 **3** **13.** 7)49 **7** **14.** 7)56 **8**

15. 7)63 **9** **16.** 7)14 **2** **17.** 5)35 **7** **18.** 7)42 **6**

Solve.

Remember: 7 days = 1 week

19. Devon has 21 days to learn her lines for the play. How many weeks does she have?

Devon has 3 weeks.

20. It takes 28 days to make the costumes for the play. How many weeks does it take? Explain.

4 weeks; 28 days ÷ 7 = 4 weeks

21. Mrs. Kelly ordered 63 yards of fabric. Each costume takes 7 yards. How many costumes is she making?

9 costumes; 63 ÷ 7 = 9

 Use with Grade 3, text pages 332–333.

Reteach

Dividing by 7

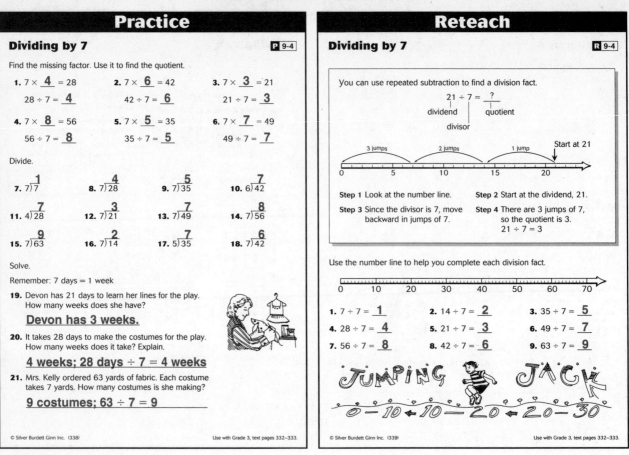

You can use repeated subtraction to find a division fact.

21 ÷ 7 = ?
dividend — divisor — quotient

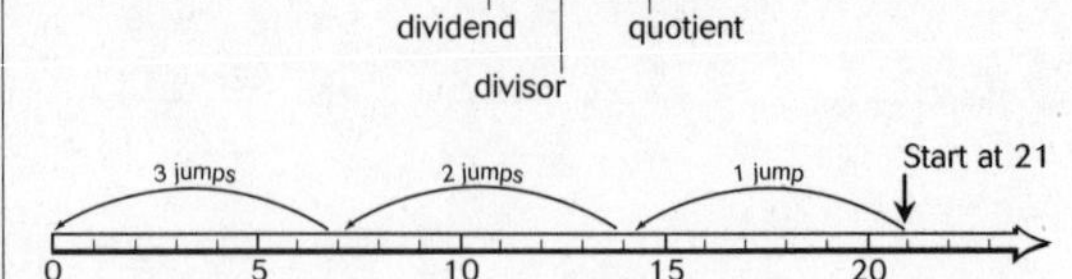

Step 1 Look at the number line.

Step 2 Start at the dividend, 21.

Step 3 Since the divisor is 7, move backward in jumps of 7.

Step 4 There are 3 jumps of 7, so the quotient is 3.
21 ÷ 7 = 3

Use the number line to help you complete each division fact.

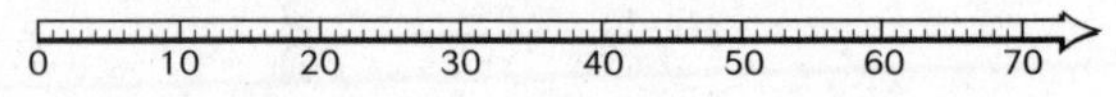

1. 7 ÷ 7 = **1** **2.** 14 ÷ 7 = **2** **3.** 35 ÷ 7 = **5**

4. 28 ÷ 7 = **4** **5.** 21 ÷ 7 = **3** **6.** 49 ÷ 7 = **7**

7. 56 ÷ 7 = **8** **8.** 42 ÷ 7 = **6** **9.** 63 ÷ 7 = **9**

 Use with Grade 3, text pages 332–333.

Extend

Mystery Numbers

E 9-4
NUMBER SENSE

Follow the directions in each box below to find the mystery number.

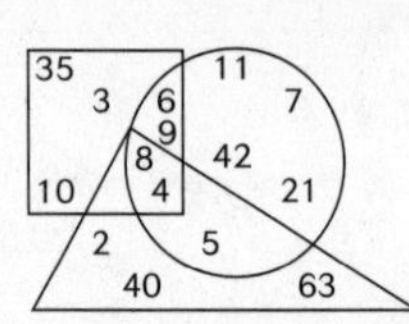

1. List the numbers in the square.

3, 4, 6, 8, 9, 10, 35

Look at all the numbers in the shapes. List the numbers that can be divided evenly by 7.

7, 21, 35, 42, 63

The mystery number is in both lists. It is **35**.

2. Look at all the numbers. List the numbers less than 7.

2, 3, 4, 5, 6

List the missing numbers:

63 = ? × 7 ? × 7 = 14
? ÷ 7 = 4 ? = 56 ÷ 7

9, 2, 28, 8

The mystery number is in both lists. It is **2**.

3. Look at all the numbers. List the numbers greater than 8.

9, 10, 11, 21, 35, 40, 42, 63

List the missing numbers:

? ÷ 7 = 6 35 ÷ 7 = ?
? ÷ 7 = 7 0 ÷ 7 = ?

42, 5, 49, 0

The mystery number is in both lists. It is **42**.

4. List the numbers in the triangle.

2, 4, 5, 8, 40, 63

List the missing numbers:

7 × 1 = ? 7 − 1 = ?
1 + 7 = ? 7 ÷ ? = 7

7, 6, 8, 1

The mystery number is in both lists. It is **8**.

 Use with Grade 3, text pages 332–333.

Daily Review

Name ______________________

Daily Review 9-4

Dividing by 7

Find each missing factor. Then use it to find the quotient.

1. 7 × **4** = 28
28 ÷ 7 = **4**

2. 7 × **9** = 63
63 ÷ 7 = **9**

3. 7 × **3** = 21
21 ÷ 7 = **3**

Find each quotient.

4. 7)21 **3** **5.** 7)7 **1** **6.** 7)42 **6** **7.** 7)49 **7** **8.** 7)28 **4**

9. 7)14 **2** **10.** 1)7 **7** **11.** 7)21 **3** **12.** 7)35 **5** **13.** 7)56 **8**

14. 28 ÷ 7 = **4** **15.** 49 ÷ 7 = **7** **16.** 42 ÷ 7 = **6** **17.** 14 ÷ 7 = **2**

Problem Solving

18. There are 42 dancers backstage. They will form 7 equal groups. How many dancers are in each group?

6 dancers

19. At a dance school, 15 girls and 6 boys have signed up for a class. The teacher decides to form 3 different classes of equal size. How many students will be in each class?

7 students

Review and Remember

Find each answer.

20. 62 + 34 = **96** **21.** 7 × 8 = **56** **22.** 67 − 8 = **59** **23.** 64 ÷ 8 = **8**

24. 53 − 9 = **44** **25.** 36 ÷ 6 = **6** **26.** 5 × 9 = **45** **27.** 27 + 38 = **65**

Chapter 9 • Lesson 5

Practice

Problem Solving P 9-5

Choose the Operation

Circle the best choice for each question.

Stone Mill School is having a school play. They are serving ice cream after the play. They have 85 chocolate cones and 212 vanilla cones.

1. Which operation would you use to find how many cones are made altogether?

(a.) addition

b. subtraction

c. multiplication

2. Which number sentence tells how many cones are made altogether?

(a.) 85 + 212 = 297

b. 85 + 85 = 170

c. 212 − 85 = 127

3. Which operation would you use to find out how many more vanilla cones than chocolate cones are made?

a. addition

(b.) subtraction

c. division

4. Which number sentence tells how many more vanilla than chocolate cones are made?

a. 212 + 212 = 424

(b.) 212 − 85 = 127

c. 212 − 212 = 0

Solve.

5. The refreshment table has cardboard cone trays. Each tray can hold 4 cones. The school estimates that they will set out 128 cones in trays. How can you find the number of trays they will need?

divide; 128 ÷ 4 = 32 holders

6. At the end of the evening, 21 packages of wafer cones are left. Each package contains 5 cones. How could you find the total number of cones in all 21 packages?

multiply; 21 x 5 = 105 cones

 Use with Grade 3, text pages 334–335.

Reteach

Problem Solving R 9-5

Choose the Operation

To solve a problem, think about what you need to find out.

The students in Ms. Metz's class collect leaves. Rajim picks up 34 leaves, and Gordon picks up 20. Ms. Metz puts 6 leaves on each page of a nature scrapbook. How many leaves do Rajim and Gordon have altogether? How many pages does Ms. Metz need for all the leaves?

Add if you need to put groups together.

Subtract if you need to find out how many more are in one group than another.

Multiply if you need to put equal groups together.

Divide if you need to separate items into equal groups.

To find out how many leaves Rajim and Gordon have altogether, you put groups together. **Add** 34 + 20. They have 54 leaves.

To find out how many pages Ms. Metz needs, separate items into equal groups. **Divide** 54 by 6. Ms. Metz needs 9 pages.

Solve.

1. Suppose you want to find out how many more leaves Rajim found than Gordon. Which operation would you choose? Explain.

Subtraction; you are comparing two amounts.

2. Will division help you find the number of pages Rajim will fill with his leaves? Explain.

Yes; you are separating things into equal groups.

3. Suppose Gordon uses some of his leaves to fill 3 pages. Which operation would you use to find the total number of leaves on the three pages?

Multiplication; you are adding equal groups.

 Use with Grade 3, text pages 334–335.

Extend

On Target

E 9-5 NUMBER SENSE

Decide how you will solve each problem. Write *add, subtract, multiply,* or *divide.* Then write the number sentence to solve the problem.

5 6 7 8 9

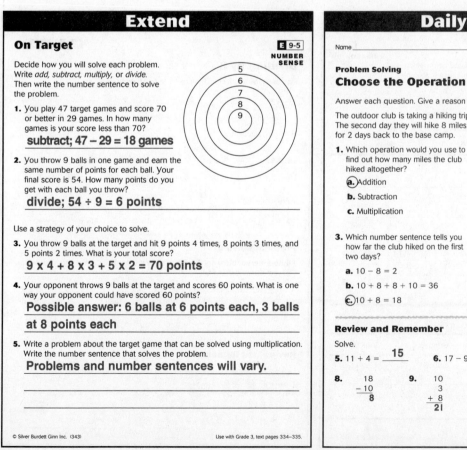

1. You play 47 target games and score 70 or better in 29 games. In how many games is your score less than 70?

subtract; 47 – 29 = 18 games

2. You throw 9 balls in one game and earn the same number of points for each ball. Your final score is 54. How many points do you get with each ball you throw?

divide; 54 ÷ 9 = 6 points

Use a strategy of your choice to solve.

3. You throw 9 balls at the target and hit 9 points 4 times, 8 points 3 times, and 5 points 2 times. What is your total score?

9 x 4 + 8 x 3 + 5 x 2 = 70 points

4. Your opponent throws 9 balls at the target and scores 60 points. What is one way your opponent could have scored 60 points?

Possible answer: 6 balls at 6 points each, 3 balls at 8 points each

5. Write a problem about the target game that can be solved using multiplication. Write the number sentence that solves the problem.

Problems and number sentences will vary.

 Use with Grade 3, text pages 334–335.

Daily Review

Name ____________ Daily Review 9-5

Problem Solving

Choose the Operation

Answer each question. Give a reason for your choice.

The outdoor club is taking a hiking trip. The first day the club will hike 10 miles. The second day they will hike 8 miles. Then they will then turn around and hike for 2 days back to the base camp.

1. Which operation would you use to find out how many miles the club hiked altogether?

(a.) Addition

b. Subtraction

c. Multiplication

2. Which operation would you use to find out how many more miles the club hiked the first day than on the second day?

a. Addition

(b.) Subtraction

c. Multiplication

3. Which number sentence tells you how far the club hiked on the first two days?

a. 10 − 8 = 2

b. 10 + 8 + 8 + 10 = 36

(c.) 10 + 8 = 18

4. Which number sentence tells you how far the club hiked altogether on the trip?

(a.) 10 + 8 + 8 + 10 = 36

b. 10 × 2 = 20

c. 10 + 8 = 18

Review and Remember

Solve.

5. 11 + 4 = 15 **6.** 17 − 9 = 8 **7.** 25 + 8 = 33

8. 18 − 10 = 8

9. 10 + 3 + 8 = 21

10. 4 + 9 + 6 = 19

11. 19 − 6 = 13

Practice

Dividing by 8

P 9-6

Write the product or quotient. Shade the square with that answer. The shaded squares will form a path from start to the circus tent.

1. 32 ÷ 8 = 4
2. 8 × 9 = 72
3. 40 ÷ 8 = 5
4. 8 ÷ 8 = 1
5. 7 × 7 = 49
6. 2 × 8 = 16
7. 8 × 4 = 32
8. 5 × 7 = 35
9. 56 ÷ 8 = 7
10. 8 × 6 = 48
11. 8 × 7 = 56
12. 24 ÷ 8 = 3
13. 64 ÷ 8 = 8
14. 8 × 3 = 24
15. 16 ÷ 8 = 2
16. 48 ÷ 8 = 6
17. 72 ÷ 8 = 9
18. 0 × 8 = 0

START

8	16	25	48	56	7
45	24	32	35	40	72
55	65	11	17	64	9
14	3	4	5	6	49
12	2	26	29	23	37
0	1	89	41	61	71

 Use with Grade 3, text pages 338–339.

Reteach

Dividing by 8

R 9-6

You can use multiplication to help you divide.

24 ÷ 8 = ?

Step 1 You need to know how many groups of 8 are in 24.

Step 2 Make one group of 8, then another, then another.

3 groups of 8 make 24. So,

3 × 8 = 24, so,

24 ÷ 3 = 8

Complete each multiplication fact. Then divide.

1. 2 × 8 = 16; 16 ÷ 8 = 2
2. 4 × 8 = 32; 32 ÷ 8 = 4
3. 6 × 8 = 48; 48 ÷ 8 = 6
4. 5 × 8 = 40; 40 ÷ 8 = 5
5. 8 × 8 = 64; 64 ÷ 8 = 8
6. 7 × 8 = 56; 56 ÷ 8 = 7
7. 9 × 8 = 72; 72 ÷ 8 = 9
8. 1 × 8 = 8; 8 ÷ 8 = 1
9. 4 × 6 = 24; 24 ÷ 6 = 4

Divide.

10. $8\overline{)32}$ 4
11. $8\overline{)48}$ 6
12. $8\overline{)56}$ 7

 Use with Grade 3, text pages 338–339.

Extend

Crossing Paths

E 9-6 REASONING

Complete the chart. Find where each item listed below belongs. Use the category heads to help you. Write the item in the chart. Then write the missing category heads.

banana	polar bear	cardinal	roses
canary	snow lily	caution light	frog
strawberry	stoplight	sunshine daisy	peas
go light	weed	white light	milk

Categories	Kinds of Food	Kinds of Lights	Kinds of Animals	Kinds of Plants
Yellow Things	banana	caution light	canary	sunshine daisy
Green Things	peas	go light	frog	weed
Red Things	strawberry	stoplight	cardinal	roses
White Things	milk	white light	polar bear	snow lily

Write names of foods or colors on this chart. Check students' reasoning

	Red	Green	Yellow
Grow on Trees		apples, pears	
Grow on Small Plants	tomatoes, cranberries		

 Use with Grade 3, text pages 338–339.

Daily Review

Name __________ Daily Review 9-6

Dividing by 8

Find each missing factor. Then use it to find the quotient.

1. 8 × [3] = 24; 24 ÷ 8 = [3]
2. 8 × [9] = 72; 72 ÷ 8 = [9]
3. 8 × [5] = 40; 40 ÷ 8 = [5]

Find each quotient.

4. $8\overline{)32}$ 4
5. $8\overline{)64}$ 8
6. $8\overline{)8}$ 1
7. $8\overline{)48}$ 6
8. $8\overline{)24}$ 3
9. 16 ÷ 8 = 2
10. 40 ÷ 8 = 5
11. 56 ÷ 8 = 7
12. 72 ÷ 8 = 9

Write × or ÷ for each □.

13. 4 [×] 8 = 32
14. 24 [÷] 8 = 3
15. 8 [×] 5 = 40

Problem Solving

16. In a theater, there are 8 seats in each row. How many rows are needed to seat 40 children? 5 rows

17. There are 24 different puppets in one show. Each puppeteer takes care of 3 different puppets. How many puppeteers are needed for the show? 8 puppeteers

Review and Remember

Use paper and pencil or mental math to solve. Tell which method you used. Methods will vary.

18. 844 + 353 — 1,197; paper and pencil
19. 1,560 + 200 — 1,760; mental math
20. 689 − 20 — 669; mental math
21. 726 − 469 — 257; paper and pencil

Practice

Dividing by 9

P 9-7

Write the product or quotient.

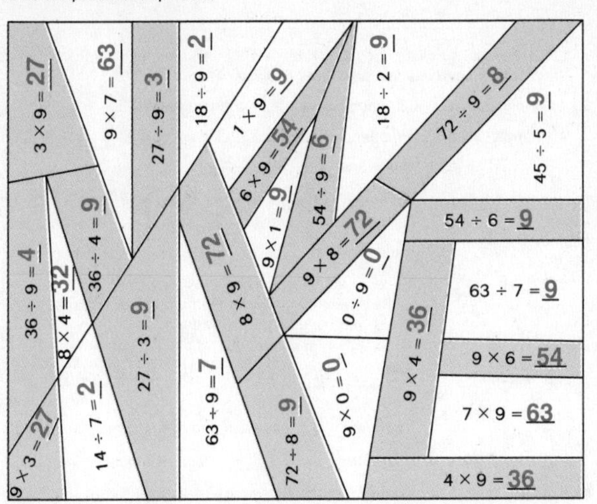

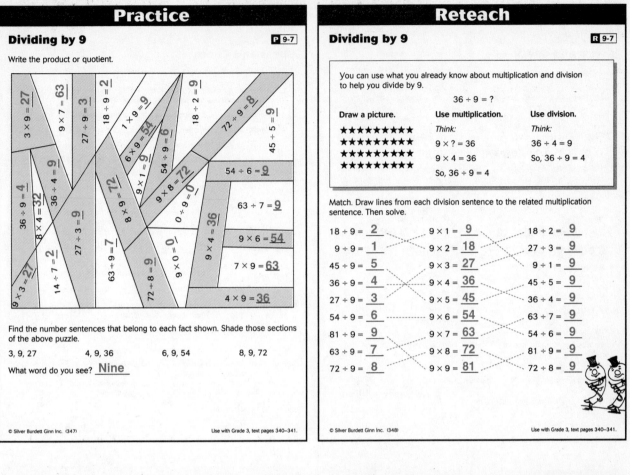

Find the number sentences that belong to each fact shown. Shade those sections of the above puzzle.

3, 9, 27 4, 9, 36 6, 9, 54 8, 9, 72

What word do you see? Nine

 Use with Grade 3, text pages 340–341.

Reteach

Dividing by 9

R 9-7

You can use what you already know about multiplication and division to help you divide by 9.

36 ÷ 9 = ?

Draw a picture.	Use multiplication.	Use division.
★★★★★★★★★	*Think:*	*Think:*
★★★★★★★★★	9 × ? = 36	36 ÷ 4 = 9
★★★★★★★★★	9 × 4 = 36	So, 36 ÷ 9 = 4
★★★★★★★★★	So, 36 ÷ 9 = 4	

Match. Draw lines from each division sentence to the related multiplication sentence. Then solve.

18 ÷ 9 = 2	9 × 1 = 9	18 ÷ 2 = 9
9 ÷ 9 = 1	9 × 2 = 18	27 ÷ 3 = 9
45 ÷ 9 = 5	9 × 3 = 27	9 ÷ 1 = 9
36 ÷ 9 = 4	9 × 4 = 36	45 ÷ 5 = 9
27 ÷ 9 = 3	9 × 5 = 45	36 ÷ 4 = 9
54 ÷ 9 = 6	9 × 6 = 54	63 ÷ 7 = 9
81 ÷ 9 = 9	9 × 7 = 63	54 ÷ 6 = 9
63 ÷ 9 = 7	9 × 8 = 72	81 ÷ 9 = 9
72 ÷ 9 = 8	9 × 9 = 81	72 ÷ 8 = 9

 Use with Grade 3, text pages 340–341.

Extend

Fill It Up

E 9-7

REASONING

Write a number in each box in the chart to fit the rule for that column and row. Do not use any number more than once.

	9 as a factor	has three digits	has 4 as a factor
has the digit 4 in it	54	400	24
has 3 as a factor	27	150	12
is an even number	90	822	8
has zero in tens place	900	201	200
is greater than 30	36	932	32

Check the accuracy of students' numbers, which will vary. Possible answers are shown.

Create Your Own

On the back of this page, make a chart like the one above and give it to a classmate to complete. Make sure your chart does not ask for a number that cannot be made, such as "an even number that ends in 3."

Check students' methods and figures.

 Use with Grade 3, text pages 340–341.

Daily Review

Name________________

Daily Review 9-7

Dividing by 9

Divide.

1. $9\overline{)36}$ 4
2. $9\overline{)27}$ 3
3. $9\overline{)54}$ 6
4. $9\overline{)72}$ 8
5. $9\overline{)9}$ 1
6. $9\overline{)18}$ 2
7. $9\overline{)45}$ 5
8. $9\overline{)81}$ 9
9. $1\overline{)9}$ 9
10. $9\overline{)63}$ 7

Follow the rule to complete each chart.

	Rule: Divide by 9 Input	Output
11.	81	9
12.	63	7
13.	45	5
14.	27	3

	Rule: Divide by 6 Input	Output
15.	42	7
16.	48	8
17.	36	6
18.	54	9

	Rule: Divide by 8 Input	Output
19.	24	3
20.	72	9
21.	40	5
22.	64	8

Problem Solving

23. Each of the 45 students in the chorus will hold up a flower during the performance. There will be 5 different-colored flowers. An equal number of students will hold up the same color flower. How many students will have the same color flower?

9 students

24. Nine chorus members are on the decorating team for a show. They must put together 18 bouquets of flowers. If each student works on the same number of bouquets, how many will each student do?

2 bouquets

Review and Remember

Find each answer.

25. 8 × 9 = 72
26. 432 + 251 = 683
27. 328 − 142 = 186
28. 49 ÷ 7 = 7

Practice

Problem Solving P 9-8

Guess and Check

Use guess and check to solve each problem.

1. There are 17 clowns in one circus act. They ride unicycles and walk on stilts. Seven more clowns walk on stilts than ride on unicycles. How many clowns walk on stilts? How many clowns ride on unicycles?

   12 on stilts, 5 on unicycles

2. In another circus act, half of the clowns are people and half are dogs. They are all wearing clown shoes! There are 24 shoes in all. How many dogs are wearing clown shoes?

   4 dogs

3. The circus charges $2 for a child under 12 and $5 for a child over 12. Suni spent $18 for 6 children. How many children are under 12? How many children are over 12?

   4 children under 12;
   2 children over 12

4. There are 174 human and animal circus performers. There are 28 more animal performers than human performers. How many animal performers are there? How many human performers?

   101 animal performers;
   73 human performers

5. A clown says, "The sum of my numbers is 10, and their product is 21. What are my numbers?" Write the numbers here.

   7 and 3

Create Your Own

6. Choose two numbers between 1 and 10. Find their sum and their product. Record them below. Ask a classmate to guess the numbers you chose. Then write the numbers in below as well.

   The sum of my numbers is _____ and their product is _____.

   What are my numbers? My numbers are _____ and _____.

   Answers will vary.

Reteach

Problem Solving R 9-8

Guess and Check

There are 13 goldfish in a pond. There are 5 more large fish than small fish. How many large fish are there? How many small fish?

1. How can you find the number of large fish and small fish?

Understand You need to know the total number of fish.

There are **13** fish altogether.

You need to know how many more large fish than small fish there are.

There are **5** more large fish than small fish.

Plan Write a number pair whose sum is 13.
Is the difference between the numbers equal to 5?
If it is, you have found the answer!
If it is not, try another number pair whose sum is 13.

Solve **9** + **4** = 13 **9** – **4** = 5

There are **9** large fish and **4** small fish.

Look Back **9** large fish and **4** small fish make 13 fish.

There are 5 more large fish than small fish.
The answer makes sense.

Use guess and check to solve the problems.

2. Hal spends $16 at a book store. He spends $2 more on a fish book than he does on a sports book. How much is each book?

   fish book **$9**; sports book **$7**

3. Marla has 17 fish. She has 5 more lionhead fish than fantail fish. How many of each kind of fish does Marla have?

   lionhead **11**; fantail **6**

Extend

Guess Again!

E 9-8 NUMBER SENSE

1. Penny is twice as old as Pat. When Penny is 20, Pat will be 16. How old is Penny now? How old is Pat?

   Penny is 8, Pat is 4.

2. The sum of Eve's age and Alan's age is 48. Alan is 12 years younger than Eve. How old are Eve and Alan?

   Eve is 30, Alan is 18.

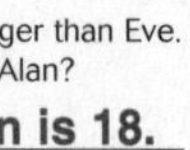

3. Jackie is half as old as Jill. Jill is half as old as Bob. Bob is 40. How old are Jackie and Jill?

   Jill is 20, Jackie is 10.

4. Mrs. Tang is 4 years more than twice as old as Kim. Kim is 15. How old is Mrs. Tang?

   34 years old

5. Thuy is 1 year older than Boris. Boris is 1 year older than Val. The sum of their ages is 30. How old are Thuy, Boris, and Val?

   Val is 9, Boris is 10, and Thuy is 11.

6. When Sally's age is multiplied by Gwen's age, the product is 24. Sally is 10 years younger than Gwen. How old is Sally? How old is Gwen?

   Sally is 2, Gwen is 12.

Write a number sentence to solve.

7. In the school play, Amy's character is 27 years older than Amy's real age. Amy is 9 years old. How old is the character she is playing?

   27 + 9 = 36 years old

8. Alice takes 36 pictures of the play. She takes 4 equal groups of pictures, one for each scene in the play. How many pictures does Alice have of each scene?

   36 ÷ 4 = 9 pictures

Daily Review

Name ____________________ Daily Review 9-8

Problem Solving

Guess and Check

Use guess and check to solve these problems.

1. Solve this riddle. I am twice as old as my brother. I am half as old as my sister. Together, our ages total 14. How old are we?

   2, 4, and 8

2. Tickets for the ferris wheel cost $0.25 each. A book of 5 tickets costs $1.00. The Cruz family spent $2.50 on tickets. What is the greatest number of tickets they can have?

   12 tickets

3. Together John and Jose collected 9 crates of newspaper for the recycling center. Jose collected twice as many crates as John. How many crates did each boy collect?

   John collected 3 crates; Jose collected 6 crates.

4. I am a 3-digit number. The sum of my digits is 14. My first digit is 3 times my third digit. My second digit is one less than my third digit. What number am I?

   923

Review and Remember

Solve.

5. $116 + 34 + 76 =$ **226**
6. $145 + 756 + 645 =$ **1,546**
7. $487 + 761 + 32 =$ **1,280**
8. $679 + 231 + 452 =$ **1,362**
9. $762 - 384 =$ **378**
10. $901 - 27 =$ **874**
11. $8{,}330 - 1{,}290 =$ **7,040**
12. $427 - 188 =$ **239**

Chapter 9 • Lesson 9

Practice

Using Strategies in Division

P 9-9

Find each quotient.

1. 35 ÷ 5 = 7 **2.** 32 ÷ 4 = 8 **3.** 42 ÷ 6 = 7

4. 36 ÷ 6 = 6 **5.** 40 ÷ 8 = 5 **6.** 24 ÷ 8 = 3

Divide.

7. 2)18 9 **8.** 6)48 8 **9.** 6)30 5

10. 3)12 4 **11.** 9)45 5 **12.** 7)49 7

13. 8)64 8 **14.** 9)54 6 **15.** 5)35 7

Compare. Write <, >, or = for each ◯.

16. 12 ÷ 6 (<) 3 **17.** 16 ÷ 8 (=) 2 **18.** 56 ÷ 8 (>) 5

19. 36 ÷ 9 (<) 6 **20.** 48 ÷ 8 (=) 6 **21.** 27 ÷ 9 (>) 2

Solve and tell what strategy you used.

22. Fifteen dancers are asked to form three equal groups. How many dancers will be in each group?

5. Strategies will vary.

Make up your own question using division. Ask a classmate to solve.

23. Answers will vary. Check students' methods.

 Use with Grade 3, text pages 344–345.

Reteach

Using Strategies in Division

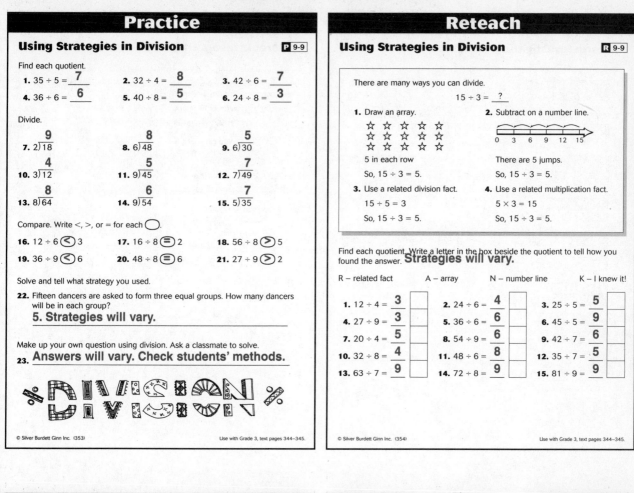

There are many ways you can divide.

15 ÷ 3 = ?

1. Draw an array.

☆ ☆ ☆ ☆ ☆
☆ ☆ ☆ ☆ ☆
☆ ☆ ☆ ☆ ☆

5 in each row

So, 15 ÷ 3 = 5.

2. Subtract on a number line.

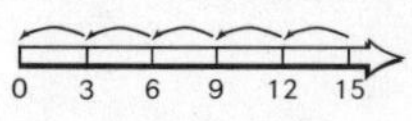

There are 5 jumps.

So, 15 ÷ 3 = 5.

3. Use a related division fact.

15 ÷ 5 = 3

So, 15 ÷ 3 = 5.

4. Use a related multiplication fact.

5 × 3 = 15

So, 15 ÷ 3 = 5.

Find each quotient. Write a letter in the box beside the quotient to tell how you found the answer. Strategies will vary.

R – related fact A – array N – number line K – I knew it!

1. 12 ÷ 4 = 3 ☐ **2.** 24 ÷ 6 = 4 ☐ **3.** 25 ÷ 5 = 5 ☐

4. 27 ÷ 9 = 3 ☐ **5.** 36 ÷ 6 = 6 ☐ **6.** 45 ÷ 5 = 9 ☐

7. 20 ÷ 4 = 5 ☐ **8.** 54 ÷ 9 = 6 ☐ **9.** 42 ÷ 7 = 6 ☐

10. 32 ÷ 8 = 4 ☐ **11.** 48 ÷ 6 = 8 ☐ **12.** 35 ÷ 7 = 5 ☐

13. 63 ÷ 7 = 9 ☐ **14.** 72 ÷ 8 = 9 ☐ **15.** 81 ÷ 9 = 9 ☐

 Use with Grade 3, text pages 344–345.

Extend

Symbol Search

E 9-9 VISUAL THINKING

Find the above symbols in the larger box below and circle them in red. Each symbol must match exactly. Time yourself to see how long it takes to find all of the symbols.

How long did it take? Times will vary.

Now find these figures in the puzzle and put a check by each one. They will be upside down in the puzzle.

Share Your Ideas

Compare the way you did both tasks with a classmate.

 Use with Grade 3, text pages 344–345.

Daily Review

Name________________ Daily Review 9-9

Using Strategies in Division

Divide.

1. 6)36 6 **2.** 9)81 9 **3.** 8)56 7 **4.** 8)72 9 **5.** 9)0 0

6. 7)35 5 **7.** 6)48 8 **8.** 7)63 9 **9.** 6)30 5 **10.** 8)64 8

Compare. Write >, <, or = for each ◯.

11. 27 ÷ 9 (<) 4 **12.** 42 ÷ 6 (=) 7 **13.** 40 ÷ 8 (>) 3

14. 32 ÷ 4 (>) 3 × 2 **15.** 18 ÷ 6 (<) 2 × 2 **16.** 54 ÷ 6 (=) 3 × 3

Problem Solving

17. The singing part of the talent show will last exactly 18 minutes. There are 6 singers. Each singer is given an equal amount of time. How much time does each singer get?

3 minutes

18. Tickets for the talent show cost $5. A family spends $25 on tickets. How many tickets did the family buy?

5 tickets

Review and Remember

Find each answer.

19. 85 − 48 = 37 **20.** 7 × 6 = 42 **21.** 229 + 17 = 246

22. 48 ÷ 6 = 8 **23.** 8 × 7 = 56 **24.** 27 ÷ 3 = 9

25. 456 − 127 = 329 **26.** 68 + 44 = 112 **27.** 63 ÷ 9 = 7

Chapter 9 • Lesson 10

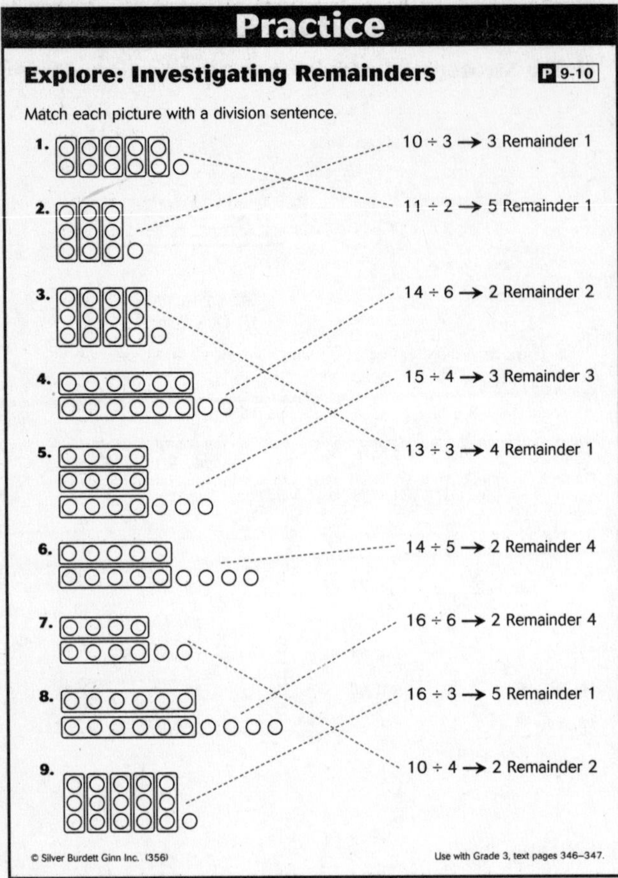

Practice

Explore: Investigating Remainders

P 9-10

Match each picture with a division sentence.

1.
2.
3.
4.
5.
6.
7.
8.
9.

- 10 ÷ 3 → 3 Remainder 1
- 11 ÷ 2 → 5 Remainder 1
- 14 ÷ 6 → 2 Remainder 2
- 15 ÷ 4 → 3 Remainder 3
- 13 ÷ 3 → 4 Remainder 1
- 14 ÷ 5 → 2 Remainder 4
- 16 ÷ 6 → 2 Remainder 4
- 16 ÷ 3 → 5 Remainder 1
- 10 ÷ 4 → 2 Remainder 2

 Use with Grade 3, text pages 346–347.

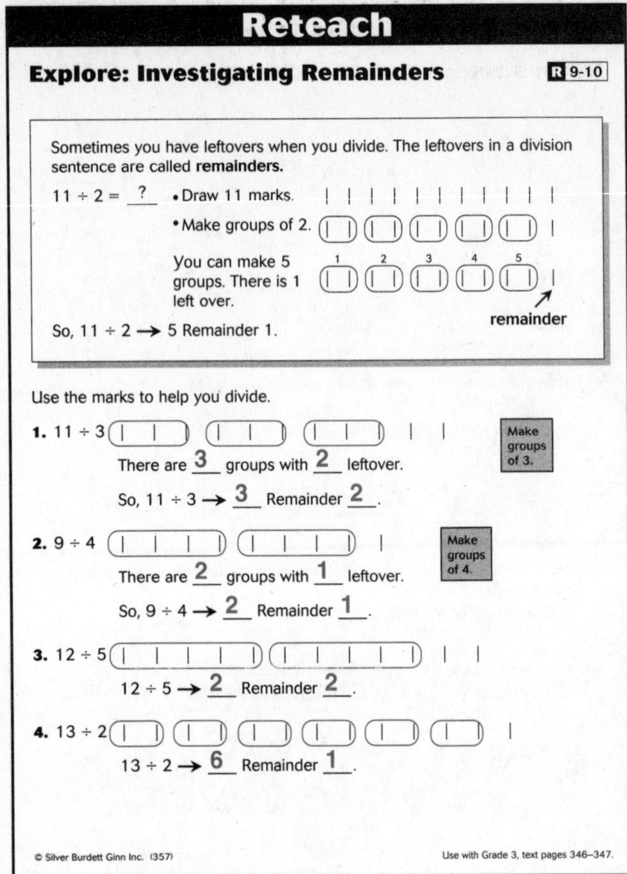

Reteach

Explore: Investigating Remainders

R 9-10

Sometimes you have leftovers when you divide. The leftovers in a division sentence are called **remainders.**

11 ÷ 2 = ?
- Draw 11 marks.
- Make groups of 2.

You can make 5 groups. There is 1 left over.

remainder

So, 11 ÷ 2 → 5 Remainder 1.

Use the marks to help you divide.

1. 11 ÷ 3 — Make groups of 3.
   There are 3 groups with 2 leftover.
   So, 11 ÷ 3 → 3 Remainder 2.
2. 9 ÷ 4 — Make groups of 4.
   There are 2 groups with 1 leftover.
   So, 9 ÷ 4 → 2 Remainder 1.
3. 12 ÷ 5
   12 ÷ 5 → 2 Remainder 2.
4. 13 ÷ 2
   13 ÷ 2 → 6 Remainder 1.

 Use with Grade 3, text pages 346–347.

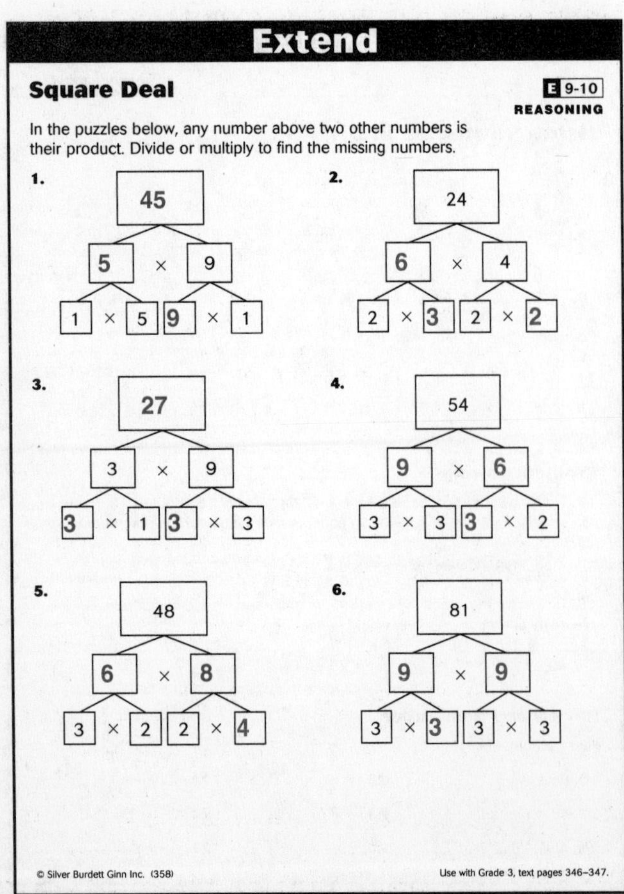

Extend

Square Deal

E 9-10
REASONING

In the puzzles below, any number above two other numbers is their product. Divide or multiply to find the missing numbers.

1. 45; 5 × 9; 1 × 5, 9 × 1
2. 24; 6 × 4; 2 × 3, 2 × 2
3. 27; 3 × 9; 3 × 1, 3 × 3
4. 54; 9 × 6; 3 × 3, 3 × 2
5. 48; 6 × 8; 3 × 2, 2 × 4
6. 81; 9 × 9; 3 × 3, 3 × 3

 Use with Grade 3, text pages 346–347.

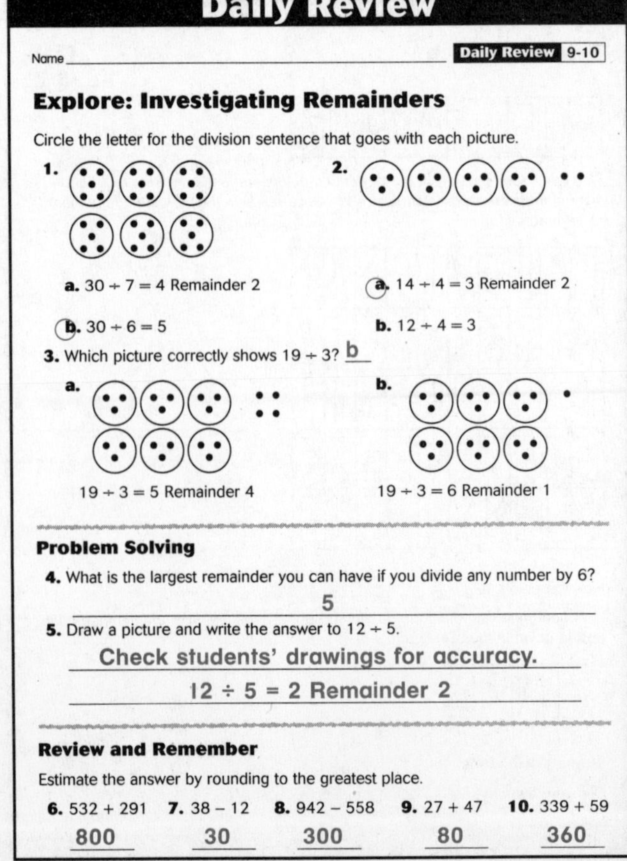

Daily Review

Name ____________

Daily Review 9-10

Explore: Investigating Remainders

Circle the letter for the division sentence that goes with each picture.

1. a. 30 ÷ 7 = 4 Remainder 2
   (b.) 30 ÷ 6 = 5
2. (a.) 14 ÷ 4 = 3 Remainder 2
   b. 12 ÷ 4 = 3
3. Which picture correctly shows 19 ÷ 3? b
   a. 19 ÷ 3 = 5 Remainder 4
   b. 19 ÷ 3 = 6 Remainder 1

Problem Solving

4. What is the largest remainder you can have if you divide any number by 6?
   5
5. Draw a picture and write the answer to 12 ÷ 5.
   Check students' drawings for accuracy.
   12 ÷ 5 = 2 Remainder 2

Review and Remember

Estimate the answer by rounding to the greatest place.

6. 532 + 291	7. 38 − 12	8. 942 − 558	9. 27 + 47	10. 339 + 59
800	30	300	80	360

Chapter 9 • Lesson 11

Practice

Problem Solving P 9-11

Using Operations

Solve.

1. Wendy went to the mall at 11:00. She shopped for an hour, and then ate lunch for 30 minutes. She met Jeri right after lunch. What time was it then?
   12:30
2. Wendy bought a sandwich for \$3.79, French fries for \$1.99, and a drink for \$1.25. About how much did Wendy spend for lunch?
   about \$7
3. Wendy and Jeri buy hair clips for \$5.50 and ribbons for \$2.50. If they share the cost equally, how much will it cost each girl?
   \$4
4. Wendy and Jeri shop in three stores. They spend 15 minutes in each store. How long do they spend shopping?
   45 minutes
5. At 3:20, Wendy and Jeri stop for a snack. They spend 5 minutes in line and 10 minutes eating. They must be home from the mall by 4:00. How much time do they have to get home?
   25 minutes
6. The mall has two school choruses performing. The Junior chorus has 75 singers. The Senior chorus has 48 more singers than the Junior chorus. How many singers are there in the Senior chorus?
   123 singers

Create Your Own

7. Write a problem about shopping in the mall. Solve your problem. Then give it to a classmate to solve.
   Problems and solutions will vary.

 Use with Grade 3, text pages 348–349.

Reteach

Problem Solving R 9-11

Using Operations

Today is the day for class pictures! It takes about 5 minutes for each class to have its picture taken. The photographer starts at 12:00 P.M. and is finished at 12:30 P.M. How many pictures did he take?

1. How long does the photographer spend taking pictures? How many pictures can he take in that amount of time?

Understand You need to know the total amount of time spent taking pictures. You also need to know how long it takes to take one picture.

Plan Step 1 Subtract to find the total number of minutes spent taking pictures.

Step 2 Divide to find the number of pictures taken.

Solve Step 1 12:30 P.M. – 12:00 P.M. = 30 minutes

Step 2 30 (total minutes) ÷ 5 (minutes per picture) = 6 (number of pictures)

Look Back Check your answer. Each picture takes 5 minutes.

5 × 6 = 30. So, the answer makes sense.

2. Ms. Wingate's class spends 10 minutes lining up from shortest to tallest. It takes 5 minutes to have their picture taken. If they begin at 12:10, what time will they be finished?
   12:25
3. The photographer takes a picture of the chess club. There are 3 rows of students with 5 students in each row. How many students are in the picture?
   15 students

 Use with Grade 3, text pages 348–349.

Extend

Newspaper Route

E 9-11 NUMBER SENSE

Seth delivers newspapers. Today he collects money from everyone who receives a daily newspaper. It takes about 7 minutes to get to each customer's house and collect money. Seth collects money for 3 hours.

1. On Third Street, Seth needs almost an hour to collect money from all of his customers. How many customers might he have on Third Street? Explain.
   Possible answer: 60 minutes ÷ 7 minutes = 8 R4 minutes; 8 customers
2. Seth collected \$10 from each customer on his route. Would you predict that Seth collected less than \$100? Explain.
   No; Seth collected about \$80 in just one hour.
3. Estimate the number of customers Seth collected money from. Give a reason for your estimate.
   8 customers x 3 hours = 24; about 24 or 25 customers

Use Guess and Check to solve.

4. The students below want to play tug of war. They want to make two teams, with each team weighing a total of 80 kilograms.

Ann	26 kg	Ben	18 kg	Cal	28 kg
Don	32 kg	Ed	34 kg	Fez	22 kg

Which children should play on each team?
Team 1: Ann, Don, and Fez
Team 2: Ben, Cal, and Ed

 Use with Grade 3, text pages 348–349.

Daily Review

Name ____________ Daily Review 9-11

Problem Solving

Using Operations

Solve each problem.

1. Rosan and Eric are playing a card game. Rosan has 16 cards and Eric has 6 cards. To play the game they each need the same number of cards. How many cards should Rosan give Eric?
   5 cards
2. There are 7 dogs in the park with their owners. Six more people bring their dogs into the park. Then 4 dogs leave with their owners. How many dogs are left in the park?
   9 dogs
3. Kelly and Monique are building a clubhouse. They want to get 2 sets of curtains and some wooden boards. Each set of curtains cost \$2.75. The wood costs \$4.50 altogether. If they split the cost equally, how much money does each girl have to pay?
   \$5.00 each
4. John has a flower garden. The garden has 4 rows of 6 flower plants. If one half of the flower plants are begonias how many plants are not begonias?
   12 plants

Review and Remember

Find each difference.

5. \$4.25 – \$1.25 = \$3.00
6. 367 – 254 = 113
7. \$6.50 – \$4.25 = \$2.25
8. 466 – 328 = 138
9. \$7.35 – \$1.80 = \$5.55
10. 897 – 604 = 293
11. \$8.75 – \$7.50 = \$1.25
12. 722 – 227 = 495

Chapter 10 • Lesson 1

Practice

Plane Figures

P 10-1

Write the name of each figure. Then write the letter of the same figure.

	Figure	Name	Letter of Same Figure	Same Figure
1.		rectangle	h.	a. b.
2.		circle	j.	c. d.
3.		triangle	a.	e. f.
4.		square	e.	g. h.
5.		pentagon	d.	i. j.
6.		hexagon	c.	k. l.
7.		trapezoid	i.	

Use the figure to answer Questions 8–10.

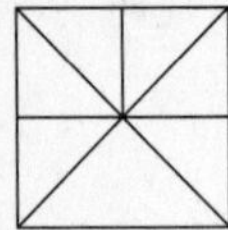

8. How many different squares can you find? 3
9. How many different triangles can you find? 14
10. How many different rectangles can you find? 5, including the squares

 Use with Grade 3, text pages 362–365.

Reteach

Plane Figures

R 10-1

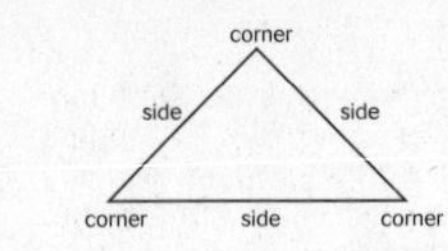

- A triangle has three sides and three corners.
- Some triangles, like this one, have sides that are equal.

circle triangle rectangle square quadrilateral 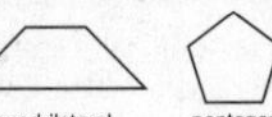 pentagon 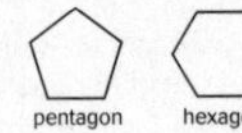 hexagon

Look at each plane figure. Then complete the chart.

Plane Figure	Number of Sides	Number of Corners	Are the Sides Equal?
	6	6	yes
	3	3	yes
	0	0	n/a
	4	4	no
	4	4	no
	5	5	yes
	4	4	yes

 Use with Grade 3, text pages 362–365.

Extend

Shape Scores

E 10-1 MENTAL MATH

Use the pictures to help you answer the questions.

1. You throw 4 balls. Each ball hits the target. You score 12 points. Which rings in the target did you hit?
   5 twice and 1 twice

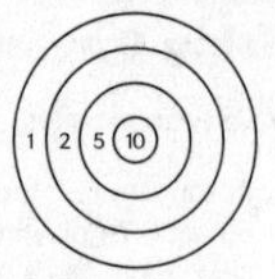

2. You score 20 points with 3 disks on this shuffleboard court. Each disk scores points. On which parts of the board did your disks land?
   5 twice and 10 once

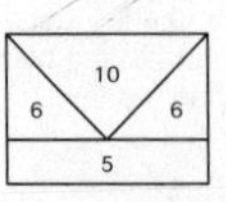

3. You throw 3 balls and score 18 points on this target. Each ball hits the target. Which rings did you hit?
   9, 6, and 3; 6 three times

4. How could you score 19 points with 3 spins on this wheel?
   9, 7, and 3; 9, 9, and 1;
   9, 5, and 5; 7, 7, and 5

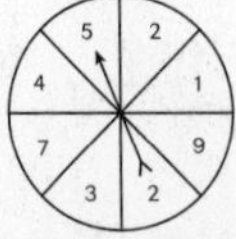

 Use with Grade 3, text pages 362–365.

Daily Review

Name ____________________ Daily Review 10-1

Plane Figures

Name each plane figure. Then tell the number of sides and the number of corners each figure has.

1. square, rectangle, or quadrilateral; 4, 4
2. pentagon; 5, 5
3. triangle; 3, 3
4. hexagon; 6, 6
5. circle; 0, 0
6. quadrilateral; 4, 4
7. triangle; 3, 3
8. rectangle or quadrilateral; 4, 4

Problem Solving

9. Use 5 different-colored crayons or markers. Create a design with the following shapes: 2 rectangles, 1 square, 3 pentagons, 1 hexagon, and 4 circles. Use a different color for each shape.
   Check students' designs for accuracy.
10. How many of the quadrilaterals in the design are squares? How many are rectangles? Are all squares rectangles? Explain. 1 square, 2 rectangles; the opposite sides of a rectangle are equal; all sides of all squares are equal; so all squares are rectangles.

Review and Remember

Use mental math to find each sum or difference.

11. 230 + 60 = 290
12. 3,000 − 400 = 2,600

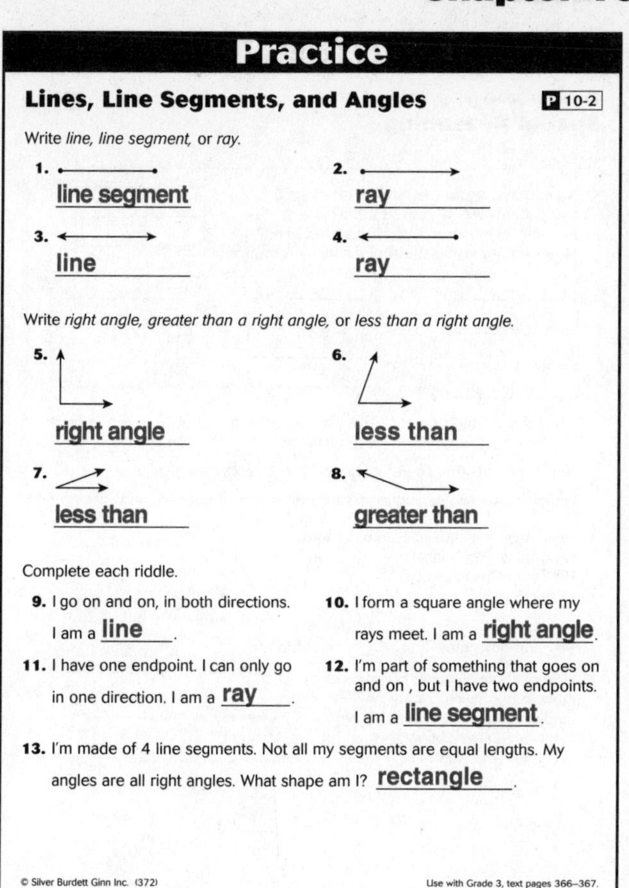

Practice

Lines, Line Segments, and Angles

P 10-2

Write *line, line segment,* or *ray.*

1. line segment
2. ray
3. line
4. ray

Write *right angle, greater than a right angle,* or *less than a right angle.*

5. right angle
6. less than
7. less than
8. greater than

Complete each riddle.

9. I go on and on, in both directions. I am a line.
10. I form a square angle where my rays meet. I am a right angle.
11. I have one endpoint. I can only go in one direction. I am a ray.
12. I'm part of something that goes on and on, but I have two endpoints. I am a line segment.
13. I'm made of 4 line segments. Not all my segments are equal lengths. My angles are all right angles. What shape am I? rectangle.

 Use with Grade 3, text pages 366–367.

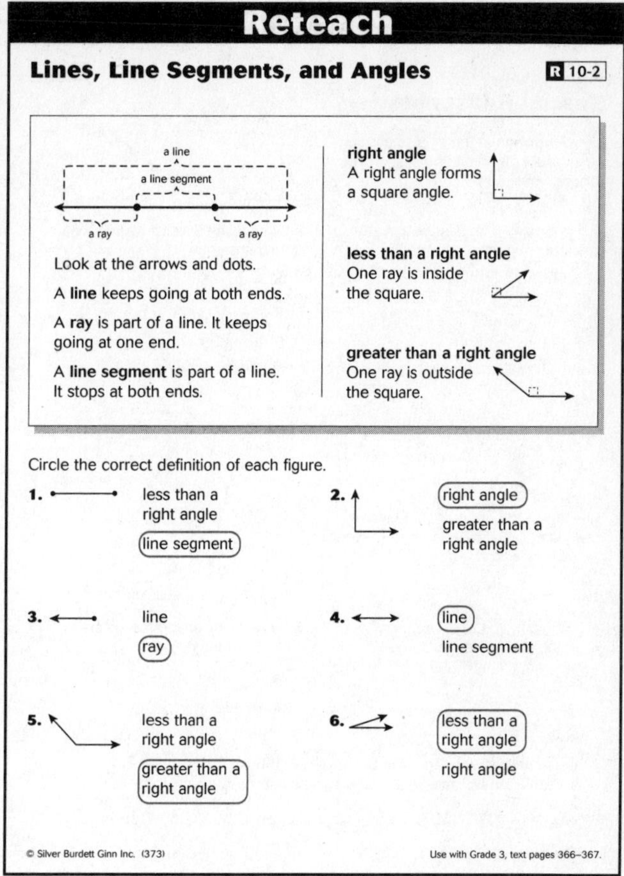

Reteach

Lines, Line Segments, and Angles

R 10-2

Look at the arrows and dots.

A **line** keeps going at both ends.

A **ray** is part of a line. It keeps going at one end.

A **line segment** is part of a line. It stops at both ends.

right angle
A right angle forms a square angle.

less than a right angle
One ray is inside the square.

greater than a right angle
One ray is outside the square.

Circle the correct definition of each figure.

1. less than a right angle / (line segment)
2. (right angle) / greater than a right angle
3. line / (ray)
4. (line) / line segment
5. less than a right angle / (greater than a right angle)
6. (less than a right angle) / right angle

 Use with Grade 3, text pages 366–367.

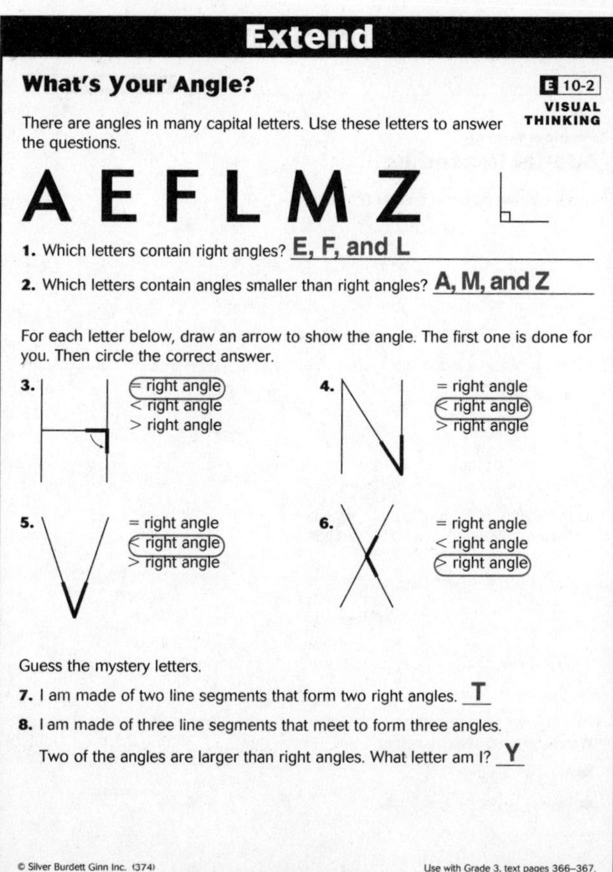

Extend

What's Your Angle?

E 10-2

VISUAL THINKING

There are angles in many capital letters. Use these letters to answer the questions.

A E F L M Z

1. Which letters contain right angles? E, F, and L
2. Which letters contain angles smaller than right angles? A, M, and Z

For each letter below, draw an arrow to show the angle. The first one is done for you. Then circle the correct answer.

3. (= right angle) / < right angle / > right angle
4. = right angle / (< right angle) / > right angle
5. = right angle / (< right angle) / > right angle
6. = right angle / < right angle / (> right angle)

Guess the mystery letters.

7. I am made of two line segments that form two right angles. T
8. I am made of three line segments that meet to form three angles. Two of the angles are larger than right angles. What letter am I? Y

 Use with Grade 3, text pages 366–367.

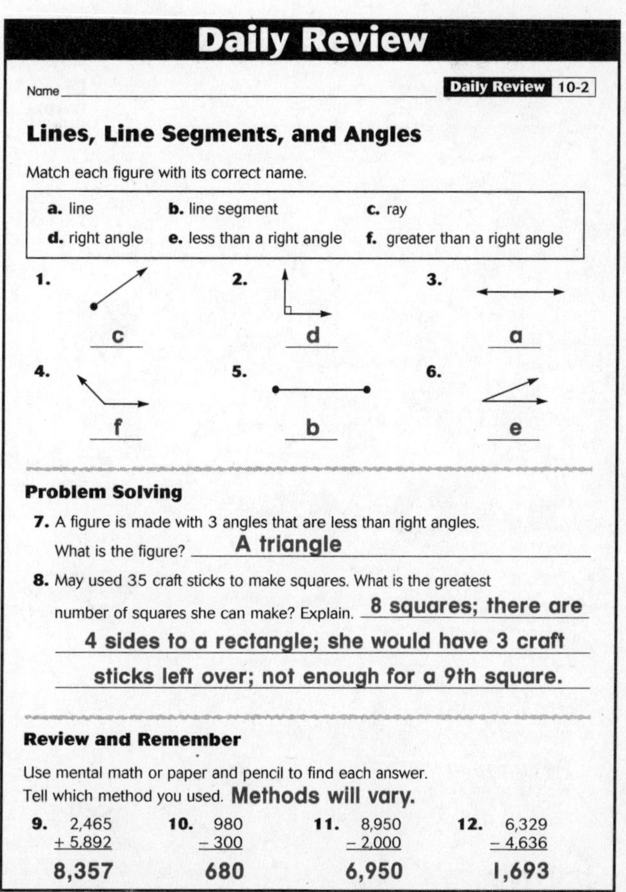

Daily Review

Name ____________________ Daily Review 10-2

Lines, Line Segments, and Angles

Match each figure with its correct name.

a. line	**b.** line segment	**c.** ray
d. right angle	**e.** less than a right angle	**f.** greater than a right angle

1. c
2. d
3. a
4. f
5. b
6. e

Problem Solving

7. A figure is made with 3 angles that are less than right angles. What is the figure? A triangle
8. May used 35 craft sticks to make squares. What is the greatest number of squares she can make? Explain. 8 squares; there are 4 sides to a rectangle; she would have 3 craft sticks left over; not enough for a 9th square.

Review and Remember

Use mental math or paper and pencil to find each answer. Tell which method you used. Methods will vary.

9. 2,465 + 5,892 = 8,357
10. 980 − 300 = 680
11. 8,950 − 2,000 = 6,950
12. 6,329 − 4,636 = 1,693

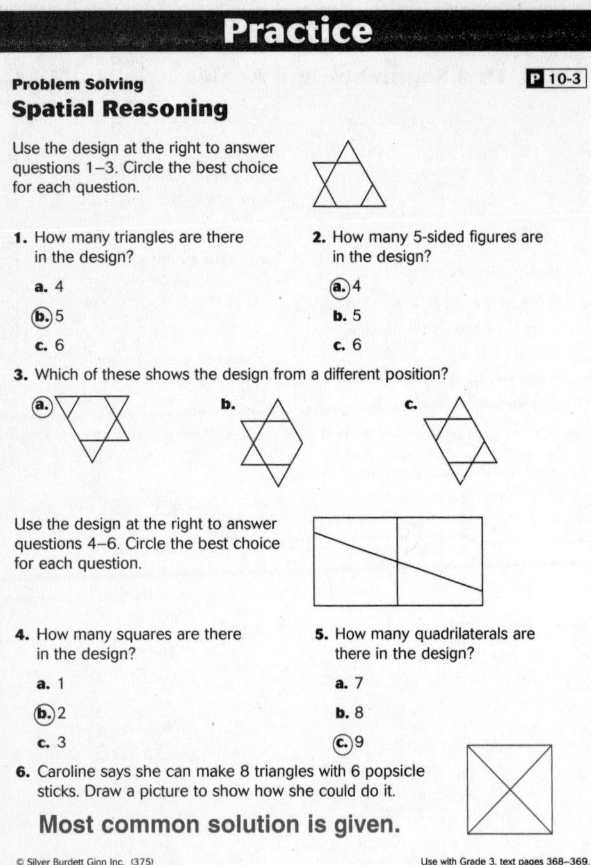

Practice

Problem Solving P 10-3

Spatial Reasoning

Use the design at the right to answer questions 1–3. Circle the best choice for each question.

1. How many triangles are there in the design?
   a. 4
   (b.) 5
   c. 6

2. How many 5-sided figures are in the design?
   (a.) 4
   b. 5
   c. 6

3. Which of these shows the design from a different position?
   (a.) b. c.

Use the design at the right to answer questions 4–6. Circle the best choice for each question.

4. How many squares are there in the design?
   a. 1
   (b.) 2
   c. 3

5. How many quadrilaterals are there in the design?
   a. 7
   b. 8
   (c.) 9

6. Caroline says she can make 8 triangles with 6 popsicle sticks. Draw a picture to show how she could do it.

Most common solution is given.

 Use with Grade 3, text pages 368–369.

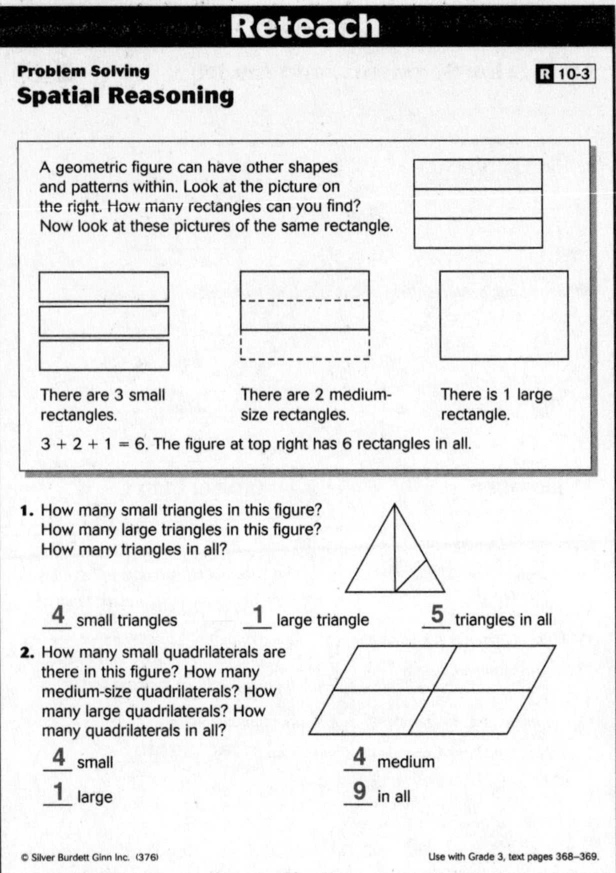

Reteach

Problem Solving R 10-3

Spatial Reasoning

A geometric figure can have other shapes and patterns within. Look at the picture on the right. How many rectangles can you find? Now look at these pictures of the same rectangle.

There are 3 small rectangles. There are 2 medium-size rectangles. There is 1 large rectangle.

3 + 2 + 1 = 6. The figure at top right has 6 rectangles in all.

1. How many small triangles in this figure? How many large triangles in this figure? How many triangles in all?
   4 small triangles 1 large triangle 5 triangles in all

2. How many small quadrilaterals are there in this figure? How many medium-size quadrilaterals? How many large quadrilaterals? How many quadrilaterals in all?
   4 small 4 medium
   1 large 9 in all

 Use with Grade 3, text pages 368–369.

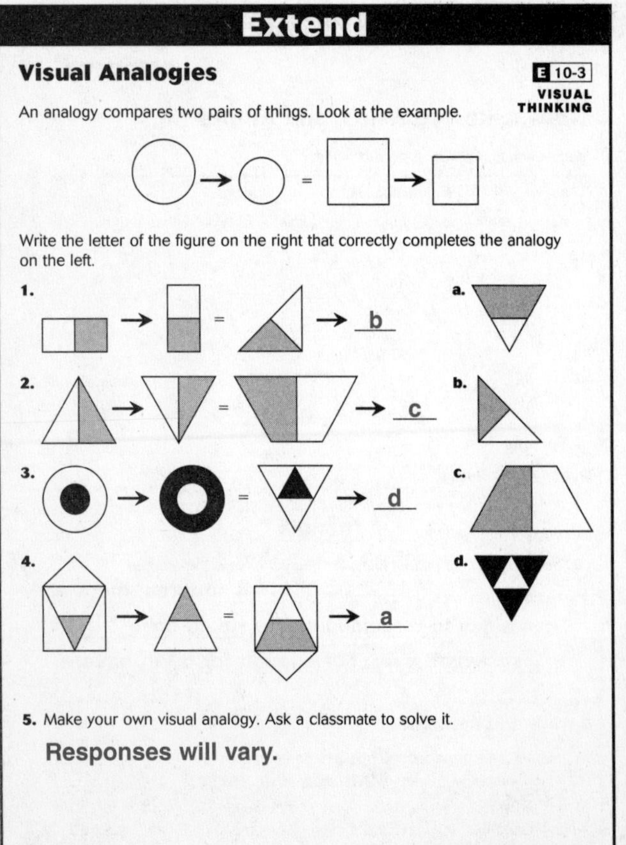

Extend

Visual Analogies

E 10-3 VISUAL THINKING

An analogy compares two pairs of things. Look at the example.

Write the letter of the figure on the right that correctly completes the analogy on the left.

1. → = → b
2. → = → c
3. → = → d
4. → = → a

a. b. c. d.

5. Make your own visual analogy. Ask a classmate to solve it.

Responses will vary.

 Use with Grade 3, text pages 368–369.

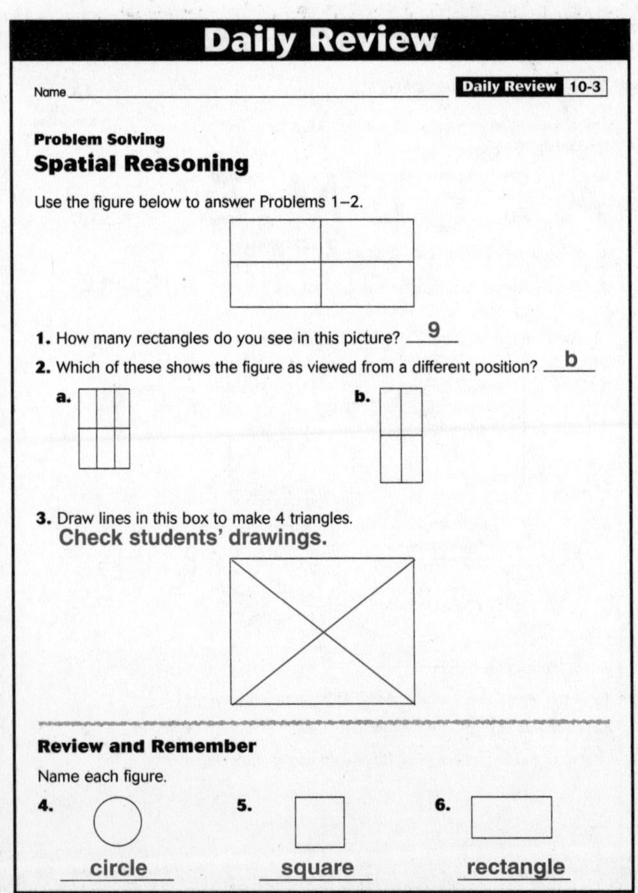

Daily Review

Name ______ Daily Review 10-3

Problem Solving

Spatial Reasoning

Use the figure below to answer Problems 1–2.

1. How many rectangles do you see in this picture? 9
2. Which of these shows the figure as viewed from a different position? b
   a. b.
3. Draw lines in this box to make 4 triangles.
   Check students' drawings.

Review and Remember

Name each figure.

4. circle
5. square
6. rectangle

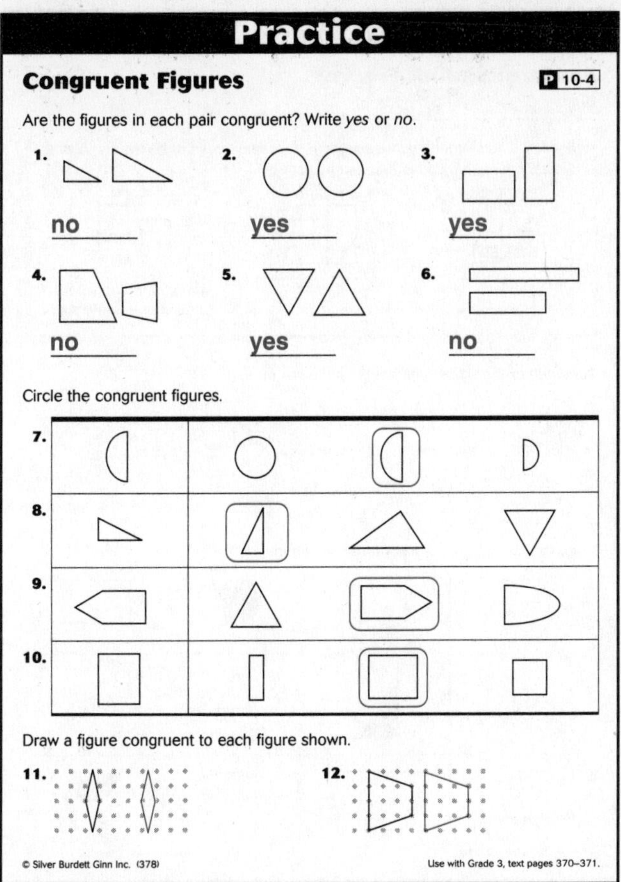

Practice

Congruent Figures

P 10-4

Are the figures in each pair congruent? Write *yes* or *no*.

1. no
2. yes
3. yes
4. no
5. yes
6. no

Circle the congruent figures.

7.
8.
9.
10.

Draw a figure congruent to each figure shown.

11.
12.

 Use with Grade 3, text pages 370–371.

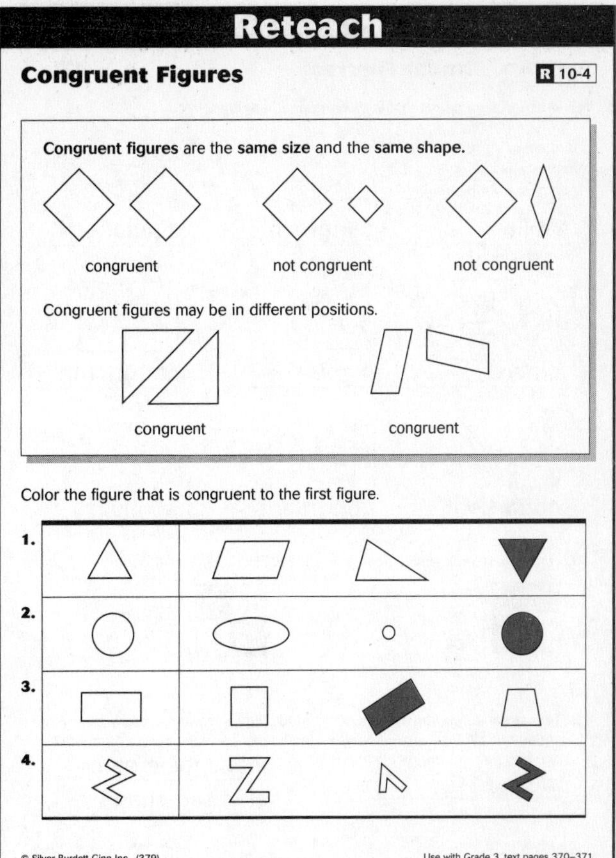

Reteach

Congruent Figures

R 10-4

Congruent figures are the **same size** and the **same shape.**

congruent | not congruent | not congruent

Congruent figures may be in different positions.

congruent | congruent

Color the figure that is congruent to the first figure.

1.
2.
3.
4.

 Use with Grade 3, text pages 370–371.

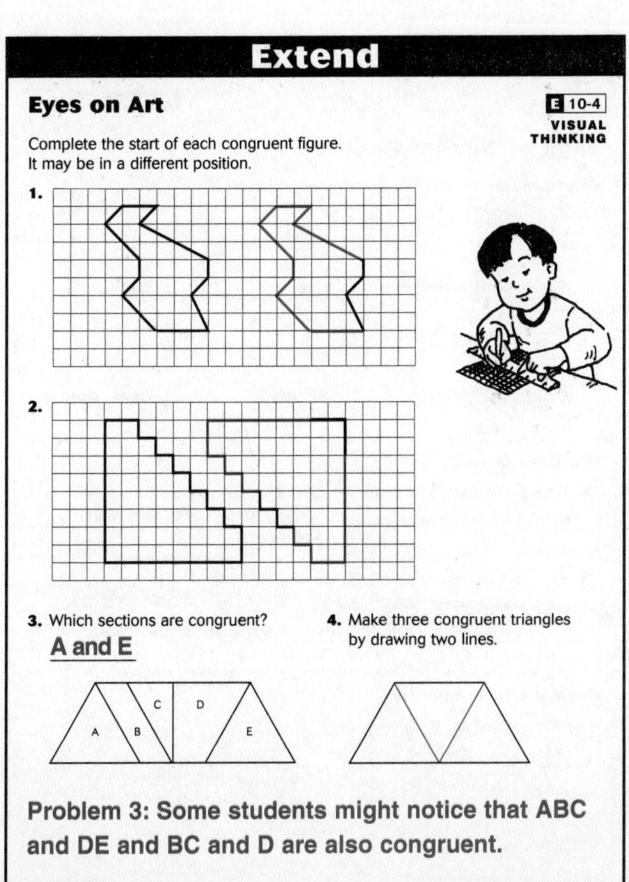

Extend

Eyes on Art

E 10-4

VISUAL THINKING

Complete the start of each congruent figure. It may be in a different position.

1.

2.

3. Which sections are congruent?
A and E

4. Make three congruent triangles by drawing two lines.

Problem 3: Some students might notice that ABC and DE and BC and D are also congruent.

 Use with Grade 3, text pages 370–371.

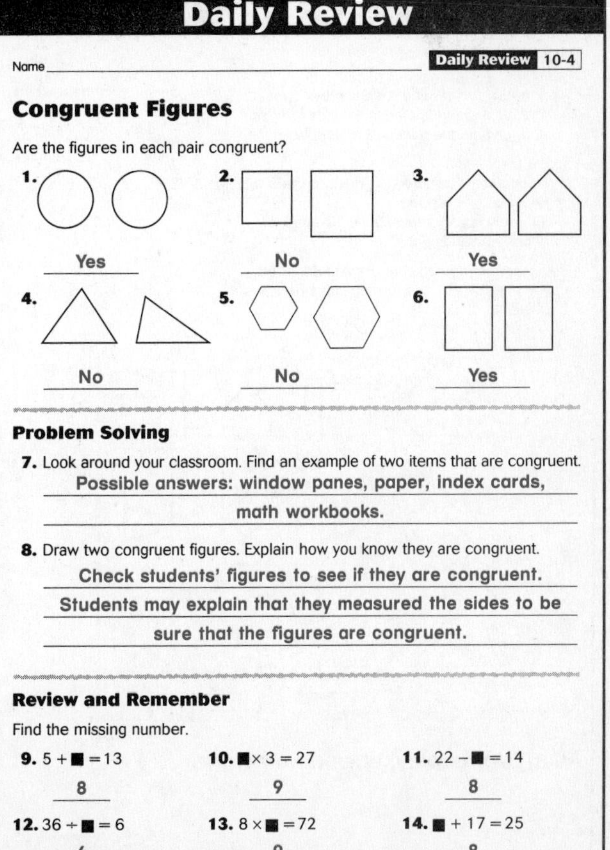

Daily Review

Name____________________ **Daily Review** 10-4

Congruent Figures

Are the figures in each pair congruent?

1. Yes
2. No
3. Yes
4. No
5. No
6. Yes

Problem Solving

7. Look around your classroom. Find an example of two items that are congruent.
Possible answers: window panes, paper, index cards, math workbooks.

8. Draw two congruent figures. Explain how you know they are congruent.
Check students' figures to see if they are congruent. Students may explain that they measured the sides to be sure that the figures are congruent.

Review and Remember

Find the missing number.

9. 5 + ■ = 13 — 8
10. ■ × 3 = 27 — 9
11. 22 − ■ = 14 — 8
12. 36 ÷ ■ = 6 — 6
13. 8 × ■ = 72 — 9
14. ■ + 17 = 25 — 8

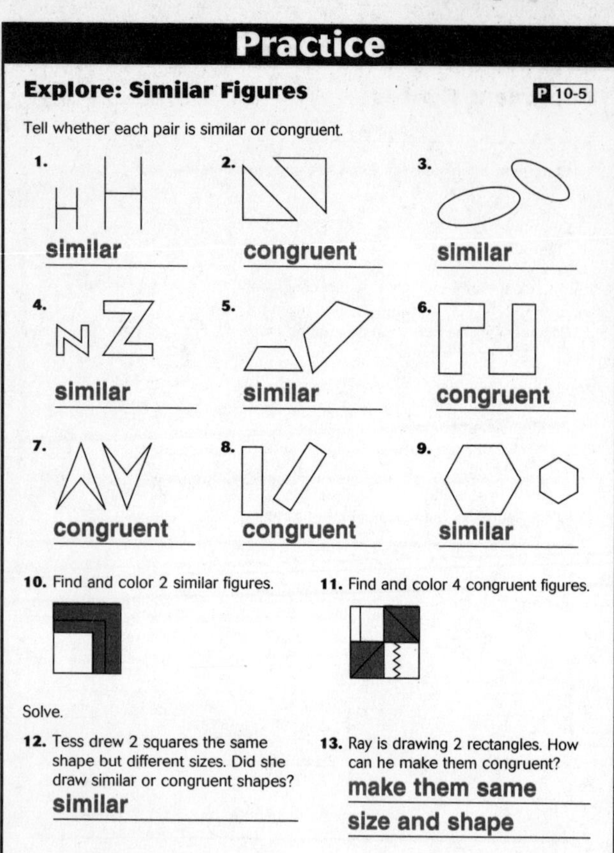
Practice
Explore: Similar Figures
P 10-5
Tell whether each pair is similar or congruent.
1. similar
2. congruent
3. similar
4. similar
5. similar
6. congruent
7. congruent
8. congruent
9. similar
10. Find and color 2 similar figures.
11. Find and color 4 congruent figures.
Solve.
12. Tess drew 2 squares the same shape but different sizes. Did she draw similar or congruent shapes?
similar
13. Ray is drawing 2 rectangles. How can he make them congruent?
make them same size and shape
© Silver Burdett Ginn Inc. (381)
Use with Grade 3, text pages 372–373.

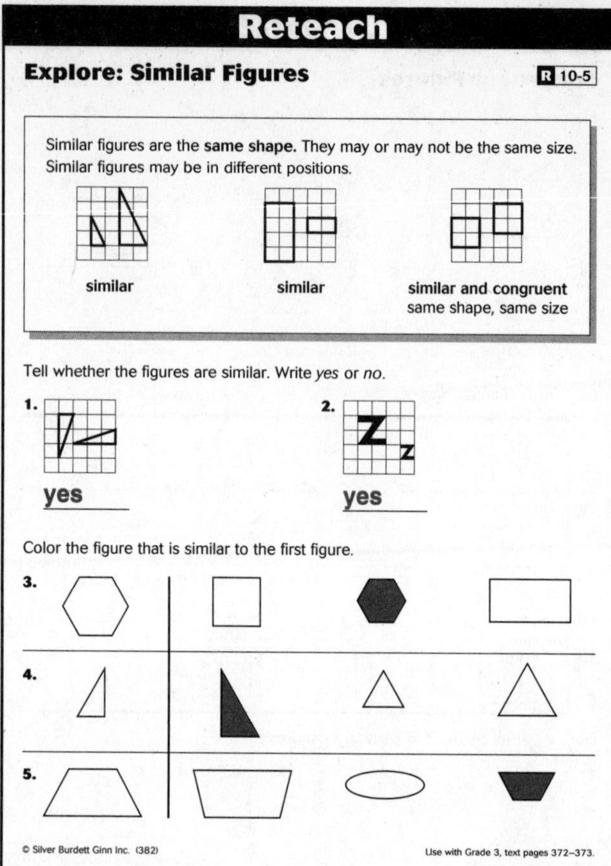
Reteach
Explore: Similar Figures
R 10-5
Similar figures are the same shape. They may or may not be the same size.
Similar figures may be in different positions.
similar
similar
similar and congruent
same shape, same size
Tell whether the figures are similar. Write yes or no.
1. yes
2. yes
Color the figure that is similar to the first figure.
3.
4.
5.
© Silver Burdett Ginn Inc. (382)
Use with Grade 3, text pages 372–373.

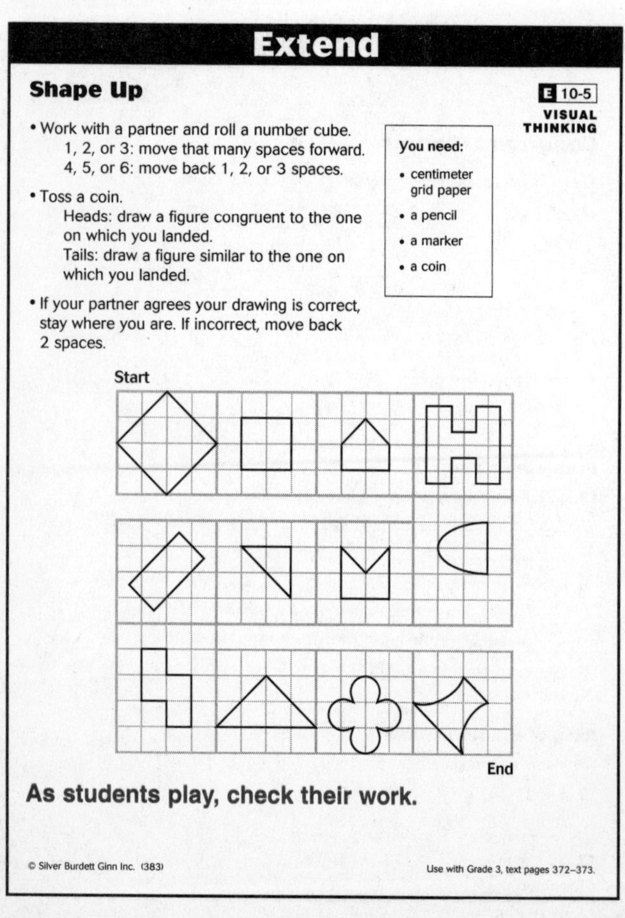
Extend
Shape Up
E 10-5
VISUAL THINKING
• Work with a partner and roll a number cube.
1, 2, or 3: move that many spaces forward.
4, 5, or 6: move back 1, 2, or 3 spaces.
• Toss a coin.
Heads: draw a figure congruent to the one on which you landed.
Tails: draw a figure similar to the one on which you landed.
• If your partner agrees your drawing is correct, stay where you are. If incorrect, move back 2 spaces.
You need:
• centimeter grid paper
• a pencil
• a marker
• a coin
Start
End
As students play, check their work.
© Silver Burdett Ginn Inc. (383)
Use with Grade 3, text pages 372–373.

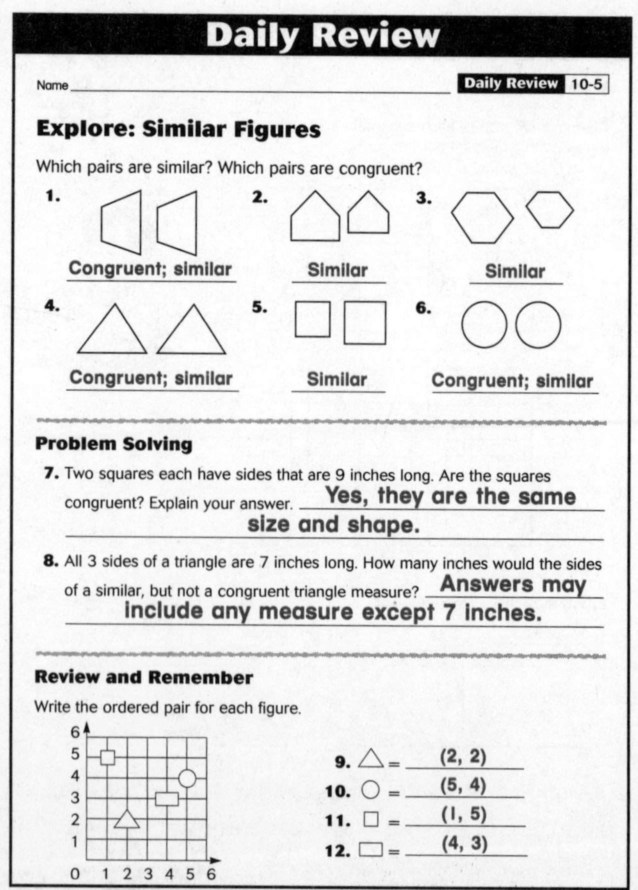
Daily Review
Name
Daily Review 10-5
Explore: Similar Figures
Which pairs are similar? Which pairs are congruent?
1. Congruent; similar
2. Similar
3. Similar
4. Congruent; similar
5. Similar
6. Congruent; similar
Problem Solving
7. Two squares each have sides that are 9 inches long. Are the squares congruent? Explain your answer. Yes, they are the same size and shape.
8. All 3 sides of a triangle are 7 inches long. How many inches would the sides of a similar, but not a congruent triangle measure? Answers may include any measure except 7 inches.
Review and Remember
Write the ordered pair for each figure.
9. △ = (2, 2)
10. ○ = (5, 4)
11. □ = (1, 5)
12. ▭ = (4, 3)
0 1 2 3 4 5 6
6 5 4 3 2 1

Chapter 10 • Lesson 6

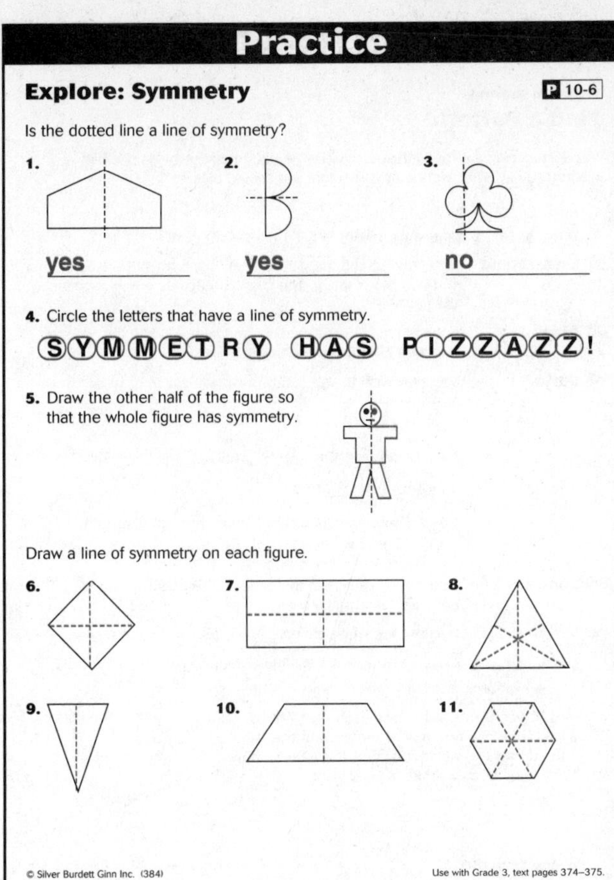

Practice

Explore: Symmetry

P 10-6

Is the dotted line a line of symmetry?

1. yes
2. yes
3. no

4. Circle the letters that have a line of symmetry.

SYMMETRY HAS PIZZAZZ!

5. Draw the other half of the figure so that the whole figure has symmetry.

Draw a line of symmetry on each figure.

6. 7. 8.

9. 10. 11.

 Use with Grade 3, text pages 374–375.

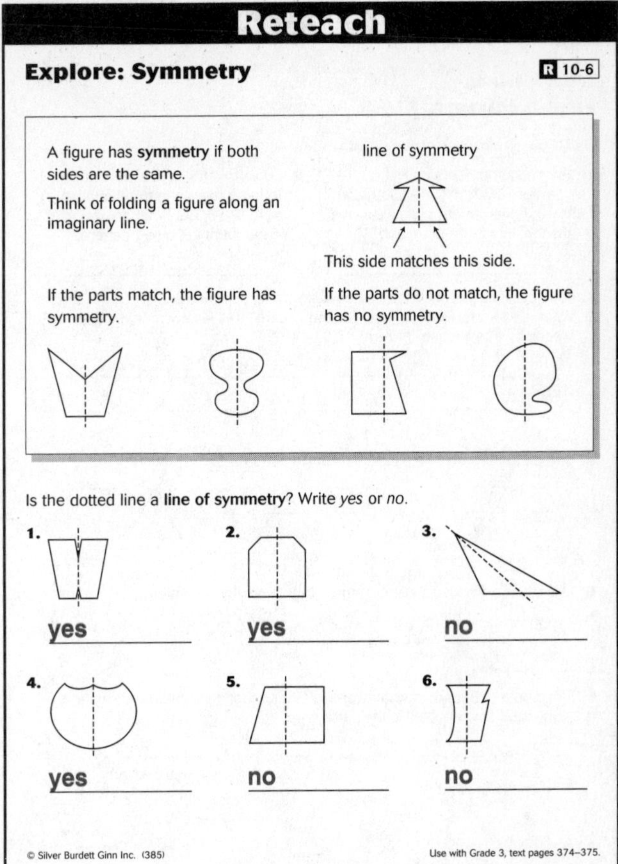

Reteach

Explore: Symmetry

R 10-6

A figure has **symmetry** if both sides are the same.

Think of folding a figure along an imaginary line.

line of symmetry

This side matches this side.

If the parts match, the figure has symmetry.

If the parts do not match, the figure has no symmetry.

Is the dotted line a **line of symmetry**? Write *yes* or *no*.

1. yes
2. yes
3. no
4. yes
5. no
6. no

 Use with Grade 3, text pages 374–375.

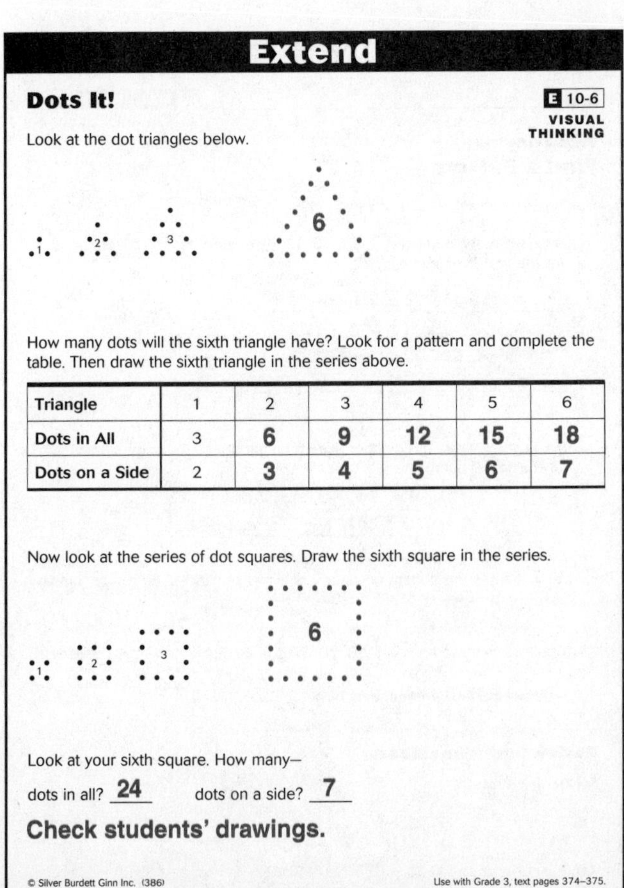

Extend

Dots It!

E 10-6 VISUAL THINKING

Look at the dot triangles below.

How many dots will the sixth triangle have? Look for a pattern and complete the table. Then draw the sixth triangle in the series above.

Triangle	1	2	3	4	5	6
Dots in All	3	6	9	12	15	18
Dots on a Side	2	3	4	5	6	7

Now look at the series of dot squares. Draw the sixth square in the series.

Look at your sixth square. How many—

dots in all? 24 dots on a side? 7

Check students' drawings.

 Use with Grade 3, text pages 374–375.

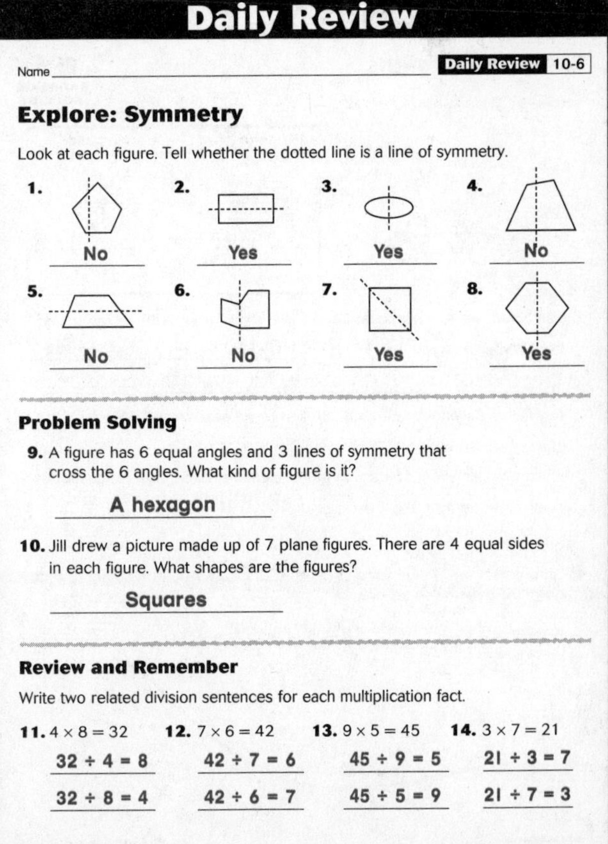

Daily Review

Name ____________ Daily Review 10-6

Explore: Symmetry

Look at each figure. Tell whether the dotted line is a line of symmetry.

1. No
2. Yes
3. Yes
4. No
5. No
6. No
7. Yes
8. Yes

Problem Solving

9. A figure has 6 equal angles and 3 lines of symmetry that cross the 6 angles. What kind of figure is it?

A hexagon

10. Jill drew a picture made up of 7 plane figures. There are 4 equal sides in each figure. What shapes are the figures?

Squares

Review and Remember

Write two related division sentences for each multiplication fact.

11. $4 \times 8 = 32$ — $32 \div 4 = 8$; $32 \div 8 = 4$

12. $7 \times 6 = 42$ — $42 \div 7 = 6$; $42 \div 6 = 7$

13. $9 \times 5 = 45$ — $45 \div 9 = 5$; $45 \div 5 = 9$

14. $3 \times 7 = 21$ — $21 \div 3 = 7$; $21 \div 7 = 3$

Practice

Problem Solving P 10-7

Find a Pattern

Find a pattern to solve each problem.

1. The house numbers on Helga's street are 1001, 1005, 1009, and 1013. If the pattern continues, what are the next three numbers?
   1017, 1021, 1025

2. Louie told his pal Jessie that he found a pattern in the numbers 1, 4, 9, 16, 25. What are the next 4 numbers in Louie's pattern?
   36, 49, 64, 81

3. Ryan calls his pattern a "staircase" pattern. His numbers are 1, 4, 3, 6, 5, 8. What are the next four numbers in the pattern? Tell what you think Ryan means by a "staircase" pattern.
   7, 10, 9, 12; the numbers go up and down like a staircase—up 3, then down 1, up 3, and so on.

4. Complete the next two figures in Trung's pattern.

5. Lee made a necklace. Draw the next four beads in the pattern.

Create Your Own

6. Make up a pattern using squares, circles, and triangles. Ask a classmate to draw the next three figures in the pattern.

___ ___ ___ ___ ___ ___ ___ ___ ___ ___ ___

Your classmate's turn

Patterns will vary.

Reteach

Problem Solving R 10-7

Find a Pattern

Mrs. Kawas plants a row of tulips. Look at the pattern of the bulbs she has planted so far. What are the next 5 colors she should plant?

red white pink pink red white pink pink red

1. How can you decide which colors Mrs. Kawas should plant?

Understand You need to find the pattern that Mrs. Kawas has used so far in her planting. Then you can decide how to continue the pattern.

Plan Look at the tulips planted so far. Once you find the pattern, continue it for five more tulips.

Solve You may wish to use cubes or draw pictures to help.

r	w	p	p	r	w	p	p	r

Mrs. Kawas plants a **red** tulip, a **white** tulip, and two **pink** tulips.

If Mrs. Kawas continues the pattern, the next five tulips will be **white, pink, pink, red, white**.

Look Back Add the new tulips to the pattern. The pattern continues. The next five tulips make sense.

2. Mrs. Kawas plants yellow and white daffodils in the pattern shown below. If she continues the pattern, what color will the sixteenth daffodil be? **yellow**
   yellow white yellow yellow white white yellow yellow yellow

3. Mrs. Kawas plants baby trees each year. She plants 2 new trees the first year, 4 the second year, and 6 the third year. If she continues this pattern, how many baby trees will Mrs. Kawas plant the fifth year?
   10 baby trees

Extend

Delightful Designs

E 10-7 PROBLEM SOLVING

Natalia has these beads in her case:

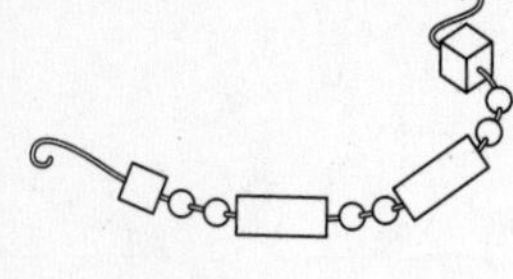

Type of Bead	Number
□ (square)	15
▭ (rectangle)	25
○ (circle)	20

1. Can Natalia make 4 necklaces like the one shown using the beads she has? Explain your answer. **No; she can make only 3 necklaces; she is short 4 round beads for a fourth necklace.**

2. Natalia buys square beads for \$2.50 and round beads for \$3.50. How much change will she get from \$10? **\$4**

3. It takes Natalia about 15 minutes to make one necklace. How many minutes does it take her to make 3 necklaces? **45 minutes**

Create Your Own

4. Draw a necklace design using all of Natalia's beads. Ask a classmate to write down the pattern you used.

Pattern: **Answers will vary.**

Daily Review

Name ______________________ Daily Review 10-7

Problem Solving

Find a Pattern

Find a pattern to solve each problem.

1. Nigel wrote the numbers 1, 4, 7, 10, 13. If he continues the pattern, what will the next five numbers be?
   16, 19, 22, 25, 28

2. Anna made the pattern below using beads. Draw the next 6 beads.
   Check students' drawings.
   □□△△□□□△△△□□□△△□□□□△△△△□□△

3. Ms. Ramirez wrote this number pattern on the board. Continue the pattern for the next 7 numbers.
   50, 49, 48, 40, 39, 38, 30, 29
   28, 20, 19, 18, 10, 9, 8

4. On Monday, Bill ran 4 miles. On Tuesday he ran 3 miles. On Wednesday, he ran 4 miles. If this pattern continues, how many miles will Bill run on Sunday?
   4 miles

5. Fiona wrote these numbers: 10, 20, 30, 10, 40. If she continues the pattern, what will the next five numbers be? **50, 10, 60, 70, 10**

Review and Remember

Solve.

6. 6 + 9 = **15** 7. 21 − 9 = **12** 8. 7 + 8 = **15** 9. 18 − 9 = **9**

10. 7 + 12 = **19** 11. 23 − 8 = **15** 12. 25 + 9 = **34** 13. 30 − 8 = **22**

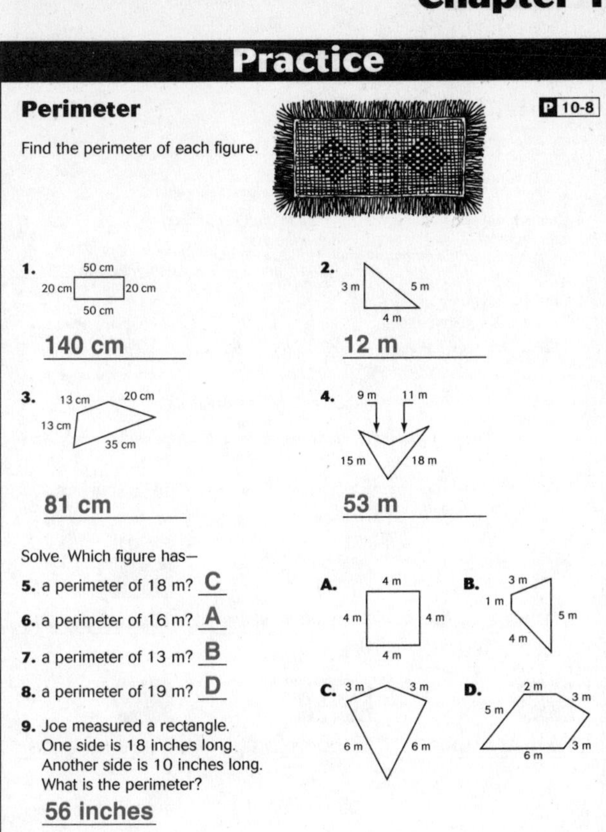
Practice
Perimeter
P 10-8
Find the perimeter of each figure.
1. 50 cm 20 cm 20 cm 50 cm
140 cm
2. 3 m 5 m 4 m
12 m
3. 13 cm 20 cm 13 cm 35 cm
81 cm
4. 9 m 11 m 15 m 18 m
53 m
Solve. Which figure has—
5. a perimeter of 18 m? C
6. a perimeter of 16 m? A
7. a perimeter of 13 m? B
8. a perimeter of 19 m? D
A. 4 m 4 m 4 m 4 m
B. 3 m 1 m 5 m 4 m
C. 3 m 3 m 6 m 6 m
D. 2 m 3 m 5 m 6 m 3 m
9. Joe measured a rectangle. One side is 18 inches long. Another side is 10 inches long. What is the perimeter?
56 inches
© Silver Burdett Ginn Inc. (390)
Use with Grade 3, text pages 380–381.

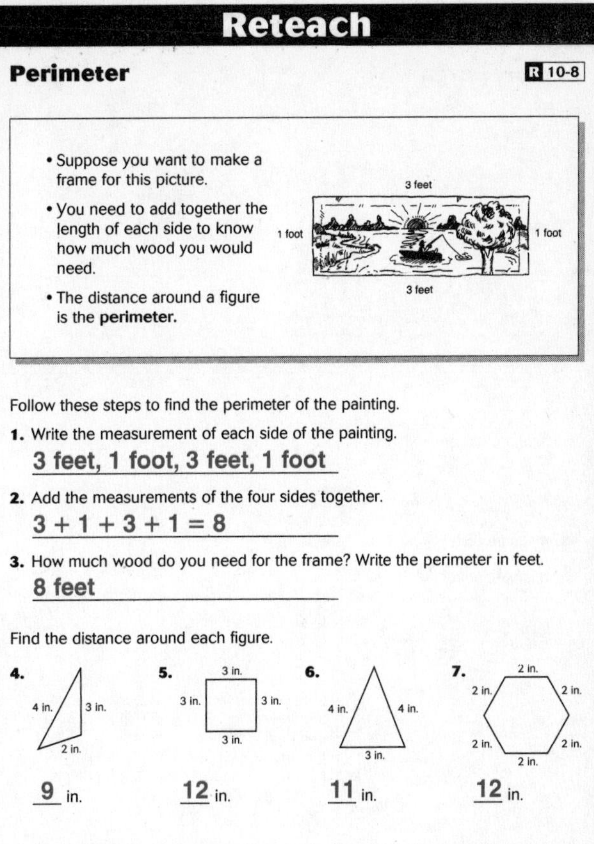
Reteach
Perimeter
R 10-8
• Suppose you want to make a frame for this picture.
• You need to add together the length of each side to know how much wood you would need.
• The distance around a figure is the perimeter.
3 feet
1 foot
1 foot
3 feet
Follow these steps to find the perimeter of the painting.
1. Write the measurement of each side of the painting.
3 feet, 1 foot, 3 feet, 1 foot
2. Add the measurements of the four sides together.
3 + 1 + 3 + 1 = 8
3. How much wood do you need for the frame? Write the perimeter in feet.
8 feet
Find the distance around each figure.
4. 4 in. 3 in. 2 in.
9 in.
5. 3 in. 3 in. 3 in. 3 in.
12 in.
6. 4 in. 4 in. 3 in.
11 in.
7. 2 in. 2 in. 2 in. 2 in. 2 in. 2 in.
12 in.
© Silver Burdett Ginn Inc. (391)
Use with Grade 3, text pages 380–381.

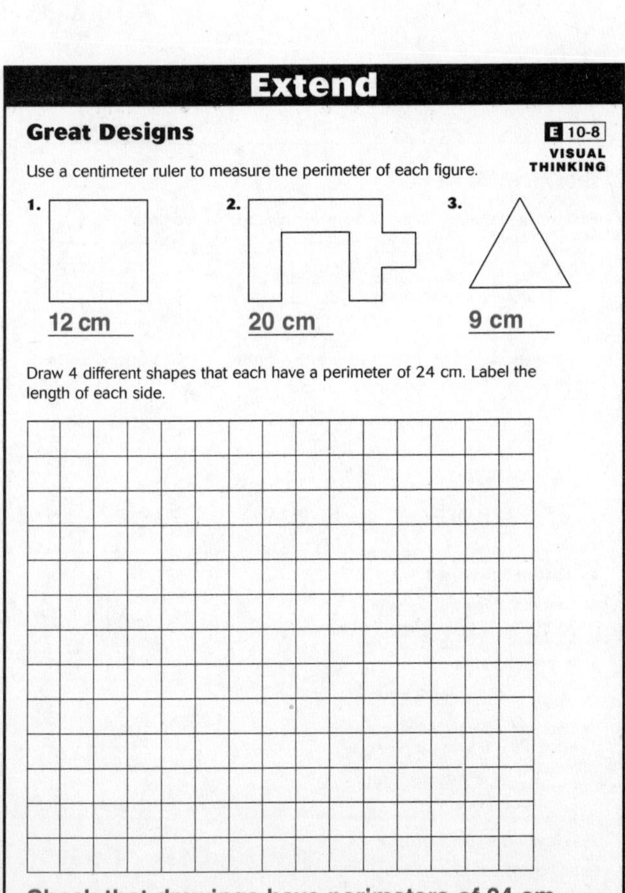
Extend
Great Designs
E 10-8
VISUAL THINKING
Use a centimeter ruler to measure the perimeter of each figure.
1. 12 cm
2. 20 cm
3. 9 cm
Draw 4 different shapes that each have a perimeter of 24 cm. Label the length of each side.
Check that drawings have perimeters of 24 cm.
© Silver Burdett Ginn Inc. (392)
Use with Grade 3, text pages 380–381.

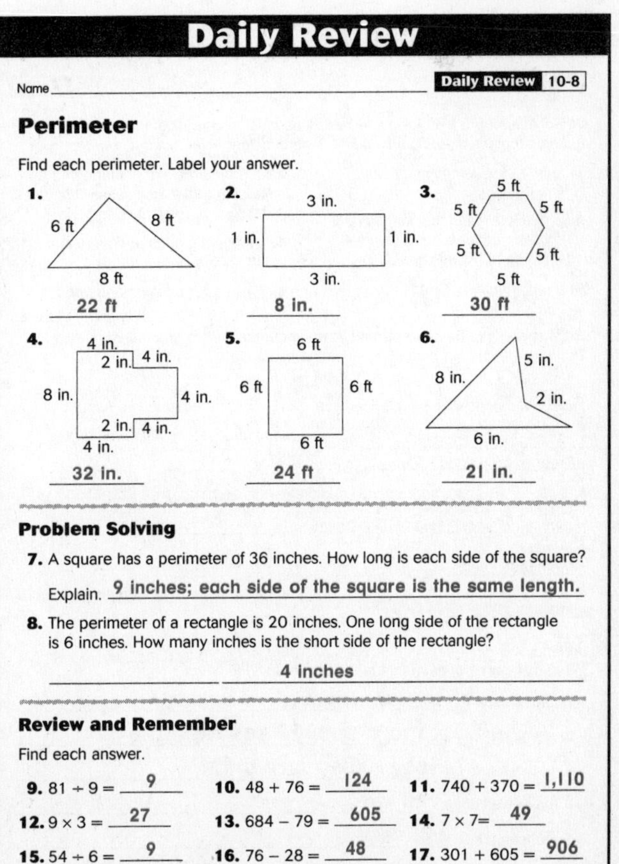
Daily Review
Name
Daily Review 10-8
Perimeter
Find each perimeter. Label your answer.
1. 6 ft 8 ft 8 ft
22 ft
2. 3 in. 1 in. 1 in. 3 in.
8 in.
3. 5 ft 5 ft 5 ft 5 ft 5 ft 5 ft
30 ft
4. 4 in. 2 in. 4 in. 8 in. 4 in. 2 in. 4 in. 4 in.
32 in.
5. 6 ft 6 ft 6 ft 6 ft
24 ft
6. 8 in. 5 in. 2 in. 6 in.
21 in.
Problem Solving
7. A square has a perimeter of 36 inches. How long is each side of the square? Explain. 9 inches; each side of the square is the same length.
8. The perimeter of a rectangle is 20 inches. One long side of the rectangle is 6 inches. How many inches is the short side of the rectangle?
4 inches
Review and Remember
Find each answer.
9. 81 ÷ 9 = 9
10. 48 + 76 = 124
11. 740 + 370 = 1,110
12. 9 × 3 = 27
13. 684 − 79 = 605
14. 7 × 7 = 49
15. 54 ÷ 6 = 9
16. 76 − 28 = 48
17. 301 + 605 = 906

Chapter 10 • Lesson 9

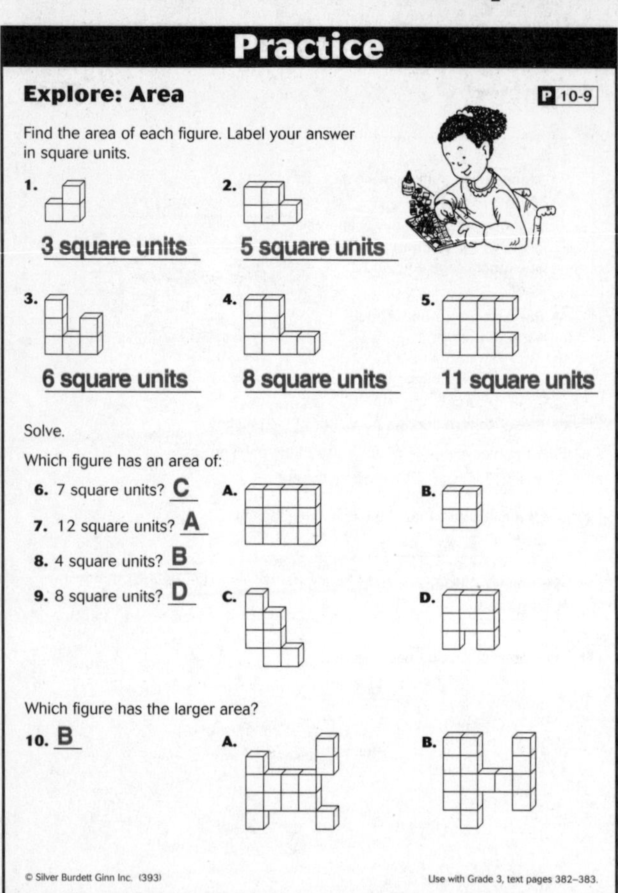

Practice

Explore: Area P 10-9

Find the area of each figure. Label your answer in square units.

1. 3 square units
2. 5 square units
3. 6 square units
4. 8 square units
5. 11 square units

Solve.

Which figure has an area of:

6. 7 square units? C
7. 12 square units? A
8. 4 square units? B
9. 8 square units? D

A. B. C. D.

Which figure has the larger area?

10. B

A. B.

 Use with Grade 3, text pages 382–383.

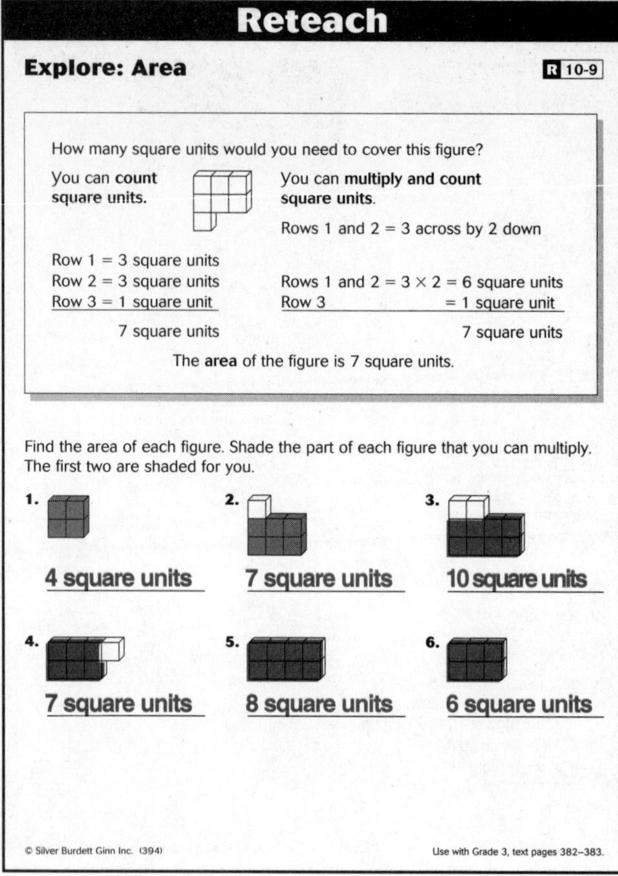

Reteach

Explore: Area R 10-9

How many square units would you need to cover this figure?

You can **count** square units.

Row 1 = 3 square units
Row 2 = 3 square units
Row 3 = 1 square unit
7 square units

You can **multiply and count** square units.

Rows 1 and 2 = 3 across by 2 down
Rows 1 and 2 = 3×2 = 6 square units
Row 3 = 1 square unit
7 square units

The **area** of the figure is 7 square units.

Find the area of each figure. Shade the part of each figure that you can multiply. The first two are shaded for you.

1. 4 square units
2. 7 square units
3. 10 square units
4. 7 square units
5. 8 square units
6. 6 square units

 Use with Grade 3, text pages 382–383.

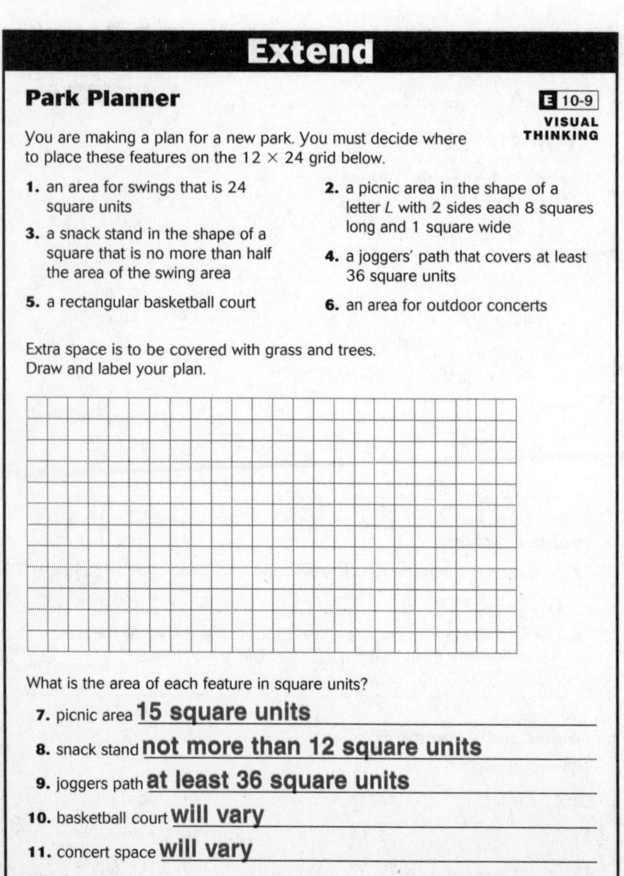

Extend

Park Planner E 10-9 VISUAL THINKING

You are making a plan for a new park. You must decide where to place these features on the 12×24 grid below.

1. an area for swings that is 24 square units
2. a picnic area in the shape of a letter *L* with 2 sides each 8 squares long and 1 square wide
3. a snack stand in the shape of a square that is no more than half the area of the swing area
4. a joggers' path that covers at least 36 square units
5. a rectangular basketball court
6. an area for outdoor concerts

Extra space is to be covered with grass and trees. Draw and label your plan.

What is the area of each feature in square units?

7. picnic area 15 square units
8. snack stand not more than 12 square units
9. joggers path at least 36 square units
10. basketball court will vary
11. concert space will vary

 Use with Grade 3, text pages 382–383.

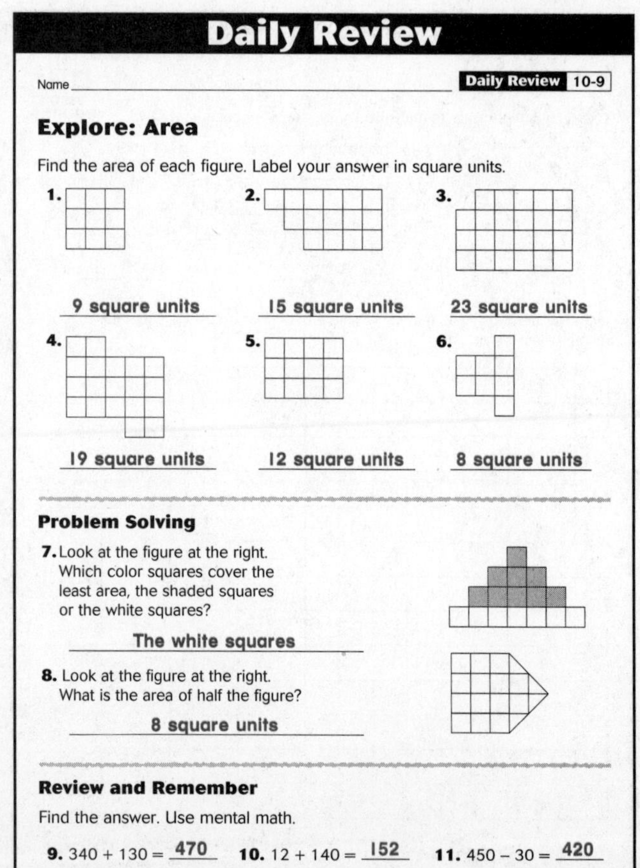

Daily Review

Name ______ Daily Review 10-9

Explore: Area

Find the area of each figure. Label your answer in square units.

1. 9 square units
2. 15 square units
3. 23 square units
4. 19 square units
5. 12 square units
6. 8 square units

Problem Solving

7. Look at the figure at the right. Which color squares cover the least area, the shaded squares or the white squares?
The white squares

8. Look at the figure at the right. What is the area of half the figure?
8 square units

Review and Remember

Find the answer. Use mental math.

9. $340 + 130 =$ 470
10. $12 + 140 =$ 152
11. $450 - 30 =$ 420

Chapter 10 • Lesson 10

Practice

Problem Solving P 10-10

Using Area and Perimeter

1. Marci wants to make a wooden picture frame that is 8 inches long and 6 inches wide. How long a piece of wood does Marci need?
28 inches

2. Marci frames a piece of Navajo cloth that measures 7 inches by 5 inches. What is the area of the cloth?
35 square inches

3. Ron is laying a tile floor in his bathroom using 1-foot-square tiles. His bathroom is 9 feet by 7 feet. How many tiles does Ron need to complete the job?
63 tiles

4. Suzanne made the design at the right. What is the area of her design?
area: **16** square units

5. James wants to fence in part of his yard for a compost garden. He wants the garden to be 6 feet on each side. Is 20 feet of fencing enough? Explain.
No; he needs 24 feet.

6. Draw a rectangle in the grid that has an area of 24 square units. Find the perimeter.
area: **24** square units
perimeter: ___ units
Answers will vary but perimeters may be:
20 [6 x 4 rectangle], 22 [8 x 3 rectangle], 28 [12 x 2 rectangle], or 50 [1 x 24 rectangle]

 Use with Grade 3, text pages 384–385.

Reteach

Problem Solving R 10-10

Using Area and Perimeter

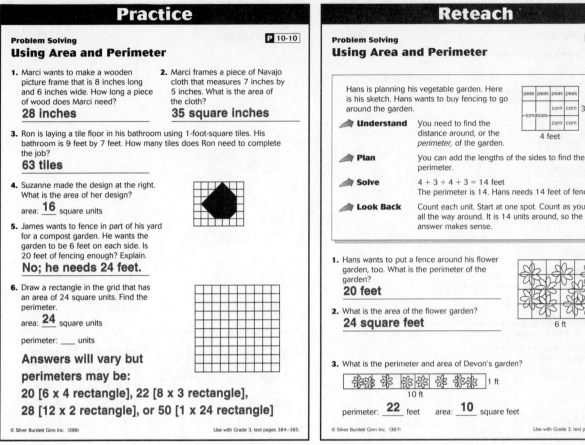

Hans is planning his vegetable garden. Here is his sketch. Hans wants to buy fencing to go around the garden.

peas	peas	peas	peas
tomatoes		corn	corn
		corn	corn

3 feet; 4 feet

Understand You need to find the distance around, or the *perimeter*, of the garden.

Plan You can add the lengths of the sides to find the perimeter.

Solve 4 + 3 + 4 + 3 = 14 feet
The perimeter is 14. Hans needs 14 feet of fencing.

Look Back Count each unit. Start at one spot. Count as you go all the way around. It is 14 units around, so the answer makes sense.

1. Hans wants to put a fence around his flower garden, too. What is the perimeter of the garden?
20 feet

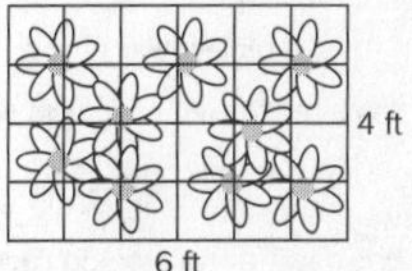
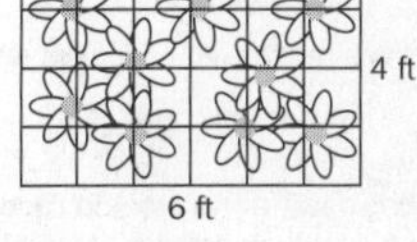

2. What is the area of the flower garden?
24 square feet

3. What is the perimeter and area of Devon's garden?

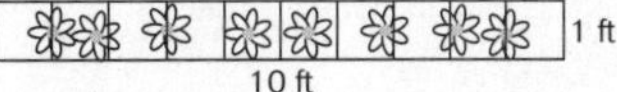

perimeter: **22** feet area: **10** square feet

 Use with Grade 3, text pages 384–385.

Extend

Make a Frame

E 10-10 NUMBER SENSE

1. Trent has 20 inches of framing. Can he make a frame 8 inches by 4 inches? If not, how many more inches of framing does he need?
no; 4 more inches

2. One side of Marcia's rectangular frame is 3 inches more than twice one of the long sides. The longer side is 21 inches. What is the shorter side?
9 inches

3. It takes about 45 minutes to make a frame in a framing shop. If Ethan finishes a frame at 5:05, what time did he begin?
4:20

4. A frame costs $2 per foot. The frame shop charges $5 for other framing materials, Joy spent $25 on a frame. How many feet of framing did she buy?
10 feet

5. Complete the table.

Frame Size	Perimeter	Area	Cost
4 feet by 6 feet	**20 feet**	**24 square feet**	$20
5 feet by 5 feet	**20 feet**	**25 square feet**	$20
3 feet by 9 feet	**24 feet**	**27 square feet**	$24
2 feet by 10 feet	**24 feet**	**20 square feet**	$24
5 feet by 8 feet	**26 feet**	**40 square feet**	$26

Use your answers from the table for Problems 6 and 7.

6. Tell how you think the cost of a frame is determined.
$1 a foot; the cost is equal to the perimeter.

7. A frame is 3 feet by 5 feet. What is the cost? **$16**

 Use with Grade 3, text pages 384–385.

Daily Review

Name ____________ Daily Review 10-10

Problem Solving

Using Area and Perimeter

Use area and perimeter to solve these problems.

1. Mr. Adams' third-grade art class is painting a mural on the school wall. The area to be painted is 6 feet long and 3 feet wide. It has been divided into 1-ft squares. Two students will paint each square. How many students will work on the mural? Draw a picture to show your answer.
36 students
Check students' drawings.

2. A wooden border will be placed around the mural when it is complete. How many feet of wood do the students need for the frame?
18 feet

3. Draw a design with an area of 12 square units in this grid.
Check students' drawings.

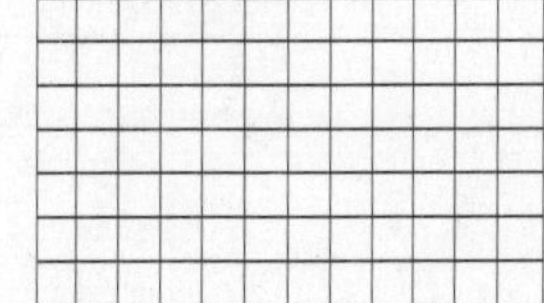

Review and Remember

Find each missing number.

4. 12 + **5** = 17
5. **4** × 3 = 12
6. 45 − **5** = 40
7. 23 + **13** = 36
8. **8** × 8 = 64
9. 77 − **44** = 33
10. 24 ÷ **6** = 4
11. 15 + **11** = 26
12. 72 ÷ **9** = 8

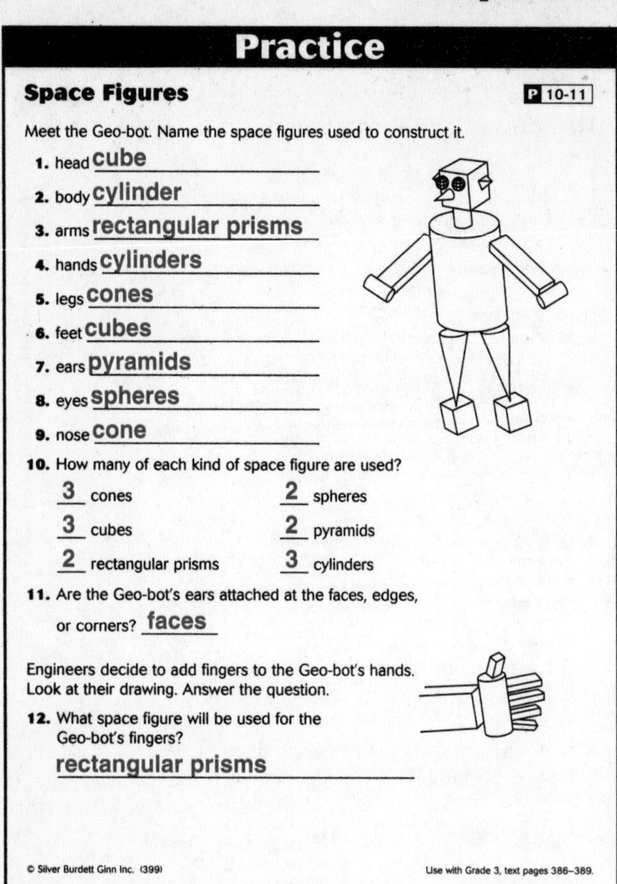

Practice

Space Figures

P 10-11

Meet the Geo-bot. Name the space figures used to construct it.

1. head cube
2. body cylinder
3. arms rectangular prisms
4. hands cylinders
5. legs cones
6. feet cubes
7. ears pyramids
8. eyes spheres
9. nose cone
10. How many of each kind of space figure are used?
    3 cones — 2 spheres
    3 cubes — 2 pyramids
    2 rectangular prisms — 3 cylinders
11. Are the Geo-bot's ears attached at the faces, edges, or corners? faces

Engineers decide to add fingers to the Geo-bot's hands. Look at their drawing. Answer the question.

12. What space figure will be used for the Geo-bot's fingers?
    rectangular prisms

 Use with Grade 3, text pages 386–389.

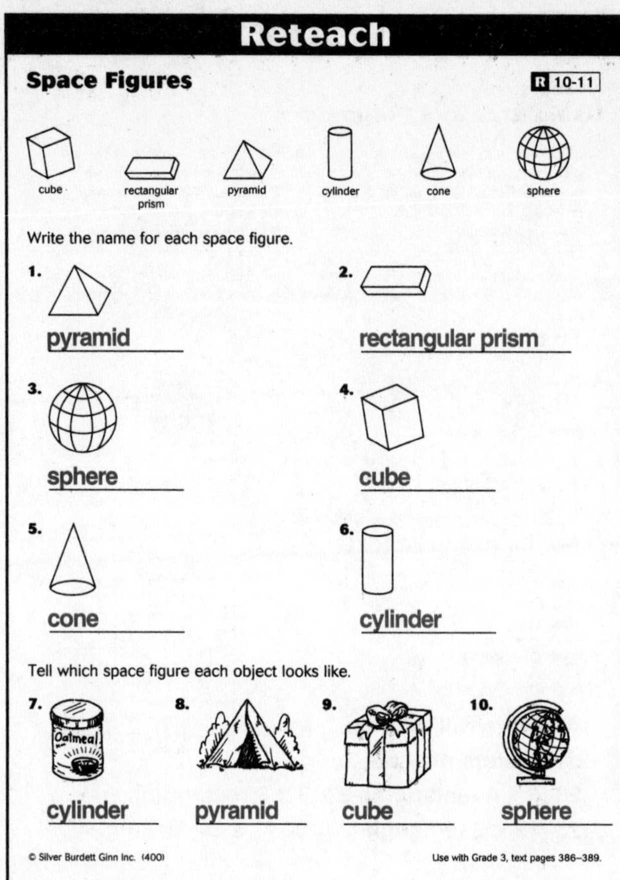

Reteach

Space Figures

R 10-11

Write the name for each space figure.

1. pyramid
2. rectangular prism
3. sphere
4. cube
5. cone
6. cylinder

Tell which space figure each object looks like.

7. cylinder
8. pyramid
9. cube
10. sphere

 Use with Grade 3, text pages 386–389.

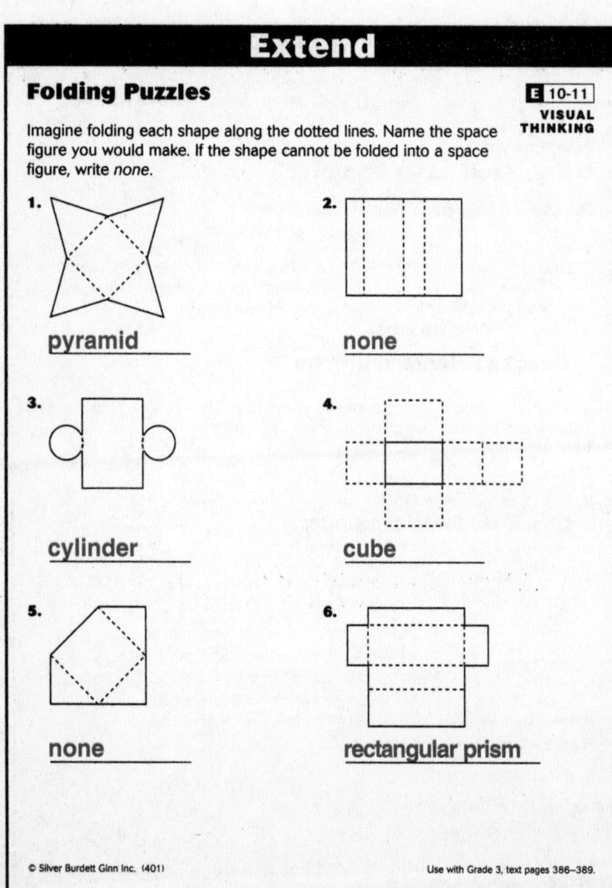

Extend

Folding Puzzles

E 10-11 VISUAL THINKING

Imagine folding each shape along the dotted lines. Name the space figure you would make. If the shape cannot be folded into a space figure, write *none*.

1. pyramid
2. none
3. cylinder
4. cube
5. none
6. rectangular prism

 Use with Grade 3, text pages 386–389.

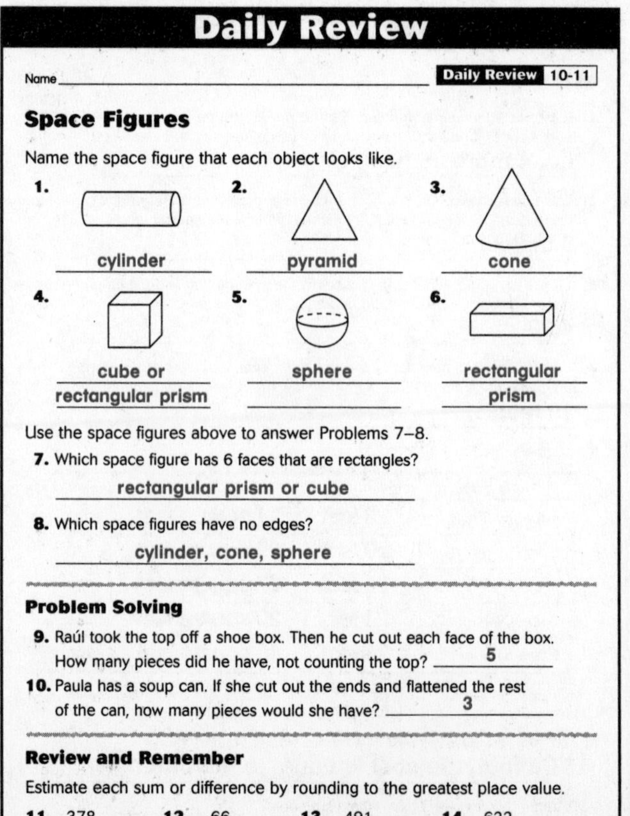

Daily Review

Name ______________________ Daily Review 10-11

Space Figures

Name the space figure that each object looks like.

1. cylinder
2. pyramid
3. cone
4. cube or rectangular prism
5. sphere
6. rectangular prism

Use the space figures above to answer Problems 7–8.

7. Which space figure has 6 faces that are rectangles?
   rectangular prism or cube
8. Which space figures have no edges?
   cylinder, cone, sphere

Problem Solving

9. Raúl took the top off a shoe box. Then he cut out each face of the box. How many pieces did he have, not counting the top? 5
10. Paula has a soup can. If she cut out the ends and flattened the rest of the can, how many pieces would she have? 3

Review and Remember

Estimate each sum or difference by rounding to the greatest place value.

11. 378 − 212 = 200
12. 66 + 35 = 110
13. 491 + 234 = 700
14. 622 + 187 = 800

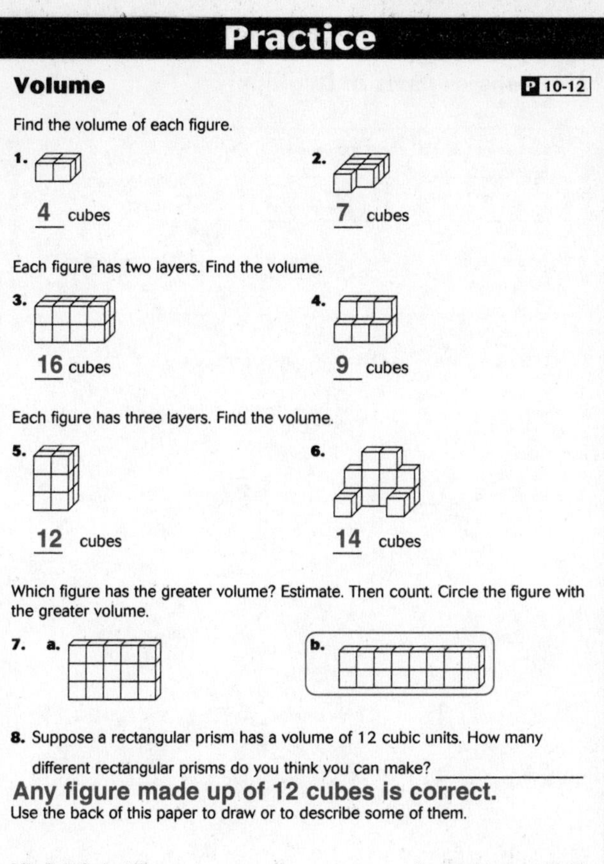

Practice

Volume

P 10-12

Find the volume of each figure.

1. 4 cubes
2. 7 cubes

Each figure has two layers. Find the volume.

3. 16 cubes
4. 9 cubes

Each figure has three layers. Find the volume.

5. 12 cubes
6. 14 cubes

Which figure has the greater volume? Estimate. Then count. Circle the figure with the greater volume.

7. a. b.

8. Suppose a rectangular prism has a volume of 12 cubic units. How many different rectangular prisms do you think you can make? ____________

Any figure made up of 12 cubes is correct.

Use the back of this paper to draw or to describe some of them.

 Use with Grade 3, text pages 390–391.

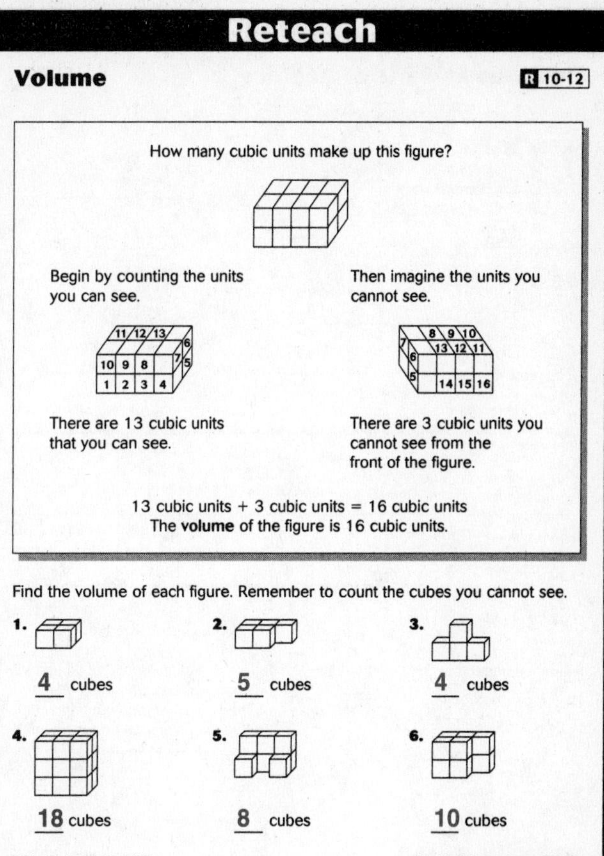

Reteach

Volume

R 10-12

How many cubic units make up this figure?

Begin by counting the units you can see.

Then imagine the units you cannot see.

There are 13 cubic units that you can see.

There are 3 cubic units you cannot see from the front of the figure.

13 cubic units + 3 cubic units = 16 cubic units

The **volume** of the figure is 16 cubic units.

Find the volume of each figure. Remember to count the cubes you cannot see.

1. 4 cubes
2. 5 cubes
3. 4 cubes
4. 18 cubes
5. 8 cubes
6. 10 cubes

 Use with Grade 3, text pages 390–391.

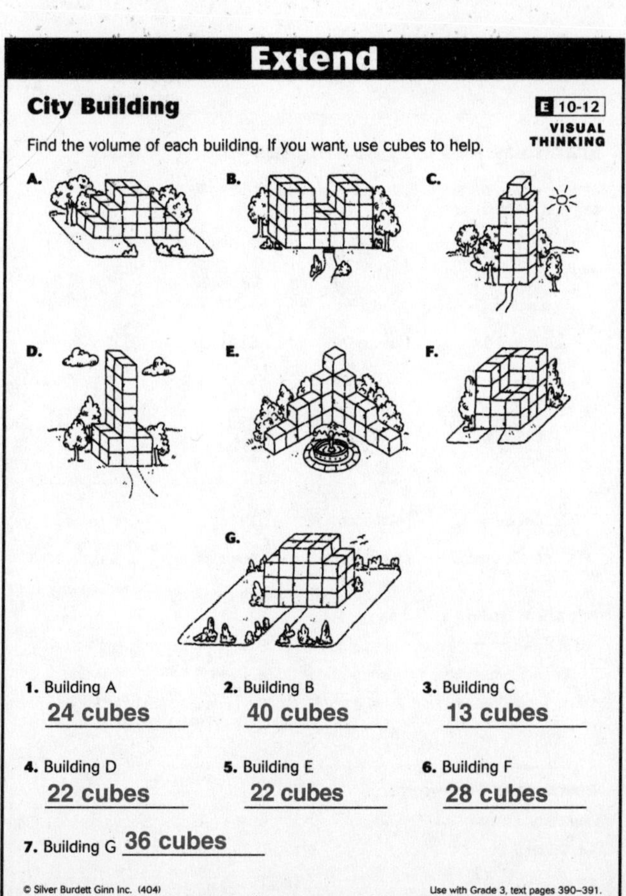

Extend

City Building

E 10-12

VISUAL THINKING

Find the volume of each building. If you want, use cubes to help.

A. B. C. D. E. F. G.

1. Building A **24 cubes**
2. Building B **40 cubes**
3. Building C **13 cubes**
4. Building D **22 cubes**
5. Building E **22 cubes**
6. Building F **28 cubes**
7. Building G **36 cubes**

 Use with Grade 3, text pages 390–391.

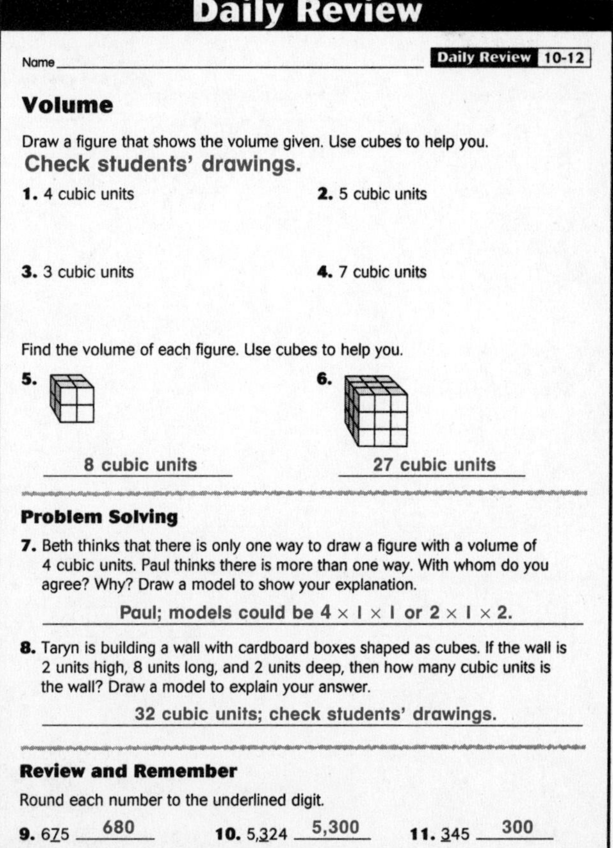

Daily Review

Name ____________________

Daily Review 10-12

Volume

Draw a figure that shows the volume given. Use cubes to help you.

Check students' drawings.

1. 4 cubic units
2. 5 cubic units
3. 3 cubic units
4. 7 cubic units

Find the volume of each figure. Use cubes to help you.

5. **8 cubic units**
6. **27 cubic units**

Problem Solving

7. Beth thinks that there is only one way to draw a figure with a volume of 4 cubic units. Paul thinks there is more than one way. With whom do you agree? Why? Draw a model to show your explanation.

Paul; models could be 4 × 1 × 1 or 2 × 1 × 2.

8. Taryn is building a wall with cardboard boxes shaped as cubes. If the wall is 2 units high, 8 units long, and 2 units deep, then how many cubic units is the wall? Draw a model to explain your answer.

32 cubic units; check students' drawings.

Review and Remember

Round each number to the underlined digit.

9. 6<u>7</u>5 **680**
10. 5,<u>3</u>24 **5,300**
11. <u>3</u>45 **300**

Chapter 11 • Lesson 1

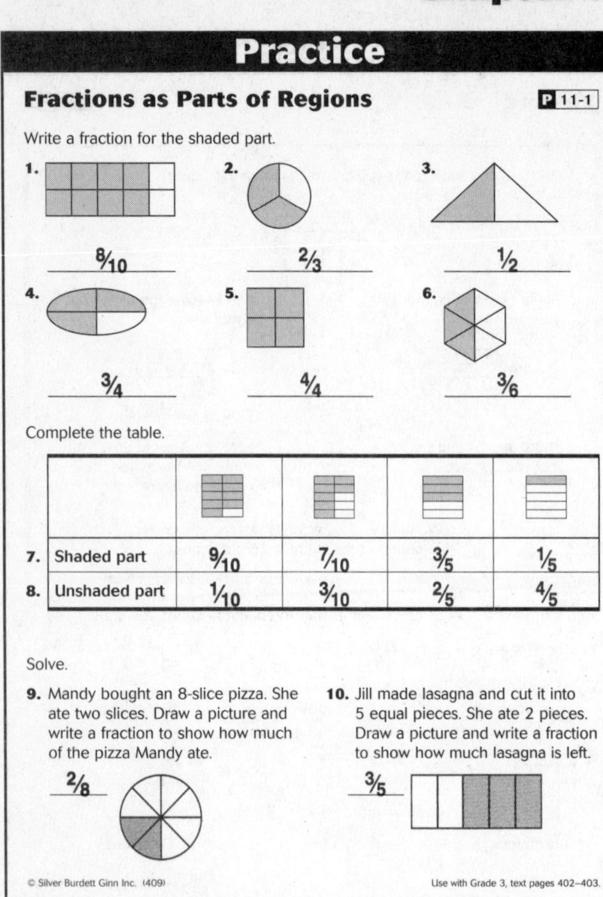

Practice

Fractions as Parts of Regions

P 11-1

Write a fraction for the shaded part.

1. 8/10
2. 2/3
3. 1/2
4. 3/4
5. 4/4
6. 3/6

Complete the table.

7. Shaded part	9/10	7/10	3/5	1/5
8. Unshaded part	1/10	3/10	2/5	4/5

Solve.

9. Mandy bought an 8-slice pizza. She ate two slices. Draw a picture and write a fraction to show how much of the pizza Mandy ate.
2/8

10. Jill made lasagna and cut it into 5 equal pieces. She ate 2 pieces. Draw a picture and write a fraction to show how much lasagna is left.
3/5

 Use with Grade 3, text pages 402–403.

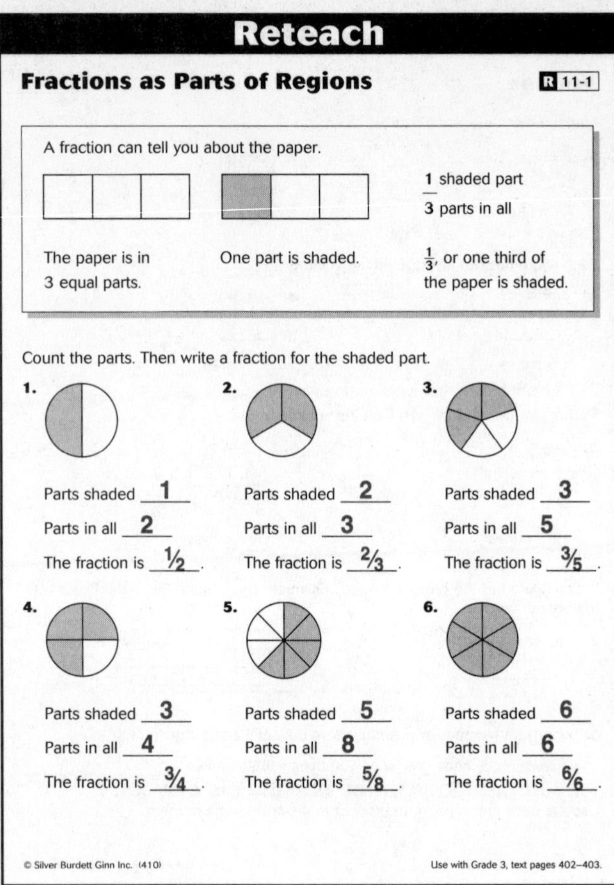

Reteach

Fractions as Parts of Regions

R 11-1

A fraction can tell you about the paper.

The paper is in 3 equal parts. One part is shaded. 1 shaded part / 3 parts in all. $\frac{1}{3}$, or one third of the paper is shaded.

Count the parts. Then write a fraction for the shaded part.

1. Parts shaded 1 Parts in all 2 The fraction is 1/2.
2. Parts shaded 2 Parts in all 3 The fraction is 2/3.
3. Parts shaded 3 Parts in all 5 The fraction is 3/5.
4. Parts shaded 3 Parts in all 4 The fraction is 3/4.
5. Parts shaded 5 Parts in all 8 The fraction is 5/8.
6. Parts shaded 6 Parts in all 6 The fraction is 6/6.

 Use with Grade 3, text pages 402–403.

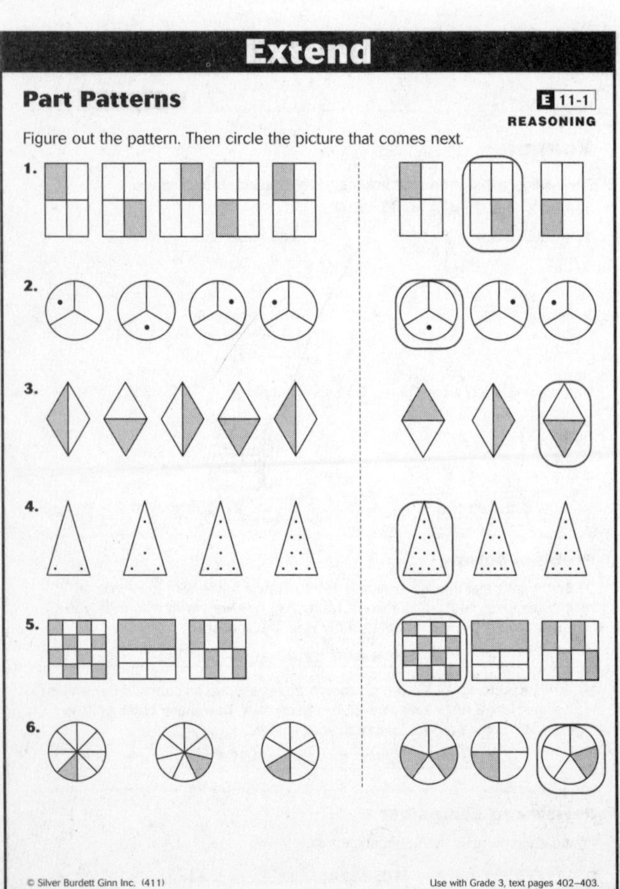

Extend

Part Patterns

E 11-1
REASONING

Figure out the pattern. Then circle the picture that comes next.

1.
2.
3.
4.
5.
6.

 Use with Grade 3, text pages 402–403.

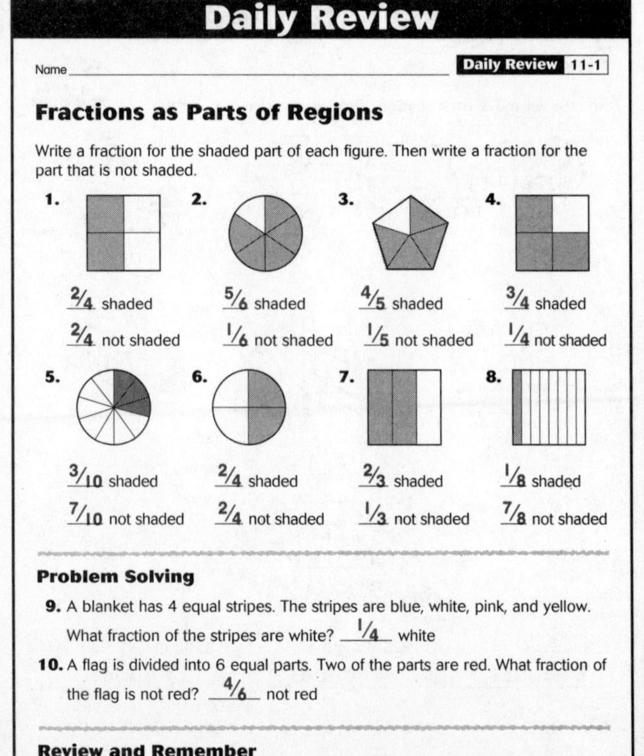

Daily Review

Name ______

Daily Review 11-1

Fractions as Parts of Regions

Write a fraction for the shaded part of each figure. Then write a fraction for the part that is not shaded.

1. 2/4 shaded, 2/4 not shaded
2. 5/6 shaded, 1/6 not shaded
3. 4/5 shaded, 1/5 not shaded
4. 3/4 shaded, 1/4 not shaded
5. 3/10 shaded, 7/10 not shaded
6. 2/4 shaded, 2/4 not shaded
7. 2/3 shaded, 1/3 not shaded
8. 1/8 shaded, 7/8 not shaded

Problem Solving

9. A blanket has 4 equal stripes. The stripes are blue, white, pink, and yellow. What fraction of the stripes are white? 1/4 white

10. A flag is divided into 6 equal parts. Two of the parts are red. What fraction of the flag is not red? 4/6 not red

Review and Remember

Find each answer.

11. 258 + 321 = 579

12. 727 – 418 = 309

13. 7 × 8 = 56

14. 81 ÷ 9 = 9

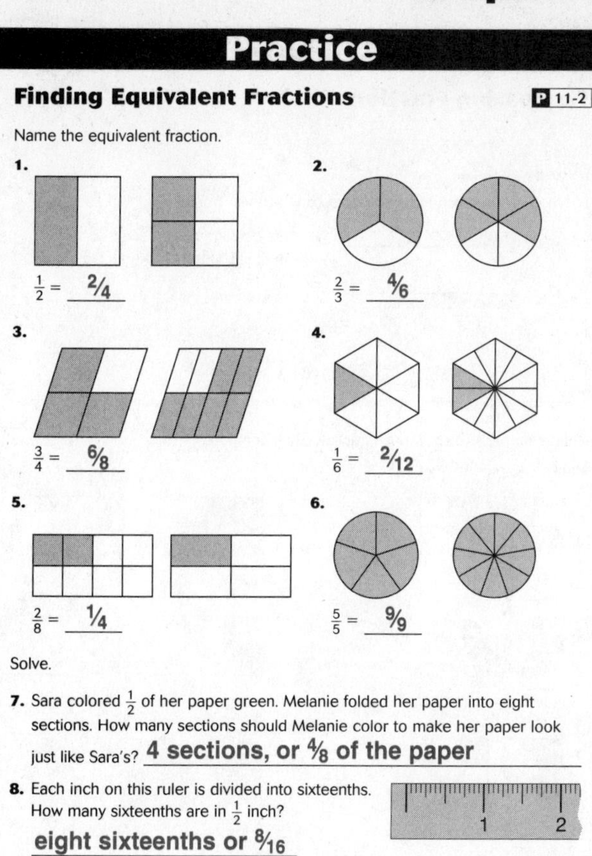

Practice

Finding Equivalent Fractions P 11-2

Name the equivalent fraction.

1. $\frac{1}{2}$ = 2/4
2. $\frac{2}{3}$ = 4/6
3. $\frac{3}{4}$ = 6/8
4. $\frac{1}{6}$ = 2/12
5. $\frac{2}{8}$ = 1/4
6. $\frac{5}{5}$ = 9/9

Solve.

7. Sara colored $\frac{1}{2}$ of her paper green. Melanie folded her paper into eight sections. How many sections should Melanie color to make her paper look just like Sara's? **4 sections, or 4/8 of the paper**
8. Each inch on this ruler is divided into sixteenths. How many sixteenths are in $\frac{1}{2}$ inch? **eight sixteenths or 8/16**

 Use with Grade 3, text pages 404–405.

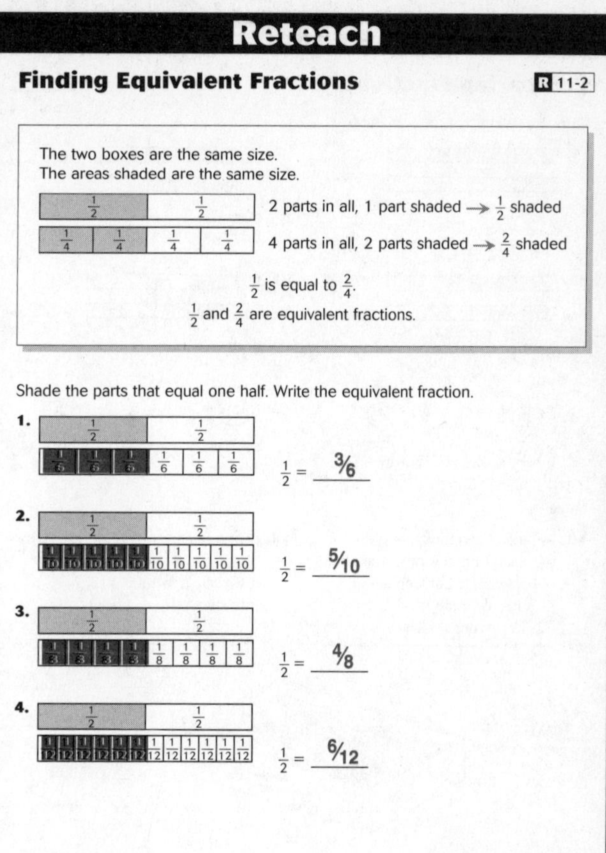

Reteach

Finding Equivalent Fractions R 11-2

The two boxes are the same size.
The areas shaded are the same size.

$\frac{1}{2}$	$\frac{1}{2}$	2 parts in all, 1 part shaded → $\frac{1}{2}$ shaded
$\frac{1}{4}$ $\frac{1}{4}$	$\frac{1}{4}$ $\frac{1}{4}$	4 parts in all, 2 parts shaded → $\frac{2}{4}$ shaded

$\frac{1}{2}$ is equal to $\frac{2}{4}$.

$\frac{1}{2}$ and $\frac{2}{4}$ are equivalent fractions.

Shade the parts that equal one half. Write the equivalent fraction.

1. $\frac{1}{2}$ = 3/6
2. $\frac{1}{2}$ = 5/10
3. $\frac{1}{2}$ = 4/8
4. $\frac{1}{2}$ = 6/12

 Use with Grade 3, text pages 404–405.

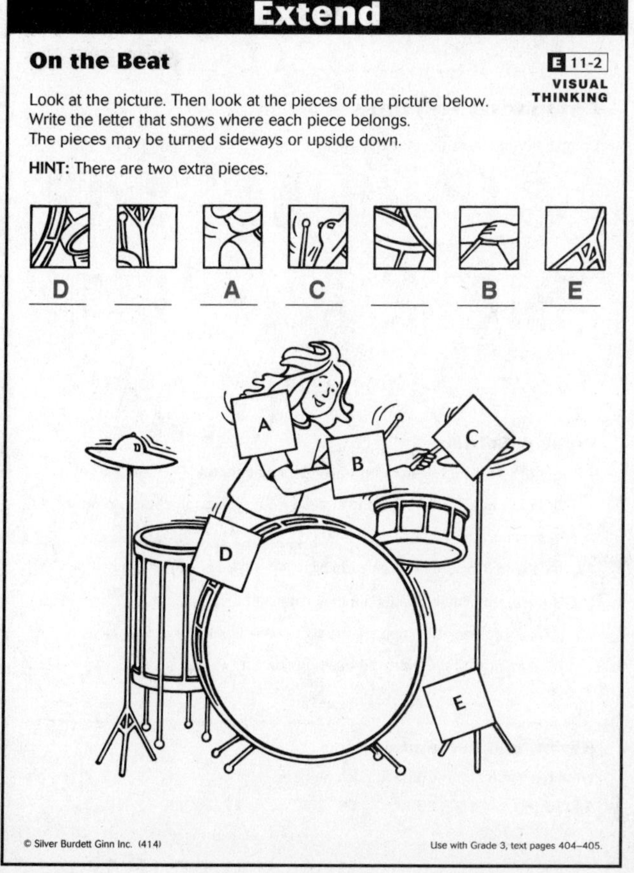

Extend

On the Beat E 11-2 VISUAL THINKING

Look at the picture. Then look at the pieces of the picture below. Write the letter that shows where each piece belongs. The pieces may be turned sideways or upside down.

HINT: There are two extra pieces.

D, ____, A, C, ____, B, E

 Use with Grade 3, text pages 404–405.

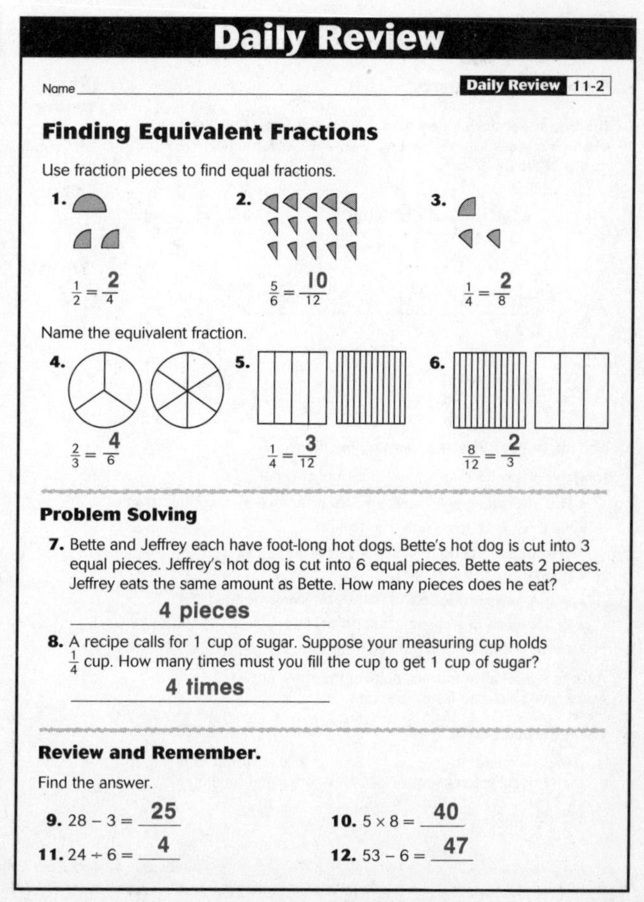

Daily Review

Name ____________ Daily Review 11-2

Finding Equivalent Fractions

Use fraction pieces to find equal fractions.

1. $\frac{1}{2} = \frac{2}{4}$
2. $\frac{5}{6} = \frac{10}{12}$
3. $\frac{1}{4} = \frac{2}{8}$

Name the equivalent fraction.

4. $\frac{2}{3} = \frac{4}{6}$
5. $\frac{1}{4} = \frac{3}{12}$
6. $\frac{8}{12} = \frac{2}{3}$

Problem Solving

7. Bette and Jeffrey each have foot-long hot dogs. Bette's hot dog is cut into 3 equal pieces. Jeffrey's hot dog is cut into 6 equal pieces. Bette eats 2 pieces. Jeffrey eats the same amount as Bette. How many pieces does he eat? **4 pieces**
8. A recipe calls for 1 cup of sugar. Suppose your measuring cup holds $\frac{1}{4}$ cup. How many times must you fill the cup to get 1 cup of sugar? **4 times**

Review and Remember.

Find the answer.

9. 28 − 3 = 25
10. 5 × 8 = 40
11. 24 ÷ 6 = 4
12. 53 − 6 = 47

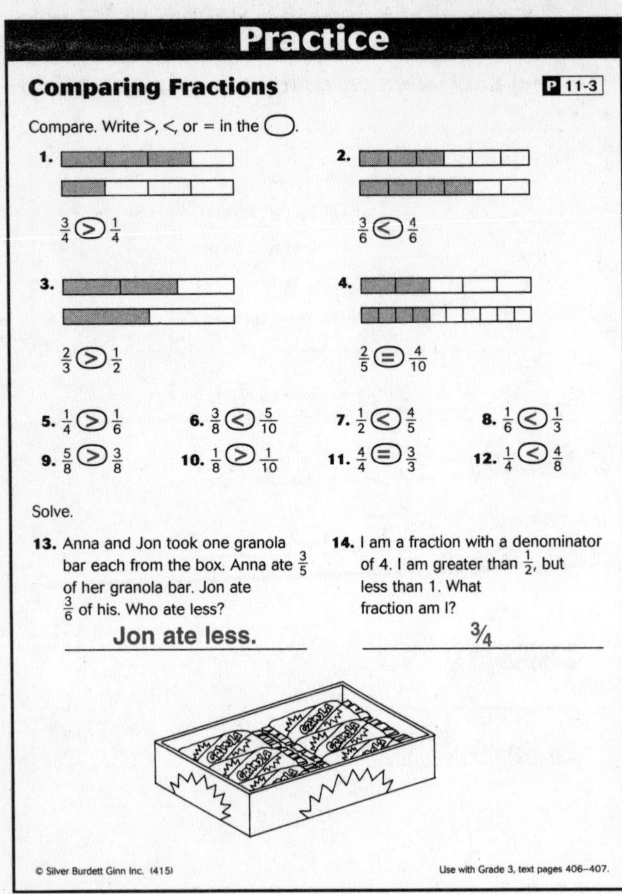

Practice

Comparing Fractions

P 11-3

Compare. Write >, <, or = in the ◯.

1. $\frac{3}{4}$ (>) $\frac{1}{4}$
2. $\frac{3}{6}$ (<) $\frac{4}{6}$
3. $\frac{2}{3}$ (>) $\frac{1}{2}$
4. $\frac{2}{5}$ (=) $\frac{4}{10}$

5. $\frac{1}{4}$ (>) $\frac{1}{6}$ 6. $\frac{3}{8}$ (<) $\frac{5}{10}$ 7. $\frac{1}{2}$ (<) $\frac{4}{5}$ 8. $\frac{1}{6}$ (<) $\frac{1}{3}$

9. $\frac{5}{8}$ (>) $\frac{3}{8}$ 10. $\frac{1}{8}$ (>) $\frac{1}{10}$ 11. $\frac{4}{4}$ (=) $\frac{3}{3}$ 12. $\frac{1}{4}$ (<) $\frac{4}{8}$

Solve.

13. Anna and Jon took one granola bar each from the box. Anna ate $\frac{3}{5}$ of her granola bar. Jon ate $\frac{3}{6}$ of his. Who ate less?
Jon ate less.

14. I am a fraction with a denominator of 4. I am greater than $\frac{1}{2}$, but less than 1. What fraction am I?
3/4

Use with Grade 3, text pages 406–407.

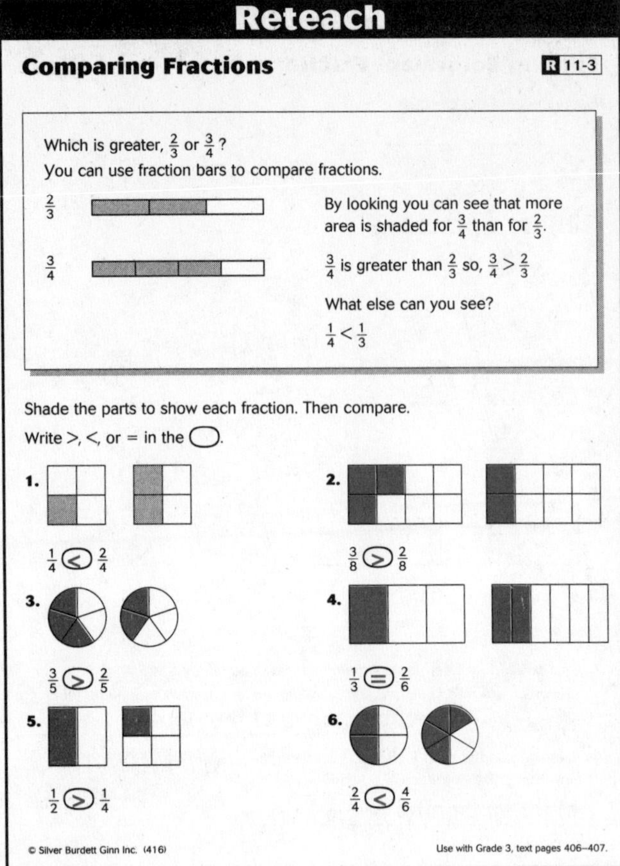

Reteach

Comparing Fractions

R 11-3

Which is greater, $\frac{2}{3}$ or $\frac{3}{4}$?
You can use fraction bars to compare fractions.

$\frac{2}{3}$

$\frac{3}{4}$

By looking you can see that more area is shaded for $\frac{3}{4}$ than for $\frac{2}{3}$.

$\frac{3}{4}$ is greater than $\frac{2}{3}$ so, $\frac{3}{4} > \frac{2}{3}$

What else can you see?

$\frac{1}{4} < \frac{1}{3}$

Shade the parts to show each fraction. Then compare.

Write >, <, or = in the ◯.

1. $\frac{1}{4}$ (<) $\frac{2}{4}$
2. $\frac{3}{8}$ (>) $\frac{2}{8}$
3. $\frac{3}{5}$ (>) $\frac{2}{5}$
4. $\frac{1}{3}$ (=) $\frac{2}{6}$
5. $\frac{1}{2}$ (>) $\frac{1}{4}$
6. $\frac{2}{4}$ (<) $\frac{4}{6}$

Use with Grade 3, text pages 406–407.

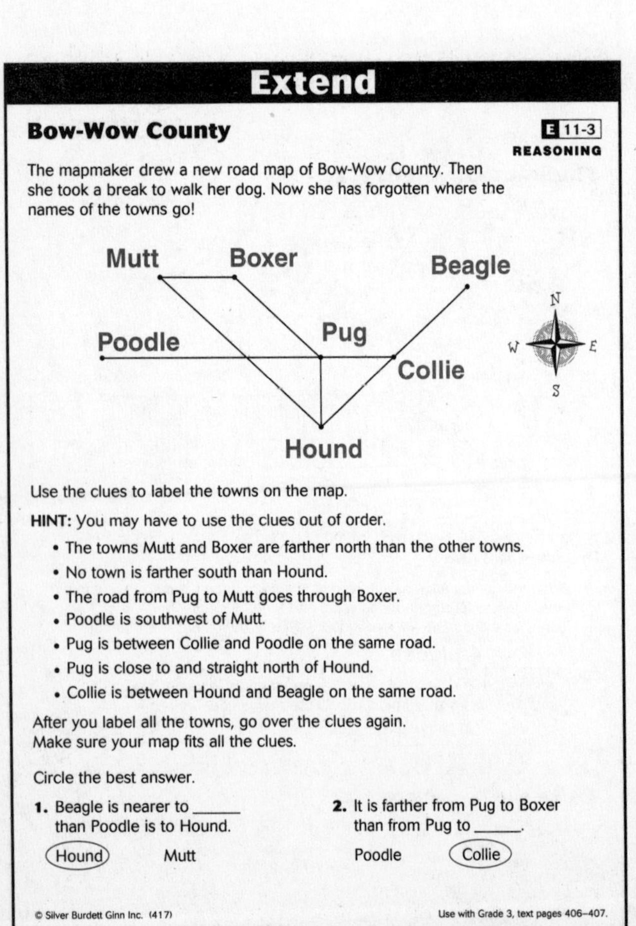

Extend

Bow-Wow County

E 11-3
REASONING

The mapmaker drew a new road map of Bow-Wow County. Then she took a break to walk her dog. Now she has forgotten where the names of the towns go!

Use the clues to label the towns on the map.

HINT: You may have to use the clues out of order.

- The towns Mutt and Boxer are farther north than the other towns.
- No town is farther south than Hound.
- The road from Pug to Mutt goes through Boxer.
- Poodle is southwest of Mutt.
- Pug is between Collie and Poodle on the same road.
- Pug is close to and straight north of Hound.
- Collie is between Hound and Beagle on the same road.

After you label all the towns, go over the clues again. Make sure your map fits all the clues.

Circle the best answer.

1. Beagle is nearer to _____ than Poodle is to Hound.
(Hound) Mutt

2. It is farther from Pug to Boxer than from Pug to _____.
Poodle (Collie)

Use with Grade 3, text pages 406–407.

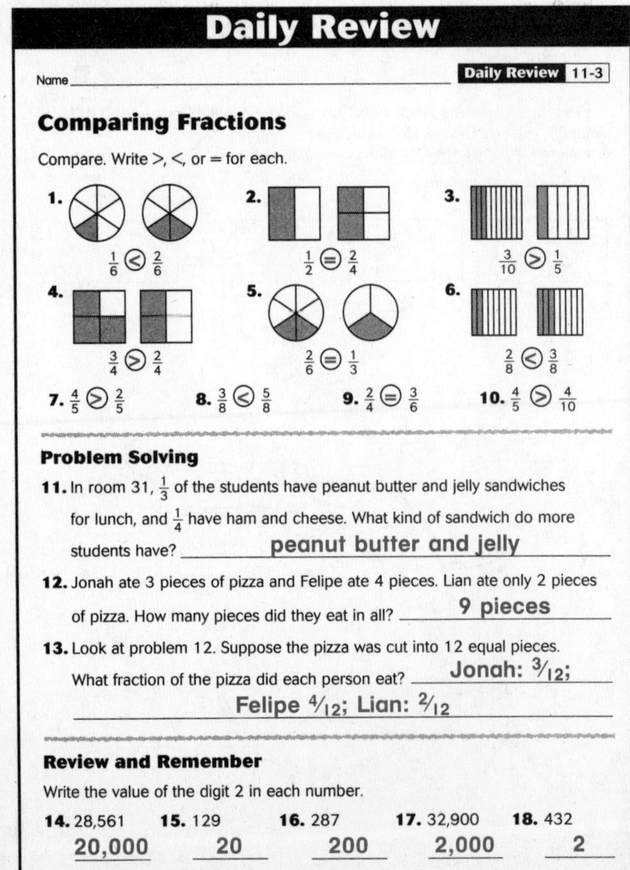

Daily Review

Name ____________________

Daily Review 11-3

Comparing Fractions

Compare. Write >, <, or = for each.

1. $\frac{1}{6}$ (<) $\frac{2}{6}$
2. $\frac{1}{2}$ (=) $\frac{2}{4}$
3. $\frac{3}{10}$ (>) $\frac{1}{5}$
4. $\frac{3}{4}$ (>) $\frac{2}{4}$
5. $\frac{2}{6}$ (=) $\frac{1}{3}$
6. $\frac{2}{8}$ (<) $\frac{3}{8}$

7. $\frac{4}{5}$ (>) $\frac{2}{5}$ 8. $\frac{3}{8}$ (<) $\frac{5}{8}$ 9. $\frac{2}{4}$ (=) $\frac{3}{6}$ 10. $\frac{4}{5}$ (>) $\frac{4}{10}$

Problem Solving

11. In room 31, $\frac{1}{3}$ of the students have peanut butter and jelly sandwiches for lunch, and $\frac{1}{4}$ have ham and cheese. What kind of sandwich do more students have? **peanut butter and jelly**

12. Jonah ate 3 pieces of pizza and Felipe ate 4 pieces. Lian ate only 2 pieces of pizza. How many pieces did they eat in all? **9 pieces**

13. Look at problem 12. Suppose the pizza was cut into 12 equal pieces. What fraction of the pizza did each person eat? **Jonah: 3/12; Felipe 4/12; Lian: 2/12**

Review and Remember

Write the value of the digit 2 in each number.

14. 28,561 **20,000** 15. 129 **20** 16. 287 **200** 17. 32,900 **2,000** 18. 432 **2**

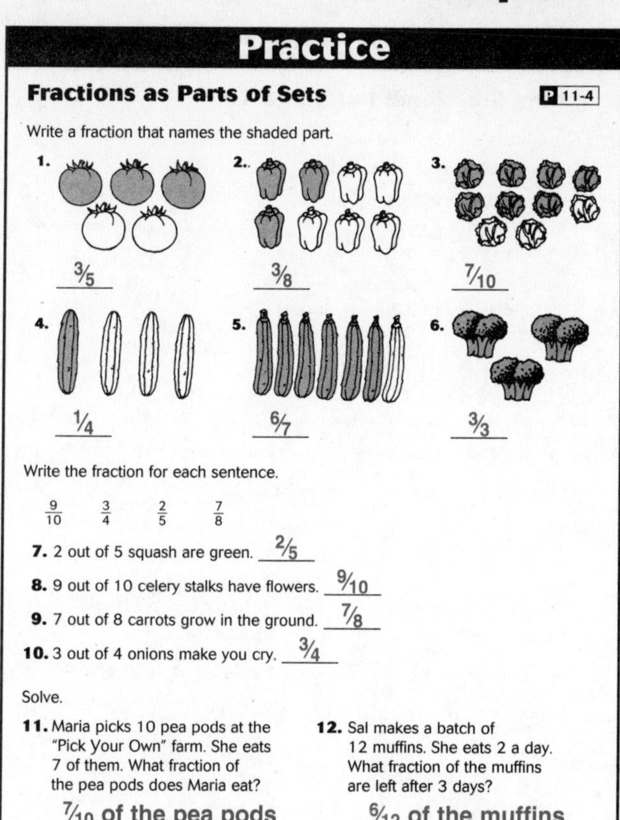

Practice

Fractions as Parts of Sets

P 11-4

Write a fraction that names the shaded part.

1. 3/5
2. 3/8
3. 7/10
4. 1/4
5. 6/7
6. 3/3

Write the fraction for each sentence.

$\frac{9}{10}$ $\frac{3}{4}$ $\frac{2}{5}$ $\frac{7}{8}$

7. 2 out of 5 squash are green. 2/5
8. 9 out of 10 celery stalks have flowers. 9/10
9. 7 out of 8 carrots grow in the ground. 7/8
10. 3 out of 4 onions make you cry. 3/4

Solve.

11. Maria picks 10 pea pods at the "Pick Your Own" farm. She eats 7 of them. What fraction of the pea pods does Maria eat? 7/10 of the pea pods
12. Sal makes a batch of 12 muffins. She eats 2 a day. What fraction of the muffins are left after 3 days? 6/12 of the muffins

 Use with Grade 3, text pages 408–409.

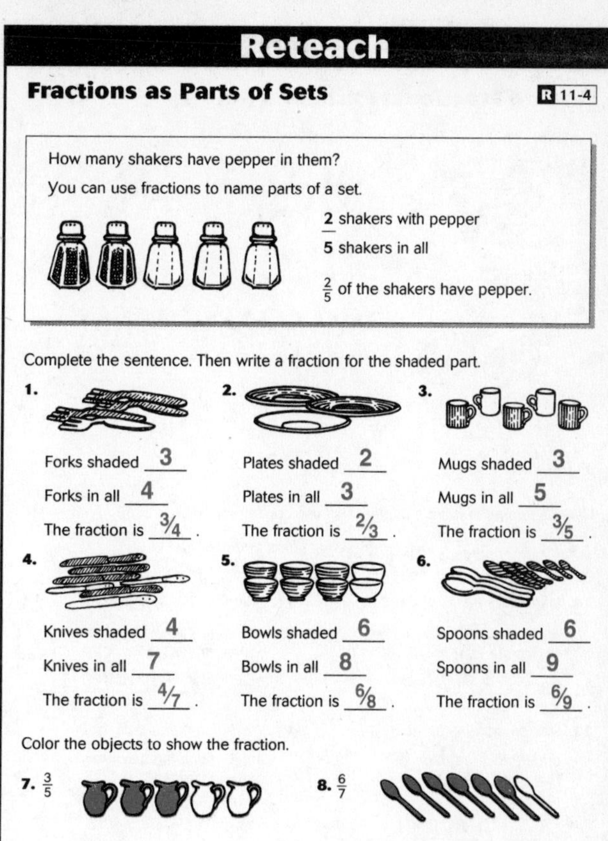

Reteach

Fractions as Parts of Sets

R 11-4

How many shakers have pepper in them?
You can use fractions to name parts of a set.

2 shakers with pepper
5 shakers in all
$\frac{2}{5}$ of the shakers have pepper.

Complete the sentence. Then write a fraction for the shaded part.

1. Forks shaded 3; Forks in all 4; The fraction is 3/4.
2. Plates shaded 2; Plates in all 3; The fraction is 2/3.
3. Mugs shaded 3; Mugs in all 5; The fraction is 3/5.
4. Knives shaded 4; Knives in all 7; The fraction is 4/7.
5. Bowls shaded 6; Bowls in all 8; The fraction is 6/8.
6. Spoons shaded 6; Spoons in all 9; The fraction is 6/9.

Color the objects to show the fraction.

7. $\frac{3}{5}$
8. $\frac{6}{7}$

 Use with Grade 3, text pages 408–409.

Extend

Musical Fractions

E 11-4
NUMBER SENSE

When you see 4/4 in music, it means 4 beats to a measure.

In $\frac{4}{4}$ time:

whole note = 4 beats
half note = 2 beats
quarter note = 1 beat
eighth note = $\frac{1}{2}$ beat
sixteenth note = $\frac{1}{4}$ beat

Add notes to make each measure have 4 beats. Possible answers given.

 Use with Grade 3, text pages 408–409.

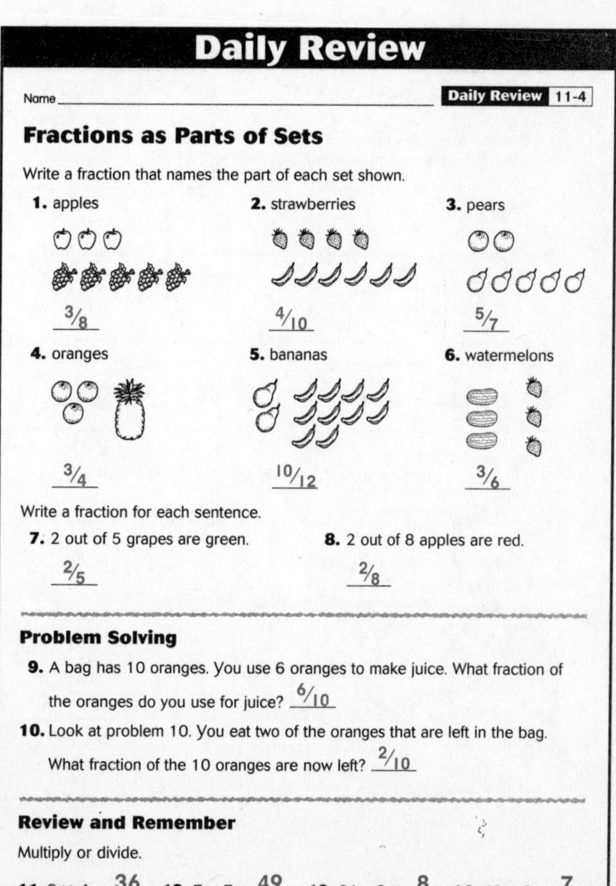

Daily Review

Name ____________

Daily Review 11-4

Fractions as Parts of Sets

Write a fraction that names the part of each set shown.

1. apples 3/8
2. strawberries 4/10
3. pears 5/7
4. oranges 3/4
5. bananas 10/12
6. watermelons 3/6

Write a fraction for each sentence.

7. 2 out of 5 grapes are green. 2/5
8. 2 out of 8 apples are red. 2/8

Problem Solving

9. A bag has 10 oranges. You use 6 oranges to make juice. What fraction of the oranges do you use for juice? 6/10
10. Look at problem 10. You eat two of the oranges that are left in the bag. What fraction of the 10 oranges are now left? 2/10

Review and Remember

Multiply or divide.

11. $9 \times 4 =$ 36
12. $7 \times 7 =$ 49
13. $64 \div 8 =$ 8
14. $42 \div 6 =$ 7

Chapter 11 • Lesson 5

Practice

Finding Fractional Parts of a Set

P 11-5

Complete. You may use counters or draw pictures to help.

1. 

$\frac{1}{4}$ of 8 = 2

2. 

$\frac{1}{3}$ of 9 = 3

3. $\frac{1}{2}$ of 14 = 7

4. 

$\frac{1}{2}$ of 2 = 1

5. 

$\frac{1}{2}$ of 16 = 8

6. 

$\frac{1}{5}$ of 10 = 2

7. $\frac{1}{3}$ of 15 = 5

8. $\frac{1}{2}$ of 10 = 5

9. $\frac{1}{4}$ of 16 = 4

Use the apples to solve. You may also use counters to help.

10. Marta says that $\frac{1}{2}$ of the apples are red. How many apples are red?

3 apples

11. Julie says that $\frac{1}{3}$ of the apples are yellow. How many apples are yellow?

2 apples

12. Stan says that $\frac{1}{6}$ of the apples are from Maryland. How many apples are from Maryland?

1 apple

13. Wayne says that $\frac{2}{3}$ of the apples taste tart. How many apples taste tart?

4 apples

Use with Grade 3, text pages 410–411.

Reteach

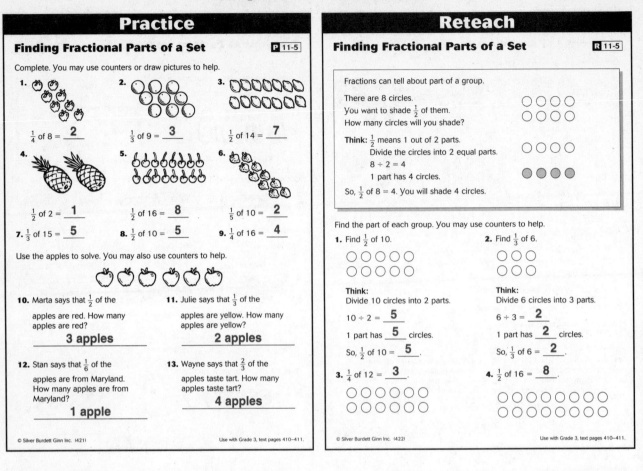

Finding Fractional Parts of a Set

R 11-5

Fractions can tell about part of a group.

There are 8 circles.
You want to shade $\frac{1}{2}$ of them.
How many circles will you shade?

Think: $\frac{1}{2}$ means 1 out of 2 parts.
Divide the circles into 2 equal parts.
$8 \div 2 = 4$
1 part has 4 circles.

So, $\frac{1}{2}$ of 8 = 4. You will shade 4 circles.

Find the part of each group. You may use counters to help.

1. Find $\frac{1}{2}$ of 10.

Think:
Divide 10 circles into 2 parts.

$10 \div 2 =$ 5

1 part has 5 circles.

So, $\frac{1}{2}$ of 10 = 5.

2. Find $\frac{1}{3}$ of 6.

Think:
Divide 6 circles into 3 parts.

$6 \div 3 =$ 2

1 part has 2 circles.

So, $\frac{1}{3}$ of 6 = 2.

3. $\frac{1}{4}$ of 12 = 3.

4. $\frac{1}{2}$ of 16 = 8.

Use with Grade 3, text pages 410–411.

Extend

Alike or Different?

E 11-5

VISUAL THINKING

Find the picture in each row that is different from the other two. Draw a picture to match the different one.

1. 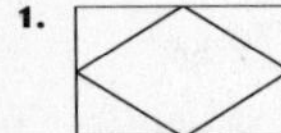

2. 

3.   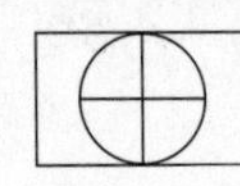 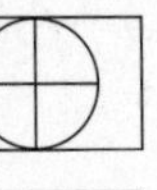 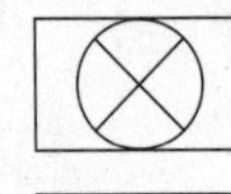 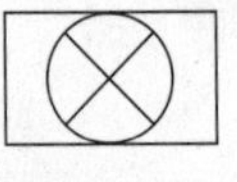 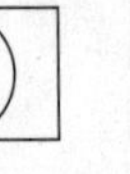  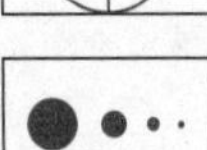

This time, find the two pictures in each row that are alike. Draw a third one just like them.

4.  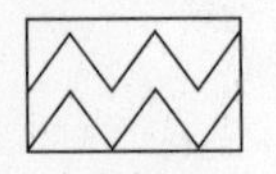 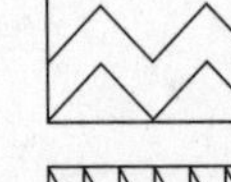 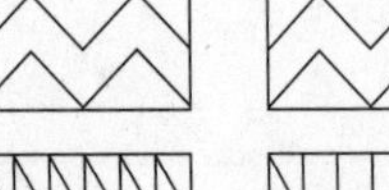

5. 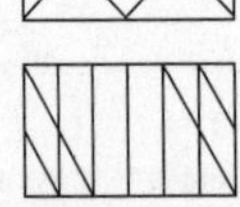  

6. 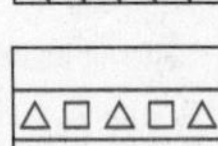

Use with Grade 3, text pages 410–411.

Daily Review

Name ____________________

Daily Review 11-5

Finding Fractional Parts of a Set

Use counters to find each answer.

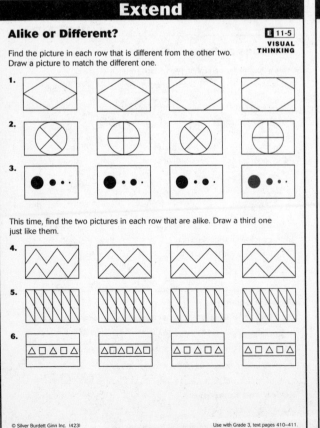

1. 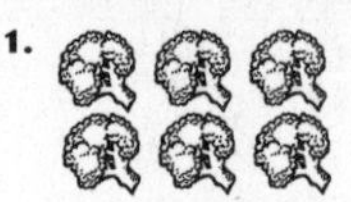  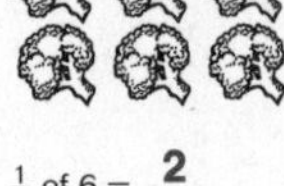    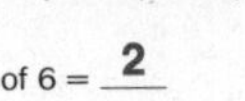 

$\frac{1}{3}$ of 6 = 2

2. $\frac{1}{5}$ of 10 = 2

3. 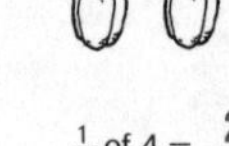

$\frac{1}{2}$ of 4 = 2

4. $\frac{1}{3}$ of 9 = 3

5. $\frac{1}{4}$ of 8 = 2

6. $\frac{1}{2}$ of 10 = 5

7. $\frac{1}{6}$ of 12 = 2

8. $\frac{1}{8}$ of 16 = 2

9. $\frac{1}{4}$ of 12 = 3

10. $\frac{1}{3}$ of 15 = 5

11. $\frac{1}{2}$ of 8 = 4

12. $\frac{1}{8}$ of 8 = 1

Problem Solving

13. There are 12 inches in a foot. How many inches are there in $\frac{1}{3}$ of a foot?

4 inches

14. There are 20 tortilla shells in a package. If you use $\frac{1}{5}$ of the package, how many tortilla shells are left? 16 shells

Review and Remember

Complete each pattern.

15. 400, 420, 440, 460, 480, 500, 520

16. 65, 70, 75, 80, 85, 90, 95

17. 350, 360, 370, 380, 390, 400, 410

Practice

Problem Solving P 11-6

Reasonable Answers

Circle the correct answer to each question.

Max the Magician put 6 rabbits in a hat. He pulled some rabbits out of the hat. There were 2 rabbits left in the hat.

1. Which number sentence shows how many rabbits Max pulled out of the hat?

a. $6 + 2 = 8$ rabbits

(b.) $6 - 2 = 4$ rabbits

c. $6 \times 2 = 12$ rabbits

2. Which fraction shows how many rabbits Max pulled out of the hat?

a. $\frac{2}{6}$ **b.** $\frac{3}{6}$ **(c.)** $\frac{4}{6}$

3. Is it reasonable to say that $\frac{2}{6}$ of the rabbits were left in the hat?

(a.) Yes; $\frac{4}{6} + \frac{2}{6} = \frac{6}{6}$, or 1

b. No; 2 rabbits = $\frac{1}{2}$

c. No; $6 - 2 = 4$, or $\frac{1}{4}$

4. Is it reasonable to say that Max pulled $\frac{1}{2}$ of the rabbits out of the hat?

a. No; $\frac{4}{6}$ is less than $\frac{1}{2}$.

b. Yes; $\frac{4}{6}$ is equal to $\frac{1}{2}$.

(c.) No; $\frac{4}{6}$ is greater than $\frac{1}{2}$.

Max uses scarves for his magic show. He ties $\frac{4}{8}$ of them together. He hides 4 of them in his hands. Is it reasonable to say that he ties together about $\frac{1}{2}$ of his scarves?

5. How many eighths are equal to $\frac{1}{2}$?

a. $\frac{1}{8}$ **(b.)** $\frac{4}{8}$ **c.** $\frac{8}{8}$

6. How many scarves does Max use to hide objects inside his hands?

a. $\frac{4}{8}$ **b.** $\frac{1}{2}$ **(c.)** 4

7. What can you say about how many scarves Max tied together?

a. He used less than $\frac{1}{2}$. **(b.)** He used exactly $\frac{1}{2}$. **c.** He used more than $\frac{1}{2}$.

 Use with Grade 3, text pages 412–413.

Reteach

Problem Solving R 11-6

Reasonable Answers

When you answer a question, decide if the answer is *reasonable.* When you read the question again, look at the facts it contains. Make sure your answer makes sense given those facts.

Renee puts 4 pictures on each page of her photo album. One page shows 3 pictures of Renee's dog and 1 picture of her family. What fraction tells what part of the page is about her dog?

Is it reasonable to think that $\frac{3}{4}$ of the pictures on Renee's photo album page are of her dog? The fraction $\frac{3}{4}$ means 3 parts out of 4, and 3 out of 4 photos are of Renee's dog.

1. Is it reasonable to think that $\frac{1}{1}$ of the pictures are of Renee's family? Explain.

No; 1/1 is the whole page, and the family doesn't cover the whole page.

2. Is it reasonable to think that $\frac{1}{4}$ of the pictures are of Renee's family? Explain.

Yes; 1 out of 4 pictures are of Renee's family, and 1 out of 4 is the same as 1/4.

3. What should you do if you find that an answer is not reasonable?

Possible answer: Reread the paragraph or problem. Try to find a different way to answer the question. See if the new answer makes sense.

 Use with Grade 3, text pages 412–413.

Extend

Analyzing Reasonableness

E 11-6 NUMBER SENSE

Use the recipe for the Cereal Snack Mix to answer the questions.

CEREAL SNACK MIX
4 cups of cereal
1 cup of nuts
3 cups of pretzels
2 cups of dried fruit

1. How could you find the part of the mix that is pretzels?

3 cups of pretzels, 8 cups in all, so pretzels are 3 out of 8, or 3/8

2. Is it reasonable to say that exactly $\frac{1}{2}$ of the mix is cereal? Explain.

Yes; 4 out of 8 cups are cereal and 4/8 is equal to 1/2.

Hallie adds dried fruit to the recipe. The new recipe makes 10 cups of mix.

3. Divide the circle on the right to show the new total number of parts.

4. What fraction shows the part of Hallie's recipe that is dried fruit?

2/10

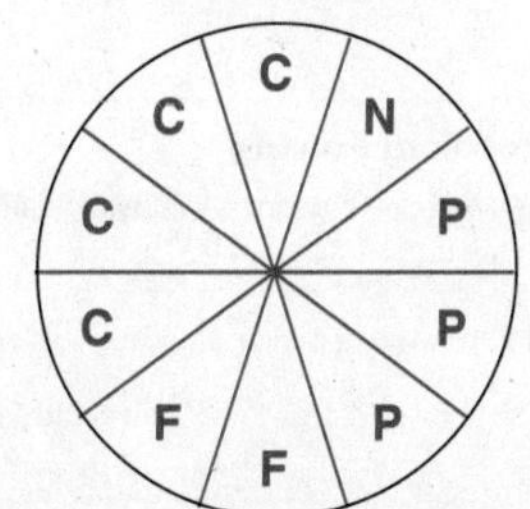

5. Label the parts of the circle *C, N, P,* and *F* to show how many cups of each ingredient goes into the mix.

6. Add the dried fruit to the recipe card above. Is it still reasonable to say that $\frac{1}{2}$ of the mix is cereal?

No; the cereal is 4/10 of the recipe now; which is less than 1/2.

 Use with Grade 3, text pages 412–413.

Daily Review

Name________________ Daily Review 11-6

Problem Solving

Reasonable Answers

Answer each question. Give a reason for your choice.

Marc paints animal figures on rocks and sells them at the beach. One day, he painted 12 rocks and sold all but 3 of them.

1. Which number sentence shows how many painted rocks Marc sold?

(a.) $12 - 3 = 9$

b. $12 + 3 = 15$

c. $12 \times 3 = 36$

2. What fraction shows how many painted rocks were sold?

a. $\frac{3}{12}$

(b.) $\frac{9}{12}$

c. $\frac{12}{12}$

3. Is it reasonable to say that more than one-half of the rocks were sold?

Yes; 1/2 of 12 is 6 — more than 6 were sold.

4. Is it reasonable to say that Marc sold about 10 rocks? Why or why not?

Yes, 9 can be rounded up to 10.

Review and Remember

Multiply.

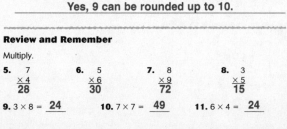

5. $7 \times 4 = $ **28** 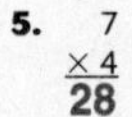 **6.** $5 \times 6 = $ **30** **7.** $8 \times 9 = $ **72** **8.** $3 \times 5 = $ **15**

9. $3 \times 8 = $ **24** **10.** $7 \times 7 = $ **49** **11.** $6 \times 4 = $ **24**

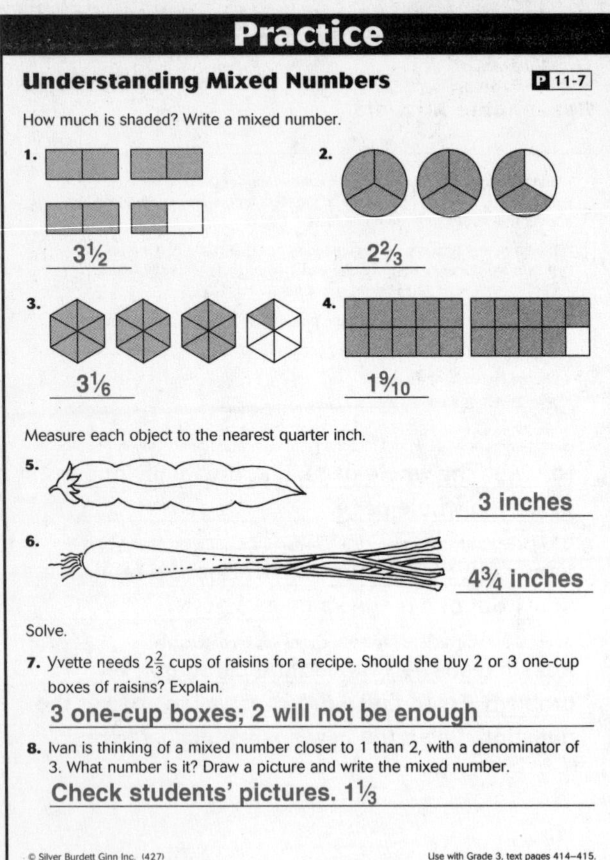

Practice

Understanding Mixed Numbers

P 11-7

How much is shaded? Write a mixed number.

1. $3\frac{1}{2}$
2. $2\frac{2}{3}$
3. $3\frac{1}{6}$
4. $1\frac{9}{10}$

Measure each object to the nearest quarter inch.

5. 3 inches
6. $4\frac{3}{4}$ inches

Solve.

7. Yvette needs $2\frac{2}{3}$ cups of raisins for a recipe. Should she buy 2 or 3 one-cup boxes of raisins? Explain.
   3 one-cup boxes; 2 will not be enough
8. Ivan is thinking of a mixed number closer to 1 than 2, with a denominator of 3. What number is it? Draw a picture and write the mixed number.
   Check students' pictures. $1\frac{1}{3}$

 Use with Grade 3, text pages 414–415.

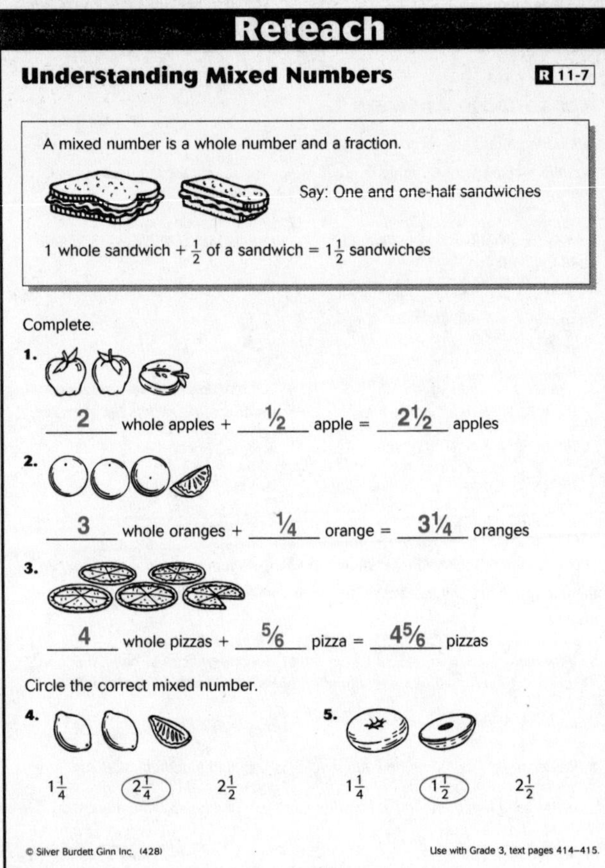

Reteach

Understanding Mixed Numbers

R 11-7

A mixed number is a whole number and a fraction.

Say: One and one-half sandwiches

1 whole sandwich + $\frac{1}{2}$ of a sandwich = $1\frac{1}{2}$ sandwiches

Complete.

1. 2 whole apples + $\frac{1}{2}$ apple = $2\frac{1}{2}$ apples
2. 3 whole oranges + $\frac{1}{4}$ orange = $3\frac{1}{4}$ oranges
3. 4 whole pizzas + $\frac{5}{6}$ pizza = $4\frac{5}{6}$ pizzas

Circle the correct mixed number.

4. $1\frac{1}{4}$ ($2\frac{1}{4}$) $2\frac{1}{2}$
5. $1\frac{1}{4}$ ($1\frac{1}{2}$) $2\frac{1}{2}$

 Use with Grade 3, text pages 414–415.

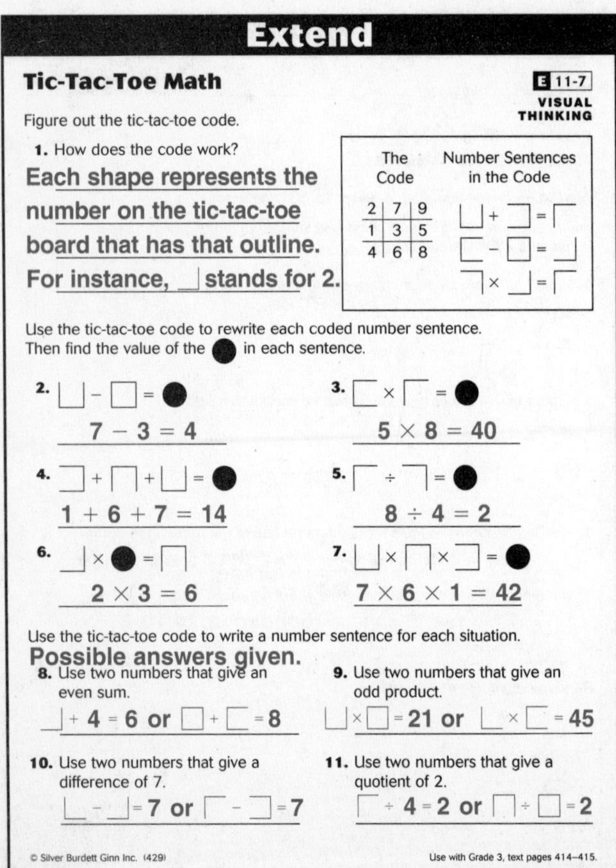

Extend

Tic-Tac-Toe Math

E 11-7

VISUAL THINKING

Figure out the tic-tac-toe code.

1. How does the code work?
   Each shape represents the number on the tic-tac-toe board that has that outline. For instance, ┘ stands for 2.

The Code		
2	7	9
1	3	5
4	6	8

Number Sentences in the Code

⊔ + ⊐ = ┌

⊏ − □ = ┘

┐ × ┘ = ┌

Use the tic-tac-toe code to rewrite each coded number sentence. Then find the value of the ● in each sentence.

2. ⊔ − □ = ●
   7 − 3 = 4
3. ⊏ × ┌ = ●
   5 × 8 = 40
4. ⊐ + ⊓ + ⊔ = ●
   1 + 6 + 7 = 14
5. ┌ ÷ ┐ = ●
   8 ÷ 4 = 2
6. ┘ × ● = ⊓
   2 × 3 = 6
7. ⊔ × ⊓ × ⊐ = ●
   7 × 6 × 1 = 42

Use the tic-tac-toe code to write a number sentence for each situation.
Possible answers given.

8. Use two numbers that give an even sum.
   ┘ + 4 = 6 or □ + ⊏ = 8
9. Use two numbers that give an odd product.
   ⊔ × □ = 21 or └ × ⊏ = 45
10. Use two numbers that give a difference of 7.
    └ − ┘ = 7 or ┌ − ⊐ = 7
11. Use two numbers that give a quotient of 2.
    ┌ ÷ 4 = 2 or ⊓ ÷ □ = 2

 Use with Grade 3, text pages 414–415.

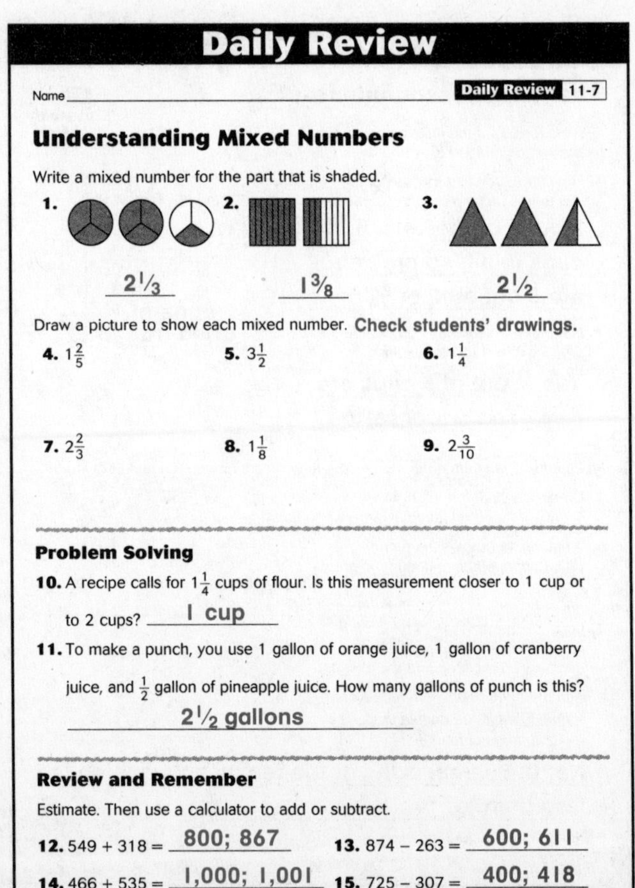

Daily Review

Name ____________________

Daily Review 11-7

Understanding Mixed Numbers

Write a mixed number for the part that is shaded.

1. $2\frac{1}{3}$
2. $1\frac{3}{8}$
3. $2\frac{1}{2}$

Draw a picture to show each mixed number. Check students' drawings.

4. $1\frac{2}{5}$
5. $3\frac{1}{2}$
6. $1\frac{1}{4}$
7. $2\frac{2}{3}$
8. $1\frac{1}{8}$
9. $2\frac{3}{10}$

Problem Solving

10. A recipe calls for $1\frac{1}{4}$ cups of flour. Is this measurement closer to 1 cup or to 2 cups? 1 cup
11. To make a punch, you use 1 gallon of orange juice, 1 gallon of cranberry juice, and $\frac{1}{2}$ gallon of pineapple juice. How many gallons of punch is this?
    $2\frac{1}{2}$ gallons

Review and Remember

Estimate. Then use a calculator to add or subtract.

12. 549 + 318 = 800; 867
13. 874 − 263 = 600; 611
14. 466 + 535 = 1,000; 1,001
15. 725 − 307 = 400; 418

Practice

Problem Solving P 11-8

Draw a Picture

Solve each problem. Draw a picture if it helps you.

Kim makes sandwiches in a snack shop. Today, she makes 2 cheese sandwiches, 3 ham and cheese sandwiches, and 1 peanut butter and jelly sandwich.

1. What fraction of the sandwiches contain cheese? **5/6 of the sandwiches**
2. Of the sandwiches Kim makes, 1 sandwich is on white bread and 3 sandwiches are on rolls. What fraction of the sandwiches are made on another kind of bread? **2/6 of the sandwiches**
3. Kim buys 8 bags of chips to sell. Only $\frac{3}{4}$ of the bags are sold. How many bags of chips did Kim sell? **6 bags**
4. There are 15 people in line at the snack shop. Only $\frac{2}{3}$ of them will order juice. How many people will not order juice? **5 people**

Try these or other strategies you have learned.

- Make a Table
- Draw a Picture
- Write a Number Sentence
- Act It Out

5. Kim bakes 10 loaves of bread. Of these, $\frac{1}{2}$ are whole wheat. How many loaves are whole wheat? **5 loaves**
6. A customer pays $12 for two lunches. One lunch costs $\frac{1}{2}$ as much as the other lunch. How much does each lunch cost? **$4 and $8**

 Use with Grade 3, text pages 416-417.

Reteach

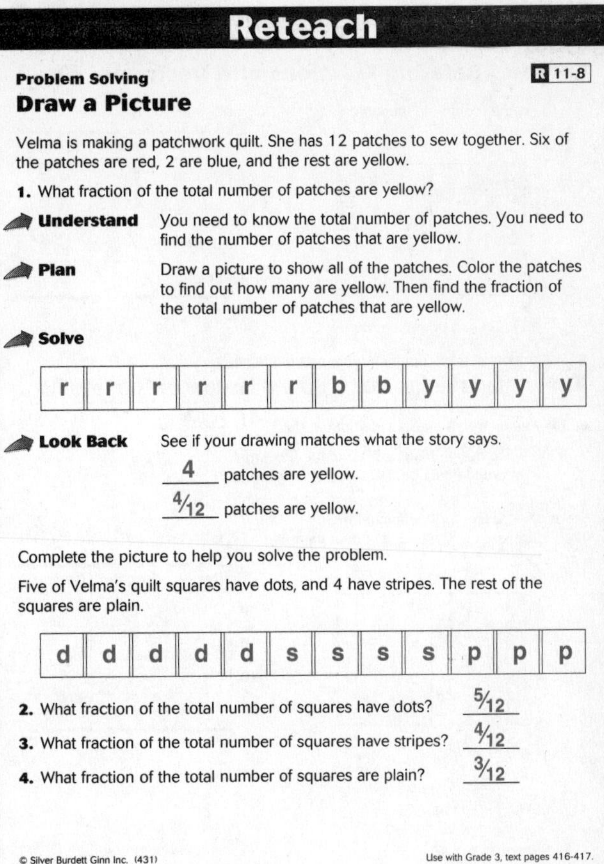

Problem Solving R 11-8

Draw a Picture

Velma is making a patchwork quilt. She has 12 patches to sew together. Six of the patches are red, 2 are blue, and the rest are yellow.

1. What fraction of the total number of patches are yellow?

Understand You need to know the total number of patches. You need to find the number of patches that are yellow.

Plan Draw a picture to show all of the patches. Color the patches to find out how many are yellow. Then find the fraction of the total number of patches that are yellow.

Solve

r	r	r	r	r	r	b	b	y	y	y	y

Look Back See if your drawing matches what the story says.

4 patches are yellow.

4/12 patches are yellow.

Complete the picture to help you solve the problem.

Five of Velma's quilt squares have dots, and 4 have stripes. The rest of the squares are plain.

d	d	d	d	d	s	s	s	s	p	p	p

2. What fraction of the total number of squares have dots? **5/12**
3. What fraction of the total number of squares have stripes? **4/12**
4. What fraction of the total number of squares are plain? **3/12**

 Use with Grade 3, text pages 416-417.

Extend

Brain Teasers

E 11-8 NUMBER SENSE

Use your favorite strategies to solve.

1. Mae picked 36 apples in 3 days. On Sunday, she picked $\frac{1}{2}$ of them. She picked $\frac{1}{6}$ of them on Monday. How many apples did Mae pick on Tuesday? What fractional part of the apples is this? **12 apples, or 1/3 of all the apples**
2. A playground has a total of 18 swings and slides. There are $\frac{1}{2}$ as many swings as there are slides. How many are there of each? **There are 6 swings and 12 slides.**
3. Fran has $30. She spends $\frac{1}{3}$ of her money for a new bike helmet. She spends $\frac{1}{6}$ of her money for a new bike horn. How much money does Fran have left? **$15**
4. Will's age is $\frac{3}{4}$ of Sloan's age. Sloan is 1 year older than Will. Will's age is $\frac{1}{4}$ of Randy's age. Sloan's age is $\frac{1}{6}$ of Wendy's age. How old is each person? **Will is 3 years old. Sloan is 4 years old. Randy is 12 years old. Wendy is 24 years old.**

Write two problems that can be solved by coloring or shading the picture. Then give them to a classmate to solve. **Problems and solutions will vary.**

5. ______________________________

6. ______________________________

 Use with Grade 3, text pages 416-417.

Daily Review

Name ______________________________ Daily Review 11-8

Problem Solving

Draw a Picture

Draw a picture to help you solve each problem.

Check students' drawings.

1. There are 10 tables in the cafeteria. One-half of them are rectangular and one-half are circular. How many tables are rectangular? **5 tables**
2. Lee has 4 crates of books. One crate holds history books, 1 crate is full of picture books, and 2 crates contain mysteries. What fraction of these crates contain picture books? **1/4**
3. Anthony is sorting playground balls. He has 1 softball, 2 basketballs, and 2 kickballs. What fraction of the balls are kickballs? **2/5**

Review and Remember

Multiply.

4. $5 \times 5 =$ **25** 5. $6 \times 2 =$ **12** 6. $8 \times 1 =$ **8** 7. $9 \times 3 =$ **27**

Practice

Explore: Relating Fractions and Decimals P 11-9

Use the flag to complete the table.

	Design	Fraction	Decimal
1.	Shaded	3/10	0.3
2.	White	2/10	0.2
3.	Dotted	4/10	0.4
4.	Striped	1/10	0.1

5. Which design takes up the largest part of the flag?
The dotted design takes up the largest part of the flag.

6. How many tenths are in the whole design? **10 tenths**

7. If the white design takes up 0.2 of the flag, what decimal would describe the part that is not white? **0.8**

Make up a design for the flag below.
Then complete the table to tell about your flag. **Answers will vary.**

	Design	Fraction	Decimal
8.	Shaded	$\frac{1}{10}$	0.1
9.			
10.			
11.			

 Use with Grade 3, text pages 420–421.

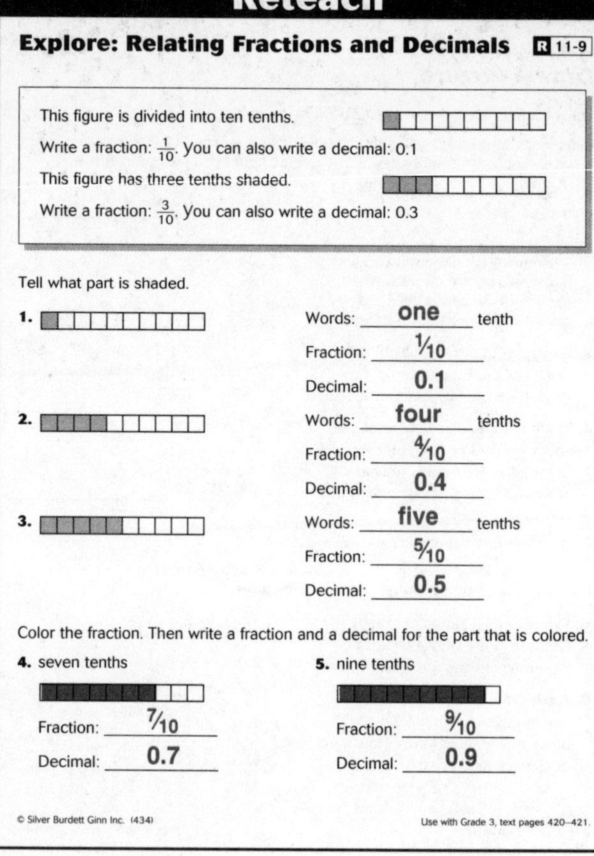

Reteach

Explore: Relating Fractions and Decimals R 11-9

This figure is divided into ten tenths.
Write a fraction: $\frac{1}{10}$. You can also write a decimal: 0.1
This figure has three tenths shaded.
Write a fraction: $\frac{3}{10}$. You can also write a decimal: 0.3

Tell what part is shaded.

1. Words: **one** tenth
Fraction: **1/10**
Decimal: **0.1**

2. Words: **four** tenths
Fraction: **4/10**
Decimal: **0.4**

3. Words: **five** tenths
Fraction: **5/10**
Decimal: **0.5**

Color the fraction. Then write a fraction and a decimal for the part that is colored.

4. seven tenths
Fraction: **7/10**
Decimal: **0.7**

5. nine tenths
Fraction: **9/10**
Decimal: **0.9**

 Use with Grade 3, text pages 420–421.

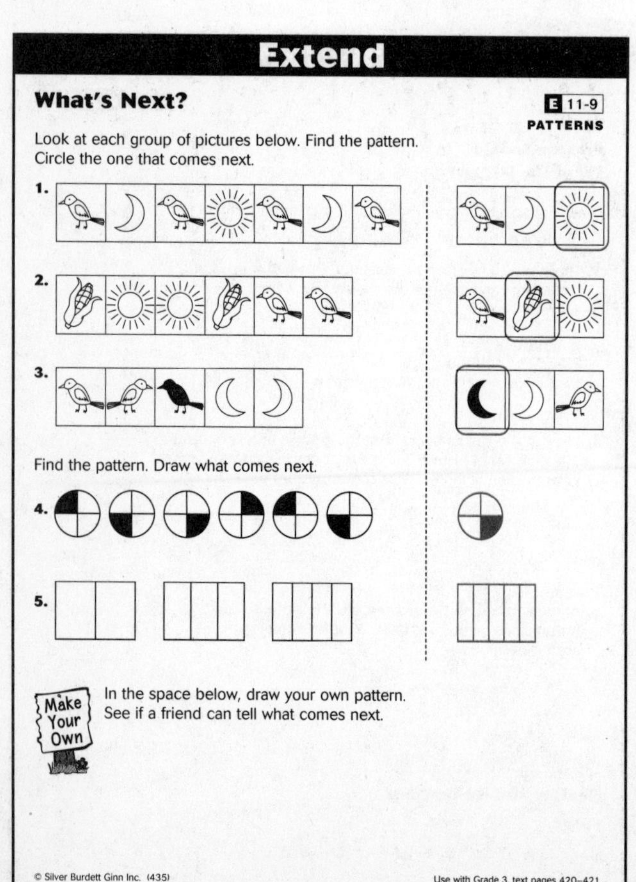

Extend

What's Next? E 11-9

PATTERNS

Look at each group of pictures below. Find the pattern. Circle the one that comes next.

1.

2.

3.

Find the pattern. Draw what comes next.

4.

5.

Make Your Own

In the space below, draw your own pattern. See if a friend can tell what comes next.

 Use with Grade 3, text pages 420–421.

Daily Review

Name _____ Daily Review 11-9

EXPLORE: Relating Fractions and Decimals

Follow the directions.

1. You are planning a garden. You divide the garden into 2 parts beans, 1 part cucumbers, 3 parts squash, and 4 parts tomatoes. Draw a garden plan on a separate sheet of paper. Color the rows. Use a different color for each kind of vegetable.

Complete the chart to tell about the parts of your garden.
Colors students use will vary.

	Plant	Color	Fraction	Decimal
2.	Cucumbers	green	1/10	0.1
3.	Beans	yellow	2/10	0.2
4.	Squash	orange	3/10	0.3
5.	Tomatoes	red	4/10	0.4

Problem Solving

6. Lettuce, cucumbers, beans, and peppers make up 0.7 of a garden. The rest of the garden is tomatoes. What decimal would describe the tomatoes? **0.3**

7. Your garden has 10 equal parts. It includes beans, peas, broccoli, lettuce, and tomatoes. Each kind of vegetable has an equal part of the garden. What decimal would describe each part? **0.2**

Review and Remember

Use mental math to find the answer.

8. 410 + 80 = **490**
9. 720 − 40 = **680**
10. 88 − 38 = **50**
11. 300 + 129 = **429**

Practice

Decimals in Tenths

P 11-10

Write a fraction and a decimal for the shaded part.

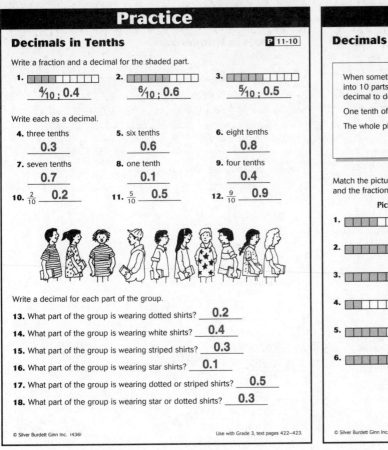

1. 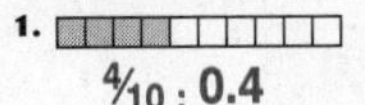
4/10 ; 0.4

2. 6/10 ; 0.6

3. 5/10 ; 0.5

Write each as a decimal.

4. three tenths 0.3
5. six tenths 0.6
6. eight tenths 0.8
7. seven tenths 0.7
8. one tenth 0.1
9. four tenths 0.4
10. $\frac{2}{10}$ 0.2
11. $\frac{5}{10}$ 0.5
12. $\frac{9}{10}$ 0.9

Write a decimal for each part of the group.

13. What part of the group is wearing dotted shirts? 0.2
14. What part of the group is wearing white shirts? 0.4
15. What part of the group is wearing striped shirts? 0.3
16. What part of the group is wearing star shirts? 0.1
17. What part of the group is wearing dotted or striped shirts? 0.5
18. What part of the group is wearing star or dotted shirts? 0.3

Use with Grade 3, text pages 422–423.

Reteach

Decimals in Tenths

R 11-10

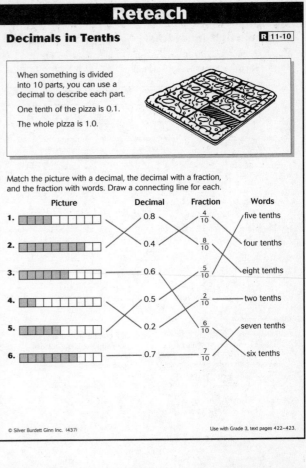

When something is divided into 10 parts, you can use a decimal to describe each part.

One tenth of the pizza is 0.1.

The whole pizza is 1.0.

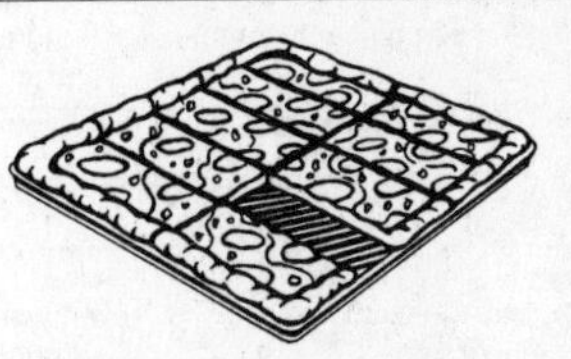

Match the picture with a decimal, the decimal with a fraction, and the fraction with words. Draw a connecting line for each.

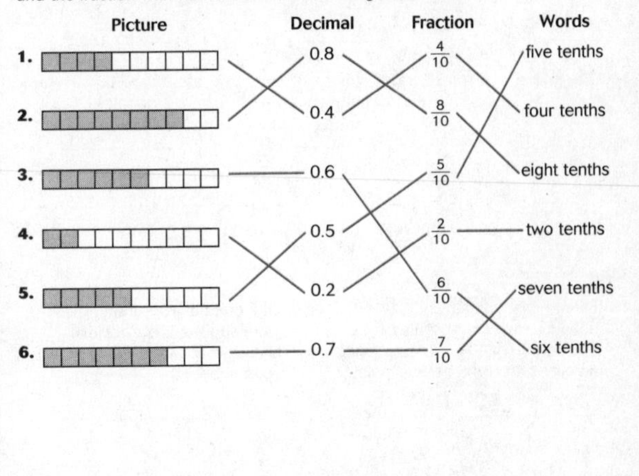

Picture	Decimal	Fraction	Words
1.	0.8	$\frac{4}{10}$	five tenths
2.	0.4	$\frac{8}{10}$	four tenths
3.	0.6	$\frac{5}{10}$	eight tenths
4.	0.5	$\frac{2}{10}$	two tenths
5.	0.2	$\frac{6}{10}$	seven tenths
6.	0.7	$\frac{7}{10}$	six tenths

Use with Grade 3, text pages 422–423.

Extend

Mix-Up

E 11-10 NUMBER SENSE

Mix-Up is a game in which you try to find as many of the number sentences as you can that are hidden on a game board. You can only write a number sentence if the numbers are all touching one another on the game board.

For example, if you had a section of a game board that looked like the one at the right, you could write 7 + 4 = 11, and 9 × 4 = 36, but not 36 − 11 = 25, because those numbers are not all touching each other.

7	9	11
25	4	36

Answers may vary. Possible answers:

1. Use this Mix-Up board to try to find 5 multiplication sentences and 5 addition sentences. Write them in the spaces below.

4	7	42	40
1	6	5	30
48	8	2	12
6	3	10	11

7 × 6 = 42 | 6 + 1 = 7
6 × 8 = 48 | 5 + 1 = 6
5 × 6 = 30 | 5 + 2 = 7
2 × 6 = 12 | 10 + 2 = 12
3 × 2 = 6 | 3 + 2 = 5

2. Now use this Mix-Up board to try to find 5 division and 5 subtraction sentences.

31	50	20	45
30	81	5	18
3	4	9	2
27	72	12	6

20 ÷ 5 = 4 | 30 − 3 = 27
72 ÷ 6 = 12 | 50 − 20 = 30
18 ÷ 2 = 9 | 9 − 5 = 4
12 ÷ 3 = 4 | 81 − 50 = 31
45 ÷ 5 = 9 | 50 − 5 = 45

Use with Grade 3, text pages 422–423.

Daily Review

Name ______________________

Daily Review 11-10

Decimals in Tenths

Write a fraction and a decimal for the shaded part.

1. 2/10, 0.2

2. 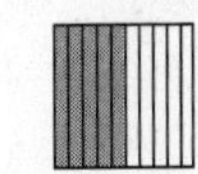
5/10, 0.5

3. 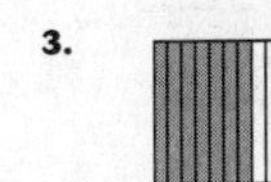
7/10, 0.7

Write each as a decimal.

4. $\frac{1}{10}$ = 0.1
5. $\frac{3}{10}$ = 0.3
6. $\frac{9}{10}$ = 0.9
7. $\frac{6}{10}$ = 0.6
8. $\frac{8}{10}$ = 0.8
9. $\frac{4}{10}$ = 0.4
10. two tenths = 0.2
11. seven tenths = 0.7
12. nine tenths = 0.9
13. three tenths = 0.3
14. five tenths = 0.5
15. one tenth = 0.1

Problem Solving Check students' drawings for accuracy.

16. Draw a picture to show $\frac{2}{10}$. Then write the decimal shown in your picture. 0.2

17. Draw a picture to show 0.9. Then write the fraction shown in your picture. 9/10

Review and Remember

Round to the nearest hundred.

18. 941 900
19. 573 600
20. 289 300
21. 966 1,000
22. 835 800
23. 749 700

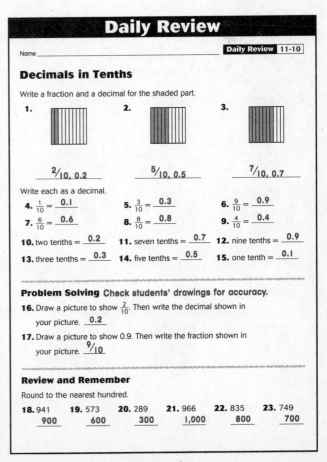

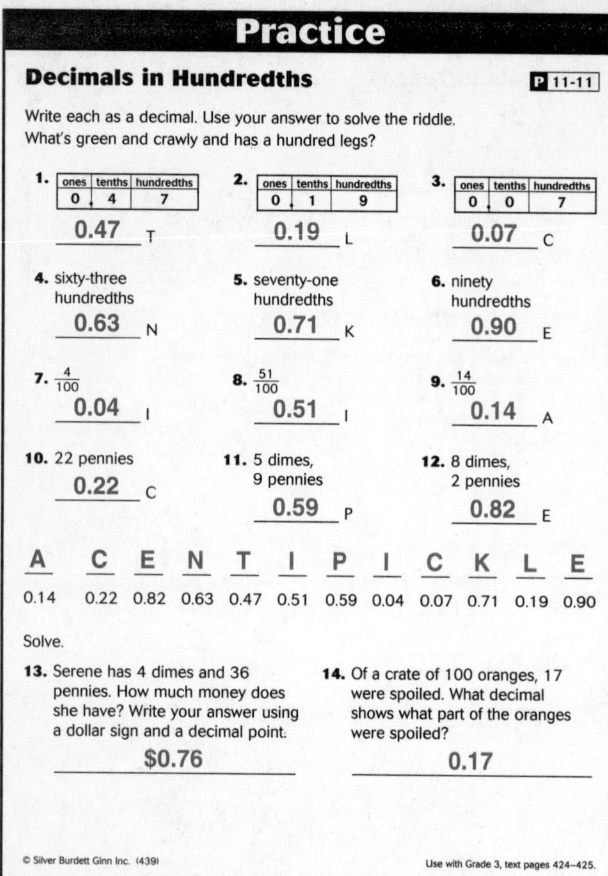

Practice

Decimals in Hundredths

P 11-11

Write each as a decimal. Use your answer to solve the riddle.
What's green and crawly and has a hundred legs?

1.

ones	tenths	hundredths
0	4	7

0.47 T

2.

ones	tenths	hundredths
0	1	9

0.19 L

3.

ones	tenths	hundredths
0	0	7

0.07 C

4. sixty-three hundredths 0.63 N

5. seventy-one hundredths 0.71 K

6. ninety hundredths 0.90 E

7. $\frac{4}{100}$ 0.04 I

8. $\frac{51}{100}$ 0.51 I

9. $\frac{14}{100}$ 0.14 A

10. 22 pennies 0.22 C

11. 5 dimes, 9 pennies 0.59 P

12. 8 dimes, 2 pennies 0.82 E

A	C	E	N	T	I	P	I	C	K	L	E
0.14	0.22	0.82	0.63	0.47	0.51	0.59	0.04	0.07	0.71	0.19	0.90

Solve.

13. Serene has 4 dimes and 36 pennies. How much money does she have? Write your answer using a dollar sign and a decimal point. $0.76

14. Of a crate of 100 oranges, 17 were spoiled. What decimal shows what part of the oranges were spoiled? 0.17

 Use with Grade 3, text pages 424–425.

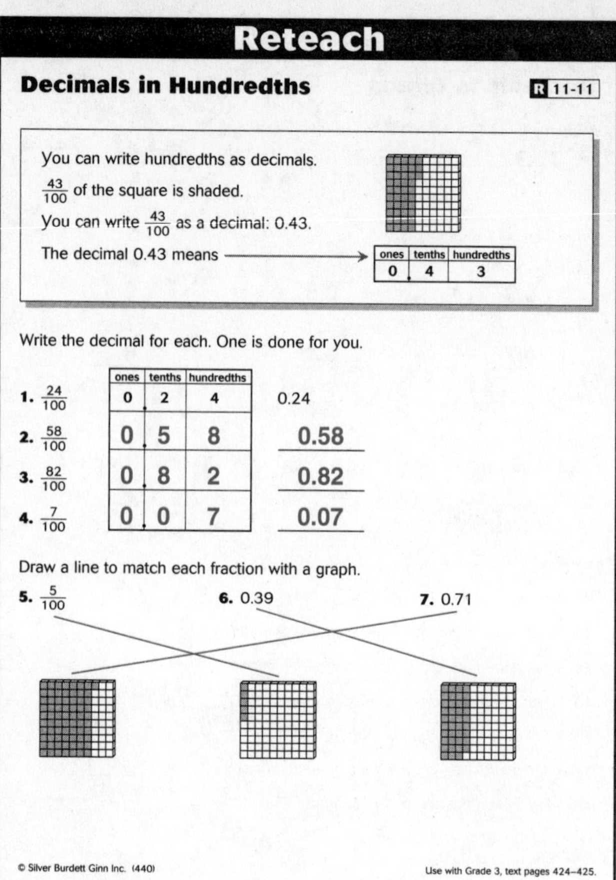

Reteach

Decimals in Hundredths

R 11-11

You can write hundredths as decimals.
$\frac{43}{100}$ of the square is shaded.
You can write $\frac{43}{100}$ as a decimal: 0.43.
The decimal 0.43 means →

ones	tenths	hundredths
0	4	3

Write the decimal for each. One is done for you.

	ones	tenths	hundredths	
1. $\frac{24}{100}$	0	2	4	0.24
2. $\frac{58}{100}$	0	5	8	0.58
3. $\frac{82}{100}$	0	8	2	0.82
4. $\frac{7}{100}$	0	0	7	0.07

Draw a line to match each fraction with a graph.

5. $\frac{5}{100}$ 6. 0.39 7. 0.71

 Use with Grade 3, text pages 424–425.

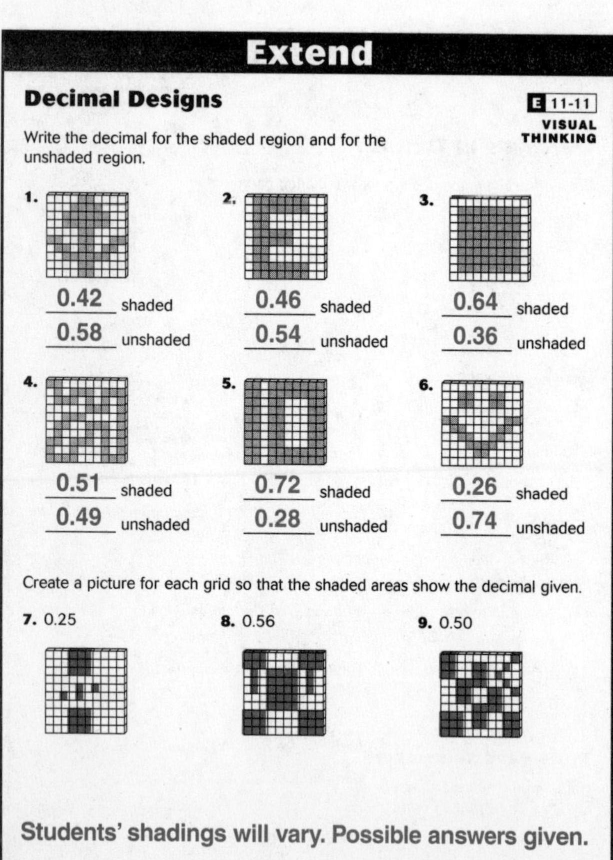

Extend

Decimal Designs

E 11-11 VISUAL THINKING

Write the decimal for the shaded region and for the unshaded region.

1. 0.42 shaded 0.58 unshaded

2. 0.46 shaded 0.54 unshaded

3. 0.64 shaded 0.36 unshaded

4. 0.51 shaded 0.49 unshaded

5. 0.72 shaded 0.28 unshaded

6. 0.26 shaded 0.74 unshaded

Create a picture for each grid so that the shaded areas show the decimal given.

7. 0.25 8. 0.56 9. 0.50

Students' shadings will vary. Possible answers given.

 Use with Grade 3, text pages 424–425.

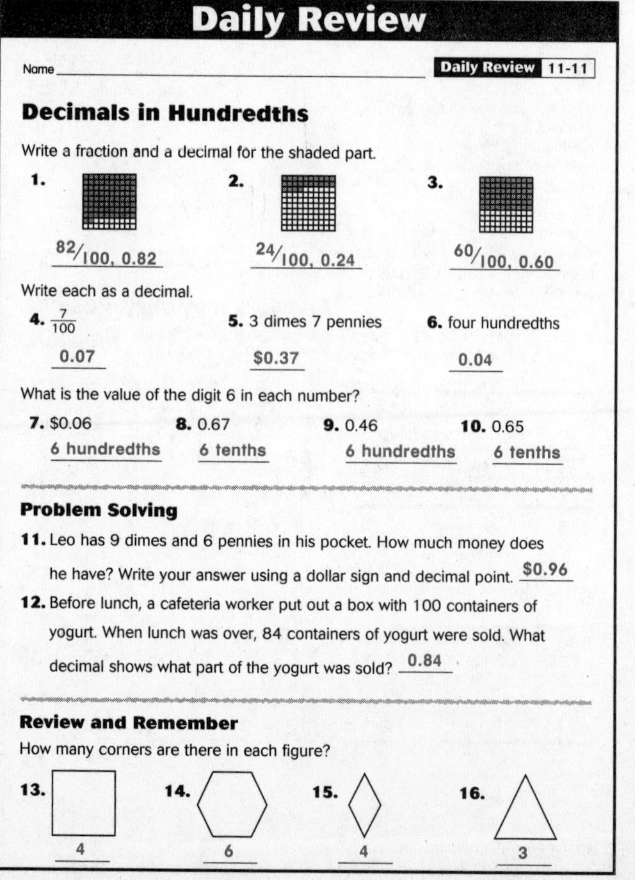

Daily Review

Name ____________

Daily Review 11-11

Decimals in Hundredths

Write a fraction and a decimal for the shaded part.

1. 82/100, 0.82

2. 24/100, 0.24

3. 60/100, 0.60

Write each as a decimal.

4. $\frac{7}{100}$ 0.07

5. 3 dimes 7 pennies $0.37

6. four hundredths 0.04

What is the value of the digit 6 in each number?

7. $0.06 6 hundredths

8. 0.67 6 tenths

9. 0.46 6 hundredths

10. 0.65 6 tenths

Problem Solving

11. Leo has 9 dimes and 6 pennies in his pocket. How much money does he have? Write your answer using a dollar sign and decimal point. $0.96

12. Before lunch, a cafeteria worker put out a box with 100 containers of yogurt. When lunch was over, 84 containers of yogurt were sold. What decimal shows what part of the yogurt was sold? 0.84

Review and Remember

How many corners are there in each figure?

13. 4 14. 6 15. 4 16. 3

Chapter 6

Practice Workbook

Multiplying Three Numbers

Multiply.

1. 2 × 2 × 3 = 12
2. 3 × 2 × 1 = 6
3. 7 × 0 × 4 = 0
4. 5 × 1 × 4 = 20
5. 4 × 1 × 8 = 32
6. 3 × 4 × 1 = 12
7. 7 × 1 × 8 = 56
8. 8 × 0 × 9 = 0
9. 3 × 1 × 8 = 24
10. 2 × 3 × 1 = 6
11. 5 × 4 × 1 = 20
12. 3 × 2 × 4 = 24
13. 2 × 2 × 4 = 16
14. 2 × 3 × 2 = 12
15. 2 × 3 × 3 = 18
16. 4 × 1 × 2 = 8
17. 2 × 4 × 2 = 16
18. 5 × 1 × 3 = 15
19. 6 × 9 × 0 = 0
20. 4 × 2 × 8 = 64

Review and Remember

Add or subtract. Use mental math or paper and pencil.

1. 3 + 5 + 4 = 12
2. 1 + 8 + 1 = 10
3. 8 + 6 + 1 = 15
4. 5 + 5 + 2 = 12
5. 4 + 4 + 3 = 11
6. 3 + 2 + 5 = 10
7. 961 − 479 = 482
8. 887 − 635 = 252
9. 745 − 378 = 367
10. 268 − 194 = 74

Practice Workbook

Finding Facts from Pictures

Use the picture to answer each question.

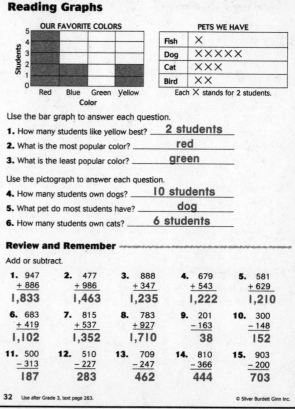

1. How many apples are there? 8 apples
2. How many peaches are there? 6 peaches
3. How many lemons are there? 7 lemons
4. How many pumpkins and peaches are there? 15
5. How many lemons and peaches are there? 13
6. Are there more lemons or more apples? apples
7. Mark bought 4 pumpkins. How many are left? 5 pumpkins

Review and Remember

Add or subtract.

1. 5 + 2 + 7 = 14
2. 6 + 1 + 8 = 15
3. 3 + 4 + 0 = 7
4. 4 + 1 + 8 = 13
5. 983 − 165 = 818
6. 841 − 322 = 519
7. 629 − 431 = 198
8. 739 − 553 = 186

Chapter 7

Practice Workbook

Making a List

1. Anne has white bread, rye bread, turkey, and cheese. How many different sandwiches can she make? Make a list to show the sandwiches.

number of sandwiches 6

Bread	Filling
white	turkey
white	cheese
white	turkey and cheese
rye	turkey
rye	cheese
rye	turkey and cheese

2. Jim has a white sweater, a blue sweater, red pants, and blue pants. How many different ways can he wear the sweaters and pants? Make a list to show the outfits.

number of outfits 4

Sweater	Pants
white	red
white	blue
blue	red
blue	blue

Review and Remember

Solve by using problem-solving strategies.

1. Jill has 3 cats, 2 dogs, and 2 hamsters. How many pets does Jill own? 7 pets

2. Kim invited 8 friends to her party. Each friend brought 2 gifts. How many gifts did Kim receive? 16 gifts

Add or subtract.

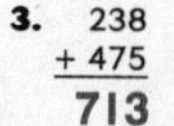

3. 238 + 475 = 713
4. 542 + 349 = 891
5. 74 − 43 = 31
6. 55 − 9 = 46
7. 96 − 85 = 11

Practice Workbook

Reading Graphs

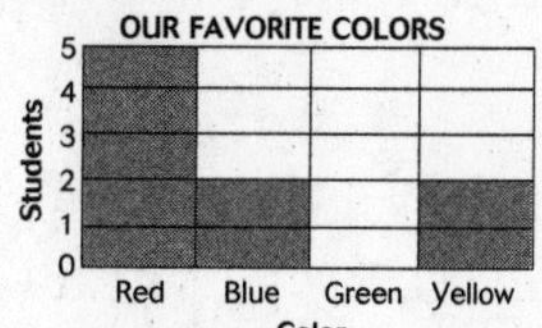

PETS WE HAVE

Fish	X
Dog	XXXXX
Cat	XXX
Bird	XX

Each X stands for 2 students.

Use the bar graph to answer each question.

1. How many students like yellow best? 2 students
2. What is the most popular color? red
3. What is the least popular color? green

Use the pictograph to answer each question.

4. How many students own dogs? 10 students
5. What pet do most students have? dog
6. How many students own cats? 6 students

Review and Remember

Add or subtract.

1. 947 + 886 = 1,833
2. 477 + 986 = 1,463
3. 888 + 347 = 1,235
4. 679 + 543 = 1,222
5. 581 + 629 = 1,210
6. 683 + 419 = 1,102
7. 815 + 537 = 1,352
8. 783 + 927 = 1,710
9. 201 − 163 = 38
10. 300 − 148 = 152
11. 500 − 313 = 187
12. 510 − 227 = 283
13. 709 − 247 = 462
14. 810 − 366 = 444
15. 903 − 200 = 703

Chapter 7

Practice Workbook

Using Ordered Pairs to Locate Points

Use the grid to answer each question.

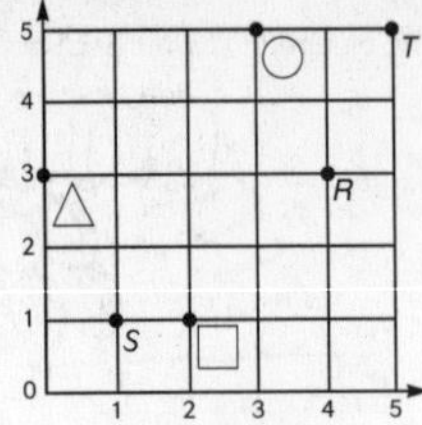

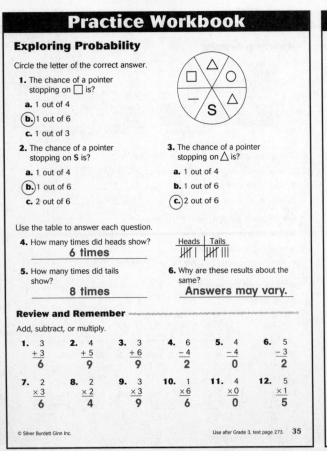

1. What ordered pair gives the location of the square? **(2, 1)**
2. What ordered pair gives the location of R? **(4, 3)**
3. What ordered pair gives the location of the circle? **(3, 5)**
4. What ordered pair gives the location of the triangle? **(0, 3)**
5. What ordered pair gives the location of S? **(1, 1)**
6. What ordered pair gives the location of T? **(5, 5)**

Review and Remember

Add or subtract.

1. 28 + 31 + 45 = **104**
2. 72 + 83 + 9 = **164**
3. 16 + 83 + 94 = **193**
4. 321 − 198 = **123**
5. 611 − 294 = **317**
6. 323 − 167 = **156**
7. 227 − 105 = **122**
8. 643 − 271 = **372**
9. 62 + 47 + 15 **124**
10. 17 + 21 + 84 **122**
11. 12 + 38 + 92 **142**
12. 57 + 22 + 10 **89**

Practice Workbook

Making Graphs

Use the grid.

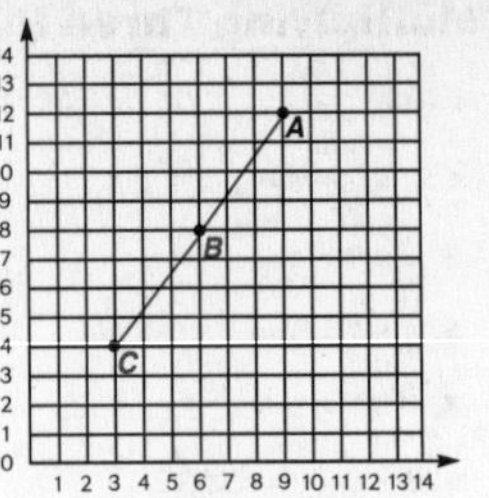

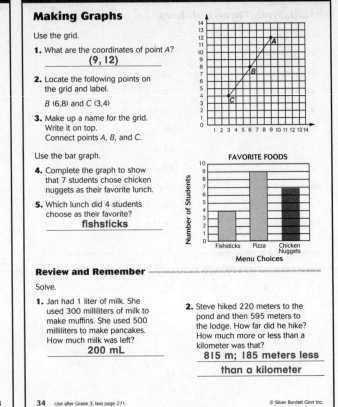

1. What are the coordinates of point A? **(9, 12)**
2. Locate the following points on the grid and label.
   B (6,8) and C (3,4)
3. Make up a name for the grid. Write it on top. Connect points A, B, and C.

Use the bar graph.

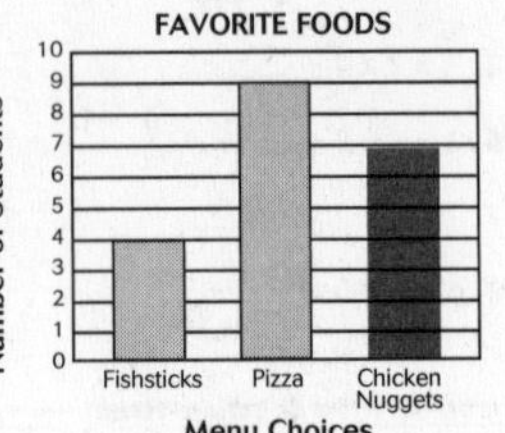

4. Complete the graph to show that 7 students chose chicken nuggets as their favorite lunch.
5. Which lunch did 4 students choose as their favorite? **fishsticks**

Review and Remember

Solve.

1. Jan had 1 liter of milk. She used 300 milliliters of milk to make muffins. She used 500 milliliters to make pancakes. How much milk was left? **200 mL**
2. Steve hiked 220 meters to the pond and then 595 meters to the lodge. How far did he hike? How much more or less than a kilometer was that? **815 m; 185 meters less than a kilometer**

Chapter 7

Practice Workbook

Exploring Probability

Circle the letter of the correct answer.

1. The chance of a pointer stopping on □ is?
   a. 1 out of 4
   (b.) 1 out of 6
   c. 1 out of 3
2. The chance of a pointer stopping on S is?
   a. 1 out of 4
   (b.) 1 out of 6
   c. 2 out of 6
3. The chance of a pointer stopping on △ is?
   a. 1 out of 4
   b. 1 out of 6
   (c.) 2 out of 6

Use the table to answer each question.

Heads	Tails
𝍸 I	𝍸 III

4. How many times did heads show? **6 times**
5. How many times did tails show? **8 times**
6. Why are these results about the same? **Answers may vary.**

Review and Remember

Add, subtract, or multiply.

1. 3 + 3 = **6**
2. 4 + 5 = **9**
3. 3 + 6 = **9**
4. 6 − 4 = **2**
5. 4 − 4 = **0**
6. 5 − 3 = **2**
7. 2 × 3 = **6**
8. 2 × 2 = **4**
9. 3 × 3 = **9**
10. 1 × 6 = **6**
11. 4 × 0 = **0**
12. 5 × 1 = **5**

Chapter 8

Practice Workbook

Relating Multiplication and Division

Multiply or divide.

1. 3 × 6 = **18**; 6 × 3 = **18**; 18 ÷ 3 = **6**; 18 ÷ 6 = **3**
2. 2 × 5 = **10**; 5 × 2 = **10**; 10 ÷ 2 = **5**; 10 ÷ 5 = **2**
3. 3 × 4 = **12**; 4 × 3 = **12**; 12 ÷ 4 = **3**; 12 ÷ 3 = **4**

Multiply. Then write two division sentences.

4. 3 × 5 = **15**; 5 × 3 = **15**; **15** ÷ **3** = 5; **15** ÷ **5** = 3
5. 3 × 7 = **21**; 7 × 3 = **21**; **21** ÷ **3** = 7; **21** ÷ **7** = 3
6. 2 × 6 = **12**; 6 × 2 = **12**; **12** ÷ **2** = **6**; **12** ÷ **6** = **2**

Review and Remember

Choose the correct word to complete each sentence.

gram centimeter kilogram

1. To measure lengths, use the **centimeter**.
2. To measure the weight of light objects, use the **gram**.
3. To measure the weight of heavy objects, use the **kilogram**.

Chapter 8

Practice Workbook

Using 2 and 3 as Divisors

Write a division fact for each.
Then write how many are in each group.

1. 8 animals
4 equal groups
8 ÷ 4 = 2, 2 animals

2. 9 birds
3 equal groups
9 ÷ 3 = 3, 3 birds

Divide.

3. 12 ÷ 3 = 4 **4.** 2 ÷ 2 = 1 **5.** 14 ÷ 2 = 7

6. 18 ÷ 3 = 6 **7.** 12 ÷ 2 = 6 **8.** 27 ÷ 3 = 9

9. 21 ÷ 3 = 7 **10.** 18 ÷ 2 = 9 **11.** 10 ÷ 2 = 5

12. 16 ÷ 2 = 8 **13.** 15 ÷ 3 = 5 **14.** 6 ÷ 3 = 2

15. 2)6 = 3 **16.** 3)24 = 8 **17.** 3)18 = 6 **18.** 3)27 = 9

Review and Remember

Add, subtract, or multiply.

1. 23 + 41 = 64 **2.** 12 + 23 = 35 **3.** 16 + 33 = 49 **4.** 45 + 34 = 79

5. 35 − 12 = 23 **6.** 67 − 43 = 24 **7.** 89 − 25 = 64 **8.** 93 − 71 = 22

9. 6 × 2 = 12 **10.** 5 × 3 = 15 **11.** 8 × 2 = 16 **12.** 9 × 3 = 27

Practice Workbook

Two-Step Problems

Read each problem and solve.

1. Jean had $5.00. She spent $2.25 in one store and $1.30 in another store. How much money does she have left? **$1.45**

2. Frank, Sal, and Travis were in a 500 m relay race. Frank ran 150 m, Sal ran 175 m. How far did Travis run? **175 m**

3. Cindy picked 3 bunches of flowers. Each bunch had 6 flowers. She gave 1 bunch of flowers to her mother. How many flowers does Cindy have left? **12 flowers**

4. Lisa's sister baby-sat for the Johnsons for 3 hours. She then baby-sat for the Millers for 2 hours. She was paid $2 an hour for baby-sitting. How much money was Lisa's sister paid? **$10**

5. Marie read 21 pages in her book before lunch. She read 17 pages after lunch. Tommy read 32 pages after lunch. How many more pages did Marie read than Tommy? **6 pages**

Review and Remember

Solve.

1. Marsha read 175 pages. The book has 202 pages. How many pages does Marsha have left to read? **27 pages**

2. There are 124 pages in a book, 216 in another, and 439 in another. How many pages in all are in the 3 books? **779 pages**

Chapter 8

Practice Workbook

Using 4 and 5 as Divisors

Divide.

1. 8 ÷ 4 = 2 **2.** 12 ÷ 4 = 3 **3.** 4 ÷ 4 = 1

4. 16 ÷ 4 = 4 **5.** 10 ÷ 5 = 2 **6.** 25 ÷ 5 = 5

7. 24 ÷ 4 = 6 **8.** 36 ÷ 4 = 9 **9.** 15 ÷ 5 = 3

10. 36 ÷ 4 = 9 **11.** 45 ÷ 5 = 9 **12.** 40 ÷ 5 = 8

Complete. Follow each rule.

Rule: Divide by 5

	Input	Output
13.	5	1
14.	10	2
15.	15	3
16.	20	4

Rule: Divide by 4

	Input	Output
17.	4	1
18.	12	3
19.	16	4
20.	28	7

Review and Remember

Add, subtract, or multiply.

1. 27 + 17 = 44 **2.** 15 + 26 = 41 **3.** 71 − 19 = 52 **4.** 63 − 34 = 29

5. 7 × 4 = 28 **6.** 3 × 4 = 12 **7.** 9 × 4 = 36 **8.** 6 × 4 = 24

9. 13 + 27 = 40 **10.** 35 + 19 = 54 **11.** 84 − 56 = 28 **12.** 72 − 39 = 33

Practice Workbook

Using 0 and 1 in Division

Find each quotient.

1. 5 ÷ 5 = 1 **2.** 0 ÷ 5 = 0 **3.** 9 ÷ 9 = 1

4. 6 ÷ 1 = 6 **5.** 8 ÷ 1 = 8 **6.** 2 ÷ 1 = 2

7. 0 ÷ 3 = 0 **8.** 0 ÷ 5 = 0 **9.** 0 ÷ 7 = 0

10. 6 ÷ 6 = 1 **11.** 0 ÷ 8 = 0 **12.** 5 ÷ 1 = 5

13. 4)0 = 0 **14.** 7)7 = 1 **15.** 1)3 = 3 **16.** 4)4 = 1

Solve.

17. Vanessa has 6 pictures. She pastes 6 pictures on each poster. How many posters can she make? **1 poster**

18. Mark made 4 birthday cards. He put 1 in each envelope. How many envelopes did he have? **4 envelopes**

Review and Remember

Add, subtract, or multiply. Use mental math or paper and pencil.

1. 31 + 82 = 113 **2.** 71 + 63 = 134 **3.** 80 + 94 = 174 **4.** 36 + 72 = 108

5. 478 − 312 = 166 **6.** 894 − 123 = 771 **7.** 675 − 461 = 214 **8.** 549 − 123 = 426

9. 8 × 5 = 40 **10.** 6 × 5 = 30 **11.** 9 × 5 = 45 **12.** 3 × 5 = 15

Chapter 9

Practice Workbook

Dividing by 6

Complete each sentence. Multiply or divide.

1. 6 × [4] = 24   24 ÷ 6 = [4]
2. 6 × [8] = 48   48 ÷ 6 = [8]
3. 6 × [0] = 0   0 ÷ 6 = [0]
4. 6 × [3] = 18   18 ÷ 6 = [3]
5. 6 × [6] = 36   36 ÷ 6 = [6]
6. 5 × [4] = 20   20 ÷ 5 = [4]
7. 6 × [2] = 12   12 ÷ 6 = [2]
8. 3 × [8] = 24   24 ÷ 3 = [8]

Divide.

9. 6)48 — 8   10. 6)24 — 4   11. 4)36 — 9   12. 6)30 — 5   13. 6)12 — 2

14. 6)6 — 1   15. 2)6 — 3   16. 6)42 — 7   17. 3)24 — 8   18. 6)54 — 9

19. 3)18 — 6   20. 6)0 — 0   21. 4)32 — 8   22. 6)18 — 3   23. 6)36 — 6

24. 48 ÷ 6 = [8]   25. 6 ÷ [6] = 1   26. [24] ÷ 6 = 4   27. [18] ÷ 6 = 3

28. 54 ÷ 6 = [9]   29. 18 ÷ [6] = 3   30. [42] ÷ 6 = 7   31. [30] ÷ 5 = 6

32. 12 ÷ [6] = 2   33. 24 ÷ [4] = 6   34. 6 ÷ [1] = 6   35. [36] ÷ 6 = 6

Review and Remember

Add or subtract.

1. 345 + 534 = 879
2. 198 + 764 = 962
3. 549 + 429 = 978
4. 397 − 218 = 179
5. 617 − 338 = 279
6. 645 − 223 = 422

Practice Workbook

Using 8 and 9 as Divisors

Find each quotient.

1. 8)32 — 4   2. 8)48 — 6   3. 9)27 — 3   4. 9)45 — 5

5. 9)81 — 9   6. 8)72 — 9   7. 9)54 — 6   8. 8)24 — 3

9. 8)0 — 0   10. 8)40 — 5   11. 9)18 — 2   12. 9)63 — 7

13. 9)9 — 1   14. 9)0 — 0   15. 8)64 — 8   16. 8)56 — 7

17. 36 ÷ 9 = 4   18. 32 ÷ 8 = 4   19. 45 ÷ 9 = 5   20. 8 ÷ 8 = 1

21. 24 ÷ 8 = 3   22. 27 ÷ 9 = 3   23. 9 ÷ 9 = 1   24. 18 ÷ 9 = 2

Circle the letter of the correct number sentence. Then solve the problem.

25. There were 48 chairs in the classroom. There were 8 equal rows of chairs. How many chairs were in each row?

6 chairs

a. 48 + 8 = □
b. 48 − 8 = □
c. 48 × 8 = □
(d.) 48 ÷ 8 = □

Review and Remember

Multiply or divide.

1. 6 × 7 = 42   2. 4 × 8 = 32   3. 7 × 3 = 21

4. 25 ÷ 5 = 5   5. 7 ÷ 7 = 1   6. 14 ÷ 2 = 7

7. 6 × 3 = 18   8. 2 × 8 = 16   9. 9 × 7 = 63   10. 7 × 8 = 56

Chapter 9

Practice Workbook

Multiplication and Division Facts

Complete each fact family.

1. 7 × 2 = 14   2 × 7 = 14   14 ÷ 2 = 7   14 ÷ 7 = 2
2. 4 × 3 = 12   3 × 4 = 12   12 ÷ 4 = 3   12 ÷ 3 = 4
3. 5 × 8 = 40   8 × 5 = 40   40 ÷ 8 = 5   40 ÷ 5 = 8

Give the other facts in each family.

4. 6 × 8 = 48   8 × 6 = 48   48 ÷ 8 = 6   48 ÷ 6 = 8
5. 8 × 3 = 24   3 × 8 = 24   24 ÷ 3 = 8   24 ÷ 8 = 3
6. 4 × 7 = 28   7 × 4 = 28   28 ÷ 7 = 4   28 ÷ 4 = 7

Find the missing number.

7. 7 × 0 = 0   8. 45 ÷ 9 = 5   9. 6 × 4 = 24

10. 8 × 1 = 8   11. 9 ÷ 1 = 9   12. 8 × 2 = 16

13. 5 × 5 = 25   14. 24 ÷ 4 = 6   15. 5 × 3 = 15

16. 3 × 2 = 6   17. 18 ÷ 2 = 9   18. 4 × 3 = 12

Review and Remember

Add or subtract.

1. 87 + 53 = 140
2. 97 + 66 = 163
3. 67 + 54 = 121
4. 87 + 49 = 136
5. 317 − 125 = 192
6. 252 − 161 = 91
7. 348 − 119 = 229
8. 246 − 158 = 88

Practice Workbook

Division Practice

Divide.

1. 2)14 — 7   2. 2)18 — 9   3. 3)24 — 8   4. 3)22 — 7 R1   5. 4)20 — 5   6. 4)32 — 8

7. 5)35 — 7   8. 5)45 — 9   9. 6)0 — 0   10. 7)0 — 0   11. 1)9 — 9   12. 1)3 — 3

13. 6)24 — 4   14. 6)54 — 9   15. 6)19 — 3 R1   16. 7)49 — 7   17. 7)42 — 6   18. 7)63 — 9

Complete each fact family.

19. 7 × 5 = 35   5 × 7 = 35   35 ÷ 7 = 5   35 ÷ 5 = 7
20. 8 × 6 = 48   6 × 8 = 48   48 ÷ 8 = 6   48 ÷ 6 = 8
21. 9 × 8 = 72   8 × 9 = 72   72 ÷ 9 = 8   72 ÷ 8 = 9
22. 6 × 4 = 24   4 × 6 = 24   24 ÷ 6 = 4   24 ÷ 4 = 6
23. 6 × 7 = 42   7 × 6 = 42   42 ÷ 6 = 7   42 ÷ 7 = 6
24. 8 × 5 = 40   5 × 8 = 40   40 ÷ 8 = 5   40 ÷ 5 = 8

Review and Remember

Add or subtract.

1. 341 + 232 = 573
2. 172 + 413 = 585
3. 300 + 161 = 461
4. 401 + 183 = 584
5. 310 − 140 = 170
6. 701 − 451 = 250
7. 600 − 361 = 239
8. 810 − 643 = 167

Chapter 9

Practice Workbook

Using Operations

Library
Opens 7:50 A.M. Closes 3:45 P.M.
Return books by 3:30 P.M.

Bookstore
Opens 8:00 A.M. Closes 4:00 P.M.

Math book	$3.95
Science book	$3.95
Notebook	$0.39
Pencil	$0.25
Pen	$0.17

Cross out any extra information. Use the signs to solve.

1. Connie has $5. Can she buy a new math book and a pencil? **yes**
2. Jeremy arrived at school at 7:45 A.M. How long will he have to wait for the library to open? **5 minutes**
3. Mrs. Petrie works in the bookstore from the time it opens until it closes. ~~Miss Galen works in the cafeteria.~~ How long does Mrs. Petrie work each day if she has a 30 minute lunch? **7½ hours**
4. Timmy had 60¢. He bought 2 items at the bookstore. What items could he buy? **pen and notebook or pen and pencil**
5. Emily begins putting books on the shelves at 3:30. Emily can put 2 books on shelves every minute. How many books will Emily put on the shelves by the time the library closes? **30 books**

Review and Remember

Multiply.

1. 8 × 4 = **32**
2. 5 × 7 = **35**
3. 4 × 3 = **12**
4. 9 × 8 = **72**
5. 7 × 6 = **42**
6. 6 × 3 = **18**
7. 0 × 5 = **0**
8. 5 × 9 = **45**
9. 6 × 6 = **36**

Chapter 10

Practice Workbook

Name Plane Figures

Name each plane figure.

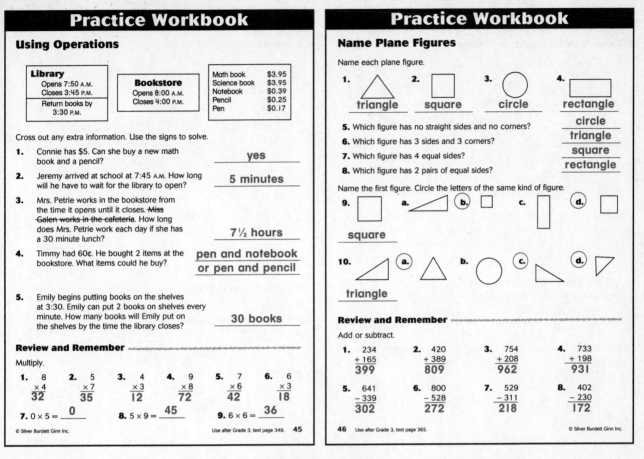

1. **triangle**
2. **square**
3. **circle**
4. **rectangle**

5. Which figure has no straight sides and no corners? **circle**
6. Which figure has 3 sides and 3 corners? **triangle**
7. Which figure has 4 equal sides? **square**
8. Which figure has 2 pairs of equal sides? **rectangle**

Name the first figure. Circle the letters of the same kind of figure.

9. **square** — a. b. (circled) c. d. (circled)
10. **triangle** — a. (circled) b. c. (circled) d. (circled)

Review and Remember

Add or subtract.

1. 234 + 165 = **399**
2. 420 + 389 = **809**
3. 754 + 208 = **962**
4. 733 + 198 = **931**
5. 641 − 339 = **302**
6. 800 − 528 = **272**
7. 529 − 311 = **218**
8. 402 − 230 = **172**

Chapter 10

Practice Workbook

Lines, Line Segments, Rays, and Right Angles

Name each figure.

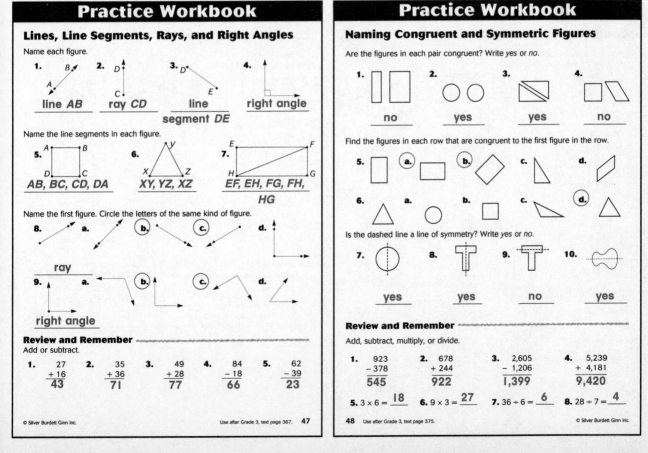

1. **line *AB***
2. **ray *CD***
3. **line segment *DE***
4. **right angle**

Name the line segments in each figure.

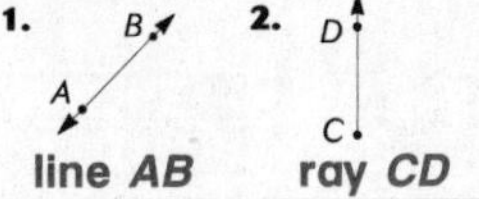

5. ***AB, BC, CD, DA***

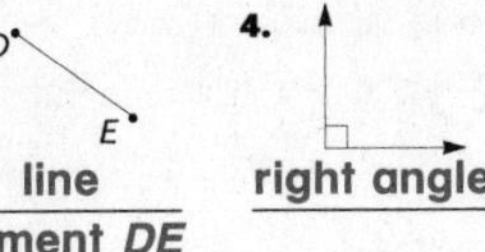

6. ***XY, YZ, XZ***

7. ***EF, EH, FG, FH, HG***

Name the first figure. Circle the letters of the same kind of figure.

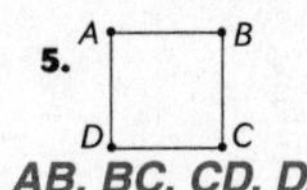

8. **ray** — a. b. (circled) c. (circled) d.

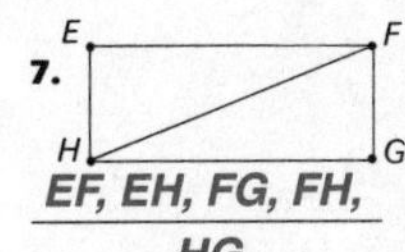

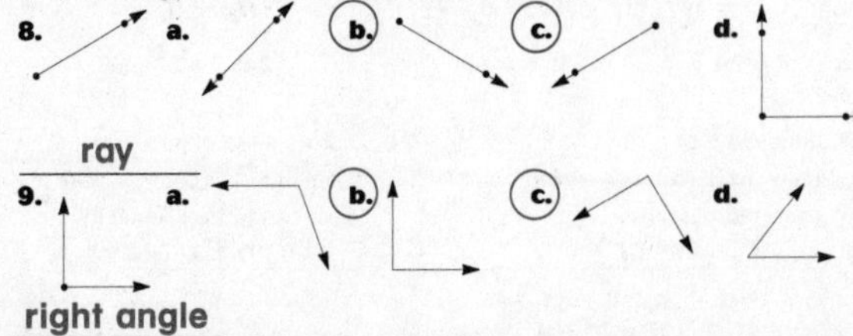

9. **right angle** — a. b. (circled) c. (circled) d.

Review and Remember

Add or subtract.

1. 27 + 16 = **43**
2. 35 + 36 = **71**
3. 49 + 28 = **77**
4. 84 − 18 = **66**
5. 62 − 39 = **23**

Practice Workbook

Naming Congruent and Symmetric Figures

Are the figures in each pair congruent? Write *yes* or *no*.

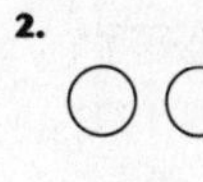

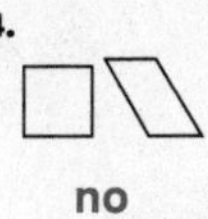

1. **no**
2. **yes**
3. **yes**
4. **no**

Find the figures in each row that are congruent to the first figure in the row.

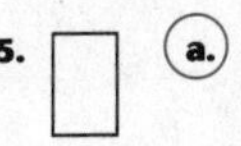
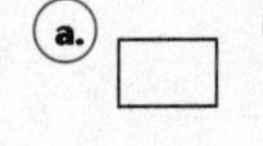
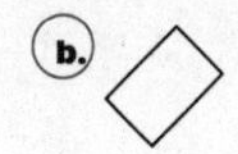
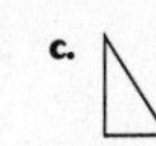
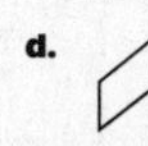

5. a. (circled) b. (circled) c. d.

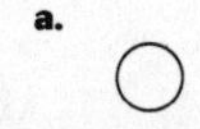
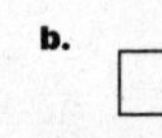
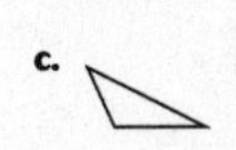
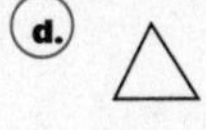

6. a. b. c. d. (circled)

Is the dashed line a line of symmetry? Write *yes* or *no*.

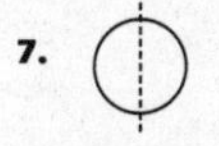

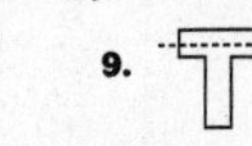
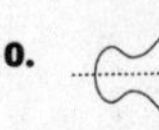

7. **yes**
8. **yes**
9. **no**
10. **yes**

Review and Remember

Add, subtract, multiply, or divide.

1. 923 − 378 = **545**
2. 678 + 244 = **922**
3. 2,605 − 1,206 = **1,399**
4. 5,239 + 4,181 = **9,420**
5. 3 × 6 = **18**
6. 9 × 3 = **27**
7. 36 ÷ 6 = **6**
8. 28 ÷ 7 = **4**

Chapter 10

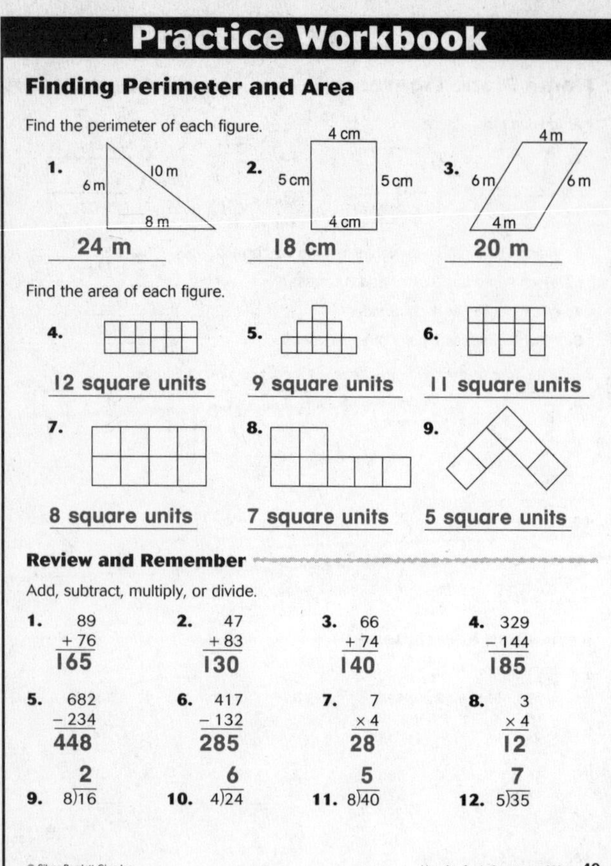

Practice Workbook

Finding Perimeter and Area

Find the perimeter of each figure.

1. 6 m, 10 m, 8 m — **24 m**
2. 4 cm, 5 cm, 5 cm, 4 cm — **18 cm**
3. 4 m, 6 m, 6 m, 4 m — **20 m**

Find the area of each figure.

4. **12 square units**
5. **9 square units**
6. **11 square units**
7. **8 square units**
8. **7 square units**
9. **5 square units**

Review and Remember

Add, subtract, multiply, or divide.

1. 89 + 76 = **165**
2. 47 + 83 = **130**
3. 66 + 74 = **140**
4. 329 − 144 = **185**
5. 682 − 234 = **448**
6. 417 − 132 = **285**
7. 7 × 4 = **28**
8. 3 × 4 = **12**
9. 8)16 = **2**
10. 4)24 = **6**
11. 8)40 = **5**
12. 5)35 = **7**

 Use after Grade 3, text page 383. 49

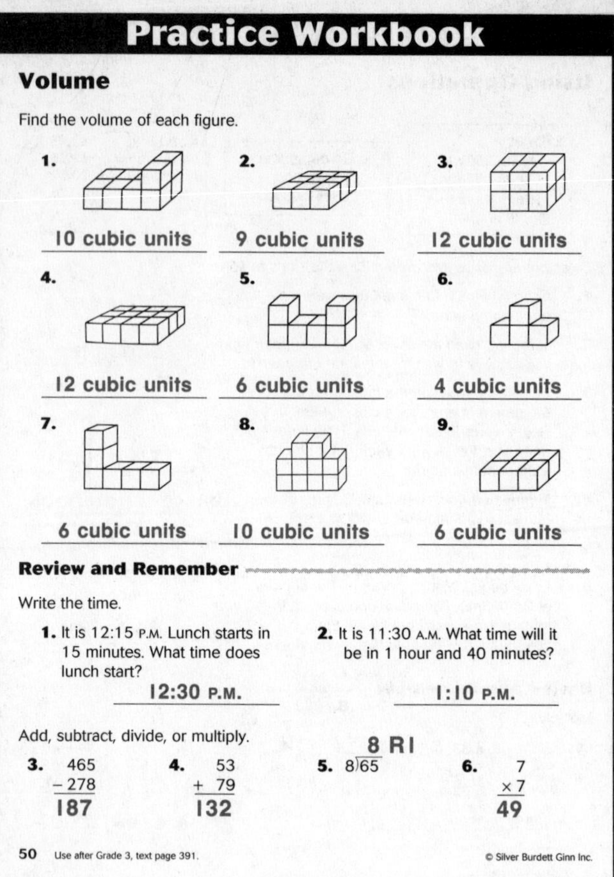

Practice Workbook

Volume

Find the volume of each figure.

1. **10 cubic units**
2. **9 cubic units**
3. **12 cubic units**
4. **12 cubic units**
5. **6 cubic units**
6. **4 cubic units**
7. **6 cubic units**
8. **10 cubic units**
9. **6 cubic units**

Review and Remember

Write the time.

1. It is 12:15 P.M. Lunch starts in 15 minutes. What time does lunch start? **12:30 P.M.**
2. It is 11:30 A.M. What time will it be in 1 hour and 40 minutes? **1:10 P.M.**

Add, subtract, divide, or multiply.

3. 465 − 278 = **187**
4. 53 + 79 = **132**
5. 8)65 = **8 R1**
6. 7 × 7 = **49**

50 Use after Grade 3, text page 391.

Chapter 11

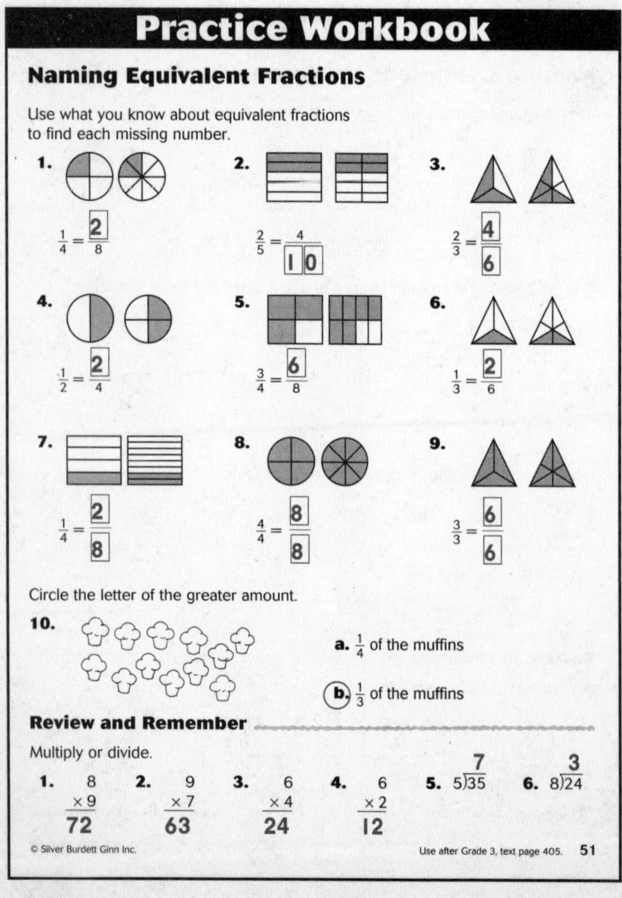

Practice Workbook

Naming Equivalent Fractions

Use what you know about equivalent fractions to find each missing number.

1. $\frac{1}{4} = \frac{\boxed{2}}{8}$
2. $\frac{2}{5} = \frac{4}{\boxed{10}}$
3. $\frac{2}{3} = \frac{\boxed{4}}{\boxed{6}}$
4. $\frac{1}{2} = \frac{\boxed{2}}{4}$
5. $\frac{3}{4} = \frac{\boxed{6}}{8}$
6. $\frac{1}{3} = \frac{\boxed{2}}{6}$
7. $\frac{1}{4} = \frac{\boxed{2}}{\boxed{8}}$
8. $\frac{4}{4} = \frac{\boxed{8}}{\boxed{8}}$
9. $\frac{3}{3} = \frac{\boxed{6}}{\boxed{6}}$

Circle the letter of the greater amount.

10. a. $\frac{1}{4}$ of the muffins
(b.) $\frac{1}{3}$ of the muffins

Review and Remember

Multiply or divide.

1. 8 × 9 = **72**
2. 9 × 7 = **63**
3. 6 × 4 = **24**
4. 6 × 2 = **12**
5. 5)35 = **7**
6. 8)24 = **3**

 Use after Grade 3, text page 405. 51

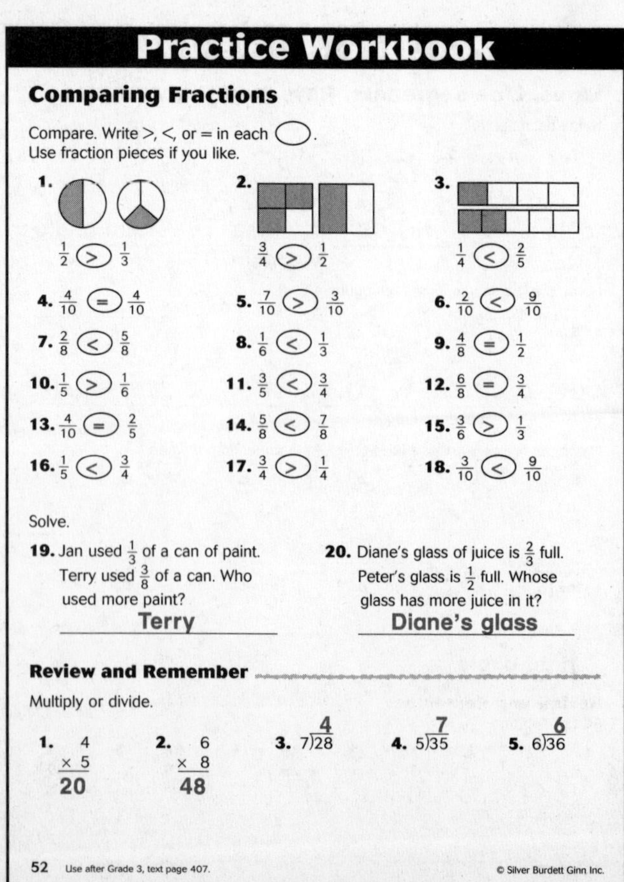

Practice Workbook

Comparing Fractions

Compare. Write >, <, or = in each ◯. Use fraction pieces if you like.

1. $\frac{1}{2}$ (>) $\frac{1}{3}$
2. $\frac{3}{4}$ (>) $\frac{1}{2}$
3. $\frac{1}{4}$ (<) $\frac{2}{5}$
4. $\frac{4}{10}$ (=) $\frac{4}{10}$
5. $\frac{7}{10}$ (>) $\frac{3}{10}$
6. $\frac{2}{10}$ (<) $\frac{9}{10}$
7. $\frac{2}{8}$ (<) $\frac{5}{8}$
8. $\frac{1}{6}$ (<) $\frac{1}{3}$
9. $\frac{4}{8}$ (=) $\frac{1}{2}$
10. $\frac{1}{5}$ (>) $\frac{1}{6}$
11. $\frac{3}{5}$ (<) $\frac{3}{4}$
12. $\frac{6}{8}$ (=) $\frac{3}{4}$
13. $\frac{4}{10}$ (=) $\frac{2}{5}$
14. $\frac{5}{8}$ (<) $\frac{7}{8}$
15. $\frac{3}{6}$ (>) $\frac{1}{3}$
16. $\frac{1}{5}$ (<) $\frac{3}{4}$
17. $\frac{3}{4}$ (>) $\frac{1}{4}$
18. $\frac{3}{10}$ (<) $\frac{9}{10}$

Solve.

19. Jan used $\frac{1}{3}$ of a can of paint. Terry used $\frac{3}{8}$ of a can. Who used more paint? **Terry**
20. Diane's glass of juice is $\frac{2}{3}$ full. Peter's glass is $\frac{1}{2}$ full. Whose glass has more juice in it? **Diane's glass**

Review and Remember

Multiply or divide.

1. 4 × 5 = **20**
2. 6 × 8 = **48**
3. 7)28 = **4**
4. 5)35 = **7**
5. 6)36 = **6**

52 Use after Grade 3, text page 407.

Chapter 11

Practice Workbook

Finding Fractional Parts

Complete.

1. $\frac{1}{2}$ of 6 = **3**
2. $\frac{1}{3}$ of 9 = **3**
3. $\frac{1}{2}$ of 2 = **1**
4. $\frac{1}{8}$ of 64 = **8**
5. $\frac{1}{5}$ of 10 = **2**
6. $\frac{1}{9}$ of 81 = **9**
7. $\frac{1}{7}$ of 21 = **3**
8. $\frac{1}{4}$ of 24 = **6**
9. $\frac{1}{6}$ of 18 = **3**
10. $\frac{1}{8}$ of 56 = **7**
11. $\frac{1}{2}$ of 14 = **7**
12. $\frac{1}{3}$ of 24 = **8**
13. $\frac{1}{6}$ of 30 = **5**
14. $\frac{1}{5}$ of 25 = **5**
15. $\frac{1}{7}$ of 49 = **7**
16. $\frac{1}{4}$ of 32 = **8**
17. $\frac{1}{2}$ of 18 = **9**
18. $\frac{1}{6}$ of 6 = **1**

Solve.

19. There are 72 students in the band and $\frac{1}{9}$ of them are third-graders. How many students are third-graders? **8 students**

20. Fourth-graders make up $\frac{1}{8}$ of the band. How many students are fourth-graders? **9 students**

Review and Remember

Multiply, divide, or add.

1. 7 × 3 = **21**
2. 8 × 5 = **40**
3. 6 × 0 = **0**
4. 5 × 3 = **15**
5. 1 × 8 = **8**
6. $7\overline{)49}$ **7**
7. $8\overline{)24}$ **3**
8. $4\overline{)16}$ **4**
9. $8\overline{)40}$ **5**
10. $9\overline{)63}$ **7**
11. 24 + 69 + 33 **126**
12. 15 + 92 + 47 **154**

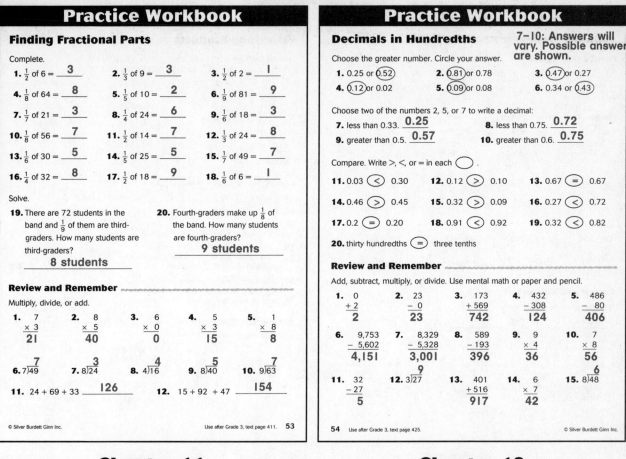

Practice Workbook

Decimals in Hundredths

7–10: Answers will vary. Possible answers are shown.

Choose the greater number. Circle your answer.

1. 0.25 or (0.52)
2. (0.81) or 0.78
3. (0.47) or 0.27
4. (0.12) or 0.02
5. (0.09) or 0.08
6. 0.34 or (0.43)

Choose two of the numbers 2, 5, or 7 to write a decimal:

7. less than 0.33. **0.25**
8. less than 0.75. **0.72**
9. greater than 0.5. **0.57**
10. greater than 0.6. **0.75**

Compare. Write >, <, or = in each ◯.

11. 0.03 (<) 0.30
12. 0.12 (>) 0.10
13. 0.67 (=) 0.67
14. 0.46 (>) 0.45
15. 0.32 (>) 0.09
16. 0.27 (<) 0.72
17. 0.2 (=) 0.20
18. 0.91 (<) 0.92
19. 0.32 (<) 0.82
20. thirty hundredths (=) three tenths

Review and Remember

Add, subtract, multiply, or divide. Use mental math or paper and pencil.

1. 0 + 2 = **2**
2. 23 − 0 = **23**
3. 173 + 569 = **742**
4. 432 − 308 = **124**
5. 486 − 80 = **406**
6. 9,753 − 5,602 = **4,151**
7. 8,329 − 5,328 = **3,001**
8. 589 − 193 = **396**
9. 9 × 4 = **36**
10. 7 × 8 = **56**
11. 32 − 27 = **5**
12. $3\overline{)27}$ **9**
13. 401 + 516 = **917**
14. 6 × 7 = **42**
15. $8\overline{)48}$ **6**

Chapter 11

Practice Workbook

Reading and Writing Decimals Greater Than 1

Write a decimal for the shaded part.

1. 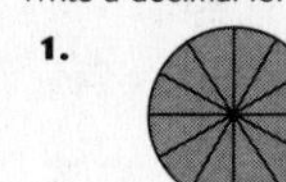 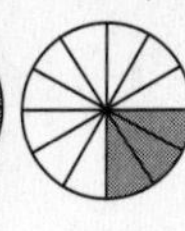 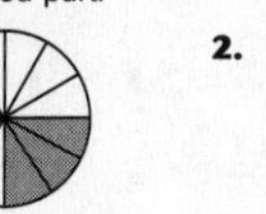 **1.3**

2. 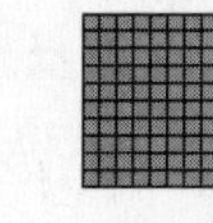 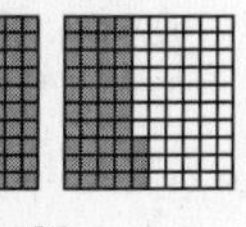 **1.43**

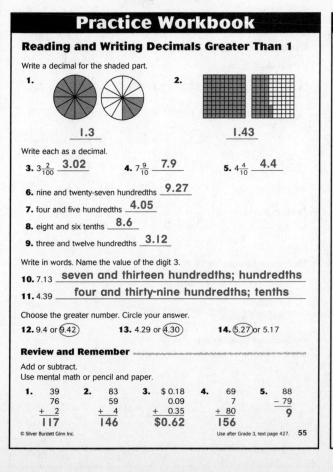

Write each as a decimal.

3. $3\frac{2}{100}$ **3.02**
4. $7\frac{9}{10}$ **7.9**
5. $4\frac{4}{10}$ **4.4**
6. nine and twenty-seven hundredths **9.27**
7. four and five hundredths **4.05**
8. eight and six tenths **8.6**
9. three and twelve hundredths **3.12**

Write in words. Name the value of the digit 3.

10. 7.13 **seven and thirteen hundredths; hundredths**
11. 4.39 **four and thirty-nine hundredths; tenths**

Choose the greater number. Circle your answer.

12. 9.4 or (9.42)
13. 4.29 or (4.30)
14. (5.27) or 5.17

Review and Remember

Add or subtract.
Use mental math or pencil and paper.

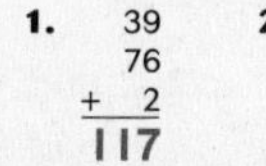 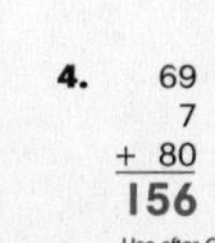

1. 39 + 76 + 2 = **117**
2. 83 + 59 + 4 = **146**
3. \$0.18 + 0.09 + 0.35 = **\$0.62**
4. 69 + 7 + 80 = **156**
5. 88 − 79 = **9**

Chapter 12

Practice Workbook

Multiplying Three-Digit Numbers

Multiply.

1. 222 × 4 = **888**
2. 142 × 2 = **284**
3. 101 × 8 = **808**
4. 103 × 3 = **309**
5. 210 × 3 = **630**
6. 105 × 8 = **840**
7. 106 × 9 = **954**
8. 108 × 7 = **756**
9. 112 × 7 = **784**
10. 115 × 5 = **575**
11. 120 × 6 = **720**
12. 121 × 6 = **726**
13. 140 × 5 = **700**
14. 141 × 5 = **705**
15. 162 × 4 = **648**
16. 412 × 6 = **2,472**
17. 500 × 6 = **3,000**
18. 580 × 4 = **2,320**
19. 900 × 9 = **8,100**
20. 400 × 7 = **2,800**
21. 401 × 4 = **1,604**
22. 517 × 5 = **2,585**
23. 327 × 3 = **981**
24. 202 × 8 = **1,616**
25. 900 × 0 = **0**

Review and Remember

Name each figure.

1. four equal straight sides **square**
2. no straight sides and no corners **circle**
3. three straight sides and three corners **triangle**

4. **ray**

5. **right angle**

6. 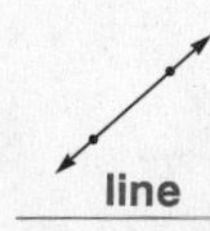 **line**

Chapter 12

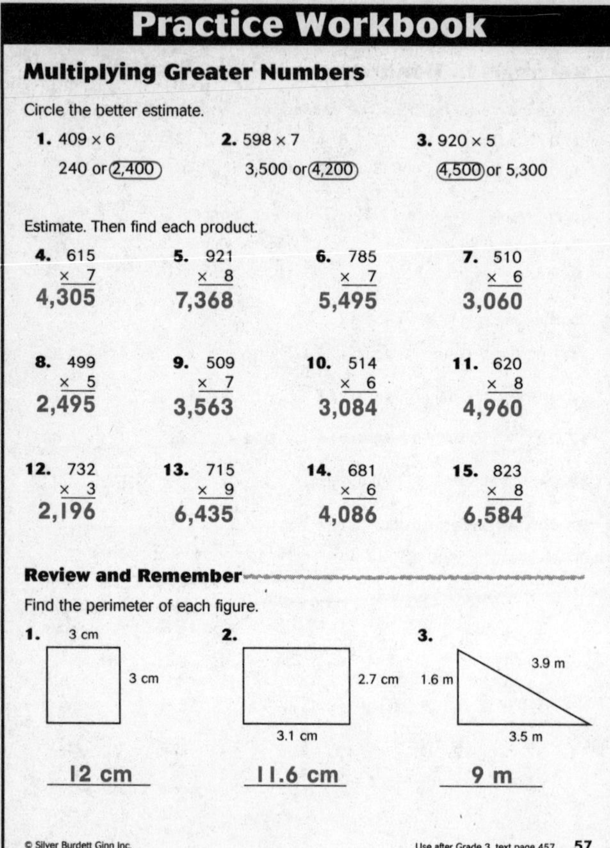

Practice Workbook

Multiplying Greater Numbers

Circle the better estimate.

1. 409 × 6 — 240 or **(2,400)**
2. 598 × 7 — 3,500 or **(4,200)**
3. 920 × 5 — **(4,500)** or 5,300

Estimate. Then find each product.

4. 615 × 7 = **4,305**
5. 921 × 8 = **7,368**
6. 785 × 7 = **5,495**
7. 510 × 6 = **3,060**
8. 499 × 5 = **2,495**
9. 509 × 7 = **3,563**
10. 514 × 6 = **3,084**
11. 620 × 8 = **4,960**
12. 732 × 3 = **2,196**
13. 715 × 9 = **6,435**
14. 681 × 6 = **4,086**
15. 823 × 8 = **6,584**

Review and Remember

Find the perimeter of each figure.

1. **12 cm**
2. **11.6 cm**
3. **9 m**

Practice Workbook

Estimating Products

Estimate each product. **Estimates will vary. Possible answers are shown.**

1. 72 × 3 = **210**
2. 38 × 4 = **160**
3. 93 × 7 = **630**
4. 66 × 3 = **210**
5. 377 × 6 = **2,400**
6. 213 × 8 = **1,600**
7. 623 × 2 = **1,200**
8. 782 × 7 = **5,600**
9. 7 × 78 **560**
10. 5 × 495 **2,500**
11. 3 × 828 **2,400**

Estimate. Write >, <, or = in each ◯.

12. 7 × 38 **(<)** 300
13. 40 × 6 **(=)** 8 × 30
14. 6 × 71 **(>)** 49 × 8
15. 120 × 7 **(>)** 2 × 308

Use estimation to solve. **Estimates will vary.**

16. Lorna is making jewelry. Each necklace has 8 beads. About how many beads does she need to make 27 necklaces? **240** beads
17. Theo has 23 math problems for homework each night. About how many problems does he have in 7 nights? **140** problems

Review and Remember

Add, subtract, or multiply.

1. 6.4 + 2.8 = **9.2**
2. 2.4 − 1.5 = **0.9**
3. 4.7 + 3.7 = **8.4**
4. 3.8 − 2.2 = **1.6**
5. 8 × 6 = **48**
6. 5 × 7 = **35**
7. 6 × 4 = **24**
8. 12 × 0 = **0**

Chapter 12

Practice Workbook

Using Remainders

Find each quotient.

1. 2)16 **8**
2. 5)18 **3 R3**
3. 4)29 **7 R1**
4. 5)27 **5 R2**
5. 6)62 **10 R2**
6. 5)60 **12**
7. 5)86 **17 R1**
8. 4)87 **21 R3**
9. 78 ÷ 7 **11 R1**
10. 84 ÷ 9 **9 R3**
11. 72 ÷ 8 **9**
12. 76 ÷ 5 **15 R1**
13. 95 ÷ 3 **31 R2**
14. 87 ÷ 2 **43 R1**

Compare. Write >, <, or = in each ◯.

15. 90 ÷ 3 **(>)** 90 ÷ 4
16. 38 ÷ 4 **(<)** 29 ÷ 3
17. 96 ÷ 3 **(=)** 16 × 2
18. 47 ÷ 6 **(>)** 53 ÷ 8
19. 31 ÷ 3 **(<)** 43 ÷ 4
20. 50 ÷ 7 **(<)** 60 ÷ 8

Review and Remember

Add, subtract, multiply, or divide.
Use mental math or paper and pencil.

1. 378 + 287 = **665**
2. 429 − 197 = **232**
3. 335 + 479 = **814**
4. 8,674 − 3,012 = **5,662**
5. 72 × 6 = **432**
6. 937 − 258 = **679**
7. 682 + 357 = **1,039**
8. 504 − 375 = **129**
9. 5,682 + 3,241 = **8,923**
10. 59 × 5 = **295**
11. 210 × 0 **0**
12. 9)0 **0**
13. 6)48 **8**
14. 49 ÷ 7 **7**

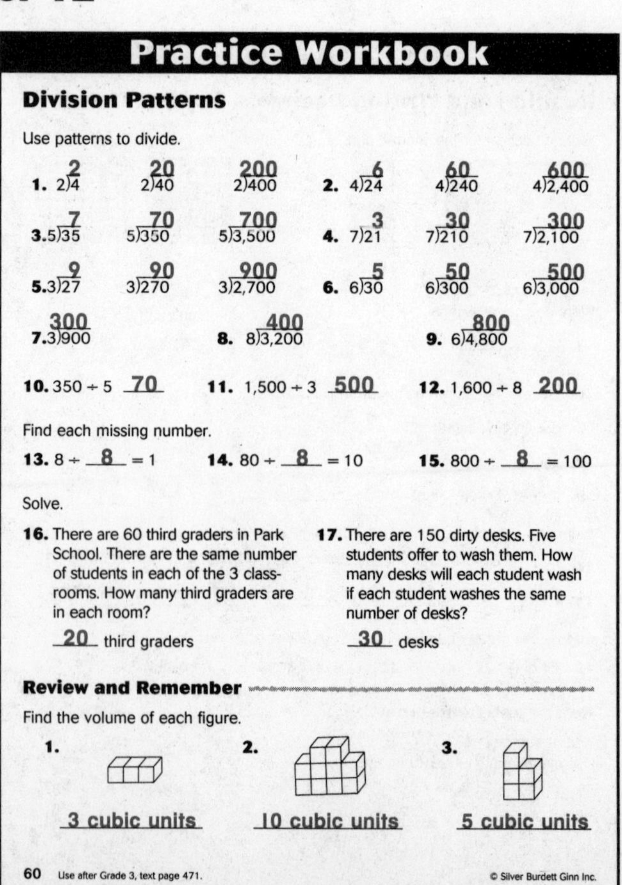

Practice Workbook

Division Patterns

Use patterns to divide.

1. 2)4 **2** 2)40 **20** 2)400 **200**
2. 4)24 **6** 4)240 **60** 4)2,400 **600**
3. 5)35 **7** 5)350 **70** 5)3,500 **700**
4. 7)21 **3** 7)210 **30** 7)2,100 **300**
5. 3)27 **9** 3)270 **90** 3)2,700 **900**
6. 6)30 **5** 6)300 **50** 6)3,000 **500**
7. 3)900 **300**
8. 8)3,200 **400**
9. 6)4,800 **800**
10. 350 ÷ 5 **70**
11. 1,500 ÷ 3 **500**
12. 1,600 ÷ 8 **200**

Find each missing number.

13. 8 ÷ **8** = 1
14. 80 ÷ **8** = 10
15. 800 ÷ **8** = 100

Solve.

16. There are 60 third graders in Park School. There are the same number of students in each of the 3 classrooms. How many third graders are in each room? **20** third graders
17. There are 150 dirty desks. Five students offer to wash them. How many desks will each student wash if each student washes the same number of desks? **30** desks

Review and Remember

Find the volume of each figure.

1. **3 cubic units**
2. **10 cubic units**
3. **5 cubic units**

Chapter 11 • Lesson 12

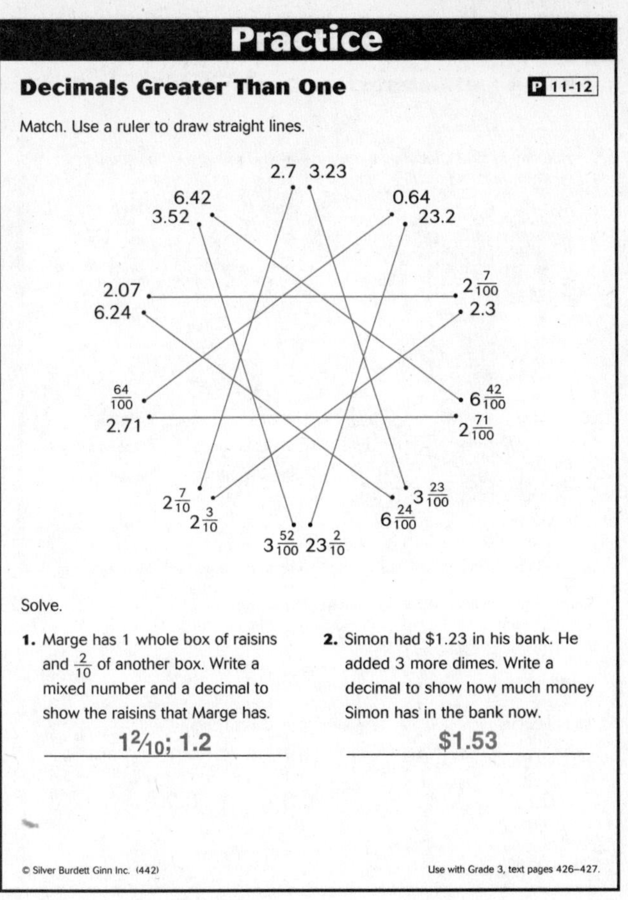

Practice

Decimals Greater Than One

P 11-12

Match. Use a ruler to draw straight lines.

Solve.

1. Marge has 1 whole box of raisins and $\frac{2}{10}$ of another box. Write a mixed number and a decimal to show the raisins that Marge has. **1 2/10; 1.2**

2. Simon had $1.23 in his bank. He added 3 more dimes. Write a decimal to show how much money Simon has in the bank now. **$1.53**

 Use with Grade 3, text pages 426–427.

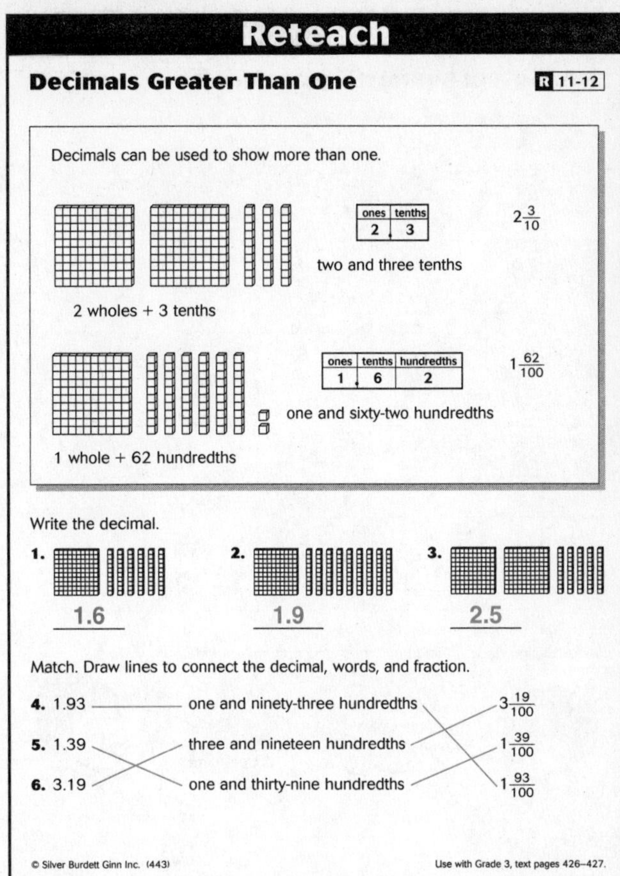

Reteach

Decimals Greater Than One

R 11-12

Decimals can be used to show more than one.

ones	tenths
2 .	3

$2\frac{3}{10}$

two and three tenths

2 wholes + 3 tenths

ones	tenths	hundredths
1 .	6	2

$1\frac{62}{100}$

one and sixty-two hundredths

1 whole + 62 hundredths

Write the decimal.

1. 1.6
2. 1.9
3. 2.5

Match. Draw lines to connect the decimal, words, and fraction.

4. 1.93 — one and ninety-three hundredths — $3\frac{19}{100}$
5. 1.39 — three and nineteen hundredths — $1\frac{39}{100}$
6. 3.19 — one and thirty-nine hundredths — $1\frac{93}{100}$

 Use with Grade 3, text pages 426–427.

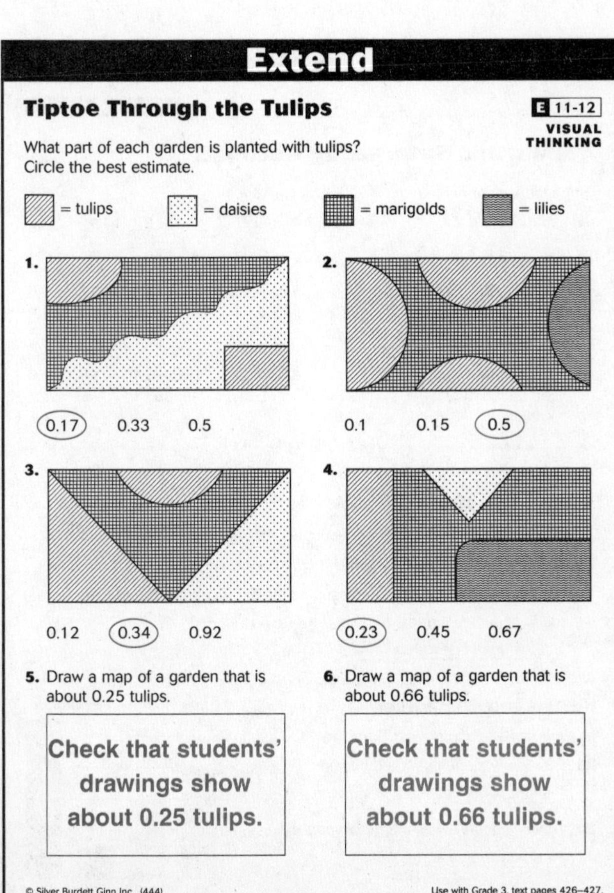

Extend

Tiptoe Through the Tulips

E 11-12 VISUAL THINKING

What part of each garden is planted with tulips? Circle the best estimate.

= tulips = daisies = marigolds = lilies

1. (0.17) 0.33 0.5
2. 0.1 0.15 (0.5)
3. 0.12 (0.34) 0.92
4. (0.23) 0.45 0.67

5. Draw a map of a garden that is about 0.25 tulips.

Check that students' drawings show about 0.25 tulips.

6. Draw a map of a garden that is about 0.66 tulips.

Check that students' drawings show about 0.66 tulips.

 Use with Grade 3, text pages 426–427.

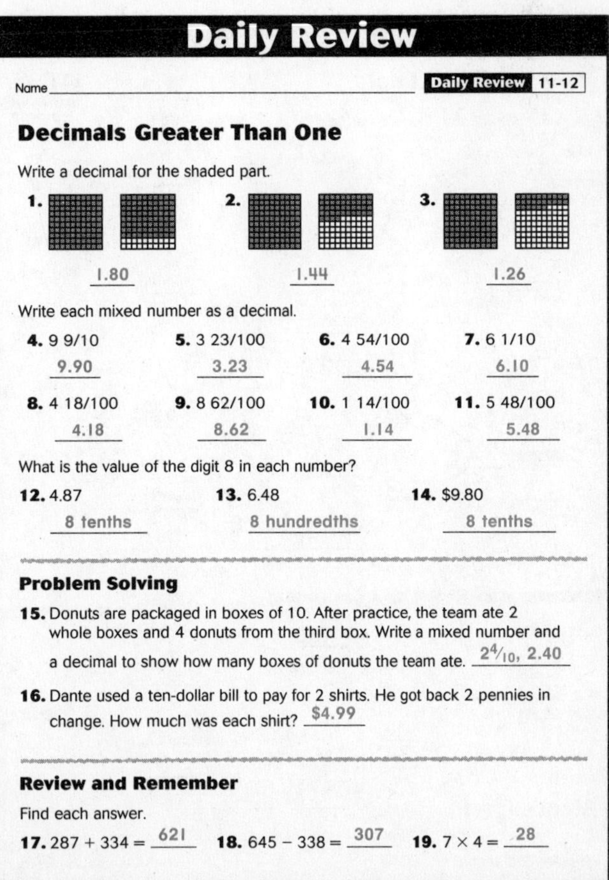

Daily Review

Name ________ Daily Review 11-12

Decimals Greater Than One

Write a decimal for the shaded part.

1. 1.80
2. 1.44
3. 1.26

Write each mixed number as a decimal.

4. 9 9/10 — 9.90
5. 3 23/100 — 3.23
6. 4 54/100 — 4.54
7. 6 1/10 — 6.10
8. 4 18/100 — 4.18
9. 8 62/100 — 8.62
10. 1 14/100 — 1.14
11. 5 48/100 — 5.48

What is the value of the digit 8 in each number?

12. 4.87 — 8 tenths
13. 6.48 — 8 hundredths
14. $9.80 — 8 tenths

Problem Solving

15. Donuts are packaged in boxes of 10. After practice, the team ate 2 whole boxes and 4 donuts from the third box. Write a mixed number and a decimal to show how many boxes of donuts the team ate. 2 4/10, 2.40

16. Dante used a ten-dollar bill to pay for 2 shirts. He got back 2 pennies in change. How much was each shirt? $4.99

Review and Remember

Find each answer.

17. 287 + 334 = 621
18. 645 − 338 = 307
19. 7 × 4 = 28

Chapter 11 • Lesson 13

Practice

Adding and Subtracting Decimals

P 11-13

Find each sum or difference. Shade the section if you need to regroup.

1. 0.2 + 0.3 = **0.5**	2. 0.4 + 0.7 = **1.1**	3. 0.9 + 1.4 = **2.3**	4. 1.8 + 0.7 = **2.5**	5. 3.2 + 2.1 = **5.3**
6. 1.2 − 0.9 = **0.3**	7. 2.4 − 1.3 = **1.1**	8. 3.5 − 1.8 = **1.7**	9. 3.6 − 1.2 = **2.4**	10. 4.7 − 2.8 = **1.9**
11. 4.3 − 1.4 = **2.9**	12. 5.2 − 3.6 = **1.6**	13. 6.8 − 2.6 = **4.2**	14. 2.4 + 5.7 = **8.1**	15. 4.7 + 2.7 = **7.4**
16. 1.5 − 0.9 = **0.6**	17. 8.9 − 5.4 = **3.5**	18. 8.1 − 5.9 = **2.2**	19. 2.4 + 5.4 = **7.8**	20. 4.7 + 2.7 = **7.4**
21. 3.5 − 1.4 = **2.1**	22. 5.4 − 1.7 = **3.7**	23. 2.0 − 1.2 = **0.8**	24. 3.2 − 1.9 = **1.3**	25. 6.6 − 2.6 = **4.0**

What design do you find in the unshaded section? **the letter X**

What do you get if you draw part of an animal?
A decianimal!

 Use with Grade 3, text pages 428–431.

Reteach

Adding and Subtracting Decimals

R 11-13

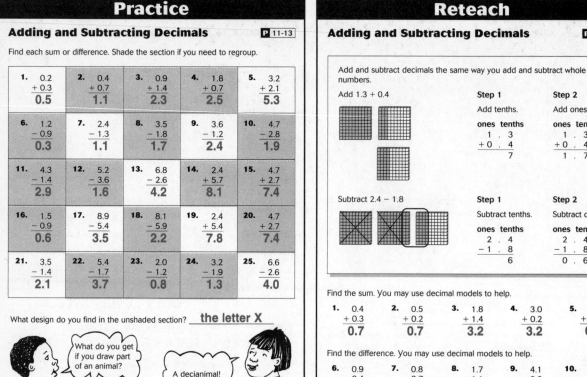

Add and subtract decimals the same way you add and subtract whole numbers.

Add 1.3 + 0.4

Step 1 Add tenths.

ones	.	tenths
1	.	3
+0	.	4
		7

Step 2 Add ones.

ones	.	tenths
1	.	3
+0	.	4
1	.	7

Subtract 2.4 − 1.8

Step 1 Subtract tenths.

ones	.	tenths
2	.	4
−1	.	8
		6

Step 2 Subtract ones.

ones	.	tenths
2	.	4
−1	.	8
0	.	6

Find the sum. You may use decimal models to help.

1. 0.4 + 0.3 = **0.7**
2. 0.5 + 0.2 = **0.7**
3. 1.8 + 1.4 = **3.2**
4. 3.0 + 0.2 = **3.2**
5. 3.5 + 2.6 = **6.1**

Find the difference. You may use decimal models to help.

6. 0.9 − 0.4 = **0.5**
7. 0.8 − 0.7 = **0.1**
8. 1.7 − 1.1 = **0.6**
9. 4.1 − 3.2 = **0.9**
10. 6.7 − 3.4 = **3.3**

 Use with Grade 3, text pages 428–431.

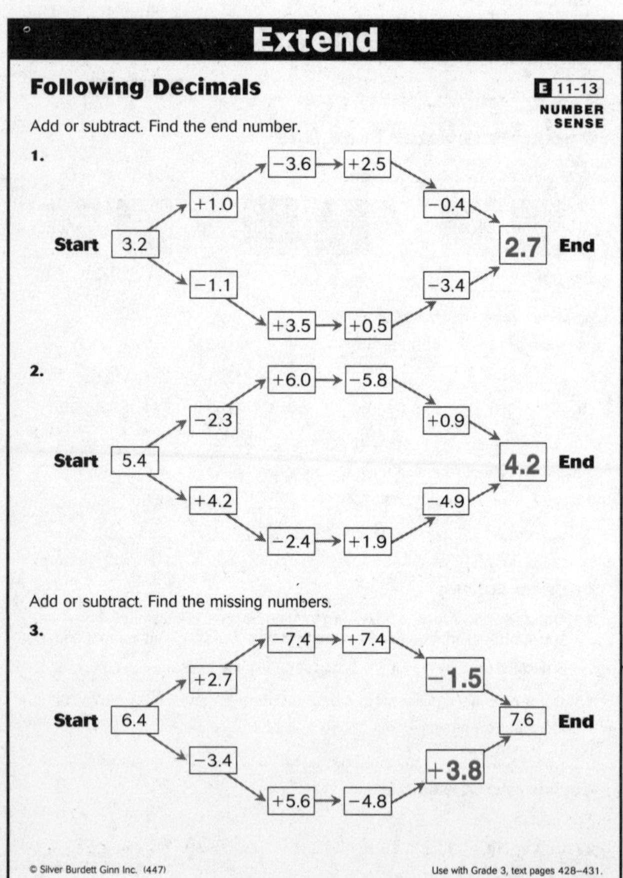

Extend

Following Decimals

E 11-13 NUMBER SENSE

Add or subtract. Find the end number.

1. Start 3.2 → +1.0 → −3.6 → +2.5 → −0.4 → End **2.7**; Start 3.2 → −1.1 → +3.5 → +0.5 → −3.4 → End **2.7**

2. Start 5.4 → −2.3 → +6.0 → −5.8 → +0.9 → End **4.2**; Start 5.4 → +4.2 → −2.4 → +1.9 → −4.9 → End **4.2**

Add or subtract. Find the missing numbers.

3. Start 6.4 → +2.7 → −7.4 → +7.4 → **−1.5** → End 7.6; Start 6.4 → −3.4 → +5.6 → −4.8 → **+3.8** → End 7.6

 Use with Grade 3, text pages 428–431.

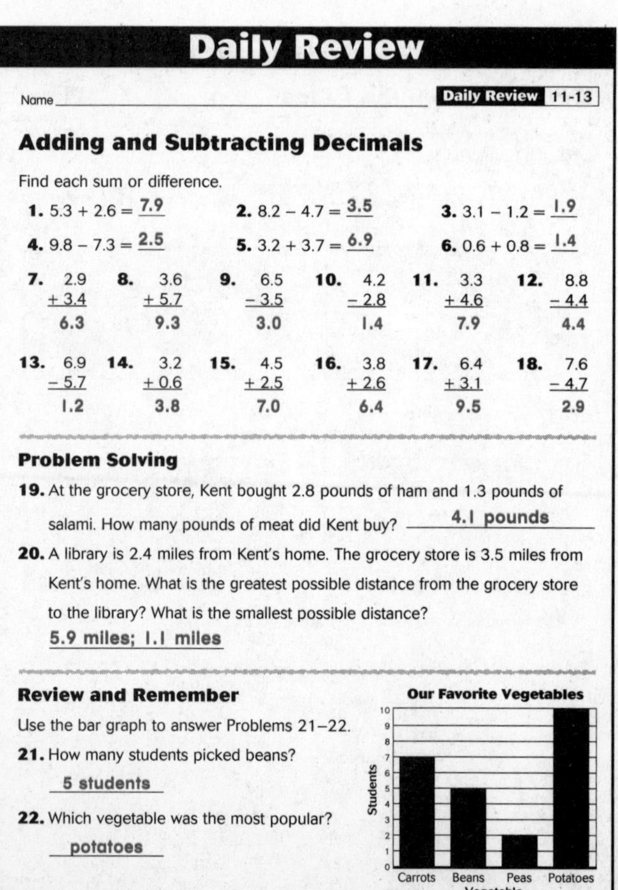

Daily Review

Name ____________________

Daily Review 11-13

Adding and Subtracting Decimals

Find each sum or difference.

1. 5.3 + 2.6 = **7.9**
2. 8.2 − 4.7 = **3.5**
3. 3.1 − 1.2 = **1.9**
4. 9.8 − 7.3 = **2.5**
5. 3.2 + 3.7 = **6.9**
6. 0.6 + 0.8 = **1.4**
7. 2.9 + 3.4 = **6.3**
8. 3.6 + 5.7 = **9.3**
9. 6.5 − 3.5 = **3.0**
10. 4.2 − 2.8 = **1.4**
11. 3.3 + 4.6 = **7.9**
12. 8.8 − 4.4 = **4.4**
13. 6.9 − 5.7 = **1.2**
14. 3.2 + 0.6 = **3.8**
15. 4.5 + 2.5 = **7.0**
16. 3.8 + 2.6 = **6.4**
17. 6.4 + 3.1 = **9.5**
18. 7.6 − 4.7 = **2.9**

Problem Solving

19. At the grocery store, Kent bought 2.8 pounds of ham and 1.3 pounds of salami. How many pounds of meat did Kent buy? **4.1 pounds**

20. A library is 2.4 miles from Kent's home. The grocery store is 3.5 miles from Kent's home. What is the greatest possible distance from the grocery store to the library? What is the smallest possible distance? **5.9 miles; 1.1 miles**

Review and Remember

Use the bar graph to answer Problems 21–22.

21. How many students picked beans? **5 students**

22. Which vegetable was the most popular? **potatoes**

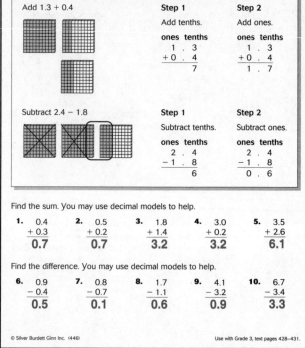

Chapter 11 • Lesson 14

Practice

Problem Solving P 11-14

Using Money

Use the price chart to answer each question.

Hannah's Health Food Store

Bulk Food		Buy a Bag of Trail Mix	
peanuts	$1.99/lb	just nuts	$6.95
raisins	$2.50/lb	nuts and raisins	$4.50
carob chips	$4.00/lb	sesame sticks	$2.75
walnuts	$5.50/lb	just fruit	$5.00

1. Kevin buys a bag of "just fruit" and a half pound of walnuts. What is his change from $10?
$2.25

2. George has $5 to spend. He wants a pound of raisins and a half pound of carob chips. Does he have enough?
Yes; total cost $4.50

3. Brenda buys a bag of sesame sticks and a pound of raisins. She pays with a $10 bill. How much change should she get back?
$4.75

4. David buys a bag of nuts and raisins and some peanuts. His total bill is $5.50. How many pounds of peanuts does David buy?
½ pound of peanuts

5. Thom gives the clerk $12 for one pound of peanuts, 2 pounds of raisins, and a pound of walnuts. Did he pay enough? If not, what does he still owe?
No; Thom still owes $0.49

6. Myra wants to buy as many bags of "just nuts" as she can with $25. How many bags can she buy? Explain.
3 bags; $6.95 is about $7, 7 × 4 > 25.

7. Would $20 be enough to buy one bag of each kind of trail mix? Tell how you know.
Yes; estimated cost $19; exact cost $19.20

 Use with Grade 3, text pages 432-433.

Reteach

Problem Solving R 11-14

Using Money

Go, Team!	
banner	$1.15
visor	$1.75
sports bag	$2.99

Milton buys a banner and a visor. Now he needs to pay the clerk.

1. How much does Milton owe the clerk for the banner and the visor?

Understand You need to find the total cost of the items.

Plan To find the total cost, you **add**.

Solve $1.15 + 1.75 = **$2.90**

Look Back You can add the numbers in a different order. The answer is correct. $1.75 + 1.15 = **$2.90** ✓

2. How much change will Milton get if he pays the clerk $5.00?

Understand You need to find the amount left from $5.00.

Plan To find the amount that is left, you **subtract**.

Solve $5.00 − 2.90 = **$2.10**

Look Back You can add the change to the cost to find the total amount. The answer is correct. $2.10 + 2.90 = **$5.00** ✓

3. Milton buys a sportsbag. What is his change from $5.00?
$2.01

4. Milton has $10. Can he buy one of everything? Explain.
Yes; total cost about $6.00

 Use with Grade 3, text pages 432-433.

Extend

All Aboard

E 11-14 **REASONING**

Make a catalog page for a toy-train supply store. List the items in order from most to least expensive. Use the clues to help you figure out the prices.

- The gas station costs $1.50 more than the $3.00 curved track.
- The least expensive item is a $1.00 shrub.
- A tree costs $0.50 more than a shrub.
- A railroad crossing sign costs $0.25 more than a telephone pole.
- A straight track costs $1.25 more than a shrub.
- A telephone pole is $0.50 less expensive than a straight track.

All Aboard at the Toy Train Supply Company!

	Item	Cost
1.	gas station	$4.50
2.	curved track	$3.00
3.	straight track	$2.25
4.	railroad crossing sign	$2.00
5.	telephone pole	$1.75
6.	tree	$1.50
7.	shrub	$1.00

8. Russell has $20 and buys 4 curved tracks. How many straight tracks can he buy?
3 straight tracks

9. Millie can buy a pack of 4 trees for $5.00. If she does that, how much is Millie paying for each tree?
$1.25 for each tree

10. Suppose you have $30. Choose what you would like to buy from the catalog. Find the total cost, then find what your change will be.
Answers will vary.

 Use with Grade 3, text pages 432-433.

Daily Review

Name ____________ Daily Review 11-14

Problem Solving

Using Money

Use the information below to help you answer each question.

Pizza	
Plain	$4.60
Green Peppers	$4.25
Onion	$3.95
Hamburger	$5.75
All slices	$1.00

1. How much change should Shad get if he pays for 2 plain pizzas with $10?
$0.80

2. Shateel ordered 1 hamburger pizza to share with Sally. Katie ordered two slices for herself. How much do they owe for the pizza?
$7.75

3. Adam has $4.25. What are his choices of pizza?
4 slices, or 1 green pepper pizza, or 1 onion pizza

4. For his birthday party, Jamie ordered 2 plain pizzas and 2 green pepper pizzas. How much did the pizzas cost? How much change should he get if he pays with a $20 bill?
$17.70; $2.30

Review and Remember

Divide.

5. 6)30 **5** 6. 2)14 **7** 7. 3)12 **4** 8. 4)36 **9** 9. 7)42 **6**

10. 8)64 **8** 11. 6)18 **3** 12. 7)28 **4** 13. 5)45 **9** 14. 5)25 **5**

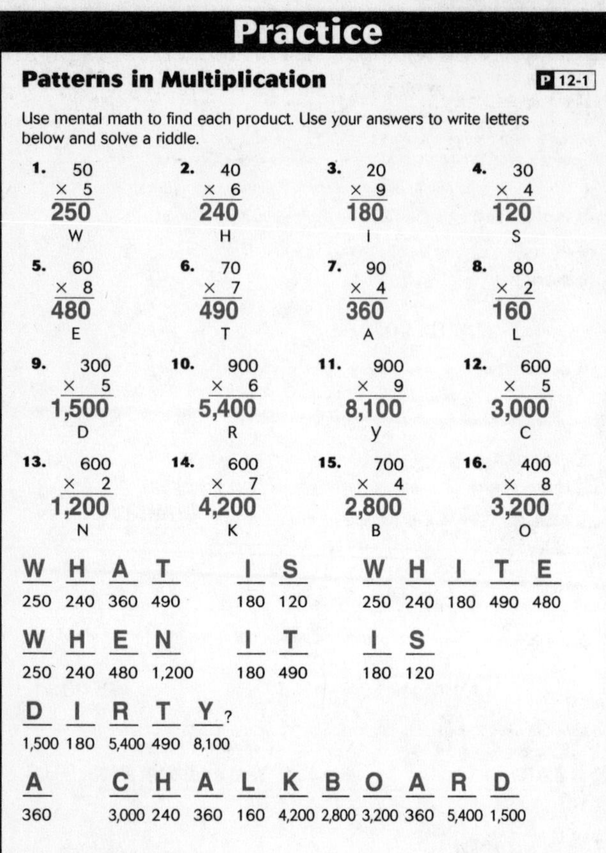

Practice

Patterns in Multiplication

P 12-1

Use mental math to find each product. Use your answers to write letters below and solve a riddle.

1. 50 × 5 = 250 W
2. 40 × 6 = 240 H
3. 20 × 9 = 180 I
4. 30 × 4 = 120 S
5. 60 × 8 = 480 E
6. 70 × 7 = 490 T
7. 90 × 4 = 360 A
8. 80 × 2 = 160 L
9. 300 × 5 = 1,500 D
10. 900 × 6 = 5,400 R
11. 900 × 9 = 8,100 y
12. 600 × 5 = 3,000 C
13. 600 × 2 = 1,200 N
14. 600 × 7 = 4,200 K
15. 700 × 4 = 2,800 B
16. 400 × 8 = 3,200 O

W H A T (250 240 360 490) I S (180 120) W H I T E (250 240 180 490 480)

W H E N (250 240 480 1,200) I T (180 490) I S (180 120)

D I R T Y? (1,500 180 5,400 490 8,100)

A (360) C H A L K B O A R D (3,000 240 360 160 4,200 2,800 3,200 360 5,400 1,500)

 Use with Grade 3, text pages 444–445.

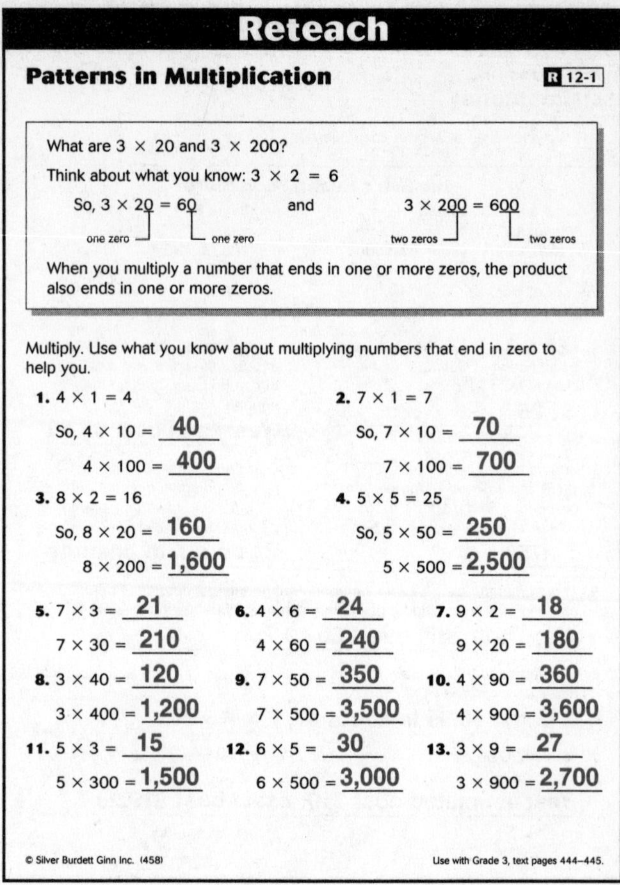

Reteach

Patterns in Multiplication

R 12-1

What are 3 × 20 and 3 × 200?

Think about what you know: 3 × 2 = 6

So, 3 × 20 = 60 (one zero — one zero) and 3 × 200 = 600 (two zeros — two zeros)

When you multiply a number that ends in one or more zeros, the product also ends in one or more zeros.

Multiply. Use what you know about multiplying numbers that end in zero to help you.

1. 4 × 1 = 4
   So, 4 × 10 = 40
   4 × 100 = 400
2. 7 × 1 = 7
   So, 7 × 10 = 70
   7 × 100 = 700
3. 8 × 2 = 16
   So, 8 × 20 = 160
   8 × 200 = 1,600
4. 5 × 5 = 25
   So, 5 × 50 = 250
   5 × 500 = 2,500
5. 7 × 3 = 21
   7 × 30 = 210
6. 4 × 6 = 24
   4 × 60 = 240
7. 9 × 2 = 18
   9 × 20 = 180
8. 3 × 40 = 120
   3 × 400 = 1,200
9. 7 × 50 = 350
   7 × 500 = 3,500
10. 4 × 90 = 360
    4 × 900 = 3,600
11. 5 × 3 = 15
    5 × 300 = 1,500
12. 6 × 5 = 30
    6 × 500 = 3,000
13. 3 × 9 = 27
    3 × 900 = 2,700

 Use with Grade 3, text pages 444–445.

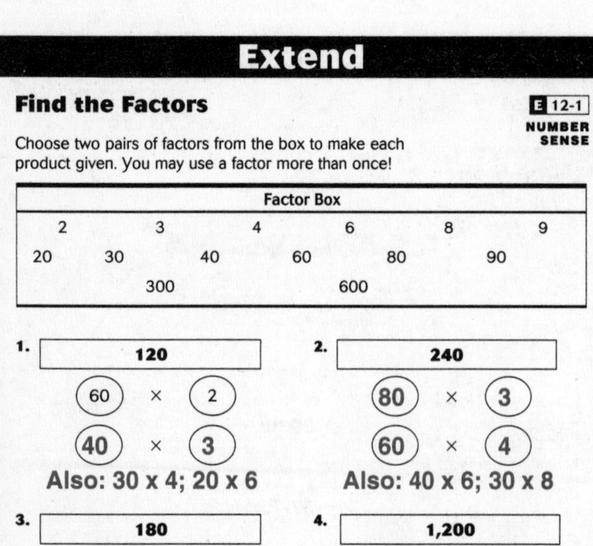

Extend

Find the Factors

E 12-1 NUMBER SENSE

Choose two pairs of factors from the box to make each product given. You may use a factor more than once!

Factor Box					
2	3	4	6	8	9
20	30	40	60	80	90
300	600				

1. 120
   60 × 2
   40 × 3
   Also: 30 x 4; 20 x 6

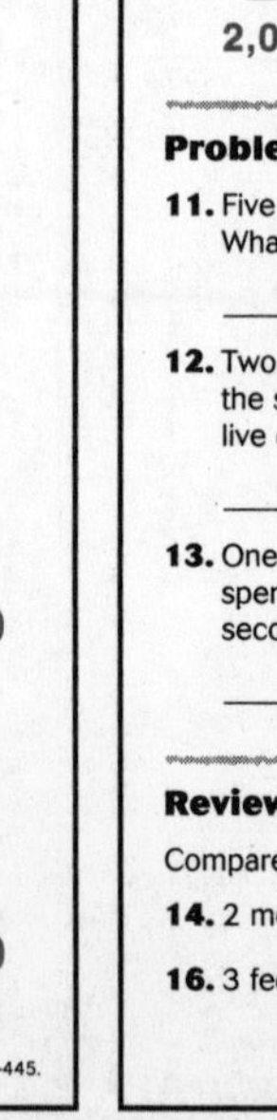

2. 240
   80 × 3
   60 × 4
   Also: 40 x 6; 30 x 8

3. 180
   90 × 2
   60 × 3
   Also: 30 x 6; 20 x 9

4. 1,200
   600 × 2
   300 × 4
   Also: 60 x 20; 40 x 30

5. 1,800
   600 × 3
   300 × 6
   Also: 90 x 20; 60 x 30

6. 2,400
   600 × 4
   300 × 8
   Also: 80 x 30; 60 x 40

 Use with Grade 3, text pages 444–445.

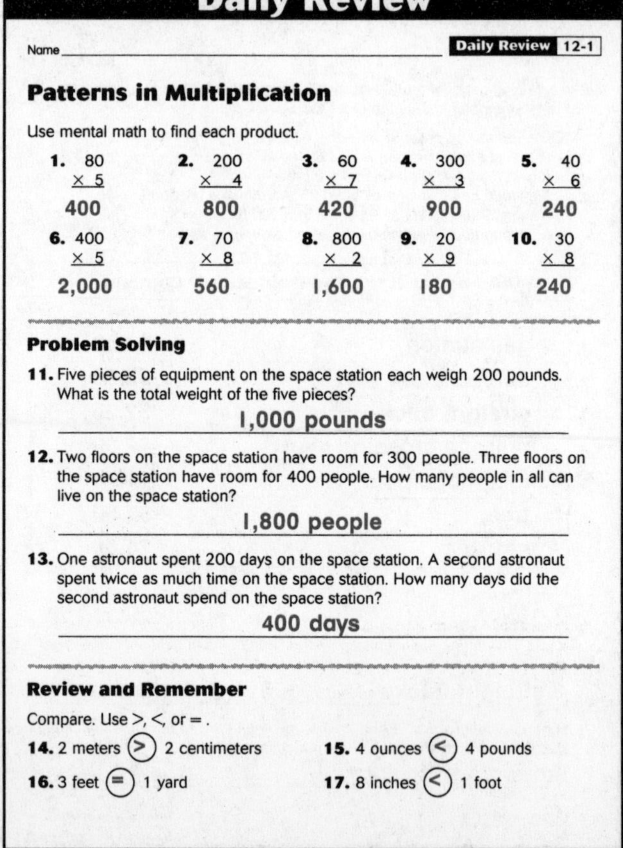

Daily Review

Name ____________________ Daily Review 12-1

Patterns in Multiplication

Use mental math to find each product.

1. 80 × 5 = 400
2. 200 × 4 = 800
3. 60 × 7 = 420
4. 300 × 3 = 900
5. 40 × 6 = 240
6. 400 × 5 = 2,000
7. 70 × 8 = 560
8. 800 × 2 = 1,600
9. 20 × 9 = 180
10. 30 × 8 = 240

Problem Solving

11. Five pieces of equipment on the space station each weigh 200 pounds. What is the total weight of the five pieces?
    1,000 pounds
12. Two floors on the space station have room for 300 people. Three floors on the space station have room for 400 people. How many people in all can live on the space station?
    1,800 people
13. One astronaut spent 200 days on the space station. A second astronaut spent twice as much time on the space station. How many days did the second astronaut spend on the space station?
    400 days

Review and Remember

Compare. Use >, <, or =.

14. 2 meters (>) 2 centimeters
15. 4 ounces (<) 4 pounds
16. 3 feet (=) 1 yard
17. 8 inches (<) 1 foot

Chapter 12 • Lesson 2

Practice

Explore: Investigating Multiplication by One-Digit Numbers

P 12-2

Draw a line from each picture to an addition sentence and from each addition sentence to a multiplication sentence.

1. 15 + 15 + 15 = 45 — 4 × 14 = 56
2. 14 + 14 + 14+ 14 = 56 — 3 × 15 = 45
3. 25 + 25 + 25 = 75 — 2 × 27 = 54
4. 27 + 27 = 54 — 3 × 25 = 75

Write your own sentences for the pictures.

5. 26 + 26 + 26 = 78

   3 × 26 = 78

6. 23 + 23 + 23 + 23 = 92

   4 × 23 = 92

Use with Grade 3, text pages 446–447.

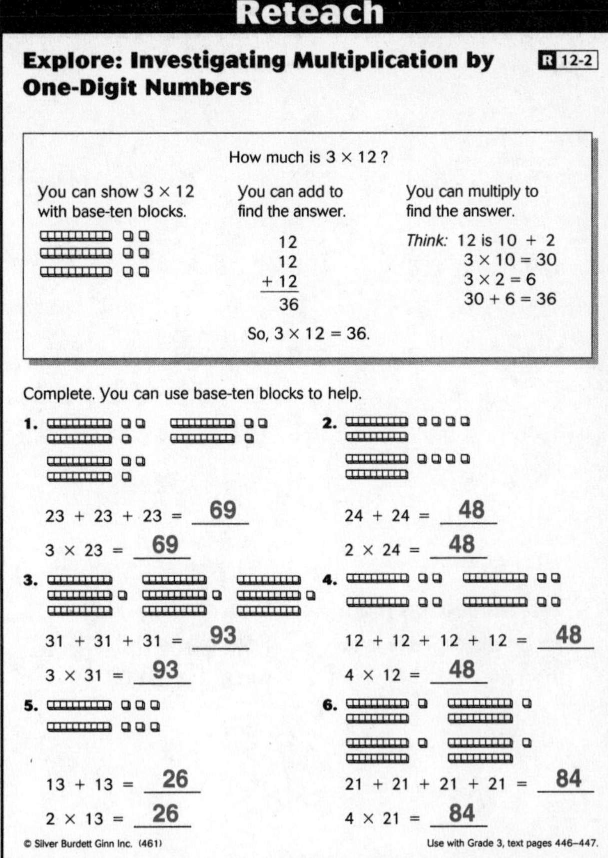

Reteach

Explore: Investigating Multiplication by One-Digit Numbers

R 12-2

How much is 3 × 12 ?

You can show 3 × 12 with base-ten blocks.

You can add to find the answer.

12
12
+ 12
36

You can multiply to find the answer.

Think: 12 is 10 + 2
3 × 10 = 30
3 × 2 = 6
30 + 6 = 36

So, 3 × 12 = 36.

Complete. You can use base-ten blocks to help.

1. 23 + 23 + 23 = 69

   3 × 23 = 69

2. 24 + 24 = 48

   2 × 24 = 48

3. 31 + 31 + 31 = 93

   3 × 31 = 93

4. 12 + 12 + 12 + 12 = 48

   4 × 12 = 48

5. 13 + 13 = 26

   2 × 13 = 26

6. 21 + 21 + 21 + 21 = 84

   4 × 21 = 84

Use with Grade 3, text pages 446–447.

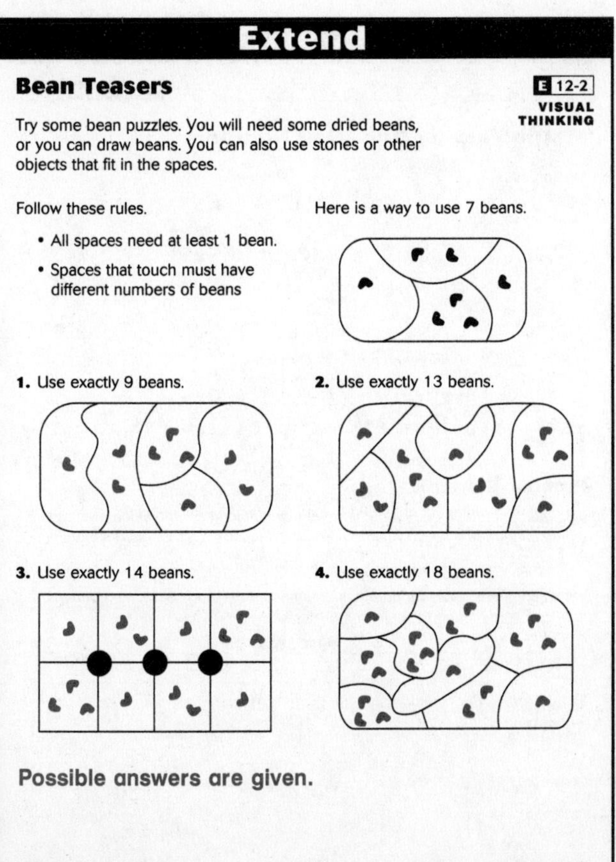

Extend

Bean Teasers

E 12-2

VISUAL THINKING

Try some bean puzzles. You will need some dried beans, or you can draw beans. You can also use stones or other objects that fit in the spaces.

Follow these rules.

- All spaces need at least 1 bean.
- Spaces that touch must have different numbers of beans

Here is a way to use 7 beans.

1. Use exactly 9 beans.
2. Use exactly 13 beans.
3. Use exactly 14 beans.
4. Use exactly 18 beans.

Possible answers are given.

Use with Grade 3, text pages 446–447.

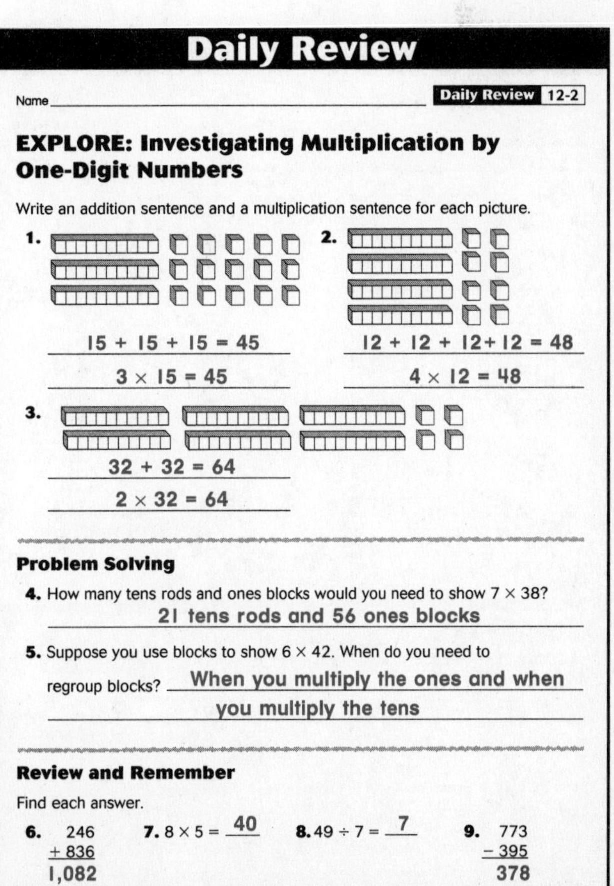

Daily Review

Name__________

Daily Review 12-2

EXPLORE: Investigating Multiplication by One-Digit Numbers

Write an addition sentence and a multiplication sentence for each picture.

1. 15 + 15 + 15 = 45

   3 × 15 = 45

2. 12 + 12 + 12+ 12 = 48

   4 × 12 = 48

3. 32 + 32 = 64

   2 × 32 = 64

Problem Solving

4. How many tens rods and ones blocks would you need to show 7 × 38? 21 tens rods and 56 ones blocks
5. Suppose you use blocks to show 6 × 42. When do you need to regroup blocks? When you multiply the ones and when you multiply the tens

Review and Remember

Find each answer.

6. $\begin{array}{r} 246 \\ +836 \\ \hline 1{,}082 \end{array}$
7. 8 × 5 = 40
8. 49 ÷ 7 = 7
9. $\begin{array}{r} 773 \\ -395 \\ \hline 378 \end{array}$

Practice

Multiplying by One-Digit Numbers

P 12-3

Multiply.

1. 13 × 5 = **65**
2. 40 × 8 = **320**
3. 29 × 3 = **87**
4. 18 × 4 = **72**
5. 82 × 2 = **164**
6. 43 × 3 = **129**
7. 53 × 2 = **106**
8. 39 × 0 = **0**
9. 14 × 6 = **84**
10. 35 × 2 = **70**
11. 82 × 6 = **492**
12. 91 × 0 = **0**
13. 47 × 8 = **376**
14. 52 × 4 = **208**
15. 16 × 5 = **80**

16. 2 × 23 = **46**
17. 4 × 15 = **60**
18. 3 × 71 = **213**
19. 0 × 54 = **0**
20. 2 × 82 = **164**
21. 5 × 12 = **60**

Solve.

22. Andrea has 78 disks to stack. She has room for 4 stacks of 21 disks each. Will all the disks fit? Explain.

Yes; Andrea has room for 84 disks; 78 is less than 84.

23. Suni has $1.00 to spend on disk labels. The labels she wants cost 27¢ each. How many can she buy? Explain.

Suni can buy 3 labels. Four labels will cost more than $1.00.

Use with Grade 3, text pages 448–451.

Reteach

Multiplying by One-Digit Numbers

R 12-3

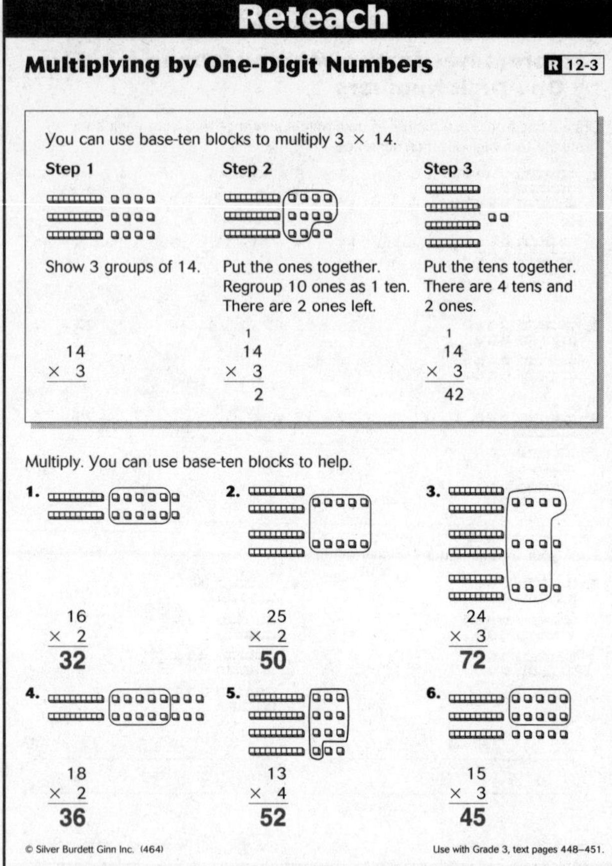

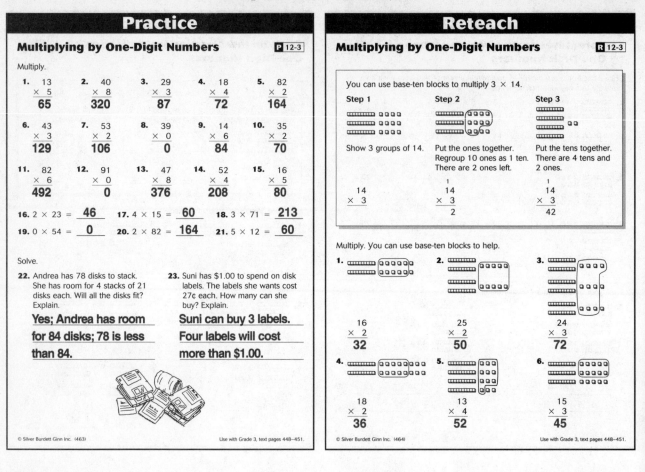

You can use base-ten blocks to multiply 3 × 14.

Step 1

Show 3 groups of 14.

14 × 3

Step 2

Put the ones together. Regroup 10 ones as 1 ten. There are 2 ones left.

14 × 3 = 2 (regroup 1)

Step 3

Put the tens together. There are 4 tens and 2 ones.

14 × 3 = 42

Multiply. You can use base-ten blocks to help.

1. 16 × 2 = **32**
2. 25 × 2 = **50**
3. 24 × 3 = **72**
4. 18 × 2 = **36**
5. 13 × 4 = **52**
6. 15 × 3 = **45**

Use with Grade 3, text pages 448–451.

Extend

Box Multiplication

E 12-3

REASONING

Arrange the three numbers in the boxes to get each product.

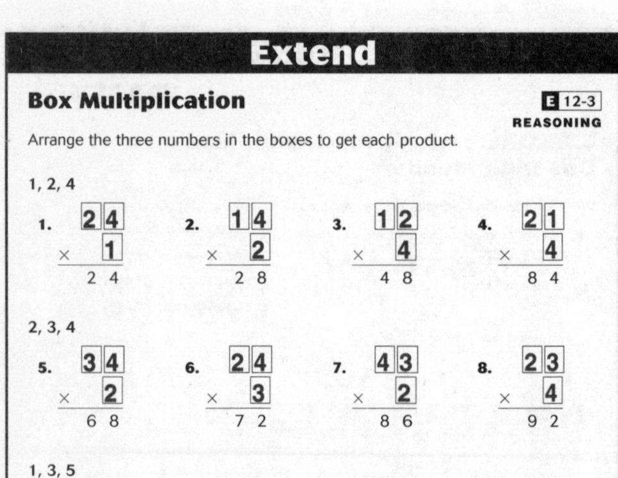

1, 2, 4

1. **24** × **1** = 24
2. **14** × **2** = 28
3. **12** × **4** = 48
4. **21** × **4** = 84

2, 3, 4

5. **34** × **2** = 68
6. **24** × **3** = 72
7. **43** × **2** = 86
8. **23** × **4** = 92

1, 3, 5

9. **35** × **1** = 35
10. **15** × **3** = 45
11. **53** × **1** = 53
12. **13** × **5** = 65

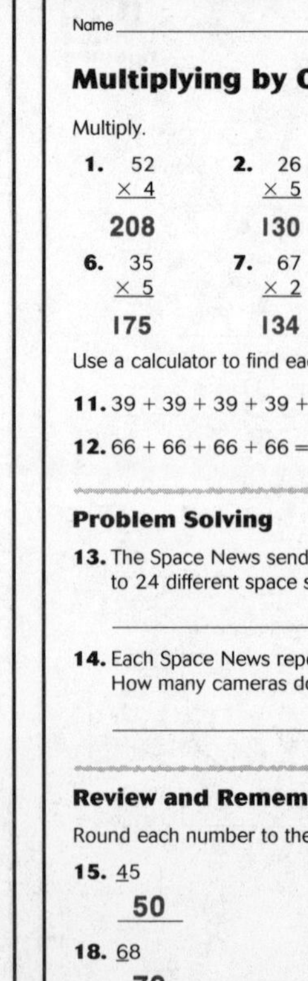

Complete the rules.

You have three digits: 3, 5, and 7. You arrange two of the digits to form a two-digit number. Then you multiply the number by the third digit.

13. To get the smallest possible product, multiply **57** × **3**.

14. To get the greatest possible product, multiply **53** × **7**.

Use with Grade 3, text pages 448–451.

Daily Review

Name ____________________

Daily Review 12-3

Multiplying by One-Digit Numbers

Multiply.

1. 52 × 4 = **208**
2. 26 × 5 = **130**
3. 42 × 3 = **126**
4. 43 × 6 = **258**
5. 81 × 3 = **243**
6. 35 × 5 = **175**
7. 67 × 2 = **134**
8. 19 × 4 = **76**
9. 54 × 6 = **324**
10. 74 × 3 = **222**

Use a calculator to find each sum and product.

11. 39 + 39 + 39 + 39 + 39 = **195**　　5 × 39 = **195**

12. 66 + 66 + 66 + 66 = **264**　　4 × 66 = **264**

Problem Solving

13. The Space News sends out 4 news videos each day. The videos are sent to 24 different space stations. How many videos are sent out each day?

96 videos

14. Each Space News reporter has 3 cameras. There are 28 news reporters. How many cameras do the reporters have in all?

84 cameras

Review and Remember

Round each number to the underlined place.

15. 45 → **50**
16. 828 → **800**
17. 732 → **730**
18. 68 → **70**
19. 343 → **300**
20. 445 → **450**

Chapter 12 • Lesson 4

Practice

More Multiplying by One-Digit Numbers
P 12-4

Multiply.

1. 25 × 7 = **175**
2. 86 × 4 = **344**
3. 34 × 8 = **272**
4. 22 × 6 = **132**
5. 43 × 5 = **215**
6. 17 × 8 = **136**
7. 52 × 5 = **260**
8. 64 × 3 = **192**
9. 98 × 2 = **196**
10. 95 × 2 = **190**

11. 6 × 44 = **264**
12. 4 × 35 = **140**
13. 0 × 98 = **0**

Find each output.

Rule: Multiply by 4

	Input	Output
14.	15	**60**
15.	25	**100**
16.	35	**140**
17.	45	**180**

Rule: Multiply by 7

	Input	Output
18.	35	**245**
19.	45	**315**
20.	55	**385**
21.	65	**455**

Solve.

22. Sal's Space Station Flower Shop is selling plants for $6.00 each. If you want 13 plants for your school, how much money do you need?

$78.00

Use with Grade 3, text pages 452–453.

Reteach

More Multiplying by One-Digit Numbers
R 12-4

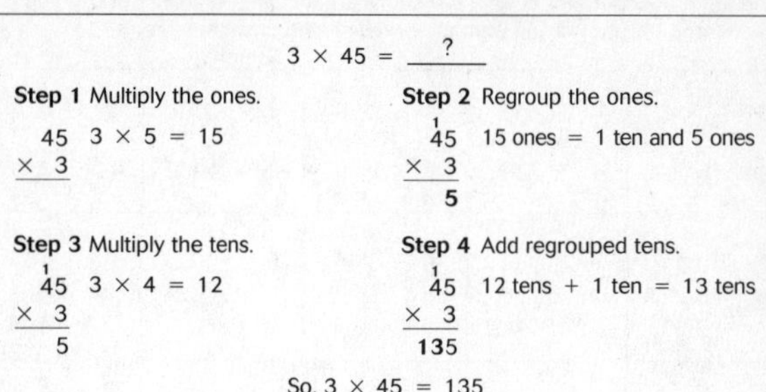

3 × 45 = ?

Step 1 Multiply the ones.
45 × 3; 3 × 5 = 15

Step 2 Regroup the ones.
45 × 3 = 5; 15 ones = 1 ten and 5 ones

Step 3 Multiply the tens.
45 × 3; 3 × 4 = 12

Step 4 Add regrouped tens.
45 × 3 = 135; 12 tens + 1 ten = 13 tens

So, 3 × 45 = 135

Do you need to regroup ones, tens, or both? Write *O*, *T*, or *B* in the box above each problem. Then multiply. You may use base-ten blocks to help.

1. **O** 25 × 3 = **75**
2. **T** 41 × 4 = **164**
3. **B** 38 × 3 = **114**
4. **B** 23 × 5 = **115**
5. **O** 28 × 2 = **56**
6. **B** 98 × 2 = **196**
7. **T** 62 × 2 = **124**
8. **B** 56 × 5 = **280**
9. **O** 19 × 5 = **95**
10. **B** 67 × 2 = **134**
11. **B** 37 × 4 = **148**
12. **O** 27 × 3 = **81**
13. **B** 49 × 3 = **147**
14. **T** 71 × 5 = **355**
15. **B** 46 × 7 = **322**

Use with Grade 3, text pages 452–453.

Extend

Circle Secrets
E 12-4
NUMBER SENSE

The numbers in each ○ have a secret. Find the product in each △. Look at the three numbers in the ○. Tell their secret. **Secrets for exercises 3 and 4 may vary.**

1.
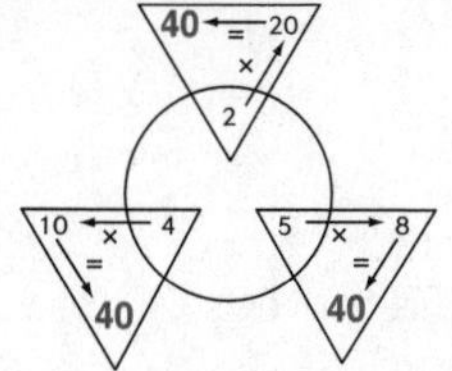

Secret: **2 × 4 × 5 = 40, the product in every triangle.**

2.
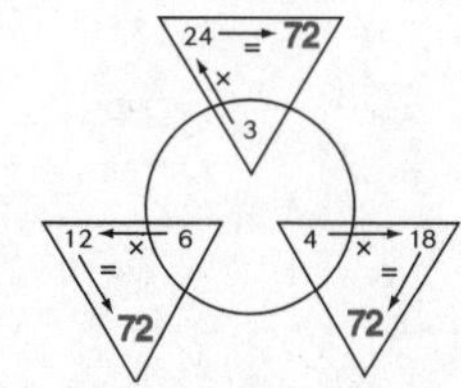

Secret: **3 × 4 × 6 = 72, the product in every triangle.**

3.
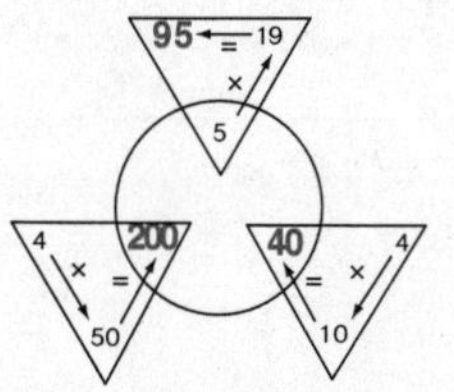

Secret: **5 × 40 = 200 The numbers form a multiplication sentence.**

4.

5 × = 90; 18; 2 × = 54; 27; 3 × = 17; 51

Secret: **3 × 18 = 54 The numbers form a multiplication sentence.**

Use with Grade 3, text pages 452–453.

Daily Review

Name ______________________

Daily Review 12-4

More Multiplying by One-Digit Numbers

Find each product.

1. 33 × 4 = **132**
2. 62 × 3 = **186**
3. 75 × 2 = **150**
4. 11 × 4 = **44**
5. 47 × 1 = **47**
6. 29 × 5 = **145**
7. 84 × 2 = **168**
8. 13 × 3 = **39**
9. 56 × 4 = **224**
10. 98 × 5 = **490**

Problem Solving

11. One tomato plant has at least 18 tomatoes. A space station garden has 6 of these tomato plants. What is the fewest number of tomatoes you would expect from this garden?

108 tomatoes

12. A farmer grows broccoli in rows of 42 plants each. There are 8 rows of broccoli plants. How many plants does the farmer have in all?

336 plants

13. The same farmer has 6 rows of pepper plants with 36 plants in each row. How many more broccoli plants are there than pepper plants?

120 more plants

Review and Remember

Find each product or quotient.

14. 81 ÷ 9 = **9**
15. 7 × 8 = **56**
16. 42 ÷ 7 = **6**
17. 4 × 8 = **32**
18. 5 × 9 = **45**
19. 63 ÷ 9 = **7**
20. 48 ÷ 6 = **8**
21. 72 ÷ 8 = **9**
22. 7 × 7 = **49**

Practice

Multiplying Greater Numbers

P 12-5

Find the products. Color in each box with a product greater than 1,000. If you color correctly, you will find your letter grade in the uncolored boxes!

1. 312 × 5 = 1,560	2. 512 × 2 = 1,024	3. 276 × 4 = 1,104	4. 371 × 5 = 1,855	5. 422 × 3 = 1,266
6. 617 × 5 = 3,085	7. 111 × 8 = 888	8. 265 × 2 = 530	9. 123 × 3 = 369	10. 481 × 3 = 1,443
11. 342 × 5 = 1,710	12. 283 × 3 = 849	13. 412 × 8 = 3,296	14. 260 × 3 = 780	15. 649 × 2 = 1,298
16. 274 × 7 = 1,918	17. 120 × 7 = 840	18. 469 × 2 = 938	19. 262 × 3 = 786	20. 568 × 4 = 2,272
21. 345 × 4 = 1,380	22. 119 × 5 = 595	23. 591 × 4 = 2,364	24. 145 × 6 = 870	25. 198 × 6 = 1,188

What is your letter grade? A

 Use with Grade 3, text pages 454–457.

Reteach

Multiplying Greater Numbers

R 12-5

Follow these steps to find the product.

Step 1 262 × 2 = 4
Multiply ones.
2 × 2 ones = 4 ones.
You do not need to regroup.

Step 2 262 × 2 = 24 (1 regrouped)
Multiply tens.
2 × 6 tens = 12 tens.
Regroup as 1 hundred and 2 tens.

Step 3 262 × 2 = 524
Multiply hundreds.
2 × 2 hundreds = 4 hundreds.
You do not need to regroup.
Add the regrouped hundred.
4 hundreds
+ 1 hundred
5 hundreds

Find each product. Regroup if you need to.

1. 151 × 4 = 604
2. 111 × 9 = 999
3. 730 × 3 = 2,190
4. 245 × 3 = 735
5. 212 × 7 = 1,484
6. 253 × 3 = 759
7. 506 × 6 = 3,036
8. 220 × 4 = 880

 Use with Grade 3, text pages 454–457.

Extend

Number Trick

E 12-5 REASONING

Read Cheryl's number trick:

① Pick any number between 0 and 10.
② Add 7 to the number.
③ Subtract the number you chose in Step①.
④ Multiply the new number by 286.
⑤ Your product is 2,002!

Try Cheryl's number trick with 3 different numbers. Show your work for each step.

Students' numbers and work will vary, but the product will always be 2,002.

1. Number: ____
Add 7: ____
Subtract the number you chose and write the new number: ____
Multiply by 286:
286 × ___ = 2,002

2. Number: ____
Add 7: ____
Subtract the number you chose and write the new number: ____
Multiply by 286:
286 × ___ = 2,002

3. Number: ____
Add 7: ____
Subtract the number you chose and write the new number: ____
Multiply by 286:
286 × ___ = 2,002

4. Look at Steps ①, ②, and ③. Why will you always get the same answer in Step ③, no matter what number you pick?
Possible answer: You add 7 to the number you chose, then subtract that number. Therefore, you always have an answer of 7 in Step 3.

5. Make up your own number trick. Try it with 2 numbers between 0 and 10. Then challenge a friend to figure out how you did your trick.
Tricks will vary.

 Use with Grade 3, text pages 454–457.

Daily Review

Name ____________ Daily Review 12-5

Multiplying Greater Numbers

Find each product.

1. 231 × 4 = 924
2. 335 × 6 = 2,010
3. $4.42 × 3 = $13.26
4. 513 × 7 = 3,591
5. 765 × 2 = 1,530
6. $6.89 × 5 = $34.45
7. 108 × 3 = 324
8. 124 × 8 = 992
9. 286 × 1 = 286
10. $3.99 × 4 = $15.96
11. 0 × 874 = 0
12. 9 × 300 = 2,700
13. 5 × $329 = $1,645
14. 6 × 113 = 678
15. 4 × 50 = 200
16. 8 × 202 = 1,616
17. 2 × 463 = 926
18. 6 × $1.20 = $7.20
19. 1 × 533 = 533

Problem Solving

20. Each person aboard the space station eats 3 packaged meals a day. If there are 248 people aboard the space station, how many packaged meals are eaten each day? 744 meals

21. At the space station cafe, lunch costs $8.75. How much would it cost a family of 4 to each lunch at the cafe? $35.00

Review and Remember

Add or subtract.

22. 872 + 346 = 1,218
23. 87 − 39 = 48
24. 475 − 136 = 339
25. 2,312 + 3,224 = 5,536
26. 29 + 88 = 117

Chapter 12 • Lesson 6

Practice

Estimating Products

P 12-6

Estimate each product. Round each number to the underlined place.

1. 59 × 5 = **300** **2.** 41 × 6 = **240** **3.** 28 × 7 = **210** **4.** 98 × 4 = **400** **5.** 47 × 8 = **400**

6. 63 × 7 = **420** **7.** 710 × 9 = **6,300** **8.** 389 × 4 = **1,600** **9.** 201 × 8 = **1,600** **10.** 802 × 6 = **4,800**

11. 313 × 5 = **1,500** **12.** 879 × 6 = **5,400** **13.** 321 × 3 = **900** **14.** 666 × 5 = **3,500** **15.** 591 × 6 = **3,600**

Complete the table. Round the number sold to find the estimated product.

	Space Rocks Sold			
	Rock Type	Cost of One	Number Sold	Estimated Product
16.	Zenox	$6	375	**$2,400**
17.	Belkon	$4	82	**$320**
18.	Dolon	$7	58	**$420**
19.	Quintox	$8	219	**$1,600**
20.	Romludar	$9	29	**$270**

Mrs. Gomez buys 295 Zenox rocks from the space miner for $6 each.

21. About how much does Mrs. Gomez spend on the Zenox rocks?
about $1,800

22. About how much does Mrs. Gomez collect if she sells each Zenox rock for $9?
about $2,700

23. About how much profit will Mrs. Gomez make? **about $900**

Reteach

Estimating Products

R 12-6

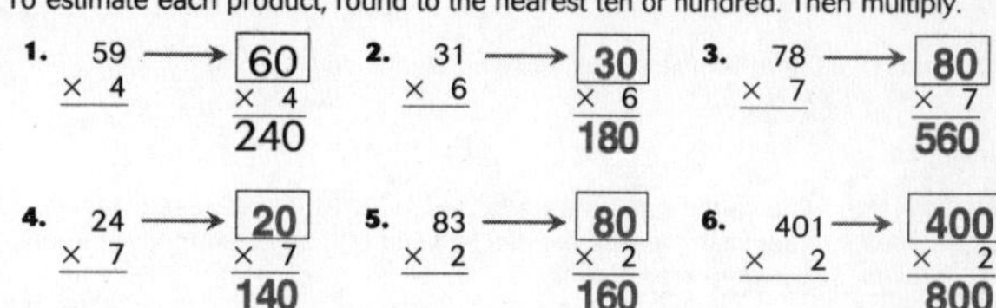

You can use rounding and mental math to estimate products.

Think: 32 rounds to 30

32 × 6 → 30 × 6 = 180. *Think:* 6 × 3 = 18, so 6 × 30 = 180.

Think: 476 rounds to 500

476 × 4 → 500 × 4 = 2,000. *Think:* 4 × 5 = 20, so 4 × 500 = 2,000.

To estimate each product, round to the nearest ten or hundred. Then multiply.

1. 59 × 4 → **60** × 4 = **240** **2.** 31 × 6 → **30** × 6 = **180** **3.** 78 × 7 → **80** × 7 = **560**

4. 24 × 7 → **20** × 7 = **140** **5.** 83 × 2 → **80** × 2 = **160** **6.** 401 × 2 → **400** × 2 = **800**

7. 219 × 3 → **200** × 3 = **600** **8.** 689 × 2 → **700** × 2 = **1,400** **9.** 329 × 9 → **300** × 9 = **2,700**

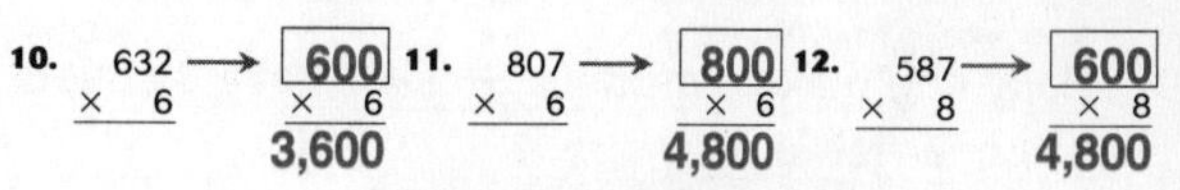

10. 632 × 6 → **600** × 6 = **3,600** **11.** 807 × 6 → **800** × 6 = **4,800** **12.** 587 × 8 → **600** × 8 = **4,800**

Extend

Who's Who?

E 12-6
REASONING

1. Hal, Sue, Lou, Kim, and Peg were in a spaceship race. As the winner of the race crossed the finish line, a picture was taken of the spaceships. In what order from the finish line were the five racers?

First, read all the clues. Then write the names of the five spaceship racers on the meter line below.

Hal is 50 meters ahead of Sue.
Sue is 10 meters behind Lou.
Kim is 20 meters behind Hal.
Lou is 50 meters behind Peg.
Peg is 30 meters ahead of Kim.
Hal is 10 meters from the finish line.

Peg Hal Kim Lou Sue

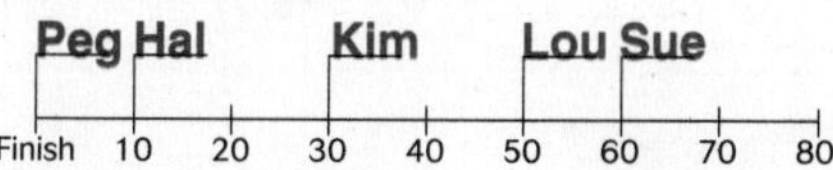

2. Eileen, Rachel, Frank, and Mickey each have a different pet shown in the picture.

Eileen is allergic to dogs and cats, so she has neither a dog nor a cat. The owner of the dog is not Mickey. Rachel is the only one who likes cats, and Eileen's mother won't let her have a bird.

What pet does each person have?

Rachel has the cat; Eileen has the fish;
Mickey has the bird; Frank has the dog.

Daily Review

Name ______________________

Daily Review 12-6

Estimating Products

Round to the underlined place. Estimate each product.

1. 5 × 13 = **50** **2.** 21 × 6 = **120** **3.** 79 × 4 = **320**

4. 9 × 56 = **540** **5.** 45 × 8 = **400** **6.** 66 × 3 = **210**

7. 42 × 4 = **160** **8.** 492 × 7 = **3,500** **9.** 842 × 8 = **6,400**

Problem Solving

10. A package of straws contains 110 straws. About how many straws are in 5 packages? **about 500 straws**

11. Four groups of students are touring the space exhibits at the science museum. Each group takes about 63 minutes to go through all of the exhibits. About how many hours does it take for all 4 groups to see the exhibits?
about 4 hours

12. A bag of peanuts contain almost 100 peanuts. In 5 bags, are there more or less than 500 peanuts? Explain **Less than 500 peanuts; since each bag contains less than 100, there will be less than 5 × 100 = 500 peanuts in 5 bags.**

Review and Remember

Multiply.

13. 8 × 2 = **16** **14.** 5 × 9 = **45** **15.** 9 × 6 = **54**

16. 7 × 8 = **56** **17.** 8 × 8 = **64** **18.** 7 × 9 = **63**

19. 9 × 3 = **27** **20.** 7 × 6 = **42** **21.** 9 × 9 = **81**

Practice

Quotients With Remainders

P 12-7

Find each quotient and its remainder. You may draw pictures or use objects to help.

1. 5)23 **4 R3** 2. 2)11 **5 R1** 3. 7)17 **2 R3** 4. 4)21 **5 R1**

5. 3)16 **5 R1** 6. 6)40 **6 R4** 7. 9)80 **8 R8** 8. 8)37 **4 R5**

9. 2)19 **9 R1** 10. 7)65 **9 R2** 11. 7)50 **7 R1** 12. 6)56 **9 R2**

13. 7)27 **3 R6** 14. 5)44 **8 R4** 15. 9)48 **5 R3** 16. 8)53 **6 R5**

17. Add all of the remainders together. What is their sum? **50**

Solve.

18. Mr. Pane has a carton holding 24 windows. He uses 7 windows for each spaceship. How many spaceships can he build with one carton of windows? How many windows are left over?

Mr. Pane can build 3 spaceships; he will have 3 windows left over.

19. Sally needs 4 sheets of paper to make a spaceship model. She has 15 sheets of paper. How many models can Sally make? How many sheets of paper will she have left over?

Sally can make 3 models. She will have 3 sheets of paper left over.

20. Jason has 30 spaceship stickers to share among 3 friends and himself. How many stickers will each child get? How many will be left over?

Each child gets 7 stickers. There will be 2 stickers left over.

 Use with Grade 3, text pages 462–463.

Reteach

Quotients With Remainders

R 12-7

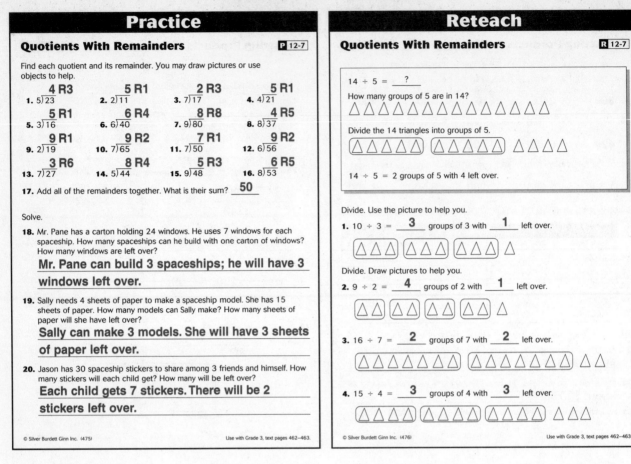

14 ÷ 5 = ?

How many groups of 5 are in 14?

△△△△△△△△△△△△△△

Divide the 14 triangles into groups of 5.

(△△△△△) (△△△△△) △△△△

14 ÷ 5 = 2 groups of 5 with 4 left over.

Divide. Use the picture to help you.

1. 10 ÷ 3 = **3** groups of 3 with **1** left over.

(△△△) (△△△) (△△△) △

Divide. Draw pictures to help you.

2. 9 ÷ 2 = **4** groups of 2 with **1** left over.

3. 16 ÷ 7 = **2** groups of 7 with **2** left over.

(△△△△△△△) (△△△△△△△) △△

4. 15 ÷ 4 = **3** groups of 4 with **3** left over.

(△△△△) (△△△△) (△△△△) △△△

 Use with Grade 3, text pages 462–463.

Extend

Next, Please!

E 12-7 REASONING

Look at each pattern. Write the number or letter that comes next. Then describe the pattern.

1. 3 6 9 12 **15**
The pattern is **adding three each time.**

2. B D F H J **L**
The pattern is **every other letter of the alphabet.**

3. 11 22 33 44 **55**
The pattern is **adding eleven each time.**

4. 3 4 6 9 13 18 24 **31**
The pattern is **adding numbers that increase by one each time.**

5. 5 50 500 5,000 **50,000**
The pattern is **multiplying by ten each time.**

6. 80 71 62 53 44 **35**
The pattern is **subtracting nine each time.**

7. 1 1 2 6 24 **120**
The pattern is **multiplying by numbers that increase by one each time.**

8. A Z B Y C **X**
The pattern is **first letter of alphabet, last letter, second letter, next to last letter, third letter, third from last.**

 Use with Grade 3, text pages 462–463.

Daily Review

Name ____________ Daily Review 12-7

Quotients With Remainders

Find each quotient.

1. 2)13 **6 R1** 2. 5)45 **9** 3. 3)25 **8 R1** 4. 1)5 **5** 5. 6)39 **6 R3**

6. 3)29 **9 R2** 7. 4)35 **8 R3** 8. 8)60 **7 R4** 9. 9)60 **6 R6** 10. 2)19 **9 R1**

11. 62 ÷ 8 = **7 R6** 12. 34 ÷ 4 = **8 R2** 13. 22 ÷ 7 = **3 R1**

14. 46 ÷ 6 = **7 R4** 15. 76 ÷ 9 = **8 R4** 16. 30 ÷ 7 = **4 R2**

17. 56 ÷ 8 = **7** 18. 15 ÷ 7 = **2 R1** 19. 47 ÷ 6 = **7 R5**

Problem Solving

20. Students are collecting cans for recycling. They place the 58 cans they have in groups of 6. How many groups of cans do they have? How many cans are left over?

9 groups of cans with 4 cans left over

21. Each recycled bottle or can is worth 5¢. A student receives 30¢ for recycled bottles and cans. How many items are recycled?

6 items

Review and Remember

Find each answer.

22. 4 × 7 = **28** 23. 53 + 46 = **99** 24. 28 ÷ 7 = **4**

25. 123 + 549 = **672** 26. 349 − 285 = **64** 27. 6 × 4 = **24**

28. 405 − 219 = **186** 29. 64 ÷ 8 = **8** 30. 627 + 189 = **816**

Practice

Problem Solving P 12-8

Interpreting Remainders

Circle the correct answer to each question.

Mrs. Patel buys fruit rolls for her 30 students to eat on a science museum field trip. The fruit rolls come in boxes of 8. How many boxes does Mrs. Patel need to buy?

1. You need to find the number of
   - a. students going on the field trip
   - b. fruit rolls in one box
   - (c.) boxes Mrs. Patel needs to buy
2. Which of the following will help you solve the problem?
   - (a.) 30 ÷ 8 = 3 R6
   - b. 30 ÷ 8 = 2 R10
   - c. 30 × 8 = 240
3. What will you do with the remainder?
   - a. subtract it from the quotient
   - (b.) use it to round the quotient up
   - c. write it beside the quotient
4. How many boxes does Mrs. Patel need to buy?
   - a. 3 boxes
   - (b.) 4 boxes
   - c. 5 boxes

Six students forgot to bring vegetable pieces for vegetable printing at the science museum. Mrs. Patel packed 16 vegetable pieces for students who forgot theirs. How can the students share these pieces equally?

5. How many vegetable pieces do the six students need to share?
   - a. 2 vegetable pieces
   - b. 6 vegetable pieces
   - (c.) 16 vegetable pieces
6. Which of the following will help you solve the problem?
   - (a.) 16 ÷ 6 = 2 R4
   - b. 16 ÷ 2 = 8
   - c. 16 × 2 = 32
7. How many pieces will each student get? What might the students do with the remainder? Tell what you think.
   2 pieces; answers will vary.

 Use with Grade 3, text pages 464–465.

Reteach

Problem Solving R 12-8

Interpreting Remainders

The *remainder* in a division problem can sometimes affect the answer. If there is a remainder, you may need to add 1 more to the solution. You may be able to just ignore a remainder. You will need to read the problem carefully to decide whether the remainder affects the answer.

CD World is selling CDs for $8 each for a one-day sale. Jermaine has $20 and wants to buy as many CDs as he can. How many can he buy?

To solve the problem, divide 20 by 8. The quotient is 2 Remainder 4.

Jermaine can buy exactly 2 CDs with $20. He will not use the remaining $4, the remainder, at all.

1. Jermaine buys cassette tapes for $6 each. He has $25 to spend. He knows that 25 ÷ 6 = 4 R1. How many cassette tapes can Jermaine buy? Explain.
   Jermaine can buy 4 cassette tapes. He will have $1 leftover.
2. Each of Jermaine's new cassette tapes runs for about 6 minutes. He has 15 minutes to listen to his tapes. Jermaine knows that 15 ÷ 6 = 2 R3. How many different complete tapes can Jermaine hear in 15 minutes? How many extra minutes does he have?
   2 complete tapes; 3 minutes.
3. Jermaine owns 43 cassette tapes. He wants to buy tape storage units. Each unit has room for 10 tapes. How many units does Jermaine need to buy?
   5 units; 43 ÷ 10 = 4 Remainder 3, so 4 units for 40 tapes plus a fifth unit for the remaining 3 tapes.

 Use with Grade 3, text pages 464–465.

Extend

Remainder Reasoning

E 12-8 PROBLEM SOLVING

For each problem, describe what you need to find in order to solve the problem. Then tell what you would do with the remainder.

1. Five friends buy a 32-sheet package of construction paper. How many sheets of construction paper will each friend get?
   How would you solve? **32 ÷ 5 = 6 Remainder 2**
   What might you do with the remainder?
   Possible answer: Cut each sheet of paper into 5 parts and share the parts equally.
2. A science class has tables at which four students can sit. How many tables are needed to seat a class of 30 students?
   How would you solve? **30 ÷ 4 = 7 Remainder 2**
   What will you do with the remainder?
   The remainder means that 8 tables, not 7, are needed.
3. Jo has 23 slices of bread. How many sandwiches can she make?
   How would you solve? **23 ÷ 2 = 11 Remainder 1**
   What will you do with the remainder?
   Possible answer: Make a half sandwich with the leftover slice.
4. Write a story problem for 20 ÷ 3 = 6 R2 where the remainder is used to round the quotient up to the next number.
   Problems will vary.
5. Write a story problem for 14 ÷ 4 = 3 R2 where the remainder doesn't matter.
   Problems will vary.

 Use with Grade 3, text pages 464–465.

Daily Review

Name ____________________ Daily Review 12-8

Problem Solving

Interpreting Remainders

Answer each question.

A tennis-ball factory makes cans of tennis balls. Each can holds 3 balls. What is the greatest number of cans that can be filled with 20 balls?

1. Which of the following could you do to solve the problem?
   - a. You could find that 20 ÷ 3 = 5 R5.
   - b. You could find that 20 × 3 = 60.
   - (c.) You could find that 20 ÷ 3 = 6 R2.
2. How should you use the remainder to solve the problem?
   - a. Use it to round up the quotient, so the answer is 7 cans.
   - (b.) Ignore the remainder so the answer is 6 cans.
   - c. Use the remainder so the answer is 6 R2 cans.

Linda is bringing baskets of flowers to a meeting. She has 47 flowers. She plans to put 7 flowers in each basket. How many baskets does she need to bring all of the flowers?

3. Which of the following could you do to solve the problem?
   - a. You could find that 47 ÷ 7 = 5 R12. Then ignore the remainder so the answer is 5 baskets.
   - (b.) You could find that 47 ÷ 7 = 6 R5. Then use the remainder to round the quotient up, so the answer is 7 baskets.
   - c. You could find that 47 ÷ 7 = 6 R5. Then use the remainder so the answer is 6 R5 baskets.

Review and Remember

Divide.

4. 36 ÷ 7 = **5 R1** 5. 25 ÷ 3 = **8 R1** 6. 46 ÷ 8 = **5 R6**

Chapter 12 • Lesson 9

Practice

Explore: Dividing by 2, 5, and 10

P 12-9

Color each box to show whether or not the number can be divided by 2, 5, or 10 without a remainder. Use this code to color the boxes.

The number can be divided by:		
Only 2	Only 5	2, 5, and 10
red	blue	yellow

1. 75 blue	**2.** 90 yellow	**3.** 88 red	**4.** 100 yellow	**5.** 45 blue
6. 36 red	**7.** 355 blue	**8.** 400 yellow	**9.** 695 blue	**10.** 502 red
11. 2,470 yellow	**12.** 7,654 red	**13.** 2,345 blue	**14.** 9,032 red	**15.** 9,710 yellow

16. How can you tell by looking at a number whether it can be divided evenly by 10? Possible answers: It ends in zero; you say it if you skip-count by ten.

17. How can you tell by looking at a number whether it can be divided evenly by 5? Possible answers: It ends in zero or five; you say it if you skip-count by five.

18. How can you tell by looking at a number whether it can be divided evenly by 2? Possible answers: It ends in 0, 2, 4, 6, or 8; you say it if you skip-count by two; it is an even number.

 Use with Grade 3, text pages 466–467.

Reteach

Explore: Dividing by 2, 5, and 10

R 12-9

You can tell whether or not a number can be evenly divided by 2, 5, or 10. Just look at the ones place!

A number can be evenly divided by:

2 if the number in the ones place is 2, 4, 6, 8, or 0.
5 if the number in the ones place is 5 or 0.
10 if the number in the ones place is 0.

34	45	60
4 in the ones place. The number can be evenly divided by 2.	5 in the ones place. The number can be evenly divided by 5.	0 in the ones place. The number can be evenly divided by 10. It can also be divided by 2 and 5.

Circle the ones place in each number. Use the number in the ones place to decide whether the number can be divided evenly by 2, 5, or all three numbers. Write 2, 5, or ALL.

1. 15 — 5	**2.** 22 — 2	**3.** 30 — ALL	**4.** 25 — 5	**5.** 34 — 2
6. 16 — 2	**7.** 26 — 2	**8.** 50 — ALL	**9.** 80 — ALL	**10.** 44 — 2
11. 35 — 5	**12.** 60 — ALL	**13.** 55 — 5	**14.** 82 — 2	**15.** 95 — 5
16. 75 — 5	**17.** 92 — 2	**18.** 100 — ALL	**19.** 68 — 2	**20.** 96 — 2

 Use with Grade 3, text pages 466–467.

Extend

Building Block Puzzle

E 12-9 VISUAL THINKING

Look at the figure on the left in each row. All but one of the shapes on the right can be used to build that figure. Circle the shape that cannot be used.

 Use with Grade 3, text pages 466–467.

Daily Review

Name ____________ Daily Review 12-9

EXPLORE: Dividing by 2, 5, and 10

Tell whether or not each number can be divided by 2, by 5, or by 10 without a remainder.

1. 340 by 2, 5, 10	**2.** 325 by 5	**3.** 422 by 2	**4.** 731 by none
5. 603 by none	**6.** 980 by 2, 5, 10	**7.** 415 by 5	**8.** 262 by 2
9. 367 by none	**10.** 145 by 5	**11.** 290 by 2, 5, 10	**12.** 505 by 5

Problem Solving

13. Write a statement to describe numbers that are divisible by 2, 5, and 10. All numbers that are divisible by 2, 5, and 10 must have a 0 in the ones place.

14. What can you say about any number that has a 0, 2, 4, 6, or 8 in the ones place? Any number that has a 0, 2, 4, 6, or 8 in the ones place is divisible by 2. Any number that has a 0 in the ones place is divisible by 2, 5, and 10.

15. Any number that is divisible by 10 is also divisible by what other numbers? Any number that is divisible by 10 is also divisible by 2 and 5.

Review and Remember

Use mental math to find each answer.

16. 370 + 400 = 770 **17.** 38 + 100 = 138 **18.** 980 − 50 = 930
19. 700 − 40 = 660 **20.** 838 − 38 = 800 **21.** 24 + 60 = 84

Chapter 12 • Lesson 10

Practice

Problem Solving P 12-10

Choose a Strategy

Choose a strategy to solve these problems. Tell which strategy you will use. Then solve. **Possible strategies are given.**

- Use Logical Reasoning
- Make a Graph
- Guess and Check
- Find a Pattern
- Write a Number Sentence
- Draw a Picture

1. The first three house numbers on Seth's street are 1234, 1238, and 1242. What is the next number?
   Strategy: **Find a Pattern**
   Solution: **1246**
2. A store sells toy trucks for $5 each. How many trucks must they sell to collect $150?
   Strategy: **Number Sentence**
   Solution: **30 trucks**
3. Carlos and Luis have 42 toy trucks. Carlos has double the number Luis has and 3 more. How many toy trucks does each boy have?
   Strategy: **Guess and Check**
   Solution: **Carlos 29; Luis 13**
4. You begin a soccer team telephone chain call at 12:45 one rainy afternoon. The last person on the team is reached by 1:15. How long did the telephone chain take?
   Strategy: **Draw a Picture**
   Solution: **30 minutes**
5. **Social Studies Connection** In 1876, Alexander Graham Bell spoke the first words through the telephone that he invented. How many years ago was that?
   Strategy: **Number Sentence**
   Solution: **Sample Answer: 122 years in 1998**
6. On Friday, 16 students bought a hot lunch, 12 students bought a cold lunch, and 24 students brought lunch. Make a graph to show the kind of lunches students had.
   Strategy: **Make a Graph**
   Solution: **Check graphs.**

 Use with Grade 3, text pages 468–469.

Reteach

Problem Solving R 12-10

Choose a Strategy

Penny's family visited her grandfather, who lives 78 miles away. On the way back they traveled 20 miles further to a friend of Penny's.

1. How many miles did Penny's family drive going and coming back?

Understand You need to find the total number of miles traveled. You need to understand you can solve this problem in different ways.

Plan What should you do?

You could *write a number sentence.* You could *make a table.*

Solve 78 + 20 + 98 = 196 miles

	Miles	Total
to Grandfather	78	78
to friend	20	98
to home	98	196

Look Back To check your work, try to solve the problem using a different plan. Your solution should be the same.

Choose a strategy to solve these problems. Tell which strategy you chose. Then solve. **Possible strategies are given.**

- Use Logical Reasoning
- Make a Graph
- Guess and Check
- Find a Pattern
- Write a Number Sentence
- Draw a Picture

2. Sam has $8, Jan has $15, Ed has $17, and Anna has $13. Which two people could put their money together and have a total of $25?
   Strategy: **Guess and Check**
   Solution: **Sam and Ed**
3. Jill finds 8 seashells on Monday, 16 on Tuesday, and 24 on Wednesday. If the pattern continues, how many will Jill find on Thursday?
   Strategy: **Find a Pattern**
   Solution: **32 seashells**

 Use with Grade 3, text pages 468–469.

Extend

Sharing Strategies

E 12-10 NUMBER SENSE

Work with a partner. Decide on a different strategy than your partner to solve each problem. Then share your solution with your partner.

1. The distance around the ball field is 76 meters. The length of the field is 1 meter less than twice its width. The width is between 10 and 15 meters. What is the length and width of the ball field?
   length: 25 m; width: 13 m
2. The music teacher works with 9 classes a week. Each class has 30 students. How many students does the music teacher work with each week?
   270 students
3. A 21-person gymnastic team makes a pyramid. Each level of the pyramid has 1 gymnast fewer than the level below it. There is one gymnast at the top. How many gymnasts are on the bottom level?
   6 gymnasts
4. Jonah is at school 30 hours for a 5-day week. School begins at 9:15 each day. When does school end each day?
   3:15
5. Kamisha is performing in a parade. The parade lasts an hour, and Kamisha performs for $\frac{1}{4}$ of the time. How many minutes will Kamisha be watching the parade rather than performing in it?
   45 minutes
6. What did you find out about the strategies you chose?
   Possible answers. Students may say they found one strategy to be quickest, most reliable, or easiest for them.

 Use with Grade 3, text pages 468–469.

Daily Review

Name ____________________ Daily Review 12-10

Problem Solving

Choose a Strategy

Use a strategy to solve each problem.

Make a Graph	Find a Pattern
Guess and Check	Write a Number Sentence
Draw a Picture	Use Logical Reasoning

1. Allison and Shaquille eat 34 crackers. Allison eats 4 fewer crackers than Shaquille. How many crackers do Allison and Shaquille each eat?
   Guess and Check; Allison: 15, Shaquille: 19
2. Marvin runs 2 miles on Monday, 4 miles on Tuesday, and 6 miles on Wednesday. How many miles will he run on Thursday if he continues this pattern?
   Find a Pattern; 8 miles
3. Sarah buys 2 new baseball cards every week. If she has 24 cards, how many weeks has she been collecting them?
   Write a Number Sentence; 12 weeks
4. Betty is 7 years old and Ryan is 10 years old. Patrick is the second youngest. His age is an odd number. What is Patrick's age?
   Use Logical Reasoning; 9 years old

Review and Remember

Multiply.

5. 27 3 3 5 **81**
6. 13 3 5 5 **65**
7. 17 3 6 5 **102**
8. 18 3 4 5 **72**
9. 21 3 6 5 **126**
10. 32 3 5 5 **160**

Practice

Division Patterns

P 12-11

Use a basic fact and mental math to find each quotient.

1. $4\overline{)80}$ **20**	2. $3\overline{)90}$ **30**	3. $4\overline{)160}$ **40**	4. $2\overline{)100}$ **50**
5. $6\overline{)180}$ **30**	6. $6\overline{)300}$ **50**	7. $2\overline{)180}$ **90**	8. $8\overline{)640}$ **80**
9. $5\overline{)1,500}$ **300**	10. $7\overline{)2,800}$ **400**	11. $7\overline{)4,900}$ **700**	12. $6\overline{)5,400}$ **900**
13. $6\overline{)4,800}$ **800**	14. $4\overline{)3,600}$ **900**	15. $9\overline{)7,200}$ **800**	16. $8\overline{)6,400}$ **800**

Solve.

17. Unity Space Station houses 240 people. If the people are divided evenly between 6 space modules, how many people are in each module?
There are 40 people in each module.

18. The Larsons traveled 1,800 light-years from Earth to Kalron. They traveled about the same distance each day for 6 days. About how far did they travel each day?
The Larsons traveled about 300 light-years each day.

Use mental math to find the mystery number.

19. Start with 250. Divide by 5 and add 10. Divide by 6. Divide by 5. What is the mystery number? **2**

20. Start with 400. Divide by 5 and add 20. Subtract 50 and divide by 25. What is the mystery number? **2**

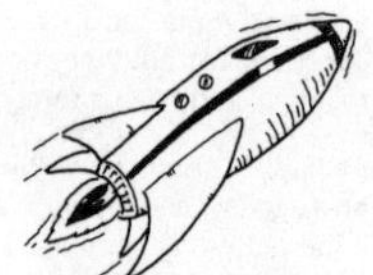

 Use with Grade 3, text pages 470–471.

Reteach

Division Patterns

R 12-11

How much are 80 ÷ 2 and 800 ÷ 2?

Step 1 Think about what you know: $2\overline{)8}$ 4

Step 2 Add one zero for tens: $2\overline{)80}$ 40

Step 3 Add two zeros for hundreds $2\overline{)800}$ 400

So, 80 ÷ 2 = 40 and 800 ÷ 2 = 400

Find each quotient. Use what you know to help you.

1. $2\overline{)4}$ **2**	$2\overline{)40}$ **20**	$2\overline{)400}$ **200**	2. $3\overline{)9}$ **3**	$3\overline{)90}$ **30**	$3\overline{)900}$ **300**
3. $2\overline{)6}$ **3**	$2\overline{)60}$ **30**	$2\overline{)600}$ **300**	4. $4\overline{)8}$ **2**	$4\overline{)80}$ **20**	$4\overline{)800}$ **200**
5. $2\overline{)10}$ **5**	$2\overline{)100}$ **50**	$2\overline{)1,000}$ **500**	6. $5\overline{)15}$ **3**	$5\overline{)150}$ **30**	$5\overline{)1,500}$ **300**
7. $7\overline{)14}$ **2**	$7\overline{)140}$ **20**	$7\overline{)1,400}$ **200**	8. $8\overline{)24}$ **3**	$8\overline{)240}$ **30**	$8\overline{)2,400}$ **300**

9. $6\overline{)600}$ **100** 10. $4\overline{)320}$ **80** 11. $7\overline{)560}$ **80** 12. $3\overline{)90}$ **30**

Solve.

13. Sally has 3 groups of stickers with 8, 80, and 800 in each group. She divides each group into 4 boxes. How many stickers will each box hold?

8 stickers in 4 boxes = **2** stickers in a box.
80 stickers in 4 boxes = **20** stickers in a box.
800 stickers in 4 boxes = **200** stickers in a box.

 Use with Grade 3, text pages 470–471.

Extend

Math Line-up

E 12-11
REASONING

Solve. Draw a picture or a diagram to help you.

1. Three kinds of birds are kept in the Space Station Pet Store. The parrots are at one end. The parakeets are between the doves and the parrots. In what order are the birds?
parrots, parakeets, doves; doves, parakeets, parrots

Draw

2. On the planet Nebron, Frost Mountain is 2,500 feet higher than Blue Mountain. High Knob Mountain is 1,000 feet lower than Frost Mountain. Which mountain is the lowest?
Blue Mountain

Draw

3. Four kinds of flowers will be planted in a row in the Space Station garden. The marigolds must be planted next to the roses and cannot be planted next to the daisies. The asters must be planted next to both the daisies and the roses. In what order will flowers be planted?
marigolds, roses, asters, daisies, or the reverse

Draw

 Use with Grade 3, text pages 470–471.

Daily Review

Name

Daily Review 12-11

Division Patterns

Use a basic fact and mental math to find each quotient.

1. $4\overline{)16}$ **4**	$4\overline{)160}$ **40**	$4\overline{)1,600}$ **400**	2. $2\overline{)6}$ **3**	$2\overline{)60}$ **30**	$2\overline{)600}$ **300**
3. $6\overline{)36}$ **6**	$6\overline{)360}$ **60**	$6\overline{)3,600}$ **600**	4. $4\overline{)28}$ **7**	$4\overline{)280}$ **70**	$4\overline{)2,800}$ **700**
5. $5\overline{)35}$ **7**	$5\overline{)350}$ **70**	$5\overline{)3,500}$ **700**	6. $3\overline{)12}$ **4**	$3\overline{)120}$ **40**	$3\overline{)1,200}$ **400**

7. 63 ÷ 9 = **7**	8. 72 ÷ 8 = **9**	9. 40 ÷ 5 = **8**
630 ÷ 9 = **70**	720 ÷ 8 = **90**	400 ÷ 5 = **80**
6,300 ÷ 9 = **700**	7,200 ÷ 8 = **900**	4,000 ÷ 5 = **800**

Problem Solving

10. Groups of 5 people can go through the travel tube at the same time. How many trips will it take for 250 people to go through the travel tube one way? **50 trips**

11. There are 80 people waiting to take the travel tubes. Groups of 4 use the travel tubes at the same time. It takes 5 seconds for each group to go through the travel tubes. How long will it take for all 80 people to go through the travel tubes one way? **100 seconds**

Review and Remember

Find each answer.

12. 19 − 4 = **15**
13. 593 − 389 = **204**
14. 306 + 441 = **747**
15. 3 × 50 = **150**

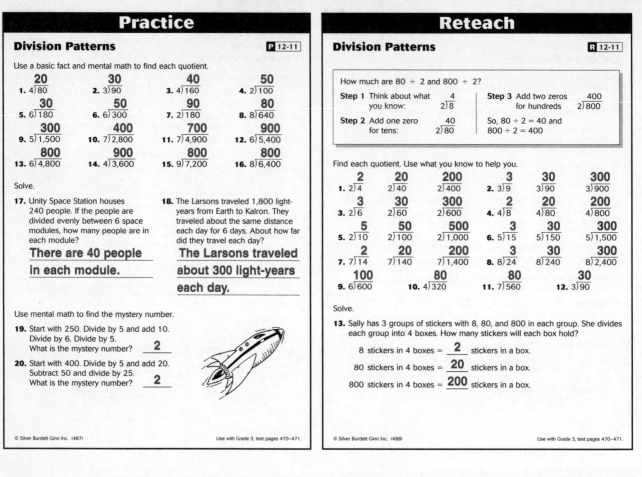

Chapter 12 • Lesson 12

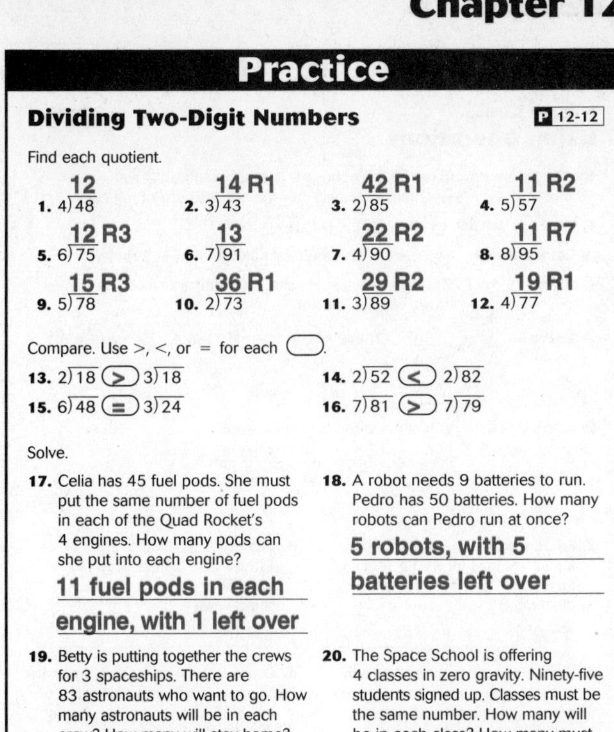

Practice

Dividing Two-Digit Numbers P 12-12

Find each quotient.

1. 4)48 **12**
2. 3)43 **14 R1**
3. 2)85 **42 R1**
4. 5)57 **11 R2**
5. 6)75 **12 R3**
6. 7)91 **13**
7. 4)90 **22 R2**
8. 8)95 **11 R7**
9. 5)78 **15 R3**
10. 2)73 **36 R1**
11. 3)89 **29 R2**
12. 4)77 **19 R1**

Compare. Use >, <, or = for each ◯.

13. 2)18 **(>)** 3)18
14. 2)52 **(<)** 2)82
15. 6)48 **(=)** 3)24
16. 7)81 **(>)** 7)79

Solve.

17. Celia has 45 fuel pods. She must put the same number of fuel pods in each of the Quad Rocket's 4 engines. How many pods can she put into each engine?
11 fuel pods in each engine, with 1 left over

18. A robot needs 9 batteries to run. Pedro has 50 batteries. How many robots can Pedro run at once?
5 robots, with 5 batteries left over

19. Betty is putting together the crews for 3 spaceships. There are 83 astronauts who want to go. How many astronauts will be in each crew? How many will stay home?
27 in each crew; 2 stay home.

20. The Space School is offering 4 classes in zero gravity. Ninety-five students signed up. Classes must be the same number. How many will be in each class? How many must wait until the class is offered again?
23 in each class; 3 must wait for next classes.

 Use with Grade 3, text pages 472–475.

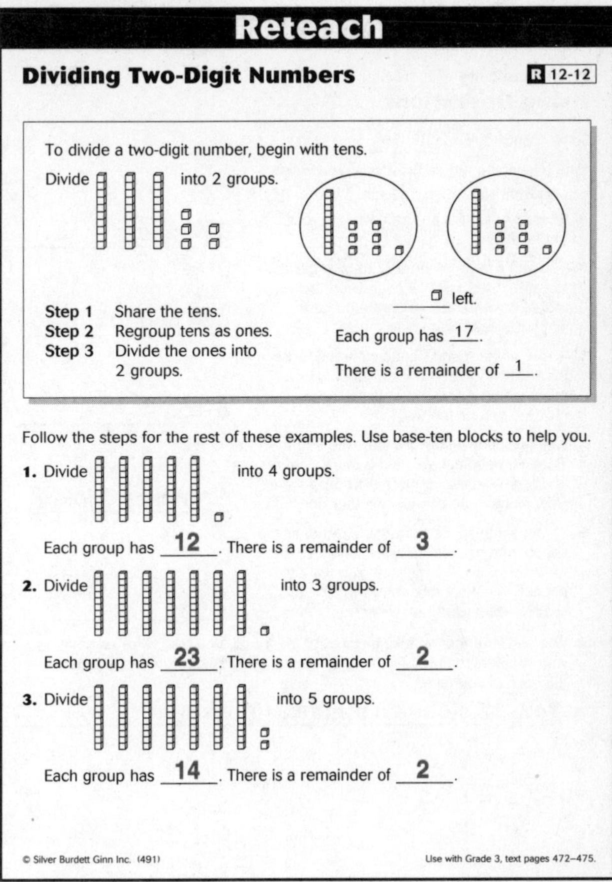

Reteach

Dividing Two-Digit Numbers R 12-12

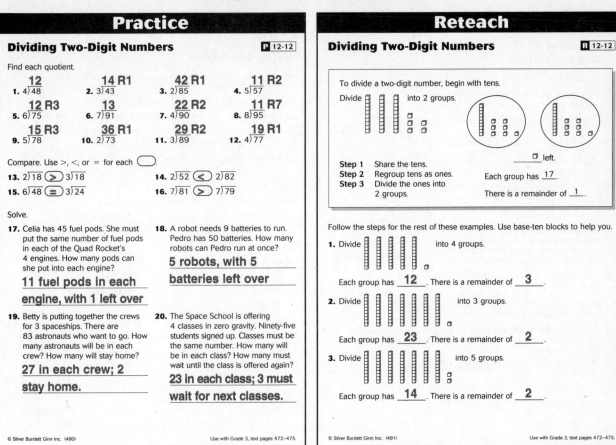

To divide a two-digit number, begin with tens.

Divide [3 tens, 5 ones] into 2 groups.

Step 1 Share the tens.
Step 2 Regroup tens as ones.
Step 3 Divide the ones into 2 groups.

1 left.
Each group has **17**.
There is a remainder of **1**.

Follow the steps for the rest of these examples. Use base-ten blocks to help you.

1. Divide [5 tens, 1 one] into 4 groups.
Each group has **12**. There is a remainder of **3**.

2. Divide [7 tens, 1 one] into 3 groups.
Each group has **23**. There is a remainder of **2**.

3. Divide [7 tens, 2 ones] into 5 groups.
Each group has **14**. There is a remainder of **2**.

 Use with Grade 3, text pages 472–475.

Extend

Find the Fake E 12-12 REASONING

Each group has three division problems that belong together and one that does not belong. Figure out how the three are alike. Circle the one that does not belong and explain why.

1. **(7)77)** 5)25 8)64 9)81
The quotient does not equal the divisor.

2. 3)600 4)800 **(5)100)** 2)400
The quotient does not equal 200.

3. **(2)120)** 4)200 5)250 6)300
The quotient does not equal 50.

4. 3)45 5)35 **(5)53)** 3)39
The quotient has a remainder.

5. 3)45 **(4)68)** 5)67 7)89
Problem not composed of consecutive numbers.

6. 3)24 **(4)52)** 6)36 8)48
The quotient is not even.

7. 4)53 6)85 7)78 **(8)98)**
The quotient does not have a remainder of 1.

 Use with Grade 3, text pages 472–475.

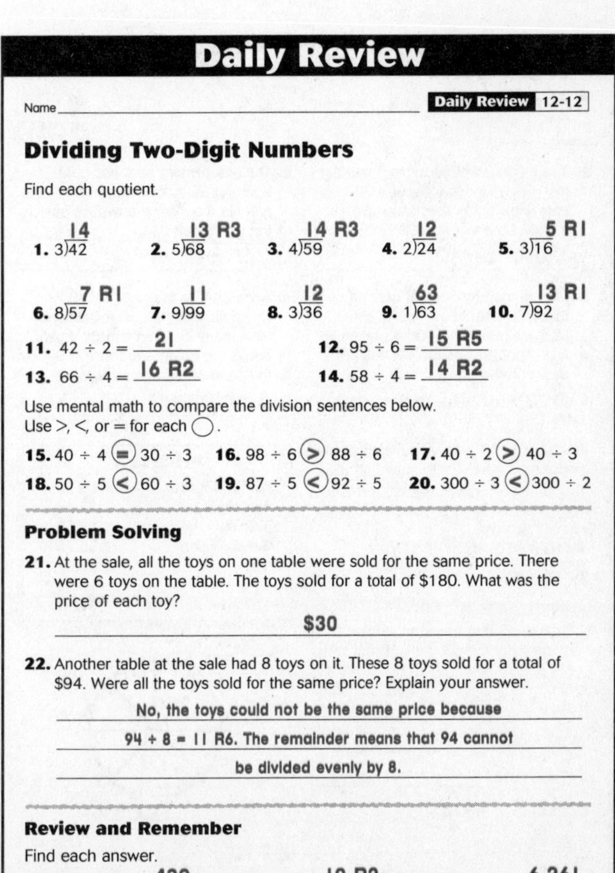

Daily Review

Name ____________ Daily Review 12-12

Dividing Two-Digit Numbers

Find each quotient.

1. 3)42 **14**
2. 5)68 **13 R3**
3. 4)59 **14 R3**
4. 2)24 **12**
5. 3)16 **5 R1**
6. 8)57 **7 R1**
7. 9)99 **11**
8. 3)36 **12**
9. 1)63 **63**
10. 7)92 **13 R1**

11. 42 ÷ 2 = **21**
12. 95 ÷ 6 = **15 R5**
13. 66 ÷ 4 = **16 R2**
14. 58 ÷ 4 = **14 R2**

Use mental math to compare the division sentences below. Use >, <, or = for each ◯.

15. 40 ÷ 4 **(=)** 30 ÷ 3
16. 98 ÷ 6 **(>)** 88 ÷ 6
17. 40 ÷ 2 **(>)** 40 ÷ 3
18. 50 ÷ 5 **(<)** 60 ÷ 3
19. 87 ÷ 5 **(<)** 92 ÷ 5
20. 300 ÷ 3 **(<)** 300 ÷ 2

Problem Solving

21. At the sale, all the toys on one table were sold for the same price. There were 6 toys on the table. The toys sold for a total of $180. What was the price of each toy?
$30

22. Another table at the sale had 8 toys on it. These 8 toys sold for a total of $94. Were all the toys sold for the same price? Explain your answer.
No, the toys could not be the same price because 94 ÷ 8 = 11 R6. The remainder means that 94 cannot be divided evenly by 8.

Review and Remember

Find each answer.

23. 401 + 38 = **439**
24. 32 ÷ 3 = **10 R2**
25. 6,328 − 67 = **6,261**

Chapter 12 • Lesson 13

Practice

Problem Solving P 12-13

Using Operations

Solve each problem.

1. Suppose you are on the moon. You weigh $\frac{1}{6}$ of what you weigh on Earth. If you weigh 54 pounds on Earth, what is your moon weight? **9 pounds**
2. You find a large moon rock to take back to Earth. It weighs 104 pounds on the moon. What will it's weight be on Earth, when it weighs 6 times as much? **624 pounds**
3. A tour of the moon's craters costs $18.85 for adults and $29.50 for children. How much would it cost for 2 adults and 4 children to take the tour? **$155.70**
4. Fifty-two people start the tour with you. Then 16 people leave, and 8 more come. The tour will take no more than 55 people. How many more can join the tour now? **11 more people**
5. To eat some space food, you need to fill the space food packet with water and let it sit for 2 hours and 15 minutes. You want to eat at 6:00. What time should you fill the space food packet with water? **3:45**
6. You and your mother take pictures of the moon. You take twice as many as your mother. Together, you take a total of 48 pictures. How many pictures did each of you take? **You, 32 pictures; mother, 16 pictures**

 Use with Grade 3, text pages 476–477.

Reteach

Problem Solving R 12-13

Using Operations

The Degas are driving to visit their cousins. They are traveling at a speed of 50 miles per hour. How many miles will they travel if they drive for 4 hours?

1. How can you find out how far the Degas will travel?

Understand You need to find the total number of miles traveled.

Plan Since the number of miles is the same for every hour they travel, you can multiply.

Solve 50 × 4 = **200** **Think:** 4 × 5 = **20**, so 4 × 50 = **200**

Look Back You can add to check your work.

50 + 50 + 50 + 50 = **200** ✓

Solve.

2. For dinner, Emmy orders a burger for $2.75, fries for $1.19, and juice for $1.35. How much does Emmy's dinner cost? **$5.29**
3. Dinner for the Degas family costs $17.35. Mrs. Degas pays with a $20 bill. How much change will she receive? **$2.65**
4. Emmy Degas has saved $3 each week to spend while she visits her cousins. She has $27. For how many weeks did she save? **9 weeks**
5. Emmy takes 4 rolls of pictures while she is with her cousins. Each roll has 36 pictures on it. How many pictures did Emmy take? **144 pictures**

 Use with Grade 3, text pages 476–477.

Extend

Amusement Park

E 12-13 NUMBER SENSE

Solve.

1. The amusement park has 8 parking lots. Each lot holds about 4,000 cars. How many cars can still park if 6/8 of the lots are full? **8,000 cars**
2. The amusement park has been open for 364 days a year for 8 years. For how many days has the park been open? **2,912 days**
3. One of the amusement park rides takes 20 people every 3 minutes. You are about the 300th person in line. About how soon will you get to go on the ride? **in about 45 minutes**
4. Admission to the park is $32.75 for adults and $23.50 for children. How many children can go if two adults are going and there is $200 to spend on admission tickets? **5 children**

You have $100 to buy souvenirs at the amusement park. Try to spend all your money. Tell what you will buy, how much you will spend, and what change you will receive.

Answers will vary.

Price List	
Stuffed Mouse	$19.95
Sweatshirt	$12.49
T-Shirt	$9.50
Baseball Cap	$8.75
Visor	$6.95
Magnet	$2.39
Keychain	$2.95

5. I will buy:

Item ________ Price ________

____

____

____

____

Total Cost ________

6. Change from $100.00 ________

 Use with Grade 3, text pages 476–477.

Daily Review

Name ________ Daily Review 12-13

Problem Solving

Using Operations

Solve each problem.

1. A bus has 22 people on it when it leaves the station. It makes 2 stops. At the first stop, 15 people get on the bus. At the second stop, 19 people get on the bus. How many people are on the bus now? **56 people**
2. One ice cream store sells 54 flavors of ice cream. Another ice cream store sells 23 flavors of ice cream. How many more flavors does the first store sell? **31 more flavors**
3. Keisha was born in 1992. How old is she now? **The answer depends on the year it is now.**
4. Brian, David, Elise, Kate, and Melissa are going on a boat trip. The trip costs $400 for 5 people. If all 5 people split the cost evenly, how much do they each pay? **$80 each**

Review and Remember

Add or subtract.

5. 49 + 7 = **56**
6. 311 + 19 = **330**
7. 237 − 34 = **203**
8. 8 + 12 + 39 = **59**
9. 602 − 183 = **419**
10. 15 + 9 + 21 = **45**
11. 589 − 37 = **552**

Practice Workbook Answers

Chapter 1

Practice Workbook

Investigating Number Patterns

Write three addition or subtraction sentences for each set. Write odd or even numbers. Then, write if the sums or differences are odd or even.

Facts will vary.

1. ODD + ODD | **2. EVEN + EVEN**

___ + ___ = ___
___ + ___ = ___
___ + ___ = ___

The sums are even. | The sums are even.

3. ODD + EVEN

___ + ___ = ___
___ + ___ = ___
___ + ___ = ___

The sums are odd.

4. ODD – EVEN

___ – ___ = ___
___ – ___ = ___
___ – ___ = ___

The differences are odd.

5. EVEN – EVEN

___ – ___ = ___
___ – ___ = ___
___ – ___ = ___

The differences are even.

6. ODD – ODD

___ – ___ = ___
___ – ___ = ___
___ – ___ = ___

The differences are even.

Review and Remember

Add or subtract.

1. 9 – 8 = 1 **2.** 4 + 4 = 8 **3.** 12 – 6 = 6

4. 4 + 3 = 7 **5.** 8 + 7 = 15 **6.** 14 – 6 = 8

Practice Workbook

Rounding to the Nearest Ten and Hundred

Round to the nearest ten.

30 31 32 33 34 35 36 37 38 39 40

1. 32 30 **2.** 35 40 **3.** 38 40

4. 34 30 **5.** 36 40 **6.** 31 30

7. 45 50 **8.** 53 50 **9.** 71 70

Round to the nearest ten. Circle the letter of the correct answer.

10. 57 — a. 50 (b.) 60 c. 70

11. 41 — a. 30 (b.) 40 c. 50

12. 75 — a. 50 b. 70 (c.) 80

13. 92 — a. 80 (b.) 90 c. 100

Round to the nearest hundred.

300 310 320 330 340 350 360 370 380 390 400

14. 341 300 **15.** 350 400 **16.** 363 400 **17.** 329 300

18. 435 400 **19.** 529 500 **20.** 617 600 **21.** 903 900

Review and Remember

Add or subtract.

1. 3 + 4 + 4 = 11 **2.** 5 + 3 + 5 = 13 **3.** 6 + 1 + 8 = 15 **4.** 4 + 2 + 7 = 13 **5.** 8 + 1 + 1 = 10 **6.** 5 + 4 + 3 = 12

7. 14 – 2 = 12 **8.** 11 – 6 = 5 **9.** 16 – 2 = 14 **10.** 18 – 9 = 9 **11.** 16 – 8 = 8 **12.** 12 – 5 = 7

Chapter 1

Practice Workbook

Reading and Writing Four-Digit Numbers

Write each number.

1. 2 thousands 4 hundreds 2 tens 5 ones 2,425

2. 6 thousands 1 hundred 0 tens 9 ones 6,109

3. 8 thousands 3 hundreds 4 tens 2 ones 8,342

4. 5 thousands 6 hundreds 9 tens 4 ones 5,694

5. 5,000 + 600 + 70 + 9 5,679 **6.** 9,000 + 800 + 20 + 1 9,821

7. 1,000 + 200 + 4 1,204 **8.** 4,000 + 200 + 50 + 7 4,257

Give the value of the digit 5.

9. 4,563 5 hundreds **10.** 5,014 5 thousands **11.** 1,250 5 tens **12.** 6,745 5 ones

Write the word name for each number.

13. 275 two hundred seventy-five

14. 3,407 three thousand, four hundred seven

15. 8,015 eight thousand, fifteen

Review and Remember

Add.

1. 5 + 2 = 7 **2.** 3 + 3 = 6 **3.** 2 + 8 = 10 **4.** 9 + 0 = 9 **5.** 3 + 7 = 10 **6.** 4 + 3 = 7

Write the numbers that come between.

7. 16 and 19 — 17, 18

8. 27 and 32 — 28, 29, 30, 31

9. 49 and 55 — 50, 51, 52, 53, 54

Practice Workbook

Comparing and Ordering Numbers

Compare. Write > or < in each ◯.

1. 322 > 321 **2.** 689 < 3,869 **3.** 5,018 < 5,118

4. 870 < 6,087 **5.** 8,432 > 4,823 **6.** 581 > 381

7. 4,960 < 4,962 **8.** 9,180 > 8,190 **9.** 2,224 < 2,325

Write the numbers in order from least to greatest.

10. 3,246 2,436 4,233 — 2,436 3,246 4,233

11. 6,198 3,427 7,866 — 3,427 6,198 7,866

12. 4,380 4,038 3,444 — 3,444 4,038 4,380

13. 1,326 3,621 6,140 — 1,326 3,621 6,140

14. 999 9 9,000 — 9 999 9,000

15. 4,022 8,042 2,048 — 2,048 4,022 8,042

16. 77 7 7,777 — 7 77 7,777

17. 3,906 9,063 6,039 — 3,906 6,039 9,063

Review and Remember

Add or subtract.

1. 8 + 9 = 17 **2.** 7 + 5 = 12 **3.** 8 + 8 = 16 **4.** 4 + 9 = 13 **5.** 2 + 9 = 11 **6.** 8 + 4 = 12

7. 13 – 5 = 8 **8.** 12 – 4 = 8 **9.** 11 – 7 = 4 **10.** 11 – 3 = 8 **11.** 13 – 7 = 6 **12.** 12 – 9 = 3

13. 9 + 8 = 17 **14.** 5 + 9 = 14 **15.** 8 + 4 = 12

16. 11 – 6 = 5 **17.** 13 – 9 = 4 **18.** 12 – 7 = 5

Chapter 1

Practice Workbook

Counting Coins and Bills

Write each value. Use a dollar sign and a decimal point.

1. forty-two cents $0.42
2. eighty-two cents $0.82
3. two dollars and twenty cents $2.20
4. three dollars and sixty cents $3.60
5. 3 dimes, 2 pennies $0.32
6. 8 one-dollar bills, 4 dimes $8.40
7. 6 one-dollar bills, 3 pennies $6.03
8. 4 one-dollar bills, 1 dime $4.10
9. 6 dimes, 8 pennies $0.68
10. 5 one-dollar bills, 9 dimes $5.90

Write the missing amount.

11. 3 one-dollar bills = 30 dimes
12. 6 quarters = 15 dimes
13. 3 one-dollar bills = 300 pennies
14. 6 quarters = 150 pennies

Review and Remember

Add or subtract.

1. 9 + 9 = 18
2. 6 + 8 = 14
3. 3 + 9 = 12
4. 6 + 9 = 15
5. 8 + 7 = 15
6. 9 + 7 = 16
7. 13 − 4 = 9
8. 11 − 2 = 9
9. 12 − 5 = 7
10. 11 − 6 = 5
11. 13 − 8 = 5
12. 12 − 4 = 8
13. 8 + 8 = 16
14. 16 − 7 = 9
15. 5 + 7 = 12
16. 3 + 6 = 9
17. 18 − 6 = 12
18. 4 + 3 = 7

Chapter 2

Practice Workbook

Using Addition Strategies

Add.

1. 6 + 5 = 11
2. 7 + 7 = 14
3. 8 + 3 = 11
4. 8 + 8 = 16
5. 6 + 7 = 13
6. 5 + 8 = 13
7. 6 + 6 = 12
8. 7 + 8 = 15
9. 9 + 4 = 13
10. 9 + 9 = 18
11. 9 + 0 = 9
12. 8 + 6 = 14
13. 5 + 7 = 12
14. 9 + 8 = 17
15. 0 + 2 = 2

16. 7 + 6 = 13
17. 9 + 6 = 15
18. 4 + 8 = 12
19. 9 + 5 = 14
20. 1 + 6 = 7
21. 4 + 5 = 9

Find the output.

Rule: Add 9

	Input	Output
22.	3	12
23.	7	16
24.	5	14
25.	8	17

Rule: Add 3

	Input	Output
26.	12	15
27.	6	9
28.	4	7
29.	9	12

Review and Remember

Molly and Tom each made 4 potholders. How many potholders did they make altogether? 8 potholders

Chapter 2

Practice Workbook

Adding Three Numbers

Add.

1. 3 + 2 + 6 = 11
2. 7 + 0 + 4 = 11
3. 5 + 4 + 4 = 13
4. 4 + 1 + 8 = 13
5. 5 + 4 + 3 = 12
6. 7 + 2 + 7 = 16
7. 7 + 1 + 8 = 16
8. 6 + 1 + 7 = 14
9. 8 + 0 + 9 = 17
10. 2 + 3 + 4 = 9
11. 5 + 0 + 8 = 13
12. 4 + 4 + 4 = 12
13. 2 + 2 + 7 = 11
14. 1 + 0 + 8 = 9
15. 7 + 2 + 6 = 15

16. 6 + 0 + 9 = 15
17. 7 + 1 + 6 = 14
18. 4 + 4 + 3 = 11

Choose the correct sum. Circle the letter of your answer.

19. 6 + 3 + 4 = ☐ **(a.)** 13 **b.** 12 **c.** 14

20. 5 + 0 + 6 = ☐ **a.** 5 **b.** 16 **(c.)** 11

Review and Remember

Add.

1. 5 + 4 = 9
2. 8 + 1 = 9
3. 3 + 7 = 10
4. 4 + 3 = 7
5. 2 + 8 = 10
6. 6 + 3 = 9
7. 7 + 1 = 8
8. 3 + 6 = 9
9. 2 + 6 = 8
10. 7 + 5 = 12
11. 6 + 3 = 9
12. 8 + 3 = 11

Practice Workbook

Using Subtraction Strategies

Subtract.

1. 15 − 7 = 8
2. 9 − 0 = 9
3. 14 − 7 = 7
4. 15 − 9 = 6
5. 14 − 6 = 8
6. 17 − 9 = 8
7. 6 − 6 = 0
8. 13 − 4 = 9
9. 16 − 8 = 8
10. 14 − 5 = 9
11. 18 − 9 = 9
12. 15 − 8 = 7
13. 16 − 9 = 7
14. 14 − 9 = 5
15. 8 − 8 = 0

16. 14 − 8 = 6
17. 7 − 7 = 0
18. 13 − 4 = 9
19. 15 − 7 = 8
20. 17 − 8 = 9
21. 12 − 8 = 4

Solve.

22. There are 15 books and 8 children. How many more books are there than children? 7 books

Review and Remember

Add or subtract. Use mental math or paper and pencil.

1. 3 + 1 + 1 = 5
2. 4 + 2 + 3 = 9
3. 3 + 0 + 3 = 6
4. 4 + 1 + 5 = 10
5. 2 + 1 + 3 = 6
6. 2 + 0 + 1 = 3
7. 10 − 4 = 6
8. 9 − 2 = 7
9. 9 − 8 = 1
10. 8 − 3 = 5
11. 10 − 3 = 7
12. 10 − 5 = 5

13. 7 − 1 = 6
14. 12 − 3 = 9
15. 9 − 5 = 4
16. 8 − 6 = 2
17. 7 + 7 = 14
18. 12 + 6 = 18

Chapter 2

Practice Workbook

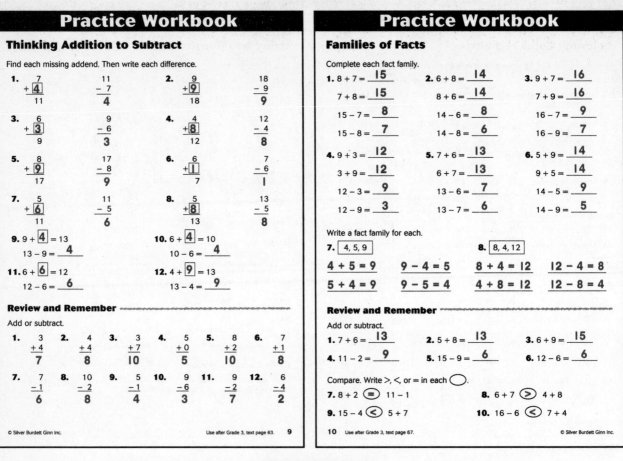

Thinking Addition to Subtract

Find each missing addend. Then write each difference.

1. 7 + [4] = 11 | 11 − 7 = **4**
2. 9 + [9] = 18 | 18 − 9 = **9**
3. 6 + [3] = 9 | 9 − 6 = **3**
4. 4 + [8] = 12 | 12 − 4 = **8**
5. 8 + [9] = 17 | 17 − 8 = **9**
6. 6 + [1] = 7 | 7 − 6 = **1**
7. 5 + [6] = 11 | 11 − 5 = **6**
8. 5 + [8] = 13 | 13 − 5 = **8**
9. 9 + [4] = 13; 13 − 9 = **4**
10. 6 + [4] = 10; 10 − 6 = **4**
11. 6 + [6] = 12; 12 − 6 = **6**
12. 4 + [9] = 13; 13 − 4 = **9**

Review and Remember

Add or subtract.

1. 3 + 4 = **7**
2. 4 + 4 = **8**
3. 3 + 7 = **10**
4. 5 + 0 = **5**
5. 8 + 2 = **10**
6. 7 + 1 = **8**
7. 7 − 1 = **6**
8. 10 − 2 = **8**
9. 5 − 1 = **4**
10. 9 − 6 = **3**
11. 9 − 2 = **7**
12. 6 − 4 = **2**

Practice Workbook

Families of Facts

Complete each fact family.

1. 8 + 7 = **15**; 7 + 8 = **15**; 15 − 7 = **8**; 15 − 8 = **7**
2. 6 + 8 = **14**; 8 + 6 = **14**; 14 − 6 = **8**; 14 − 8 = **6**
3. 9 + 7 = **16**; 7 + 9 = **16**; 16 − 7 = **9**; 16 − 9 = **7**
4. 9 + 3 = **12**; 3 + 9 = **12**; 12 − 3 = **9**; 12 − 9 = **3**
5. 7 + 6 = **13**; 6 + 7 = **13**; 13 − 6 = **7**; 13 − 7 = **6**
6. 5 + 9 = **14**; 9 + 5 = **14**; 14 − 5 = **9**; 14 − 9 = **5**

Write a fact family for each.

7. [4, 5, 9]

4 + 5 = 9 | **9 − 4 = 5**
5 + 4 = 9 | **9 − 5 = 4**

8. [8, 4, 12]

8 + 4 = 12 | **12 − 4 = 8**
4 + 8 = 12 | **12 − 8 = 4**

Review and Remember

Add or subtract.

1. 7 + 6 = **13**
2. 5 + 8 = **13**
3. 6 + 9 = **15**
4. 11 − 2 = **9**
5. 15 − 9 = **6**
6. 12 − 6 = **6**

Compare. Write >, <, or = in each ◯.

7. 8 + 2 (=) 11 − 1
8. 6 + 7 (>) 4 + 8
9. 15 − 4 (<) 5 + 7
10. 16 − 6 (<) 7 + 4

Chapter 3

Practice Workbook

Adding Greater Numbers

Add. For 1–16, check by adding up.

1. 522 + 747 = **1,269**
2. 645 + 391 = **1,036**
3. 927 + 739 = **1,666**
4. 788 + 935 = **1,723**
5. 28 + 469 + 583 = **1,080**
6. 595 + 414 + 107 = **1,116**
7. 667 + 684 + 729 = **2,080**
8. 145 + 783 + 229 = **1,157**
9. 6,894 + 8,796 = **15,690**
10. 9,678 + 4,983 = **14,661**
11. 6,825 + 5,549 = **12,374**
12. 5,634 + 8,365 = **13,999**
13. 9,843 + 5,045 = **14,888**
14. 6,945 + 6,812 = **13,757**
15. 7,648 + 8,579 = **16,227**
16. 6,543 + 7,432 = **13,975**
17. 7,983 + 6,748 **14,731**
18. 6,167 + 7,709 **13,876**
19. 8,074 + 725 **8,799**
20. 9,287 + 8,948 **18,235**

Review and Remember

Round each number to the nearest ten.

1. 37 **40**
2. 41 **40**
3. 65 **70**
4. 78 **80**

Add. Use mental math or paper and pencil.

5. 45 + 42 = **87**
6. 37 + 25 = **62**
7. 82 + 11 = **93**
8. 54 + 33 = **87**
9. 49 + 32 = **81**
10. 77 + 18 = **95**

Practice Workbook

Estimating Differences

Round to the nearest ten and estimate each difference.

1. 27 − 12 → **20**
2. 34 − 15 → **10**
3. 62 − 29 → **30**
4. 65 − 55 → **10**

Round to the nearest hundred and estimate each difference.

5. 354 − 217 → **200**
6. 716 − 280 → **400**
7. 663 − 450 → **200**
8. 749 − 552 → **100**
9. 650 − 350 → **300**
10. 352 − 176 → **200**
11. 322 − 101 → **200**
12. 682 − 552 → **100**

Compare. Write >, <, or = in each ◯.
Choose estimation, paper and pencil, or a calculator.

13. 52 − 14 (>) 75 − 47
14. 72 − 18 (>) 42 − 13
15. 63 − 32 (<) 68 − 21
16. 43 − 37 (<) 29 − 17

Review and Remember

Give the value of the digit 6.

1. 56,125 **6 thousand**
2. 612,975 **6 hundred-thousand**
3. 41,675 **6 hundred**

Give the value.

4. 

57¢

Chapter 3

Practice Workbook

Subtracting Two- and Three-Digit Numbers

Subtract. Check by adding.

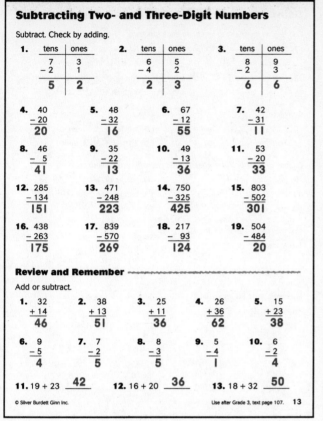

1.

tens	ones
7	3
− 2	1
5	**2**

2.

tens	ones
6	5
− 4	2
2	**3**

3.

tens	ones
8	9
− 2	3
6	**6**

4. 40 − 20 = **20** **5.** 48 − 32 = **16** **6.** 67 − 12 = **55** **7.** 42 − 31 = **11**

8. 46 − 5 = **41** **9.** 35 − 22 = **13** **10.** 49 − 13 = **36** **11.** 53 − 20 = **33**

12. 285 − 134 = **151** **13.** 471 − 248 = **223** **14.** 750 − 325 = **425** **15.** 803 − 502 = **301**

16. 438 − 263 = **175** **17.** 839 − 570 = **269** **18.** 217 − 93 = **124** **19.** 504 − 484 = **20**

Review and Remember

Add or subtract.

1. 32 + 14 = **46** **2.** 38 + 13 = **51** **3.** 25 + 11 = **36** **4.** 26 + 36 = **62** **5.** 15 + 23 = **38**

6. 9 − 5 = **4** **7.** 7 − 2 = **5** **8.** 8 − 3 = **5** **9.** 5 − 4 = **1** **10.** 6 − 2 = **4**

11. 19 + 23 **42** **12.** 16 + 20 **36** **13.** 18 + 32 **50**

Practice Workbook

Subtracting Greater Numbers

Subtract. Check by adding.

1. 8,769 − 6,548 = **2,221** **2.** 7,695 − 5,456 = **2,239** **3.** 8,740 − 2,270 = **6,470** **4.** 6,875 − 5,769 = **1,106**

5. 7,824 − 3,089 = **4,735** **6.** 9,536 − 6,287 = **3,249** **7.** 9,924 − 5,447 = **4,477** **8.** 6,943 − 2,678 = **4,265**

9. 8,521 − 6,339 = **2,182** **10.** 6,105 − 1,876 = **4,229** **11.** 3,001 − 1,246 = **1,755** **12.** 8,240 − 2,683 = **5,557**

13. 4,117 − 1,238 **2,879** **14.** 7,143 − 3,864 **3,279**

Solve.

15. The odometer on Mr. Brown's car reads 7,148 miles. It read 5,795 miles three months ago. How far did Mr. Brown drive in three months? **1,353 miles**

16. The odometer on Mrs. O'Key's car reads 9,206 miles. It read 6,789 miles two months ago. How far did Mrs. O'Key drive in two months? **2,417 miles**

Review and Remember

Add or subtract.

1. 35 + 42 + 37 = **114** **2.** 68 + 31 + 25 = **124** **3.** 73 + 64 + 89 = **226** **4.** 38 + 47 + 65 = **150** **5.** 22 + 37 + 63 = **122** **6.** 91 + 27 + 36 = **154**

7. 12 − 6 = **6** **8.** 11 − 3 = **8** **9.** 12 − 7 = **5** **10.** 13 − 9 = **4** **11.** 11 − 2 = **9** **12.** 13 − 5 = **8**

Chapter 3

Practice Workbook

Subtracting Across Zeros

Subtract. Estimate to be sure your answers make sense.

1. 600 − 563 = **37** **2.** 805 − 284 = **521** **3.** 400 − 289 = **111** **4.** 602 − 474 = **128**

5. 704 − 386 = **318** **6.** 800 − 659 = **141** **7.** 402 − 125 = **277** **8.** 702 − 196 = **506**

9. 405 − 88 = **317** **10.** 502 − 193 = **309**

11. 300 − 284 = **16** **12.** 207 − 128 = **79**

Find the correct difference. Choose mental math or paper and pencil. Circle your answer.

13. 807 − 208 — **(a.) 599**; b. 699; c. 601

14. 250 − 117 — a. 143; **(b.) 133**; c. 147

15. 600 − 256 — a. 456; b. 353; **(c.) 344**

16. 300 − 197 — a. 203; **(b.) 103**; c. 113

17. 540 − 206 — a. 236; b. 346; **(c.) 334**

18. 907 − 259 — a. 656; b. 752; **(c.) 648**

Review and Remember

Compare. Write >, <, or = in each ◯.

1. 1,742 **(>)** 1,724 **2.** 6,127 **(<)** 6,227

3. 3,110 **(>)** 3,101 **4.** 4,223 **(=)** 4,223

Use estimation to choose the letter of the correct answer. Circle your answer.

5. 592 + 215 a. 707 b. 383 **(c.) 807**

Chapter 4

Practice Workbook

Elapsed Time

Write each time in two ways.

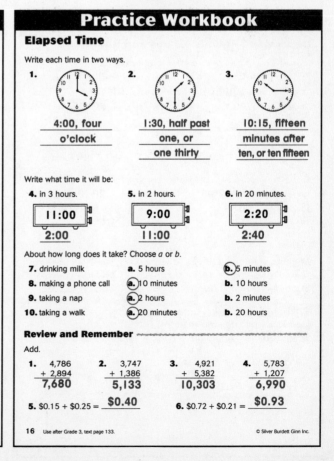

1. 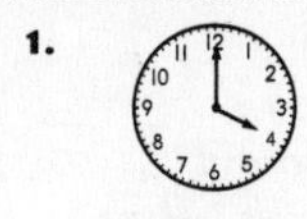

4:00, four o'clock

2. 

1:30, half past one, or one thirty

3. **10:15, fifteen minutes after ten, or ten fifteen**

Write what time it will be:

4. in 3 hours. 11:00 — **2:00**

5. in 2 hours. 9:00 — **11:00**

6. in 20 minutes. 2:20 — **2:40**

About how long does it take? Choose *a* or *b*.

7. drinking milk — a. 5 hours — **(b.) 5 minutes**

8. making a phone call — **(a.) 10 minutes** — b. 10 hours

9. taking a nap — **(a.) 2 hours** — b. 2 minutes

10. taking a walk — **(a.) 20 minutes** — b. 20 hours

Review and Remember

Add.

1. 4,786 + 2,894 = **7,680** **2.** 3,747 + 1,386 = **5,133** **3.** 4,921 + 5,382 = **10,303** **4.** 5,783 + 1,207 = **6,990**

5. \$0.15 + \$0.25 = **\$0.40** **6.** \$0.72 + \$0.21 = **\$0.93**

Chapter 4

Practice Workbook

Using Customary Units of Length and Capacity

Choose *in., ft, yd,* or *mi* to measure each length.

1. length of a hallway **yd**
2. distance from Ohio to Boston **mi**
3. width of the classroom **ft or yd**
4. width of a notebook **in.**

Complete.

5. 1 ft = **12** in.
6. 36 in. = **1** yd
7. 3 yd = **9** ft
8. 24 in. = **2** ft

Choose *cup, pint, quart,* or *gallon* to measure each amount.

9. a bathtub full of water **gallon**
10. orange juice for 2 people **pint**
11. glass of milk **cup**
12. fish tank of water **gallon**
13. pitcher of milk **quart**
14. hot cocoa for 1 person **cup**

Choose the better estimate for each.

15. a bucket of water — **(a.)** 3 gallons (circled)   b. 3 pints
16. a tank full of gasoline — a. 4 gallons   **(b.)** 14 gallons (circled)
17. yogurt for lunch — a. 1 quart   **(b.)** 1 cup (circled)
18. soup for 4 people — **(a.)** 2 pints (circled)   b. 2 gallons

Review and Remember

Add or subtract.

1. 235 + 141 = **376**
2. 342 + 451 = **793**
3. 621 + 143 = **764**
4. 340 + 127 = **467**
5. 470 − 143 = **327**
6. 593 − 24 = **569**
7. 429 − 170 = **259**
8. 362 − 238 = **124**

Practice Workbook

Using Metric Units of Length and Capacity

Choose *cm, m,* or *km* to complete each sentence.

1. The distance from St. Louis to Chicago is about 540 **km**.
2. A large paper clip is about 4 **cm** long.
3. A pencil is about 14 **cm** long.
4. The length of the school cafeteria is about 17 **m**.

Complete.

5. 1,000 m = **1** km
6. 1 m = **100** cm
7. 100 cm = **1** m
8. 2 km = **2,000** m

Choose *milliliter* or *liter* to measure the capacity of each item.

9. tank of oil **liter**
10. pitcher of milk **liter**
11. pot of water **liter**
12. teaspoon of gravy **milliliter**
13. glass of juice **milliliter**
14. raindrop **milliliter**

Choose the best estimate for each.

15. a glass of milk — a. 150 L   **(b.)** 150 mL (circled)   c. 500 mL   d. 5 mL
16. a bowl of soup — **(a.)** 300 mL (circled)   b. 30 mL   c. 300 L   d. 3 L

Review and Remember

Add or subtract.

1. 341 + 232 = **573**
2. 172 + 413 = **585**
3. 300 + 161 = **461**
4. 401 + 183 = **584**
5. 310 − 140 = **170**
6. 701 − 451 = **250**
7. 600 − 361 = **239**
8. 810 − 643 = **167**

Chapter 4

Practice Workbook

Ounces and Pounds, Grams and Kilograms

Choose *ounce* or *pound* to measure how heavy each item is.

1. a dog **pound**
2. a pencil **ounce**
3. a paper airplane **ounce**
4. a bear **pound**
5. an eraser **ounce**
6. a dictionary **pound**

Choose the better estimate for each.

7. a car — **(a.)** 3,000 pounds (circled)   b. 30 pounds
8. one apple — **(a.)** 5 ounces (circled)   b. 5 pounds

Choose *gram* or *kilogram* to measure how heavy each item is.

9. a bag of grain **kilogram**
10. a marble **gram**
11. a feather **gram**
12. a watermelon **kilogram**
13. a watch **gram**
14. a leaf **gram**

Compare. Write >, <, or = in each ◯.

15. 2 g **<** 2 kg
16. 8 g **<** 1 kg
17. 2,000 g **=** 2 kg
18. 3,000 g **>** 1 kg
19. 5 g **<** 5 kg
20. 1,000 g **=** 1 kg
21. 10 g **>** 2 g
22. 100 g **<** 100 kg
23. 3 kg **>** 300 g

Review and Remember

Round each number to the nearest ten.

1. 61 **60**
2. 26 **30**
3. 43 **40**
4. 89 **90**

Add. Use mental math or paper and pencil.

5. 33 + 27 = **60**
6. 21 + 73 = **94**
7. 65 + 28 = **93**
8. 48 + 39 = **87**
9. 17 + 55 = **72**
10. 59 + 32 = **91**

Practice Workbook

Reading a Thermometer

Write each Fahrenheit temperature shown.

1. 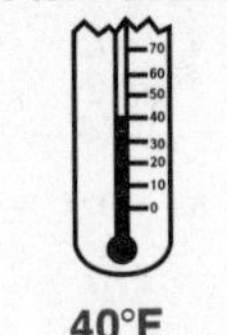
40°F

2. 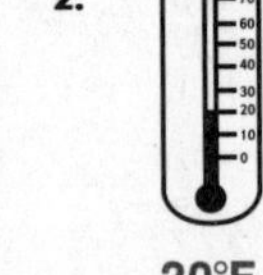
20°F

3. 
60°F

4. 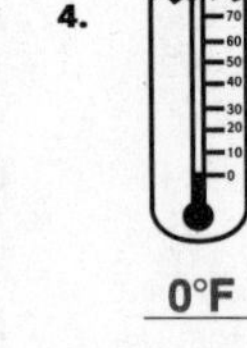
0°F

Write each Celsius temperature shown. Circle the answer that is closest to the temperature at which water freezes.

5. 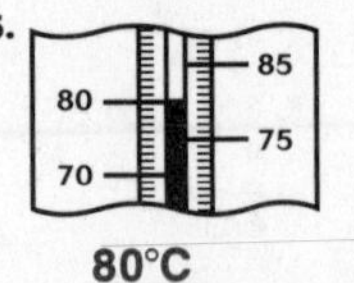

80°C

6. 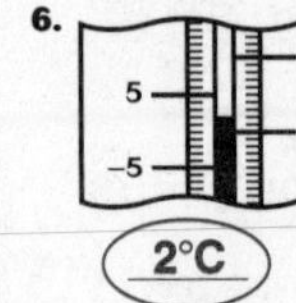

2°C (circled)

7. 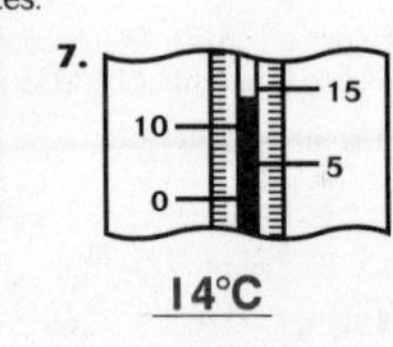

14°C

Review and Remember

Add or subtract. Use mental math or paper and pencil.

1. 3 + 3 + 7 = **13**
2. 4 + 4 + 5 = **13**
3. 7 + 0 + 8 = **15**
4. 9 + 0 + 8 = **17**
5. 5 + 2 + 9 = **16**
6. 2 + 8 + 6 = **16**
7. 17 − 8 = **9**
8. 15 − 7 = **8**
9. 15 − 9 = **6**
10. 16 − 8 = **8**
11. 18 − 9 = **9**
12. 16 − 7 = **9**
13. 14 − 6 = **8**
14. 14 − 7 = **7**
15. 17 − 2 = **15**

Chapter 5

Practice Workbook

Understanding Multiplication

Solve.

1. 2 + 2 + 2 = 6
How many 2s? 3
3 2s = 6

2. 3 + 3 + 3 = 9
How many 3s? 3
3 3s = 9

3. 4 + 4 + 4 + 4 = 16
4 × 4 = 16

4. 5 + 5 = 10
2 × 5 = 10

5. 9 + 9 = 18
2 × 9 = 18

6. 6 + 6 + 6 = 18
3 × 6 = 18

7. 5 + 5 + 5 = 15
3 × 5 = 15

8. 7 + 7 = 14
2 × 7 = 14

9. 2 + 2 + 2 + 2 = 8
4 × 2 = 8

10. 4 + 4 + 4 = 12
3 × 4 = 12

11. 3 + 3 + 3 + 3 = 12
4 × 3 = 12

12. 7 + 7 + 7 = 21
3 × 7 = 21

Review and Remember

Tell what time it will be in 3 hours.

1. 7:00 10:00
2. 10:30 1:30

Use the sign to answer.

3. Suppose it is 10:30. Can Jim eat lunch in the cafeteria? no

CAFETERIA
OPEN FOR LUNCH
FROM 11:00 – 2:00

© Silver Burdett Ginn Inc. Use after Grade 3, text page 177. 21

Practice Workbook

Using 2 and 3 as Factors

Find each product.

1. 4 × 2 = 8
2. 2 × 1 = 2
3. 6 × 2 = 12
4. 2 × 3 = 6
5. 5 × 2 = 10
6. 2 × 2 = 4
7. 7 × 2 = 14
8. 9 × 2 = 18
9. 2 × 4 = 8
10. 2 × 3 = 6
11. 3 × 3 = 9
12. 6 × 3 = 18
13. 3 × 5 = 15
14. 7 × 3 = 21
15. 3 × 8 = 24

16. 3 × 7 = 21
17. 3 × 9 = 27
18. 3 × 4 = 12
19. 8 × 3 = 24
20. 9 × 2 = 18
21. 7 × 3 = 21
22. 6 × 2 = 12
23. 9 × 3 = 27
24. 5 × 2 = 10

Solve.

25. There were 7 stools. Each stool had 3 legs. How many legs were there in all? 21 legs

26. There were 6 boys. Each boy had 2 toy cars. How many cars were there in all? 12 toy cars

Review and Remember

Add or subtract.

1. 6 + 7 = 13
2. 9 + 9 = 18
3. 8 + 7 = 15
4. 8 + 9 = 17
5. 6 + 5 = 11
6. 8 + 8 = 16
7. 34 − 19 = 15
8. 63 − 28 = 35
9. 72 − 53 = 19
10. 80 − 43 = 37
11. 58 − 29 = 29
12. 63 − 39 = 24

22 Use after Grade 3, text page 191. © Silver Burdett Ginn Inc.

Chapter 5

Practice Workbook

Using 4 and 5 as Factors

Find each product.

1. 4 × 2 = 8
2. 4 × 4 = 16
3. 5 × 7 = 35
4. 4 × 1 = 4
5. 5 × 3 = 15
6. 4 × 5 = 20
7. 9 × 4 = 36
8. 6 × 5 = 30
9. 4 × 4 = 16
10. 8 × 5 = 40
11. 6 × 4 = 24
12. 1 × 5 = 5
13. 0 × 4 = 0
14. 5 × 9 = 45
15. 0 × 5 = 0

16. 7 × 4 = 28
17. 9 × 5 = 45
18. 7 × 5 = 35
19. 8 × 4 = 32
20. 5 × 4 = 20
21. 6 × 5 = 30
22. 5 × 5 = 25
23. 4 × 3 = 12
24. 2 × 5 = 10

Solve.

25. Kim has 5 pages of pictures. She has 4 pictures on each page. How many pictures does Kim have? 20 pictures

Review and Remember

Round each number to the nearest ten.

1. 35 40
2. 21 20
3. 42 40
4. 57 60

Round each number to the nearest hundred.

5. 111 100
6. 217 200
7. 481 500
8. 154 200

© Silver Burdett Ginn Inc. Use after Grade 3, text page 193. 23

Practice Workbook

Using 0 Through 5 as Factors

Find each product.

1. 3 × 3 = 9
2. 4 × 3 = 12
3. 3 × 4 = 12
4. 5 × 2 = 10
5. 4 × 2 = 8
6. 4 × 0 = 0
7. 5 × 3 = 15
8. 2 × 7 = 14
9. 3 × 6 = 18
10. 4 × 4 = 16
11. 4 × 8 = 32
12. 6 × 4 = 24
13. 1 × 8 = 8
14. 7 × 5 = 35
15. 3 × 9 = 27

16. 1 × 2 = 2
17. 3 × 2 = 6
18. 1 × 6 = 6
19. 5 × 4 = 20
20. 3 × 7 = 21
21. 8 × 0 = 0
22. 4 × 2 = 8
23. 5 × 5 = 25
24. 0 × 1 = 0

Solve.

25. Bill has 6 boxes. He has 4 rocks in each box. How many rocks does Bill have? 24 rocks

Review and Remember

Tell what time it will be in 4 hours.

1. 3:45 7:45
2. 9:15 1:15
3. 11:00 3:00

Add.

4. 3 + 5 + 8 = 16
5. 2 + 6 + 7 = 15
6. 21 + 13 + 16 = 50
7. 12 + 42 + 23 = 77

24 Use after Grade 3, text page 197. © Silver Burdett Ginn Inc.

155

Chapter 5

Practice Workbook

Using More Patterns to Multiply

Multiply.

1. 2 × 2 = 4; 2 × 3 = 6; 2 × 4 = 8; 2 × 5 = 10
2. 4 × 2 = 8; 4 × 3 = 12; 4 × 4 = 16; 4 × 5 = 20
3. 5 × 2 = 10; 5 × 3 = 15; 5 × 4 = 20; 5 × 5 = 25
4. 3 × 7 = 21; 3 × 8 = 24; 3 × 9 = 27
5. 7 × 7 = 49; 7 × 8 = 56; 7 × 9 = 63
6. 9 × 7 = 63; 9 × 8 = 72; 9 × 9 = 81
7. 2 × 9 = 18; 9 × 2 = 18
8. 4 × 3 = 12; 3 × 4 = 12
9. 2 × 6 = 12; 6 × 2 = 12
10. 3 × 8 = 24; 8 × 3 = 24
11. 5 × 6 = 30; 6 × 5 = 30
12. 4 × 8 = 32; 8 × 4 = 32
13. 4 × 7 = 28; 7 × 4 = 28
14. 5 × 8 = 40; 8 × 5 = 40
15. 6 × 7 = 42; 7 × 6 = 42

Review and Remember

Add.

1. 5 + 5 + 5 = 15
2. 4 + 4 + 4 = 12

3.	4.	5.
2,375	4,271	6,412
+ 156	+ 327	+ 539
2,531	4,598	6,951

6.	7.	8.
4,162	1,498	5,055
+ 3,475	+ 8,364	+ 2,407
7,637	9,862	7,462

Chapter 6

Practice Workbook

Using 6 as a Factor

Find each product.

1.	2.	3.	4.	5.
6	4	2	6	6
× 3	× 6	× 6	× 5	× 1
18	24	12	30	6

6.	7.	8.	9.	10.
6	5	9	6	0
× 7	× 6	× 6	× 8	× 6
42	30	54	48	0

11. 6 × 2 = 12
12. 7 × 6 = 42
13. 1 × 6 = 6
14. 24 = 4 × 6
15. 36 = 6 × 6
16. 48 = 8 × 6
17. 6 × 3 = 18
18. 6 × 2 = 12
19. 9 × 6 = 54

Solve.

20. Lyla pasted 5 pictures on each poster. She has 6 posters. How many pictures does Lyla have? **30 pictures**
21. Terry has 6 plants. He put 3 drops of plant food in each pot. How many drops of plant food did he use? **18 drops**

Review and Remember

Add or subtract. Use mental math or paper and pencil.

1.	2.	3.	4.	5.	6.
6	5	6	2	5	9
2	1	0	4	4	0
+ 3	+ 8	+ 7	+ 5	+ 1	+ 5
11	14	13	11	10	14

7.	8.	9.	10.	11.	12.
621	333	412	622	294	721
− 189	− 145	− 143	− 153	− 187	− 539
432	188	269	469	107	182

Chapter 6

Practice Workbook

Using 7 and 8 as Factors

Find each product.

1.	2.	3.	4.	5.
7	8	6	8	3
× 3	× 2	× 7	× 4	× 8
21	16	42	32	24

6.	7.	8.	9.	10.
8	8	5	6	7
× 7	× 8	× 7	× 8	× 7
56	64	35	48	49

11. 8 × 0 = 0
12. 7 × 4 = 28
13. 5 × 8 = 40
14. 32 = 8 × 4
15. 63 = 7 × 9
16. 14 = 2 × 7

Solve.

17. Patti made 4 necklaces. She used 8 beads for each. How many beads did Patti use? **32 beads**
18. Ken rode his bike 2 miles every day. How far did he ride in 7 days? **14 miles**

Review and Remember

Add or subtract.

1.	2.	3.	4.
1,845	3,769	2,764	3,107
+ 3,569	+ 2,483	+ 4,453	+ 4,200
5,414	6,252	7,217	7,307

5.	6.	7.	8.
5,312	1,810	600	800
+ 2,418	+ 6,204	− 229	− 347
7,730	8,014	371	453

9.	10.	11.	12.
203	408	300	700
− 117	− 169	− 148	− 613
86	239	152	87

Practice Workbook

Using 9 as a Factor

Find each product.

1.	2.	3.	4.	5.
9	9	6	9	3
× 3	× 2	× 9	× 4	× 9
27	18	54	36	27

6.	7.	8.	9.	10.
9	9	5	4	9
× 7	× 8	× 9	× 9	× 9
63	72	45	36	81

11. 9 × 0 = 0
12. 9 × 4 = 36
13. 5 × 9 = 45
14. 27 = 3 × 9
15. 9 = 9 × 1
16. 54 = 9 × 6

Solve.

17. Chad has 9 model planes on each shelf in his room. He has 3 shelves. How many model planes does Chad have? **27 planes**
18. Karen put 4 pumpkin seeds in each hole. She had dug 9 holes. How many pumpkin seeds did she plant? **36 seeds**

Review and Remember

Add or subtract.

1.	2.	3.	4.
84	793	483	86
+ 76	+ 201	+ 212	+ 29
160	994	695	115

5.	6.	7.	8.
348	438	614	98
+ 929	− 129	− 289	− 47
1,277	309	325	51

9. 942 − 611 = 331
10. 764 − 531 = 233
11. 379 − 163 = 216